STANLEY W. JACOB, M.D., F.A.C.S.

Associate Professor of Surgery,
   University of Oregon Medical School;
Lecturer in Anatomy,
   University of Oregon School of Nursing;
Visiting Surgeon, University of Oregon
   Medical School Hospitals and Clinics;
First Kemper Foundation Research Scholar,
   American College of Surgeons;
Markle Scholar in Medical Sciences.

CLARICE ASHWORTH FRANCONE

Medical Illustrator,
Head of the Department of Medical Illustrations,
University of Oregon Medical School.

ILLUSTRATIONS ON 399 FIGURES
90 FIGURES IN COLOR

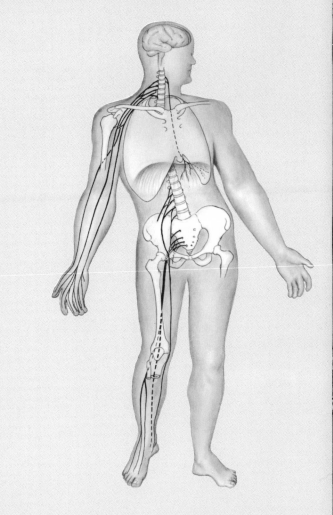

B. SAUNDERS COMPANY
Philadelphia and London

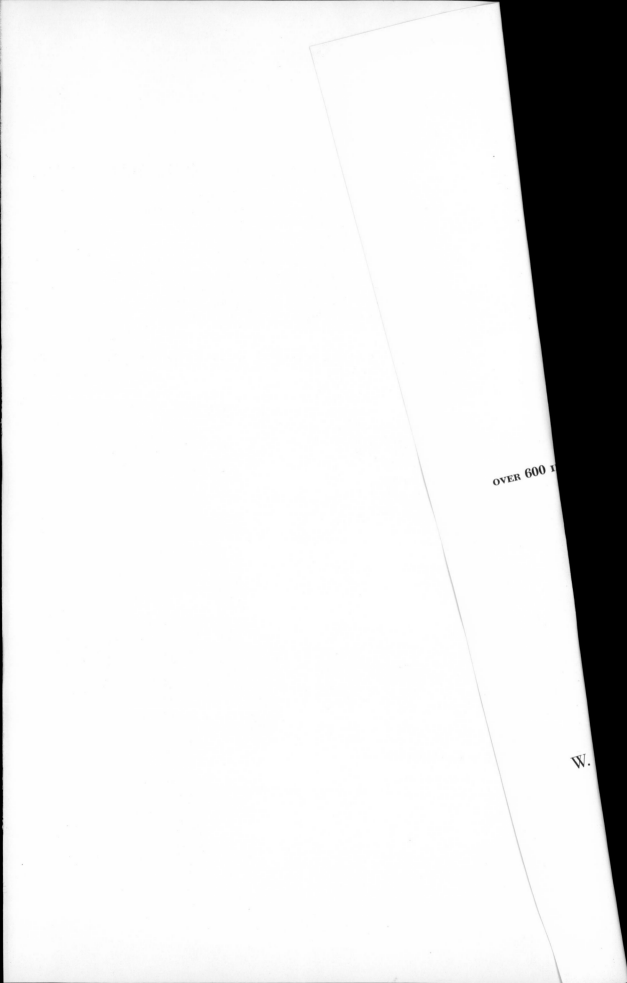

OVER 600 I

W.

STRUCTURE
AND
FUNCTION
IN
MAN

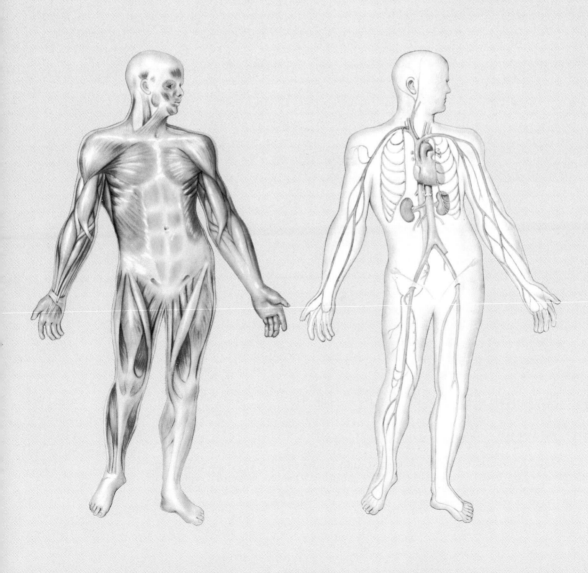

W. B. Saunders Company: West Washington Square,
Philadelphia, Pa. 19105

12 Dyott Street
London, W.C.1

Reprinted October, 1965, August, 1966, October, 1966 and July, 1967

Structure and Function in Man

Dedication

To my father, without whose encouragement
this would not have been possible.

Stanley W. Jacob

To my son Don.

Clarice Ashworth Francone

PREFACE

Many centuries ago anatomy and physiology were taught in a single course—not so much for the benefit of the student, but because the two fields of knowledge were not really separate even in the minds of researchers and educators. At the time there was insufficient knowledge of either science to warrant separate treatment. As the years passed, intensive studies were completed by methodically curious scientists in both fields. These investigations were aided by the progressive development of the physical and chemical sciences and by advances in technology providing more refined methods for observation and experimentation.

Gradually, the accumulation of facts and the elucidation of general concepts made specialization necessary; so anatomy and physiology were taught as individual sciences. Recent years have witnessed a return to the older philosophy of treating them as one integrated subject in the hope that students would more readily understand life as the truly integrated process it is.

One cannot appreciate the subject matter of physiology without first learning the basic concepts of anatomy. One cannot realize the full significance of human structure without also understanding the complex functions associated with it. Thus, while specialization is still necessary for advanced students, beginning and reviewing students at every educational level benefit from an integrated presentation of anatomy and physiology.

Structure and Function in Man is designed for use by the beginning student. This book emphasizes physiology without neglecting anatomy, an accomplishment due to the incorporation of approximately 300 new half-tone drawings depicting the anatomy of the entire body. The text employs the Nomina Anatomica (N.A.) terminology, replacing such words as *eustachian* with *auditory* and *pituitary* with *hypophysis*. A brief survey of each organ system is presented; chapters are comprehensively summarized and study questions included. Complete lists of references have not been added; to do so in a field as wide as anatomy and physiology would have created a book of inordinate length. Clues to further reading are provided in a special section at the end of the text. This book is only a beginning.

"The hardest conviction to get into the mind of the beginner is that the education he is receiving in college is not a medical course but a life course for which the work of a few years under teachers is but a preparation." —Sir William Osler.

STANLEY W. JACOB
CLARICE A. FRANCONE

Portland, Oregon

ACKNOWLEDGMENTS

If this text receives any measure of success, many associates will have made this possible. These individuals are either on the faculty or on the associate level at the University of Oregon Medical School.

At the associate level, we wish to express our appreciation to the following: Margaret Bischel, Roger Bothwell, Stanley Chism, Steven Cline, Joel Cruz, Michael Davis, Molly Day, DeWayne Ditto, Gareth Eberle, Thomas Gill, Nancy Gillespie, Earnest Hage, Marilyn Jacob, Karen Lantz, Paul Lee, Suzanne Nystrom, Alyce Page, Linda Popick, Nate Quilici, Robert Rosenbaum, Earl Sherod, James Simmerville, Cynthia Statter, Janet Stinson, Ann Sullivan, Cheryl Taubman, David Todd, Ronald Tolls, Larry Veltman, Margaret Watson, and Nancy Zimmerman.

Many individuals at the faculty level have read individual chapters or criticized figures: R. L. Bacon, Ph.D.; Rodney K. Beals, M.D.; David J. Bristow, M.D.; Robert P. Burns, M.D.; David D. DeWeese, M.D.; Raphael B. Durfee, M.D.; James H. Foster, M.D.; Philip D. Gordy, M.D.; Monte A. Greer, M.D.; James B. Haworth, M.D.; W. LeRoy Heinrichs, M.D.; Clarence V. Hodges, M.D.; Melvin P. Judkins, M.D.; John W. Kendall, M.D.; Daniel H. Labby, M.D.; Richard P. Lewis, M.D.; Adam W. Lis, Ph.D.; Richard B. Lyons, M.D.; Colin W. McCord, M.D.; Bernard Pirofsky, M.D.; Edward E. Rosenbaum, M.D.; Ivan L. Sandoz, M.D.; George W. Schemm, M.D.; Arthur J. Seaman, M.D.; Peter Sigerseth, Ph.D.; Albert Starr, M.D.; William A. Stotler, Ph.D.; Robert E. Swanson, Ph.D.; and Archie R. Tunturi, Ph.D., M.D.

The authors owe special debts of gratitude to Kay Bittick and Frances Kemper, Department of Medical Illustrations; Carol Kerr and Paul Miller, Department of Photography; Robert Brooks, Department of Pathology; and P. J. Deshpande, M.D., Research Fellow in Surgery, University of Oregon Medical School.

We want to acknowledge the editorial and production staffs of the W. B. Saunders Company, whose patience and advice contributed greatly to the completion of this manuscript.

CONTENTS

UNIT 4   REPRODUCTION

UNIT

1

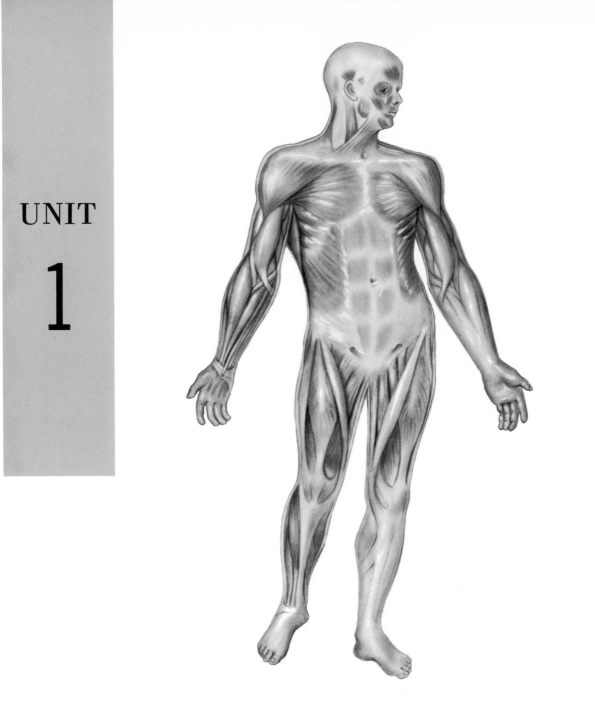

INTRODUCTORY

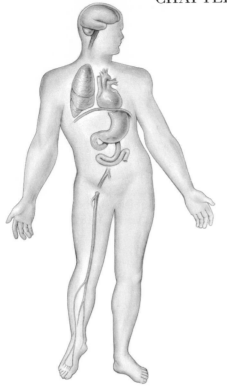

THE
BODY
AS A
WHOLE

THE HUMAN BODY

The order and plan of creation have challenged man throughout history. His world is organized into a solar system, the solar system into a galaxy, and the galaxy into a universe. In the opposite direction, his world is divided into civilizations, civilizations into societies, societies into men, and men into chemical elements. Man finds himself, like Huxley, overcome at the "wonderful unity of plan in the thousands and thousands of living constructions, and the modifications of similar apparatuses to serve diverse ends." Such is the human body.

The Complex Organism

Man as a living organism may be viewed as an assemblage of minute units called cells which are marvelously integrated both structurally and functionally. Cells eventually specialize or differentiate to a greater or lesser extent. An aggregate of similarly differentiated cells comprises a tissue, such as the fat cells of adipose tissue. Tissues, in turn, form organs; organs form systems. Ultimately, systems combine in an intricate manner to create a thinking, acting man.

3

When viewing the human body in this fashion, one stands in awe at the complexity of the organization of the body and the fine balance and interdependence of the various parts. Anatomy and physiology describe this interdependence of structure and function.

The Scientific Study of Man

Anatomy is the study of the structure of a living organism. It is subdivided into gross (macroscopic) anatomy, histology (microscopic anatomy), and embryology (developmental anatomy).

Physiology is the study of function in the living organism, and includes function at both the biochemical and gross levels.

The student is usually startled to learn that living things are composed of the same atoms and substances found on shelves in chemistry laboratories, and that these substances follow the same laws and principles as govern those reactions occurring in test tubes and flasks. When the substances are individually considered, each is obviously inanimate. What, then, is different about living substances composed of ordinarily inanimate materials? The answer seems simple, but is complex—it is *organization.*

Living tissue is composed of molecules which would *never* assume the proper configuration, structure, and relationship if energy were not supplied to maintain this level of organization. An unmended wall gradually falls to pieces, a deserted house disintegrates, and oriented cell molecules become chaotic unless energy is expended to maintain them in high energy configuration.

CONSTITUTION AND STRUCTURE

Body type or constitution is of particular interest to the physician. Body build and stature are thought to be inherited characteristics representing familial types. Individuals can be classified into four types: the sthenic type, sometimes called the "athletic type," with good musculature, broad shoulders, and a flat abdomen; the hypersthenic type, with a short, stocky build and a tendency toward obesity; the hyposthenic type, tall and thin with poorly developed musculature; and the asthenic type, in general an exaggeration of the hyposthenic characteristics, plus a disproportionately large, wide pelvis (Fig. 1).

ORGANIZATION OF THE BODY

Anatomic reference systems have been adopted to facilitate uniformity of description

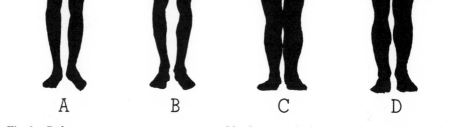

Fig. 1.   Body type or construction is represented by four main builds: *A.* hyposthenic, *B.* asthenic, *C.* hypersthenic, and *D.* sthenic.

of the body. Four basic reference systems of organization are considered: direction, planes, cavities, and structural units.

Direction

The body in the anatomic position is erect, facing forward with the arms at the sides and the palms anterior. All descriptions of location or position assume the body to be in this posture. The following directions are usually considered:

Superior (uppermost or above); for example, the head is superior to the neck.

Inferior (lowermost or below); for example, the foot is inferior to the ankle.

Anterior (toward the front); for example, the breast is on the anterior chest wall.

Posterior (refers to the back); for example, the vertebral column is posterior to the digestive tract.

Cephalad (toward the head); for example, the thoracic cavity lies cephalad or superior to the abdominal cavity.

Caudad (toward the tail); the term caudad for the most part is used only in animals which have not assumed an upright position.

Medial (nearest the midline of the body); for example, the ulna is on the medial side of the forearm.

Lateral (toward the side); that is, away from the medial side. For example, the radius is lateral to the ulna.

Proximal (nearest the point of attachment); for example, the shoulder is proximal to the elbow.

Distal (away from the point of attachment); for example, the elbow is distal to the shoulder.

The term *parietal* refers to the walls of a cavity; for example, the parietal peritoneum lines the abdominal wall. The term *visceral* refers to the covering of the organs; for example, the visceral peritoneum covers the abdominal organs.

Planes

The body is discussed with respect to planes passing through it (Fig. 2A).

Midsagittal: the plane vertically dividing the body through the midline into right and left portions.

Sagittal: any plane vertically dividing the body into right and left portions parallel to the midsagittal line.

Horizontal (transverse): any plane dividing the body into superior and inferior portions.

Frontal (coronal): any plane dividing the body into anterior, or ventral, and posterior, or dorsal, portions at right angles to the sagittal plane.

Cavities

Cavity is a term used to describe the third organizational reference system. The body has two major cavities, each subdivided into two lesser cavities (Fig. 2B). The organs of a cavity are collectively referred to as viscera.

1. Ventral cavity
   A. Thoracic: pleural and pericardial cavities
   B. Abdominopelvic
2. Dorsal cavity
   A. Cranial
   B. Spinal

Ventral cavity. Organs of the ventral cavity are involved in maintaining homeostasis.

The thoracic cavity houses the lungs, pericardium, heart, and great vessels. The mediastinum is a space between the pleural cavities, containing the thymus, lymph vessels, esophagus, trachea, and nerves.

The abdominopelvic cavity contains those organs inferior to the respiratory diaphragm but above the urogenital diaphragm, including the kidneys, stomach, large and small intestine, spleen, liver, gallbladder, ovaries, uterus, and pancreas.

Dorsal cavity. The dorsal cavity contains structures of the nervous system serving to coordinate the body's functions in a unified manner. It is divided into a cranial portion, containing the brain, and a spinal portion, containing the spinal cord.

Structural Units

The fourth and final system of reference is the structural unit, subdivided into cells, tissues, organs, and systems.

THE CELL. All living matter is composed of cells. The building material of a cell is protoplasm, an aqueous colloidal solution of protein, lipid, carbohydrate, and inorganic salts. Protoplasm is 60 to 90 per cent water, 10 to 30 per cent protein, lipid, and carbohydrate, and 1 per cent inorganic salt. *Metabolism* is the process by which protoplasm is synthesized, maintained,

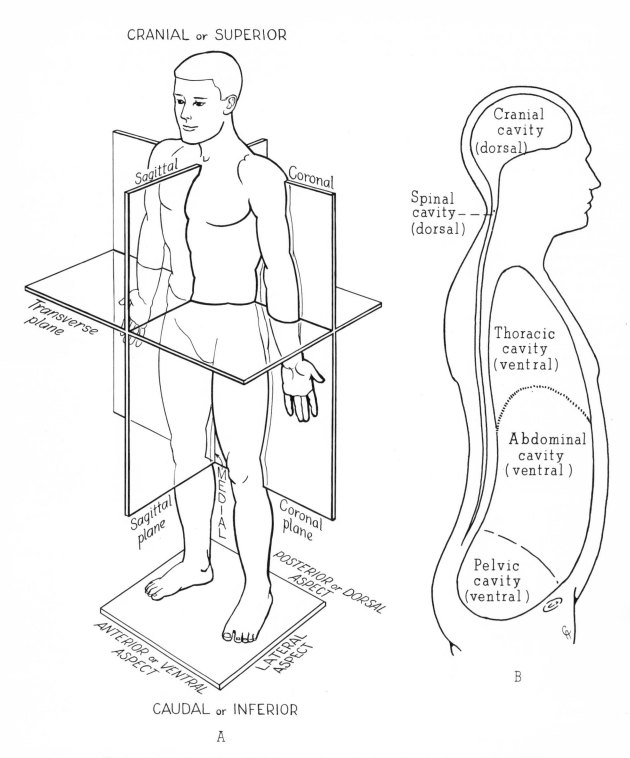

CRANIAL or SUPERIOR

Sagittal

Coronal

Transverse plane

Sagittal plane

MEDIAL

Coronal plane

POSTERIOR or DORSAL ASPECT

ANTERIOR or VENTRAL ASPECT

LATERAL ASPECT

CAUDAL or INFERIOR

A

Cranial cavity (dorsal)

Spinal cavity (dorsal)

Thoracic cavity (ventral)

Abdominal cavity (ventral)

Pelvic cavity (ventral)

B

Fig. 2. *A.* Anatomic position of body (anterior view, palms forward) with reference systems. *B.* The body has two major cavities, dorsal and ventral, each subdivided into two lesser cavities. For convenience the abdominal and pelvic cavities pictured here are referred to simply as the abdominopelvic cavity.

6

TABLE 1.   Percentage Composition of Representative Mammalian Tissues.*

TISSUE	WATER	SOLIDS	PROTEINS	LIPIDS	CARBOHYDRATES
Striated muscle	72–78	22–28	18–20	3.0	0.6
Whole blood	79	21	19	1	0.1
Liver	60–80	20–40	15	3–20	1–15
Brain	78	22	8	12–15	0.1
Skin	66	34	25	7	present
Bone (marrow-free)	20–25	75–80	30	low	present

* Source: White, A., Handler, P., Smith, E., and Stetten, D.: *Principles of Biochemistry.* New York, McGraw-Hill, 1954.

and destroyed. *Anabolism* is the component of metabolism in which protoplasm is synthesized; *catabolism* is the component breaking down protoplasm into simpler substances.

More than 12 elements enter into the composition of protoplasm, including: hydrogen, oxygen, nitrogen, chloride, calcium, carbon, iron, sodium, potassium, phosphorus, sulfur, and magnesium, and traces of copper, molybdenum, zinc, cobalt, and other elements. This "ground substance of life" performs all the activities necessary to maintain life—including metabolism, respiration, digestion, assimilation, excretion, and reproduction.

To function properly, cells require a constant internal environment. The process of homeostasis provides this environment. Homeostatic mechanisms include the control of temperature, energy, excretion, and pH. The term "homeokinesis" has been suggested to replace homeostasis, since the maintenance of life is far from a "static" phenomenon; it is an active, energy-requiring process. Homeostasis provides a balance between loss and restoration of elements in the body, including electrolytes, blood, and protein.

Body fluids are found within the vascular compartment (plasma), between cells (interstitial), or within the cells (intracellular). The *plasma* accounts for 5 per cent of the body weight; *interstitial fluid,* 15 per cent; and *intracellular fluid,* 40 per cent. Hence, approximately 60 per cent of the body weight is composed of water, two-thirds of which is found within the cells. The remaining 40 per cent of the body is composed of 18 per cent protein, 7 per cent mineral matter, and 15 per cent fat. (See Chapter Sixteen and Table 1 for additional information.)

TISSUES. Tissues are composed of cells and intercellular substance, or matrix. Generally, tissues contain cells similar in appearance, function, and embryonic origin.

All the diverse tissues of the body can be grouped under one of the following categories: epithelial, connective, muscle, or nervous tissue.

ORGANS. An organ is comprised of cells grouped into tissues serving a common function. The stomach is an organ consisting of all general types of tissues. Other examples of organs are the spleen, liver, heart, lungs, and skin.

SYSTEMS. Cells are grouped together to form tissues; tissues combine to form organs. A *system* is a group of organs. The system is the basis for the general structural plan of the body. Brief mention will be made of the various systems to gain an idea of the general organization of the body shown in the figures of the human torso (Figs. 3 to 12).

The *skeletal system* is composed of bones and cartilagenous and membranous structures associated with them. It protects and supports the soft parts of the body and supplies levers for body movement. Connective tissue predominates in this area. Articulations (joints) will be described separately.

The *muscular system* is composed of muscles, fasciae, tendon sheaths, and bursae. The three muscle types are: striated, moving the skeleton; smooth, found along the alimentary tract; and cardiac, found in the heart.

The *nervous system* consists of the brain, spinal cord, cranial nerves, peripheral nerves, and sensory and motor terminals. It is the correlating and controlling system of the body intimately connected with the other systems and with the outside world. Special senses include vision, hearing, taste, and smell.

The *circulatory system* comprises the heart, arteries, veins, lymph vessels, and capillaries. It pumps and distributes the blood carrying oxygen, nutrients, and wastes. The lymphatic system draining tissue spaces and carrying absorbed fat into the blood will be considered separately.

Text continued on page 18.

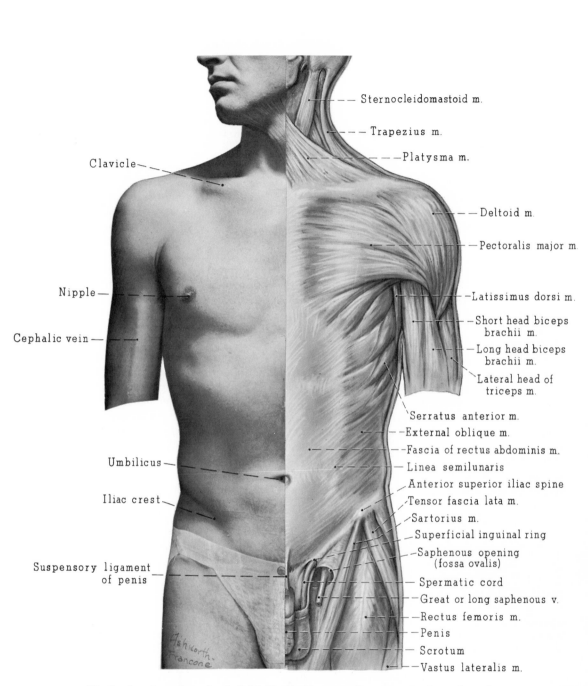

Clavicle—

Nipple—

Cephalic vein—

Umbilicus—

Iliac crest—

Suspensory ligament
of penis

— Sternocleidomastoid m.

—Trapezius m.

—Platysma m.

— —Deltoid m.

—Pectoralis major m.

—Latissimus dorsi m.

—Short head biceps
brachii m.

—Long head biceps
brachii m.

Lateral head of
triceps m.

Serratus anterior m.

—External oblique m.

—Fascia of rectus abdominis m.

—Linea semilunaris

Anterior superior iliac spine

Tensor fascia lata m.

Sartorius m.

—Superficial inguinal ring

—Saphenous opening
(fossa ovalis)

— Spermatic cord

—Great or long saphenous v.

—Rectus femoris m.

—Penis

— Scrotum

—Vastus lateralis m.

Fig. 3. Anterior surface of male; left half with skin removed, exposing first layer of muscles.

8

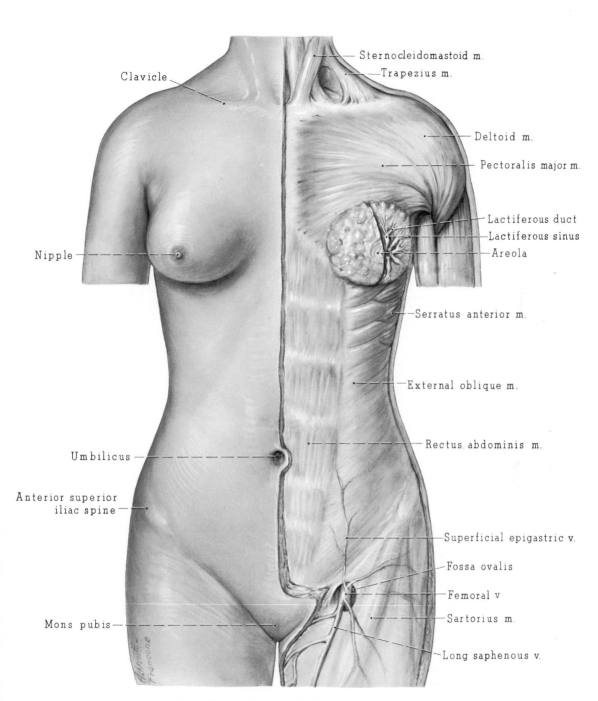

Clavicle

Nipple

Umbilicus

Anterior superior
iliac spine

Mons pubis

Sternocleidomastoid m.

Trapezius m.

Deltoid m.

Pectoralis major m.

Lactiferous duct

Lactiferous sinus

Areola

Serratus anterior m.

External oblique m.

Rectus abdominis m.

Superficial epigastric v.

Fossa ovalis

Femoral v

Sartorius m.

Long saphenous v.

Fig. 4. Anterior surface of female, left half with skin removed, exposing first layer of muscles.

9

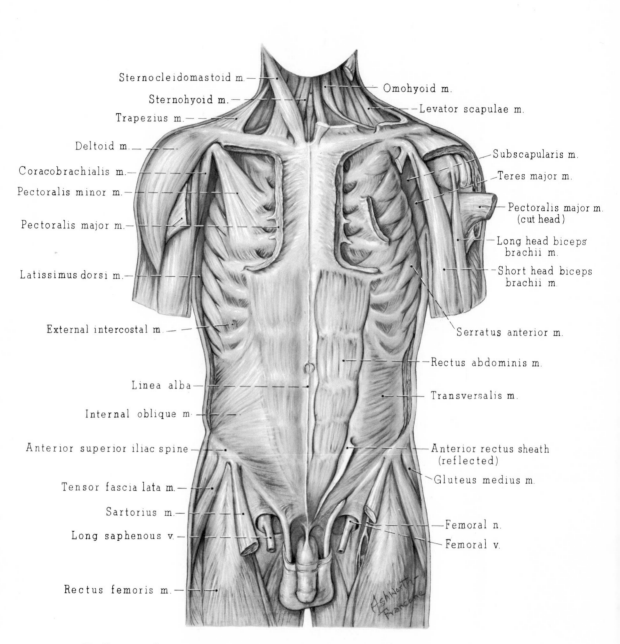

Fig. 5. Pectoralis major muscle removed on right side, pectoralis minor on left side; second and third layers of abdominal muscles exposed.

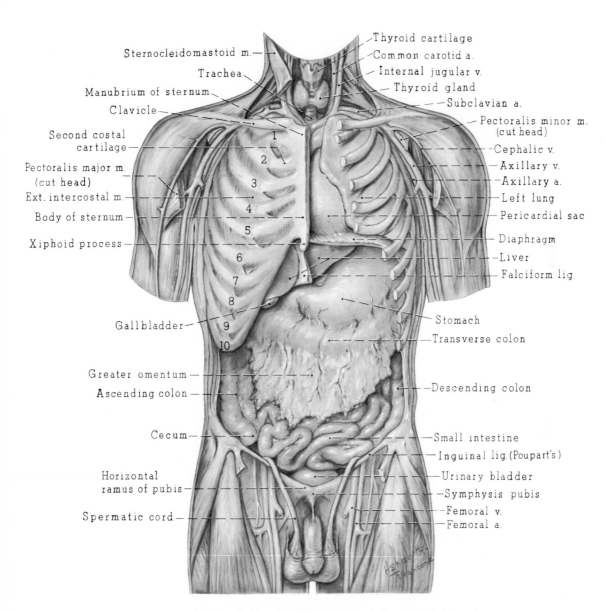

Fig. 6. Anterior muscles of chest and abdomen removed, showing underlying viscera.

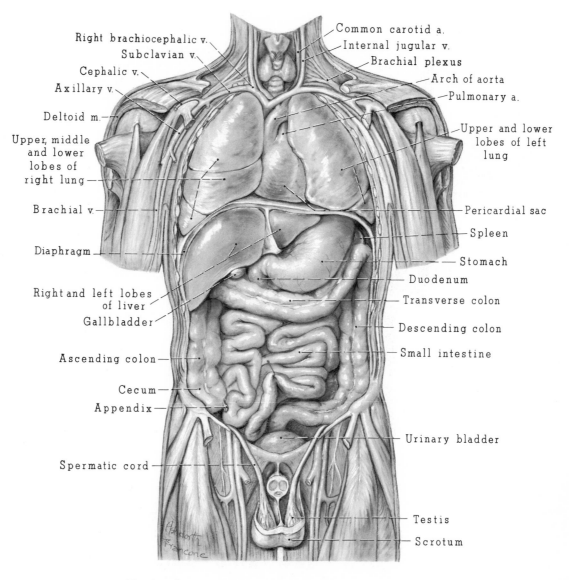

Right brachiocephalic v.
Subclavian v.
Cephalic v.
Axillary v.
Deltoid m.
Upper, middle and lower lobes of right lung
Brachial v.
Diaphragm
Right and left lobes of liver
Gallbladder
Ascending colon
Cecum
Appendix
Spermatic cord

Common carotid a.
Internal jugular v.
Brachial plexus
Arch of aorta
Pulmonary a.
Upper and lower lobes of left lung
Pericardial sac
Spleen
Stomach
Duodenum
Transverse colon
Descending colon
Small intestine
Urinary bladder
Testis
Scrotum

Fig. 7. Rib cage and omentum removed, showing visceral relations.

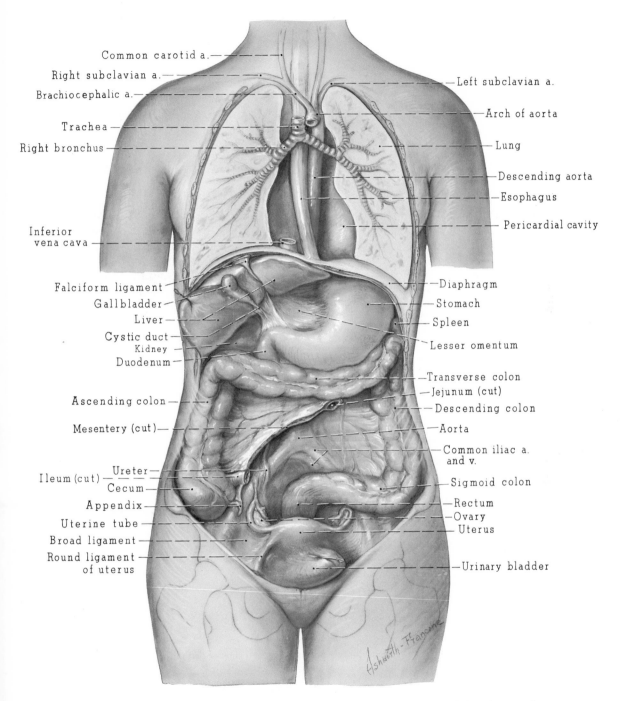

Common carotid a.

Right subclavian a.

Brachiocephalic a.

Trachea

Right bronchus

Inferior
vena cava

Falciform ligament

Gallbladder

Liver

Cystic duct

Kidney

Duodenum

Ascending colon

Mesentery (cut)

Ileum (cut)

Ureter

Cecum

Appendix

Uterine tube

Broad ligament

Round ligament
of uterus

Left subclavian a.

Arch of aorta

Lung

Descending aorta

Esophagus

Pericardial cavity

Diaphragm

Stomach

Spleen

Lesser omentum

Transverse colon

Jejunum (cut)

Descending colon

Aorta

Common iliac a.
and v.

Sigmoid colon

Rectum

Ovary

Uterus

Urinary bladder

Fig. 8. Female, demonstrating visceral relations; lungs sectioned, heart and small bowel removed.

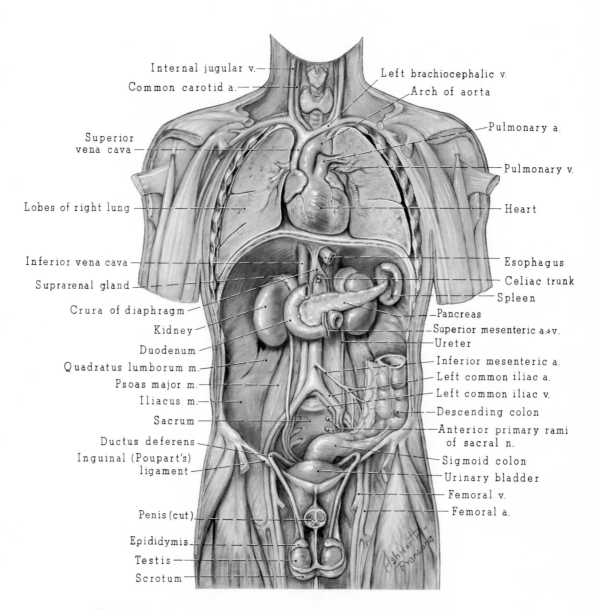

Internal jugular v.

Common carotid a.

Left brachiocephalic v.

Arch of aorta

Pulmonary a.

Superior
vena cava

Pulmonary v.

Lobes of right lung

Heart

Inferior vena cava

Esophagus

Suprarenal gland

Celiac trunk

Spleen

Crura of diaphragm

Pancreas

Kidney

Superior mesenteric a.+v.

Duodenum

Ureter

Quadratus lumborum m.

Inferior mesenteric a.

Psoas major m.

Left common iliac a.

Iliacus m.

Left common iliac v.

Sacrum

Descending colon

Ductus deferens

Anterior primary rami
of sacral n.

Inguinal (Poupart's)
ligament

Sigmoid colon

Urinary bladder

Femoral v.

Penis (cut)

Femoral a.

Epididymis

Testis

Scrotum

Fig. 9.   Male with stomach, small bowel, most of colon, and anterior part of lungs removed.

14

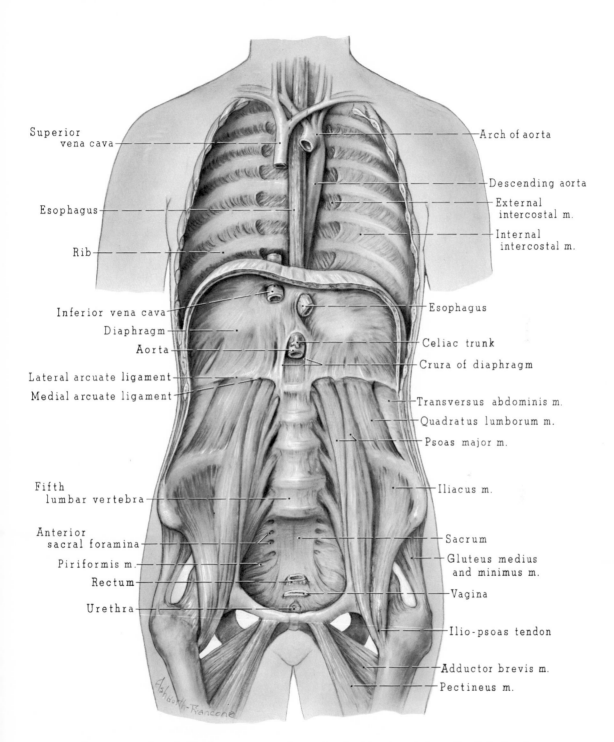

Superior vena cava

Arch of aorta

Descending aorta

External intercostal m.

Internal intercostal m.

Esophagus

Rib

Inferior vena cava

Esophagus

Diaphragm

Celiac trunk

Aorta

Crura of diaphragm

Lateral arcuate ligament

Medial arcuate ligament

Transversus abdominis m.

Quadratus lumborum m.

Psoas major m.

Fifth lumbar vertebra

Iliacus m.

Anterior sacral foramina

Sacrum

Piriformis m.

Gluteus medius and minimus m.

Rectum

Vagina

Urethra

Ilio-psoas tendon

Adductor brevis m.

Pectineus m.

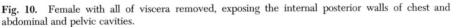

Fig. 10. Female with all of viscera removed, exposing the internal posterior walls of chest and abdominal and pelvic cavities.

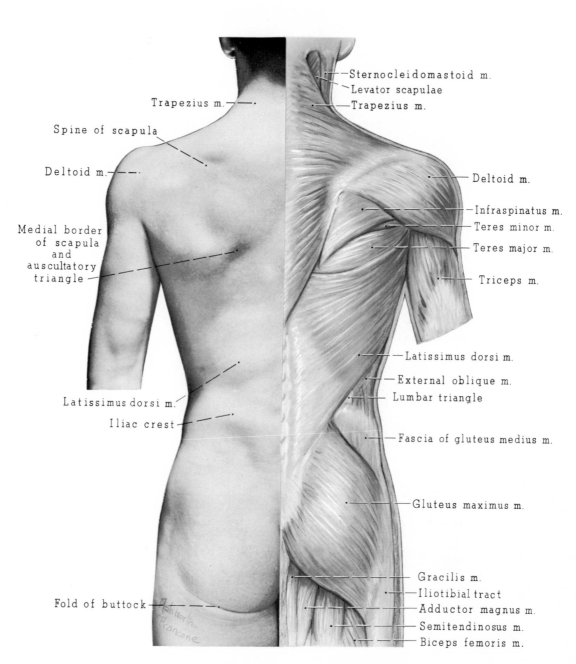

Fig. 11. Posterior view of male, showing skin removed on right side, exposing first layer of muscles.

16

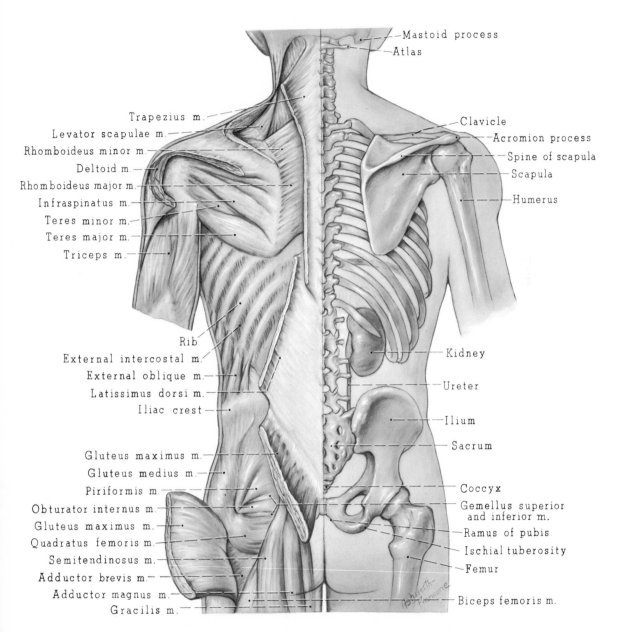

Mastoid process
Atlas

Trapezius m.
Levator scapulae m.
Rhomboideus minor m.
Deltoid m.
Rhomboideus major m.
Infraspinatus m.
Teres minor m.
Teres major m.
Triceps m.

Clavicle
Acromion process
Spine of scapula
Scapula
Humerus

Rib
External intercostal m.
External oblique m.
Latissimus dorsi m.
Iliac crest

Kidney
Ureter
Ilium
Sacrum

Gluteus maximus m.
Gluteus medius m.
Piriformis m.
Obturator internus m.
Gluteus maximus m.
Quadratus femoris m.
Semitendinosus m.
Adductor brevis m.
Adductor magnus m.
Gracilis m.

Coccyx
Gemellus superior
and inferior m.
Ramus of pubis
Ischial tuberosity
Femur
Biceps femoris m.

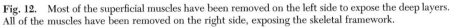

Fig. 12. Most of the superficial muscles have been removed on the left side to expose the deep layers.
All of the muscles have been removed on the right side, exposing the skeletal framework.

Continued from page 7.

The *respiratory system* is composed of the air sinuses, pharynx, larynx, trachea, bronchi, and lungs. It is involved in bringing oxygen to and in eliminating carbon dioxide from the blood.

The *digestive system* includes the alimentary tract with the associated glands from the lips to the anus. It converts food into simpler substances that can be absorbed and utilized by the body.

The *urinary system* comprises the kidneys, ureters, urinary bladder, and urethra. Its chief functions are the formation and elimination of urine and the maintenance of homeostasis.

The *endocrine system* includes the hypophysis (pituitary), thyroid, parathyroids, suprarenals, pancreatic islets in the pancreas, ovaries, testes, pineal body, and placenta (during pregnancy). The endocrine glands are involved in the chemical regulation of body functions.

The *reproductive system* consists of the ovaries, uterine tubes, uterus, vagina, and vulva in the female, and the testes, seminal vesicles, penis, prostate, and urethra in the male. It functions in perpetuation of the species.

THE INTEGRATED BODY

Though the body is studied in terms of organs and systems, functionally it can exist only as a whole. Even the simplest of tasks requires the participation of all the systems we have described.

SUMMARY: THE BODY AS A WHOLE

THE HUMAN BODY

Specialized cells are structurally and functionally integrated to form an organism.

1. Anatomy: the study of the structure of the living organism.
2. Physiology: the study of the function of the living organism.

CONSTITUTION AND STRUCTURE

1. Body build is thought to be an inherited characteristic representing familial types; four varieties are sthenic, hypersthenic, hyposthenic, and asthenic.

ORGANIZATION OF THE BODY

1. Four basic reference systems of organization are described:
   a. Direction: All descriptions of location or position assume the body to be erect, facing forward, with the arms at the side and the palms anterior. This is the so-called anatomic position. Directions include superior, inferior, anterior, posterior, cephalad, caudad, medial, lateral, proximal, and distal. Definitions of parietal and visceral are given.
   b. Planes: The body is discussed with respect to planes passing through it, including midsagittal, sagittal, horizontal, and frontal.
   c. Cavities:
      (1) Ventral cavity, subdivided into the thoracic (further divided into the pleural and pericardial) and the abdominal cavities. Organs of the visceral cavity are involved in homeostasis.
      (2) Dorsal cavity, divided into the cranial and spinal; the dorsal cavity contains structures of the nervous system.
   d. Structural units:
      (1) The cell: All living matter is composed of cells and cell products. The cell is comprised of protoplasm, an aqueous colloidal solution of protein, lipid, carbohydrate, and inorganic salts surrounded by a limiting

membrane. The necessary environment for the cell is provided by homeostasis.

(2) Tissue: Composed of cells and intercellular substance. Cells of a tissue are similar in appearance, function, and embryonic origin. The four types of tissues are epithelial, connective, muscle, and nervous.

(3) Organs: A group of tissues serving a common function brought together to form a single structure, such as the heart or lungs.

(4) System: Cells, tissues, and organs combine to form a system. The body contains the following major systems: skeletal, articular, muscular, nervous, circulatory, respiratory, digestive, urinary, endocrine, and reproductive. The special senses, skin, and lymphatic system are also considered.

THE INTEGRATED BODY

The body is studied by systems of organs but, functionally, it can exist only as a whole.

STUDY QUESTIONS: THE BODY AS A WHOLE

1. Define anatomy and physiology.
2. Body build can be classified into four types; discuss each.
3. Define the following directions: superior, inferior, anterior, posterior, cephalad, caudad, medial, lateral, proximal, and distal.
4. Differentiate parietal and visceral.
5. Explain the divisions of the four planes into which the body can be divided.
6. Compare the functions of the ventral and dorsal cavities.
7. Differentiate metabolism, anabolism, and catabolism.
8. For what reason is homeostasis necessary to the body?
9. What percentage of the body weight is comprised of water?
10. List the four types of tissue.
11. Define an organ.
12. List the ten major systems of the body.

CHAPTER TWO

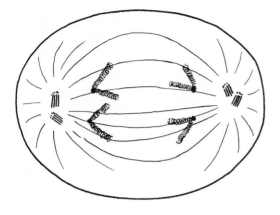

THE CELL

IMPORTANCE OF THE CELL

The human body is comprised of cells, intercellular matrix, and body fluids. Of the three, only the cells are living, with the characteristics of growth, metabolism, irritability, and reproduction.

The cell is the structural or morphologic unit of the body as well as its metabolic or physiologic unit. The human body develops from a single cell, the *fertilized ovum*. Repeated divisions of the ovum result in many types of cells differing from one another in composition and function; however, most of the basic structures of the cell are common to all.

STRUCTURE OF THE CELL
(Figs. 13 to 18)

Cells are composed of protoplasm continually carrying on dynamic biochemical processes. Protoplasm, a viscous, colloidal suspension, consists of protein, carbohydrate, lipid, electrolytes, and water. The term "protoplasm" is rapidly falling into disuse because of its nebulous description. There is some question as to the fundamental qualities of living versus non-living matter. Also, protoplasm differs markedly from cell to cell and even at different times in the same cell. It is, however, a useful term, calling attention to the fact that there is a wondrous material that one can almost analyze in chemical and physical terms forming the fundamental

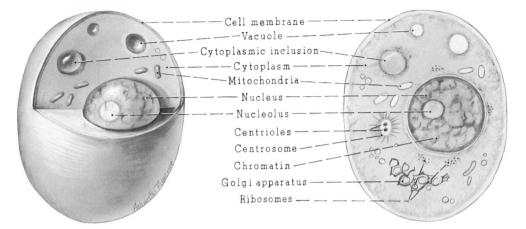

Fig. 13. Two views of a cell based on what can be seen in an electron microscope.

Labels (center): Cell membrane — Vacuole — Cytoplasmic inclusion — Cytoplasm — Mitochondria — Nucleus — Nucleolus — Centrioles — Centrosome — Chromatin — Golgi apparatus — Ribosomes

"living" substance of cells. The cell possesses numerous structural parts:
1. Cell membrane
2. Nucleus
   a. Nucleoli
   b. Chromosomes
3. Cytoplasm
   a. Cytoplasmic organelles
      (1) Endoplasmic reticulum
      (2) Ribosomes
      (3) Golgi apparatus
      (4) Mitochondria
      (5) Centrosomes
      (6) Lysosomes
      (7) Fibrils
   b. Cytoplasmic inclusions
      (1) Secretory granules
      (2) Pigment granules

Cell Membrane

The cell membrane (plasmalemma) is a thin covering of the outer surface of the cytoplasm. It approximates 75 Å (10^{-7} mm.) in thickness and consists of three layers. Electron microscopy reveals many infoldings continuous with the *endoplasmic reticulum*. These infoldings provide a route by which materials can be transported from the outside to the inside of the cell.

The cell membrane possesses the following characteristics. (1) Lipids are soluble within it and can readily move through it. (2) Chemical analyses of the red blood cell membrane have shown that it consists of a network of protein fibers with many of the spaces filled with lipid. (3) Small molecular substances not lipid soluble are able to diffuse directly through the membrane. It has been assumed that the cell membrane possesses many minute pores; however, the very nature of the plasmalemma with its multitudinous pinocytotic vesicles can also be used in the argument that the membrane has no pores. This argument is supported by many investigations showing that particulate materials are brought into the cell in a small vacuole (a pinocytotic vacuole) in the process of *pinocytosis* (see page 25). These particles are taken across the membrane in such a way that a hole or pore is not necessary. This would be a much more appealing way to accept and discharge materials into the cell, and it is now questionable whether pores are really necessary or even exist as such in ordinary cells.

The Nucleus

The nucleus consists of a nuclear membrane, nucleoli, and chromosomes within a matrix. The structure of the nucleus is important to all biological science, because the chromosomes it contains transmit the heredity of the cell from generation to generation. Each cell begins its existence with a nucleus which on occasion can be lost when the cell reaches its mature form. An example is the red blood cell, in which the nucleus is extruded before the cell reaches the blood. A few cell types, such as the megakaryocyte of bone marrow, possess multiple nuclei.

Nuclear membrane. The nucleus of the cell during interphase (the period when it is not dividing) consists of protoplasm called karyoplasm segregated from the rest of the cell by the nuclear membrane. Electron micrographs reveal that the nuclear membrane is fenestrated (perforated) and double.

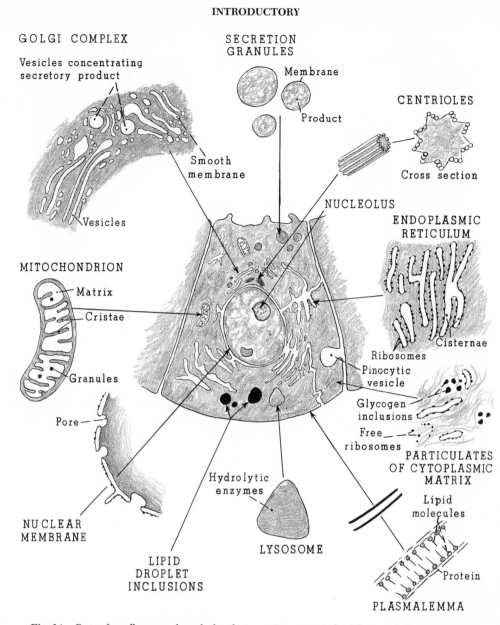

Fig. 14. Parts of a cell as seen through the electron microscope. (After Bloom and Fawcett: *A Textbook of Histology,* eighth edition. Philadelphia, W. B. Saunders, 1962.)

Nucleoli. At various times, a nucleus may possess one, several, or no *nucleoli.* Nucleoli are composed of RNA and protein lying "naked" in the karyoplasm—that is, not segregated by a membrane. Nucleoli are prominent in cells synthesizing protein (a function of RNA).

Chromosomes. During interphase, chromosomes exist in thin threads; only during mitosis do they assume the often-pictured twin helical, rod-like structure.

Forty-six chromosomes exist in the human somatic or body cell and 23 in the gametes (sperm and ova). Further analysis reveals that there are only 23 different types of chromosomes in the body cells, but each type has a mate or is duplicated. Twenty-two of these pairs (a total of 44 chromosomes) are autosomes and the 23rd pair, the sex chromosomes. The pair of sex chromosomes can be identical (called X), in which case the individual is a female, or can consist of one X- and one smaller Y-chromosome characterizing a male. Female neutrophils have a drumstick appendage attached to the nucleus that is not present on the nucleus of the neutro-

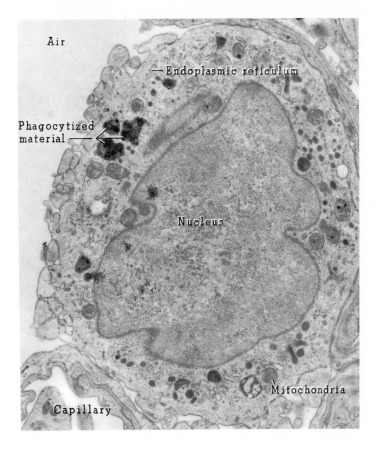

Fig. 15. A lung macrophage (alveolar macrophage) magnified 18,000×.

phils of the male. The drumstick appendage may represent the second X-chromosome.

Cytoplasm

Protoplasm outside the nucleus is called cytoplasm, the storage and working area of the cell. It contains two types of structures: organelles and inclusions. Organelles are living structures converting energy and usually possessing a surrounding membrane. Inclusions are non-living aggregations of carbohydrate, lipid, or pigment.

Cytoplasmic organelles. The most impressive organelle is the one pervading the entire cytoplasm, the *endoplasmic reticulum,* which is continuous with the plasmalemma and nuclear membrane. Two distinct varieties can be seen, each with a different function. The *smooth* type produces lipid, such as cholesterol. The *rough* type derives its name from the presence of attached ribosomes and produces protein. The endoplasmic reticulum-ribosome network synthesizes protein for cell utilization and export.

Ribosomes are dense aggregations of RNA and protein, usually attached to the endoplasmic reticulum. They are the site of protein synthesis and function in accord with the coded information carried from the nucleus by messenger RNA (see page 31).

The *Golgi complex* or *apparatus* consists of the same type of trilaminar membrane as the cell membrane, but includes an array of parallel membranes and small vesicles without ribosomes. The Golgi apparatus functions in collecting and packaging the products of cell synthesis to be stored until secreted.

Mitochondria, the "powerhouses" of the cell, contain the oxidative enzymes for breaking down glycogen and glucose into water and carbon dioxide with a release of energy. Mitochondria are found in all animals and plants. Though their shape varies according to function, they all exhibit a double membrane arrangement, with the inner membrane lifted into folds called *cristae.* The oxidative enzymes of the Krebs cycle seem to be specifically oriented in or on the inner membrane, while the enzymes involved in glycolysis float in the mitochondrial matrix.

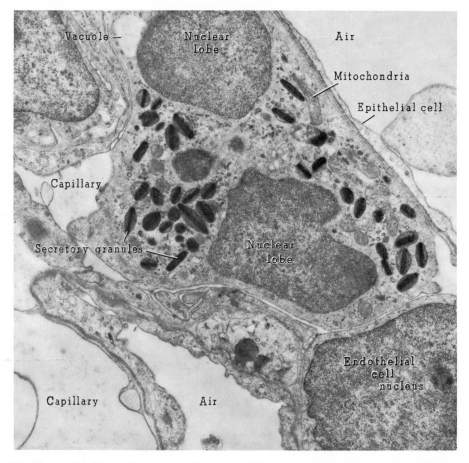

Fig. 16. A white blood cell, the eosinophil, is seen within a lung capillary. The very thin wall of the lung capillaries consists of three layers: epithelium, basement membrane, and endothelium. (Magnified 17,200×.)

The *centrosome* of the interphase cell consists of two small, hollow, cylindrical structures known as centrioles. Centrioles are involved in cell division, and are also found at the base of the cilia and flagella.

The *lysosome* is the membranous structure containing hydrolytic enzymes. Destruction of tissues after death is due in part to the release of these enzymes following disintegration of the lysosome membrane. They were referred to as the "suicide bags" by the investigators who first discovered them.

Fibrils appear during cell division. The function of fibrils will be considered on page 29.

Cytoplasmic inclusions. Inclusions are non-living aggregations of carbohydrate, lipid, or pigment and are temporary features of the cell. They serve as stores supplying raw materials for the tasks of the organelles.

Many cells contain precursors of enzymes which become active when released from the cell. These are called proenzymes or *zymogen granules* and are presumably collected inclusions seen in cells as droplets of fat, glycogen, and pigment.

PHYSIOLOGY OF THE CELL (Fig. 19)

The human body is composed of about one hundred trillion cells. Cells have different specialized functions, including movement of substances through the cell membranes, metabolism, and reproduction.

Movement Across the Cell Membrane

The plasmalemma is a semipermeable membrane permitting certain molecules to enter the

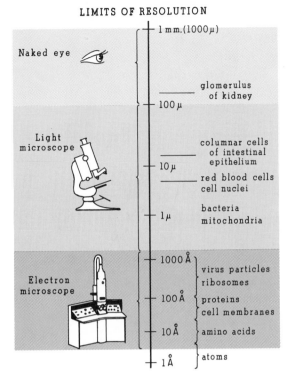

LIMITS OF RESOLUTION

Naked eye

1 mm.(1000μ)

glomerulus of kidney

100 μ

Light microscope

columnar cells of intestinal epithelium

10 μ

red blood cells cell nuclei

bacteria mitochondria

1 μ

Electron microscope

1000 Å

virus particles ribosomes

100 Å

proteins cell membranes

10 Å

amino acids

1 Å

atoms

Fig. 17. The limits of resolution of the electron microscope as contrasted to those of the eye and the light microscope. A millimeter, mm., is equal to ¹⁄₁₀₀₀ meter, or 0.03937 inch; a micron, μ, ¹⁄₁₀₀₀ millimeter; an angstrom, Å, ¹⁄₁₀,₀₀₀ micron.

brownian motion, and the end result, diffusion. Obviously, more collisions will occur in an area of higher concentration than one of lower concentration, serving to disperse the particles throughout the solution.

Osmosis. A membrane which is permeable to water, sodium, and chloride can be placed so as to divide a beaker of water into two equal portions, with sodium chloride added to only one side. Ions will migrate freely through the membrane until an equal concentration of both sodium and chloride is reached on both sides. This process is termed diffusion. On the other hand, if the membrane is impermeable to sodium and chloride, water molecules will migrate freely across the membrane in an attempt to establish equilibrium. Movement of water molecules is called *osmosis.*

If the sodium chloride solution is placed in a funnel, and the mouth sealed by a semipermeable membrane preventing the movement of sodium and chloride ions, water molecules will pass freely in either direction, but will predominantly enter the funnel. This causes a rise in the level of the solution and continues until the hydrostatic pressure exerted by a column of fluid in the funnel is equal to the pressure exerted by the water molecules passing through the membrane into the funnel. This results in an increased volume of solution causing a rise in hydrostatic pressure. The hydrostatic pressure

cell and excluding others. There are five general mechanisms allowing entry of substances into cells: pinocytosis and phagocytosis, diffusion, osmosis, filtration, and active transport (Fig. 19).

Pinocytosis is the phenomenon in which minute incuppings or invaginations are formed on the surface of cells creating fluid-filled vacuoles. These vacuoles then move to the interior of the cell.

Phagocytosis is the ingestion of solid particles. The ameba engulfs food by surrounding it and taking the substance directly into the cell. Similarly, mammalian cells, particularly macrophages (histiocytes) engulf foreign substances.

Diffusion. All molecules and ions in the body fluids, including both water and dissolved substances, are in constant motion. Each particle in the fluid medium moves in its own separate way. When one molecule bounces against another, its electrostatic forces repel the second, momentarily adding to the energy of motion of the new molecule while losing this energy itself; consequently, the new molecule moves more rapidly than before, while the other slows down. This continual movement of molecules is called

Fig. 18. The electron microscope is now being employed to study structures at a magnification of 200,000×.

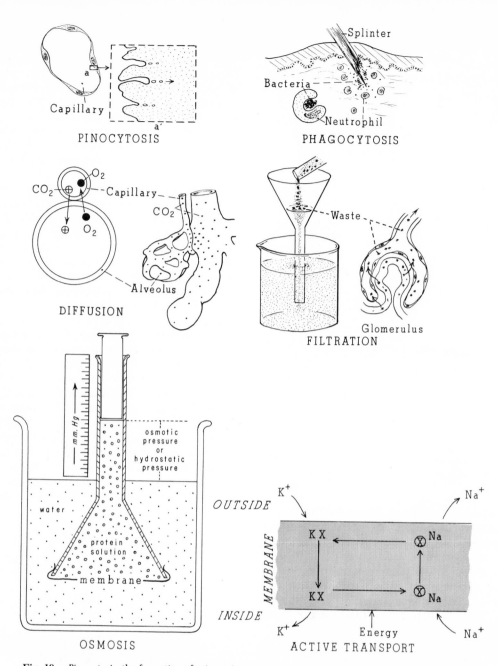

PINOCYTOSIS

PHAGOCYTOSIS

DIFFUSION

FILTRATION

OSMOSIS

ACTIVE TRANSPORT

Fig. 19. *Pinocytosis,* the formation of minute incuppings or invaginations on the surface of a cell, is illustrated by the absorption of liquid by an endothelial cell surrounding a capillary.

Phagocytosis differs from pinocytosis in that ingestion of *solid* particles takes place as in the neutrophil shown ingesting bacteria at the site of a wound.

Diffusion results from the continual movement of molecules causing collisions which occur in greater numbers in areas of higher concentration, thus dispersing the molecules to areas of lower concentration until equilibrium is established. This process is illustrated above by the dispersion of carbon dioxide and oxygen to areas of lesser concentration through the alveolar membrane of the lung.

Filtration is defined as the passage of a liquid through a filter, such as the passage of plasma through the glomerulus into the glomerular capsule.

Osmosis is demonstrated as the level of the solution in the funnel continues to rise until the hydrostatic pressure exerted by a column of fluid in the funnel is equal to the pressure exerted by the water molecules passing through the membrane.

Active transport is represented hypothetically by assuming that substances $\times$ and $\otimes$ are confined to the membrane. $\times$ has a high affinity for K^+; $\otimes$ a high affinity for Na^+. $\times$ and $\otimes$ move through the membrane only when in combination with an ion. Once $\times$ has traversed the membrane it is converted into a Na^+ specific substance, $\otimes$. This process occurs only when energy is made available to the system.

then represented by the height of the column of salt solution in the tube is the *osmotic pressure* and is dependent on the number of particles or ions of the salt in a given volume of solution. Thus, the more concentrated the salt solution, the greater the osmotic pressure; the less concentrated the solution, the lower the osmotic pressure.

Filtration. This is the process in which water and dissolved substances are "pushed" through a permeable membrane from an area of higher pressure to one of lower pressure; formation of tissue fluid is an example. The hydrostatic pressure in the first part of the capillary bed, secondary to the pumping action of the heart, is higher than the pressure of the surrounding fluid. Thus, water and dissolved substances are pushed into the tissue spaces.

Active transport. Positive ions, such as sodium and potassium, are not distributed equally across the cell membrane. More potassium ions are present intracellularly and more sodium ions extracellularly. Hence, these ions are maintained in both intracellular and extracellular locations against concentration gradients. This movement of ions against the concentration gradient or at a rate faster than can be explained by diffusion alone is called *active transport.* When an energy expenditure by the cell is required, the process is an active one. On the other hand, diffusion and osmosis do not require energy and are passive processes.

Since Na^+ can and does enter cells and since the intracellular sodium concentration does not increase, some active mechanism must exist within the cell system responsible for expelling Na^+ against its concentration gradient. The mechanism responsible is the sodium pump. The word "pump" indicates that the process is active, requiring an expenditure of energy.

Metabolism

The structural units of the cell are ultimately dependent on the three basic classes of organic compounds: carbohydrate, lipid, and protein in an aqueous ionic medium. All non-ionic molecules found in the body can be categorized into one of these three classes. Many molecules contain components of two or more of these classes such as mucoprotein, or glycoprotein with a carbohydrate molecule attached to a protein molecule.

The approximate percentage composition of a variety of tissues is presented in Table 1 (Chapter One). The differences reflect varying functional requirements of tissues in different organs of the body. For example, the brain has a high lipid content and the lipids play a vital role in the effective rapid propagation of the variable amounts of both lipid and carbohydrate present. These compounds are stored in the liver and mobilized when required.

Intermediary metabolism. Intermediary metabolism includes all the processes taking place from the moment a nutrient is ingested until the chemical products are returned to the environment. *Anabolism* includes all the synthetic or building-up processes, and *catabolism* the destructive or breaking-down processes. These chemical transformations are the basis for energy production and storage and are together known as metabolism.

The *basal metabolic rate* of an intact organism is commonly measured in the resting state and is based on the amount of oxygen consumed as related to body weight, surface area, temperature, sex, and a measured time interval. This is possible since metabolism is dependent on oxygen utilization. The large *Calorie* (1 kilocalorie) used in metabolic studies is the amount of heat required to raise the temperature of 1000 grams of water from 15 to 16 degrees centigrade (1° C.). The kilocalorie per gram value of carbohydrate and proteins is 4.1, while that of lipids is 9.3. Thus, a diet high in fat is more likely to provide adequate calories than diets high in carbohydrate and protein. It is for this reason that many attempts have been made to administer fat intravenously to patients with nutritional deficiencies. Since the body does not effectively utilize heat as a source of energy, complex chemical transformations occur in many steps, each mediated by a specific enzyme, to create energy in a form available for use by the cell.

Three major stages in this chemical transformation process include:

1. The conversion of complex molecules to simpler ones.

2. The transformation of these simple molecules in aerobic (oxygen required) and anaerobic (oxygen not required) cycles producing chemical products that can be transferred to energy storage molecules.

3. The conversion of these chemical products into the energy storage molecules which are phosphorylated compounds. Adenosine triphosphate (ATP) is the classic source of mammalian energy.

Extraction of energy from nutrients. Carbohydrates, fats, and proteins are the principal

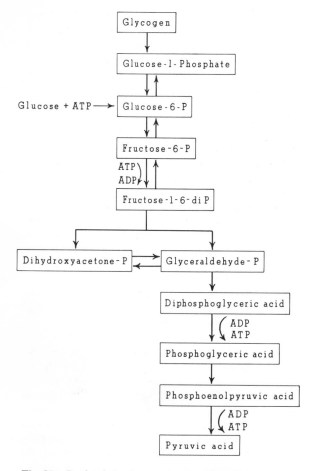

Fig. 20. In glycolysis glycogen is eventually split by a series of chemical reactions into pyruvic acid. The series of intermediate reactions is shown in abbreviated form.

through the action of another enzyme, is converted into *acetyl coenzyme A*. This compound undergoes another series of transformations collectively called the *citric acid* or *Krebs cycle*. In this series of reactions, the pyruvic acid is converted into carbon dioxide and hydrogen. The carbon dioxide leaves the cell, while the hydrogen atoms combine with the hydrogen "carriers" of the *flavoprotein cytochrome system* to be ultimately "carried" by or combined with oxygen to make water. Thus, the final products of the metabolism of glucose are carbon dioxide, water, and energy.

During the oxidation of pyruvic acid, energy is released and used to synthesize additional adenosine triphosphate (over ten times more than by the anaerobic process of glycolysis from glucose down to pyruvic acid).

Adenosine triphosphate. Adenosine triphosphate (ATP) is a nucleotide composed of the nitrogenous base adenine, the 5-carbon sugar ribose, and three molecules of phosphoric acid. Two of these phosphoric acid radicals are connected to molecules by *high energy phosphate bonds,* containing 7 kilocalories of energy per mole of ATP. These bonds are labile and can split rapidly whenever energy is required to promote other chemical reactions.

nutrient substances from which cells extract energy. Carbohydrates are digested into glucose and simple sugars. Fats are split into fatty acids. Proteins are broken down into amino acids. These materials are transported into cells and further split into still smaller compounds to liberate energy. Most of the energy is released when hydrogen is removed from the food source in the process of oxidation.

Glycolysis. Glucose is transported into the cell by means of an enzymatic carrier mechanism, where it is converted into pyruvic acid by the process of *glycolysis,* involving 14 different stages and 12 different enzyme systems. Through the process of glycolysis, glycogen is converted into pyruvic acid. (Figure 20 shows intermediate steps.)

Citric acid cycle (Krebs cycle or tricarboxylic acid cycle) (Fig. 21). Pyruvic acid formed by glycolysis diffuses into the mitochondria and,

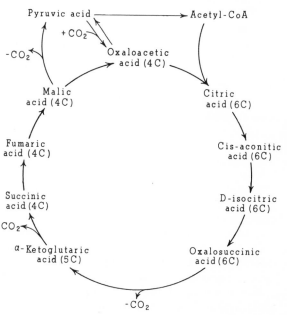

Fig. 21. Pyruvic acid undergoes a series of transformations—known collectively as the Krebs cycle—in which it is converted into carbon dioxide, water, and energy in the form of ATP.

Enzymatic Action

Biochemical reactions in the cell occur with amazing efficiency at body temperatures and pressure. If such reactions were performed in the laboratory, boiling temperatures and high pressure would be required. Even so, energy would be released abruptly and most would be lost.

How, then, does the cell circumvent these important barriers? It does so by way of *enzymes*, which are large protein molecules acting like the catalysts of inorganic chemistry, speeding the rates of intracellular chemical reactions. Without enzymes, reactions would proceed so slowly that life could not exist.

Coenzymes are small molecules attached to the large proteins and are necessary for proper enzyme function. Many of the B-complex vitamins are coenzymes.

Cell Division

Cells that are specialized or differentiated, such as the nerve or red blood cells, are unable to reproduce and must be replenished by less differentiated precursors. These primitive cells undergo a process of cell division called *mitosis*. Two daughter cells are produced identical to the parent type, or one of the two daughter cells differentiates into a special cell, while the other retains its primitive character.

Mitosis is a continuous process described in four stages. The normal functioning state of the cell is called the interphase (the "resting" phase during which most of the cellular "work" occurs). During interphase, immediately prior to the first stage of cell division, or prophase, the DNA molecule is duplicated, thus doubling the cellular DNA content. Meiosis is a form of cell division in which there is a reduction in the number of chromosomes to one-half of the original. If such a reduction did not occur, a sperm with 46 chromosomes fertilizing an ovum with 46 chromosomes would produce a zygote with 92 chromosomes. To circumvent this, *germ cells* cleave meiotically (see Chapter Seventeen). The following is a tabular account of the phase characteristics of mitosis (Fig. 22).

Prophase

1. Chromosome: The DNA protein complex (chromatin network of threads) becomes coiled, and chromosomes can easily be seen on stained sections. As the chromosomes become larger, they can be seen to be duplicated into two highly coiled parallel strands (chromatids) which are attached to one another by a centromere.

2. Nucleolus: During the last part of prophase, the nucleolus disappears.

3. Nuclear membrane: The nuclear membrane disappears during the late prophase period.

4. Centrosome: The centrosome divides equally into two smaller bodies called *centrioles* which migrate to opposite sides of the cell. As the centrioles move apart, a figure called the mitotic spindle is formed that extends from one centriole to the other. The spindle is composed of thin fibrils or *astral rays*.

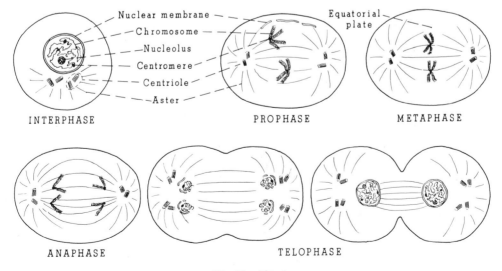

Fig. 22.   Mitosis.

METAPHASE

1. Chromosomes: The chromosomes move toward the center of the cell and arrange themselves in a plane perpendicular to a line connecting the two centrioles. This plane is called the equatorial plate.

2. Nucleolus: Absent.

3. Nuclear membrane: Absent.

4. Centrioles and spindle: The thin fibrils from the centrioles appear to be attached to the chromosomes at the centromere.

ANAPHASE

1. Chromosomes: The centromere divides, releasing the members of the chromatid pair from each other.

2. Nucleolus: Absent.

3. Nuclear membrane: Absent.

4. Centrioles and spindle: The astral rays give the appearance of pulling the chromatids toward the opposite centrioles. It is not known whether the centromeres repel each other or whether the astral rays pull the centromeres apart (however, cutting the spindle fibers does not completely prevent anaphase). When the chromatids have been separated from each other, they are again called chromosomes. The significant feature of this stage is that one chromatid from each of the 46 chromosomes finds its way into each daughter cell, giving each cell an identical complement of chromosomes.

TELOPHASE

1. Chromosomes: The chromosomes reach the general location of the centrioles and begin to uncoil.

2. Nucleolus: A nucleolus appears in each cell.

3. Nuclear membrane: The nuclear membrane reforms around each group of chromosomes.

4. Centromere and spindle: The centriole has, by now, formed a duplicate centriole and the spindle has disappeared.

5. Plasmalemma: The plasmalemma indents at the point of the equatorial plate, dividing the cytoplasm into two parts.

Mitosis permits perpetuation. There is a duplication of all cell parts with provision for transmitting a controlling mechanism into each of the cells produced. The details of the process are obscure, but the task is obviously performed with efficiency and accuracy, considering that it occurs more than a billion times during human development.

THE GENETIC CODE

The science of genetics began over a hundred years ago in what is now Czechoslovakia, when Mendel watched successive generations of peas grow. He concluded that a unit carried the genetic instructions from one generation to another with mathematical regularity. These instructions, called the genetic code, are now known to be held in the nucleus of the cells in tightly coiled strands of deoxyribose nucleic acid (DNA). DNA was isolated in 1869 by Miescher.

At the turn of the century the work of Mendel was rediscovered and is now the cornerstone of modern genetic theory. The unit Mendel discovered is the *gene*, originating from the Greek word meaning "to be born." The belief that these units of heredity are to be found among the dark, rod-like *chromosomes* in the nuclei of all cells was eventually confirmed during the second decade of this century.

Chromosomes. Chromosomes, which house the genes, are composed largely of protein and *deoxyribose nucleic acid* (DNA). In early work in the field of genetics, it was reasonable to suppose that either the protein or the DNA was the actual genetic material. For many years, it was assumed that the genetic code or specificity was carried in the chromosomal protein and that the DNA molecule was too simple to allow the production of a large number of different genes. It is now, however, accepted that DNA is the genetic material.

DNA (Fig. 23). In 1944, DNA was isolated from the nuclei of a strain of pneumonia-producing bacteria. The DNA was then given to a different bacterial strain. Soon the second strain began to act like the first. The second bacterial type had, in essence, been changed from one type of organism to another. This indicated that DNA carried the genetic code.

Everything characteristic of a living entity—its size, shape, and orderly development from infancy to death—that can be passed on to its progeny is recorded by an arrangement of molecules in its DNA. In order to understand how DNA can carry such a vast wealth of information, one must take a brief look at its structure.

Each unit comprising the DNA macromolecule consists of three different molecules, including the following.

1. *A nitrogenous base*, either one of the purines (adenine or guanine) or one of the pyrimidines (cytosine or thymine).

2. *A sugar*, deoxyribose.

3. *A phosphate*.

This repeating unit of the DNA macromolecule is called the nucleotide, named for the nitrogenous base it contains. For example, if the base is thymine, the nucleotide is thymidine phosphate.

In the actual DNA polymer, the nucleotides are held in position by ester linkages (covalent bonds) between the phosphate of one and the sugar of the other, and so forth. DNA consists of two stacks or strands of nucleotides, arranged with their nitrogenous bases facing each other. The two strands are twisted to form a double spiral or "helix."

In contrast to the covalent bonds holding the nucleotides in a stack, the weak chemical bonds that hold the two stacks together are of a different type called "hydrogen bonds." In order for the two strands of the DNA molecule to separate, only the weak bonds must be ruptured. These "hydrogen bonds" are formed between the nitrogenous bases of adjacent strands, so that the adenine of one chain is always attached to a thymine of the other, and the guanine of one to the cytosine of the other. This relationship between the two chains of DNA is thought to be constant.

Protein synthesis (Fig. 24). DNA governs the production of both the enzymatic and nonenzymatic proteins of the body and records in code form the amino acid arrangement which must be followed to synthesize a particular protein. This order of amino acids in protein is determined by the nucleotides of DNA. Thus, each amino acid must be expressed in terms of nucleotides in the DNA structure. Many different amino acids and other molecular constituents of protein exist, but only four nitrogenous bases—adenine, guanine, cytosine, and thymine—are found in DNA. These four bases, arranged in such a way as to avoid ambiguity, become the code or symbol for an amino acid.

Since DNA is a nuclear constituent, the activities discussed have been confined to the nucleus. Major protein synthesis, however, does not occur in the nucleus, but takes place in the special cytoplasmic structures called ribosomes. Information is replicated from DNA in another type of nucleic acid, *ribonucleic acid* (RNA).

RNA contains the sugar *ribose* instead of deoxyribose, uracil in place of thymine, and is single stranded, but otherwise it resembles DNA. RNA replicates of information encoded in DNA are probably made in much the same fashion as DNA replicates. Since one type of RNA carries information from the DNA of the nucleus to cytoplasmic sites, it can logically be called *messenger RNA*.

The major protein "assembly lines" of the cells are located in the *ribosomes*, consisting chiefly of ribonucleic acid. Ribosomes are found in the endoplasmic reticulum and can be considered as "factories" with access to all needed raw materials. The ribosomal machinery needs to be "programed." Messenger RNA is the carrier of these instructions from the "top office to the plant." Messenger RNA carries the program needed to manufacture one type of protein.

Amino acid activation. The basic materials of protein are amino acids. The synthesis of protein revolves around the formation of peptide bonds between the amino acids. The major source of energy for this process is ATP (see page 27). The activated amino acid must be in the place programed for it on the "assembly line." To find this position, it is necessary to read the coded instructions. Since activated amino acids cannot accomplish this, a code-reading escort, also RNA, but of a lower molecular weight than messenger RNA, is needed to lead it to its reserved spot. This is known as *transfer RNA*. It reacts with an activated amino acid transferring the amino acid to the correct spot on the "assembly line." When all amino acids are in place, the peptide bonds are established and the protein formed. Simultaneously, transfer RNA is released to repeat the process.

Genetic biology. What does genetic biology mean to medicine? Scientists are becoming increasingly aware that a number of clinical conditions may be the result of alterations in certain enzymes caused by a faulty or ineffective mechanism of the protein construction information stored in normal DNA to be relayed to synthesizing sites. Many disorders arise because the ribosomal template from which enzymatic proteins form is defective. DNA controls the configuration of the template. Abnormal hemoglobin disorders, for instance, are caused by a faulty arrangement of nucleotides in DNA leading to the substitution of one amino acid for another in the formation of the hemoglobin molecule. Substitution of only one amino acid out of a total of approximately 300 amino acids forming the hemoglobin molecule may cause sickle cell anemia (red blood cells are crescentic in shape).

Eventually it may be possible to restore the synthesis of a missing enzyme by providing the

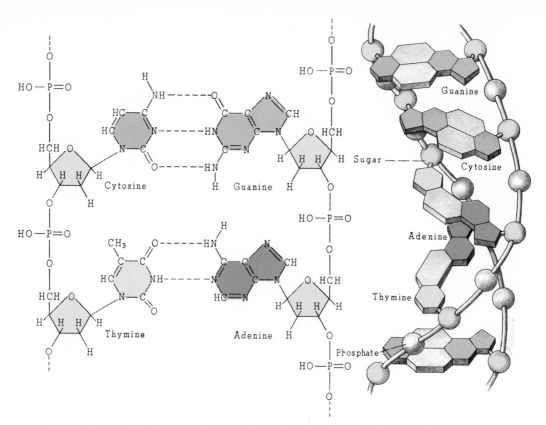

Fig. 23. Chemical structure and diagrammatic representation of DNA molecule and its components (Richard Lyons, M.D.).

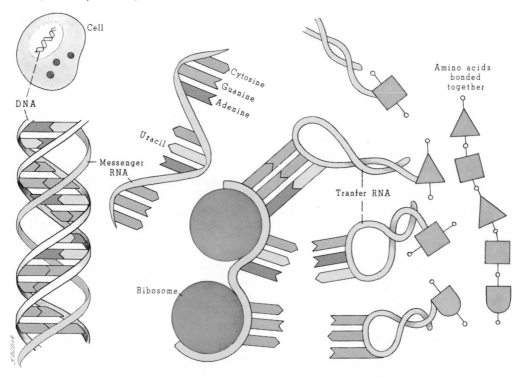

Fig. 24. Messenger RNA duplicates the information encoded in the DNA molecule and attaches itself to the ribosomes. Amino acids, carried by loops of transfer RNA, are bonded together, move away, and become a three-dimensional protein. (Modified from sketch by S. Baty.)

correct code for that enzyme in the form of RNA from normal cells. This has already been achieved in at least one experimental situation. When RNA from the liver cells of a normal rat is injected into the tumor cells of a rat with cancer, the cancer stops growing. Apparently the normal RNA supersedes the faulty genetic instructions carried by the diseased rat. These techniques are only the first step toward control of genetic diseases. If the incorrect gene could be suppressed, and the correct gene which is present but dormant, activated, it is conceivable that many illnesses could be reversed.

It is obvious that there must be some sort of control. All cells are equipped with a complete set of DNA—the equivalent of a million instructions. In some remarkable manner, suprarenal

gland cells, for example, read only a small fraction of these million instructions to produce hormones. Cells in the pancreatic islets (islets of Langerhans) produce insulin and glucagon; other instructions are ignored. The mechanism of this intricate control is not yet known.

It takes little imagination to foresee a future sequence of events. First, a particular coded gene in the formation of insulin could be located within the germ plasm of the parent. The defective gene could be removed by breaking the bonds holding it to the DNA strand. Finally, a normal gene from the donor could be installed in its place. Given power over heredity, who would exercise it and what would be its limits? This question may perplex man for generations.

SUMMARY: THE CELL

IMPORTANCE OF THE CELL

1. **The cell is the structural or morphologic unit of the body as well as its metabolic or physiologic unit.**

   a. The human body develops from a single cell, the fertilized ovum.
   b. Composition: Cells are composed of protoplasm.

STRUCTURE OF THE CELL

The cell is composed of the cell membrane, nucleus, and cytoplasm.
1. **The cell membrane or plasmalemma is a thin covering of the outer surface of the cytoplasm; it possesses many infoldings through which materials can be transported from the outside to the inside of the cell. The plasmalemma and nucleus control cell activity; the plasmalemma acts as the initial line of defense and determines the substances accepted or rejected by the cell.**

2. **Nucleus:**

   a. The nucleus can be lost when the cell matures. Most cells have a single nucleus consisting of a nuclear membrane, nucleoli, and chromosomes.
   (1) Nuclear membrane: The nuclear membrane separates the protoplasm, karyoplasm, from the rest of the cell during interphase; it is double layered and porous.
   (2) Nucleoli: One or several are found in the nucleus at various times; they are composed of RNA and protein. Nucleoli are prominent in cells synthesizing protein.
   (3) Chromosomes: Chromosomes exist in thin threads during interphase. During mitosis they assume the twin helical, rod-like structure. Forty-six chromosomes exist in the body cell and 23 in the gametes. One of the 23 pairs is the sex chromosomes. If the pair of sex chromosomes is identical (called X) the person will be female; if the pair is one X- and one Y-chromosome, the individual is a male.

3. Cytoplasm:

    a. Protoplasm outside the nucleus of the cell is called cytoplasm; this substance carries out the directions of the nucleus; organelles and inclusions are both found in the cytoplasm.

    b. Organelles: The organelles include endoplasmic reticulum, ribosomes, the Golgi complex, centrosome, lysosome, fibrils, and mitochondria; organelles are living structures converting energy.

    c. Cytoplasmic inclusions: Non-protoplasmic or non-living aggregations of molecules, carbohydrate, lipid, or pigment and are temporary features of the cell; most inclusions are stores supplying raw materials for the tasks of the organelles.

PHYSIOLOGY OF THE CELL

1. **Five general mechanisms allow entry of substances into cells: pinocytosis and phagocytosis, diffusion, osmosis, filtration, and active transport.**

    a. Pinocytosis: Minute incuppings or invaginations are formed on the surface of cells, creating fluid-filled vacuoles; the vacuoles then move to the interior of the cell. Phagocytosis: Ingestion of solid particles (ameba-like action).

    b. Diffusion: The movement of ions and molecules in solution due to the constant random motion and collision of these particles.

    c. Osmosis: If the cell membrane is impermeable to sodium and chloride, water molecules will migrate freely across the membrane in an attempt to establish equilibrium.

    d. Filtration: The passage of a liquid through a membrane due to positive pressure on one side of the membrane.

    e. Active transport: The movement of ions against a concentration gradient or at a rate faster than can be explained by diffusion alone. Active transport requires an energy expenditure by the cell.

2. **Cellular metabolism: The structural units of the cell are ultimately dependent on the three basic classes of organic compounds: carbohydrate, lipid, and protein in an aqueous ionic medium. All non-ionic molecules found in the body can be categorized into one of these classes.**

    a. Intermediary metabolism: This includes all the processes from the moment a nutrient is ingested until the chemical products are returned to the environment. The body does not effectively utilize heat as a source of energy; complex chemical transformations occur.

    b. Extraction of energy from nutrients: Carbohydrate, fat, and protein are the principal nutrient substances from which cells extract energy. Carbohydrates are digested into simple sugars such as glucose, fats split into fatty acids, and proteins are broken into amino acids; these materials are further split into smaller compounds to liberate energy.

        (1) Glycolysis: One molecule of glucose is converted into pyruvic acid and released energy takes part in the citric acid cycle.

        (2) Citric acid cycle:

            (a) Pyruvic acid diffuses into the mitochondria and through the action of another enzyme is converted into acetyl coenzyme A; this compound undergoes another transformation known as the citric acid or Kreb's cycle. The pyruvic acid is converted into carbon dioxide and hydrogen. The carbon dioxide leaves the cell, while the hydrogen atoms combine with the hydrogen "carriers" of the flavoprotein-cytochrome system to be combined with oxygen to make water. Thus, the final products of the metabolism of glucose are carbon dioxide, water, and energy.

   (b) Two of the phosphoric acid radicals found in adenosine triphosphate are connected to molecules by high energy phosphate bonds. These bonds are labile and can split rapidly whenever energy is required to promote other chemical reactions.

3. **Enzyme action: Biochemical reactions in the cell take place efficiently and at low temperatures and pressures; this is due to enzyme action. Enzymes are large protein molecules acting like the catalysts of inorganic chemistry which speed the rates of intracellular chemical reactions.**

4. **Cell division: Cells that have specialized or differentiated are unable to reproduce and must be replenished by less differentiated precursors. These primitive cells undergo a process of cell division called mitosis. Mitosis can be divided into four stages: prophase, metaphase, anaphase, and telophase.**

THE GENETIC CODE

1. **The gene, discovered by Mendel, is a unit carrying the genetic instructions from one generation to another with mathematic regularity; the instructions are called the genetic code.**

  a. Form:
    (1) DNA: The genetic code is now known to be held in the nucleus of the cells in tightly coiled strands of deoxyribose nucleic acid (DNA).
    (2) Chromosomes: Dark, rod-like structures in the nuclei of all cells containing the genes; they are largely composed of protein and DNA.

  b. DNA: Everything characteristic of a living entity—its size, shape, and orderly development—that can be passed to progeny is recorded by an arrangement of molecules in its DNA.
    (1) Structure: Each unit of the DNA macromolecule consists of a nitrogenous base, a sugar, and a phosphate; the repeating unit of the DNA macromolecule is called the nucleotide. DNA consists of two stacks or strands of nucleotides twisted to form a double spiral or "helix."

  c. Protein synthesis: DNA governs the production of both the enzymatic and non-enzymatic proteins of the body and records in code form the amino acid arrangement which must be followed to synthesize a particular protein.
    (1) Only four nitrogenous bases exist in DNA, arranged in such a way as to avoid ambiguity; they become the code or symbol for an amino acid.
    (2) Major protein synthesis takes place in the special cytoplasmic structures called *ribosomes*. Information is replicated from DNA in another type of nucleic acid, ribonucleic acid (RNA). It carries information from the DNA of the nucleus to cytoplasmic sites; thus it is called the *messenger RNA*.
    (3) Major protein "assembly lines" of the cells are located in the ribosomes. Messenger RNA carries the program needed to manufacture one type of protein to the ribosomes.

  d. Amino acid activation: The synthesis of protein revolves around the formation of peptide bonds between amino acids; the major source of energy for this process is ATP (adenosine triphosphate). The activated amino acid must be in the place programed for it on the "assembly line." A code-reading escort, transfer RNA, must read the coded instructions.

  e. Genetic biology: Many disorders arise because the ribosomal template from which enzymatic proteins form is defective. DNA controls the configuration of the template.

STUDY QUESTIONS: THE CELL

1. Describe the structures of the cell.
2. Discuss three characteristics of the cell membrane.
3. Explain the role of the chromosomes in determining sex.
4. Discuss the function of five cytoplasmic organelles.
5. List three major functions of cells.
6. Compare diffusion and osmosis.
7. Explain the term osmotic pressure.
8. Describe the process of filtration.
9. Explain intermediary metabolism.
10. Since the body does not effectively utilize heat as a source of energy, complex chemical transformations occur; review the three major stages in this transformation.
11. Discuss the manner in which energy is liberated from the following processes: glycolysis, citric acid cycle.
12. Explain the four stages of mitosis.
13. Discuss the meaning of the following terms:

genetic code   ribosome
DNA   RNA
chromosome   messenger RNA

14. Explain the role of DNA in protein synthesis.

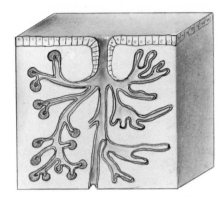

TISSUES

Tissues comprise all organs and, in turn, all organ systems. It is important to understand these components before individual organs can be studied. Even prior to the discovery of the microscope, the integrated pattern of tissues could be seen.

The basic unit of the tissue is the *cell*. Cells are either tightly packed or separated by interstitial material. Tissues are subdivided into four major categories: *epithelial, connective, muscular,* and *nervous.*

EMBRYOLOGICAL DEVELOPMENT

During embryonic development the fertilized egg cleaves, and the cells differentiate forming germ layers and tissues. The three basic germ layers are ectoderm, endoderm, and mesoderm.

The ectoderm eventually forms the nervous system, the skin, and its derivatives, including the hair, nails, and associated glands. The endoderm gives rise to the lining of the digestive tract and its derivatives. The mesoderm eventually forms connective tissue, muscle, blood, and bone.

EPITHELIAL TISSUE

Epithelial tissue is composed of mucous membranes, glandular epithelium, endothelium, and mesothelium (Fig. 25). It functions in protection, absorption, secretion, and excretion. When

37

TYPES OF EPITHELIUM

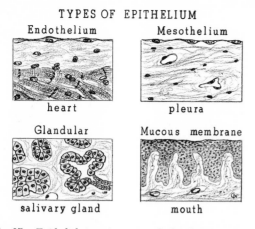

Fig. 25.   Epithelial tissue is composed of endothelium, mesothelium, glandular tissue, and mucous membranes which function to protect, absorb, secrete, and excrete.

serving a protective or absorbent function, epithelial tissue is found in sheets covering a surface such as the skin. In its secretory function, the epithelial cells involute from the surface into the underlying tissues to form gland structures specialized for secretion. Only a minimal amount of intercellular substance is found in epithelial tissue which is closely knit and not so readily penetrated as other tissues. The epidermis and associated derivatives will be discussed in Chapter Four.

In general, epithelial cells are anchored to each other or to a specialized structure called the basement membrane. The basement membrane is important, since it serves as an anchor for the inner (attached) side of cells, affording protection to the underlying tissue. It is frequently used as a landmark delineating invasion of epithelial tumors. If the tumor has invaded the basement membrane, the outlook for the patient is poor. The membrane is composed of a carbohydrate ground substance into which reticular fibers extend from adjacent connective tissue.

An epithelial tissue is named according to the outer (free) layer of cells, consisting either of one layer or several layers of different cell types. The surface of an epithelial cell can be plain or can have definite structures along the free surface, such as cilia, flagella, microvilli, and secretory vesicles.

Classification

Cells comprising epithelial tissues are classi-

fied either according to shape or to the number of layers of cells.

Classification according to shape.   Epithelial cells are classified as squamous, cuboidal, and columnar. *Squamous cells* are flat and serve as a protective layer. Other epithelial cells can become squamous if subjected to repeated irritation. *Cuboidal cells,* resembling small cubes, are found in five regions of the body, including lining tissue for ducts, acini in external secretory glands, renal tubules, germinal coverings for the ovaries, and the pigmented layer of the retina of the eye. *Columnar cells* are tall and often rectangular. They line ducts such as the urethra and are found in mucus-secreting tissues including the mucosa of the stomach, bile ducts, villi of the intestines, uterine tubes, and upper respiratory tract.

Classification according to arrangement. Four of the most common arrangements of epithelial cells are *simple, stratified, pseudostratified,* and *transitional epithelium* (Fig. 26). The *simple* arrangement is one cell thick. The *stratified* arrangement is several cells thick. The *pseudostratified* arrangement seems to consist of several layers, but in essence all cells extend from the free (outer) surface to the basement membrane. Transitional epithelium consists of several layers of closely packed, soft, pliable, and easily stretched cells. When the surface is stretched, the cells are flat; but they appear sawtoothed when the epithelium is relaxed, as in a recently emptied bladder. Transitional epithelium lines the pelvis of the kidney, the ureters, the urinary bladder, and the upper part of the urethra.

Mucous Membranes

Mucous membrane is epithelial tissue lining the digestive, respiratory, urinary, and reproductive tracts; it also lines the conjunctiva and the middle ear. Mucous membrane forms mucus, concentrates bile, and secretes or excretes enzymes for digestion of nutrients prior to absorption. The digestive tract includes the buccal cavity, pharynx, esophagus, stomach, small intestine, large intestine, and anus. The buccal cavity, lower pharynx, and esophagus are lined with stratified squamous epithelium. Simple columnar epithelium is found in the remainder of the digestive tract from the stomach to the rectum. The anus is lined with stratified squamous epithelium.

In the respiratory tract, the trachea and larynx contain *ciliated columnar epithelium.* These

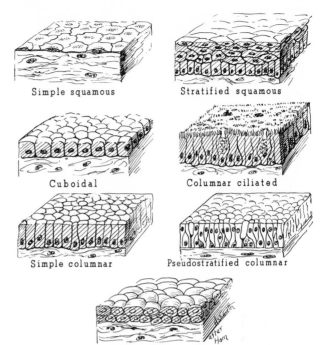

Fig. 26. Types of epithelial tissue.

Simple squamous

Stratified squamous

Cuboidal

Columnar ciliated

Simple columnar

Pseudostratified columnar

Transitional squamous

cells change to cuboidal, non-ciliated epithelium in the terminal bronchioles. Vocal cords are covered by stratified squamous epithelium.

In the urinary system, Bowman's capsule is lined with thin squamous epithelium, the convoluted tubules with cuboidal epithelium. The cuboidal epithelium becomes columnar as it approaches the pelvis of the kidney, which is lined with transitional epithelium continuing into the ureters, bladder, and upper portion of the urethra.

In the reproductive tract, the epididymis of the male is lined with columnar ciliated epithelium, the uterine tube in the female with simple columnar epithelium, and the uterus itself with ciliated columnar epithelium. The entire mucosa of the uterus contains tubular glands extending down to and sometimes entering the muscular layer. A change to stratified squamous epithelium occurs at the point at which the cervix opens into the vagina.

Mucous membranes serve four general functions: protection, support for associated structures, absorption of nutrients into the body, and secretion of mucus, enzymes, and salts.

Glandular Epithelium

Glands are involutions of epithelial cells, specializing in synthesizing and secreting cer-

tain special compounds. They can be divided into exocrine (with excretory ducts) and endocrine (ductless) glands. Exocrine glands have excretory ducts through which the secretory products pass to the surface and can be further divided into numerous gland types (Fig. 27). Simple glands, such as sweat glands, sebaceous glands, and most glands of the alimentary tract, have single, unbranched ducts. Compound glands, on the other hand, have several component lobules, and are found in the kidney, mammary glands, and large salivary glands. The shape of the gland is either tubular or saccular (see Fig. 27), and glands may secrete either mucous or serous material.

Endothelium

Endothelium is found in lymphatic vessels, blood vessels, and the lining of the heart (endocardium). The circulatory system is lined with a thin layer of endothelial cells, extending from the heart through the arteries into the capillaries and back again through the veins. The cells are a single layer of the squamous type.

Mesothelium

The third general type of epithelial tissue is the mesothelial or *serous* tissue, including the

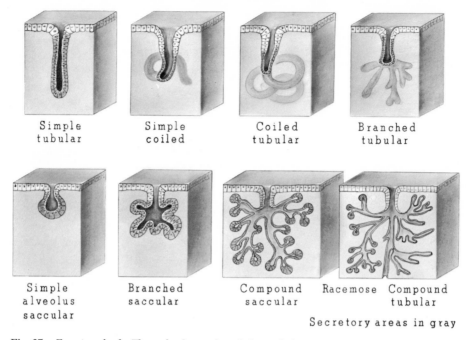

Simple tubular   Simple coiled   Coiled tubular   Branched tubular

Simple alveolus saccular   Branched saccular   Compound saccular   Racemose Compound tubular

Secretory areas in gray

Fig. 27. Exocrine glands. These glands may be tubular, coiled, saccular, or racemose (resembling a bunch of grapes on a stalk).

lining membranes of the great cavities of the body. *Mesothelial* tissue has a simple squamous cell layer overlying a sheet of connective tissue. The *pleura* is the serous membrane lining the thoracic cavity, the *pericardium* the serous membrane covering the heart, and the *peritoneum* the serous membrane lining the abdominal cavity. Serous membranes perform several functions, including protection, reduction of friction, secretion, and excretion.

CONNECTIVE TISSUE

The second major subdivision of tissue is connective tissue, in which there is an abundance of intercellular material called the matrix. Connective tissue, allowing movement and providing support, develops in the embryo as *mesenchyme* consisting of small cells with narrow branching structures, often appearing to form a fine network. Each cell in mesenchymal tissue contains a nucleus with a minimum of cytoplasm. The mesenchymal cells will develop into the various connective tissue cells. The matrix of connective tissue is variable in type and amount and is one of the main sources of difference between the types of connective tissue. It consists of various fibers embedded in a ground

substance. Occasionally the fibers are not apparent (for example, cartilage) but often they are quite obvious (for example, tendon).

Loose Connective Tissue

The fibers of loose connective tissue are not tightly woven. The tissue, filling spaces between and penetrating into the organs, is of three types: areolar, adipose, and reticular.

AREOLAR TISSUE. The most widely distributed connective tissue is pliable and crossed by many delicate threads; yet, the tissue resists tearing and is somewhat elastic. Areolar tissue contains fibroblasts, histiocytes (macrophages), leukocytes, and mast cells.

Fibroblasts are small, flattened, somewhat irregular cells with large nuclei and reduced cytoplasm. The term fibroblast refers to the ability of a cell to form fibrils. Fibroblasts are active in repair of injury. It is generally believed that suprarenal steroids inhibit and growth hormones stimulate fibroblastic activity. *Histiocytes* are phagocytic cells similar to leukocytes in blood; however, they perform phagocytic activity outside the vascular system. The histiocyte is irregular in shape and contains cytoplasmic granules. The cell is often stationary (or "fixed"). *Mast cells,* located adjacent to small blood vessels, are round or polygonal in shape and possess a cytoplasm filled with metachromatic granules. Mast cells function in the manufacture of heparin (an anticoagulant) and histamine (an inflammatory substance responsible for changes in allergic tissue). Depression in mast cell activity results from the administration of cortisol to patients. Areolar tissue is the basic supporting substance around organs, muscles, blood vessels, and nerves forming the delicate membranes around the brain and spinal cord and comprising the superficial fascia found deep in the skin.

ADIPOSE TISSUE. Adipose tissue is specialized areolar tissue with fat-containing cells. The fat or lipid cell, like other cells, has a nucleus, endoplasmic reticulum, cell membrane, mitochondria, and one or more fat droplets. Adipose tissue acts as a firm yet resilient packing around and between organs, bundles of muscle fibers, nerves, and supporting blood vessels. Since fat is a poor conductor of heat, adipose tissue protects the body from excessive heat loss or excessive rises in temperature.

RETICULAR TISSUE. Reticular fibers are abundant in the embryo and consist of fine-branching fibrils taking a silver stain as observed under the microscope. The primary cell of the reticular fiber is the reticular cell. Reticular fibers form the framework of the liver, lymphoid organs, and bone marrow.

Dense Connective Tissue

Dense connective tissue is composed of closely arranged collagen and elastic fibers. It can be classified according to the arrangement of the fibers and the proportion of elastin and collagen present. Examples of dense connective tissue having a regular arrangement of fibers are tendons, aponeuroses, and ligaments. Examples of dense connective tissue having an irregular arrangement of fibers are fasciae, capsules, and muscle sheaths.

Specialized Connective Tissue

Cartilage. Cartilage, produced by a condensation of mesenchyme, has a firm matrix consisting of protein and mucopolysaccharides. Cells of cartilage, called *chondrocytes,* are large and rounded with spherical nuclei. Collagenous and elastic fibers are embedded in the matrix, increasing the elastic and resistive properties of this tissue. The three types of cartilage are hyaline, fibrous, and elastic.

In utero, *hyaline cartilage,* the precursor of much of the skeletal system, is translucent with a clear matrix caused by abundant collagenous fibers (not visible as such) and cells scattered throughout the matrix. Hyaline cartilage is gradually replaced by bone in many parts of the body through the process of ossification; however, some remains as a covering on the articular surfaces. The hyaline costal cartilages attach the anterior ends of the upper seven pairs of ribs to the sternum. The trachea and bronchi are kept open by incomplete rings of surrounding hyaline cartilage. This type of cartilage is also found in the nose.

Fibrous cartilage contains dense masses of unbranching, collagenous fibers lying in the matrix. Cells of fibrous cartilage are present in rows between bundles of the matrix. Fibrocartilage is dense and resistant to stretching; however, it is less flexible and resilient than hyaline cartilage. Fibrous cartilage, interposed between the vertebrae in the spinal column, is also present in the symphysis pubis, permitting a minimal range of movement.

Elastic cartilage, which is more resilient than either the hyaline or the fibrous type because of a predominance of elastic fibers impregnated in its ground substance, is found in the auricle of the external ear, the auditory tube, the epiglottis, and portions of the larynx.

Bone. Bone is a firm structure formed by impregnation of the intercellular material with inorganic salts. It is living tissue supplied by blood vessels and nerves and is constantly being remodeled. The two common types are compact, forming the dense outer layer, and cancellous, forming the inner lighter tissue of the shaft of a long bone (see Fig. 37, page 64).

Dentine. The dentine of teeth is closely related to bone. The crown of the tooth is covered by enamel, the hardest substance in the body. Enamel is secreted onto the dentine by the epithelial cells of the enamel organ before the teeth are extruded through the gums. Dentine resembles bone but is harder and denser (see Fig. 316, page 384).

Blood and hematopoietic tissue. Marrow is the blood-forming (hematopoietic) tissue located in the shafts of bones. The red blood cells (erythrocytes) and most white blood cells (leukocytes) originate in the capillary sinusoids of bone marrow. Some leukocytes are formed in the lymphoid organs.

Blood is a fluid tissue circulating through the body, carrying nutrients to cells, and removing waste products (see Fig. 226, page 282).

Lymphoid tissue. Lymphoid tissue is found in lymph nodes, the thymus, spleen, tonsils, and adenoids. The germinal centers of lymph tissue produce plasma cells and lymphocytes. Lymphoid tissue functions in antibody production.

Connective tissues perform many functions, including support and nourishment for other tissues, packing material in the spaces between organs, and defense for the body by digestion and absorption of foreign material.

Reticulo-endothelial system. Connective tissue cells, carrying on the process of phagocytosis, are frequently referred to as the reticulo-endothelial system. The cells ingest solid particles similarly to the manner in which an ameba takes in nourishment. Three types of phagocytic cells belong to this classification: reticulo-endothelial cells, lining the liver (Kuppfer's cells), spleen, and bone marrow; macrophages, termed tissue histiocytes or "resting-wandering" cells; and microglia, located in the central nervous system. The reticulo-endothelial system is the body's first line of defense against infection.

MUSCLE TISSUE

There are three types of muscle tissue: voluntary (striated), involuntary (smooth), and cardiac. *Striated* or voluntary muscle has cross-striations and can be controlled at will. *Involuntary* muscle is smooth without striations and is under the control of the autonomic nervous system. *Cardiac* muscle, although striated, is found exclusively in the heart and is not under voluntary control. All muscle develops from the myomeres of the embryonic mesoderm (see Fig. 85, page 119).

NERVOUS TISSUE

The fourth type of tissue is *nervous tissue,* divided into nervous tissue proper and interstitial connective tissue (neuroglia). Nervous tissue is formed from the primitive neural plate of the ectoderm. It is the most highly organized tissue in the body, initiating, controlling, and coordinating the body's ability to adapt to its environment. In nervous tissue proper, the specialized conducting cells are *neurons,* linked together to form nerve pathways. The neuroglia (interstitial tissue) supports the neuron (see Fig. 143, page 189).

The various types of tissue are summarized in Table 2 and Figs. 28 and 29.

TISSUE TRANSPLANTATION

During the last two decades, an active interest has been taken in methods and mechanisms of tissue transplantation. The following discussion should prove useful to the student embarking on a medical or paramedical career.

DEFINITIONS

Autotransplant. A transplant to the same individual from whom the tissue was removed. For example, a skin graft from the thigh to a burned surface of the hand of the same person.

Isotransplant. A transplant between individuals of the same (identical twins) or nearly the same genetic background (inbred strains) of animals.

Homotransplant. A transplant between two individuals of the same species with a different genetic background, as from one patient to another (not his identical twin).

Heterotransplant. A transplant between members of two different species, as from a rat to a dog.

It is currently accepted that when any tissue is grafted between two individuals who are not identical twins, the graft is rejected because of the development of "actively acquired immunity." When tissues are homotransplanted, the lipoprotein of the cell membrane leaves the transplanted cell as an antigen and enters the lymphatics of the recipient organism. The antigen then travels to the regional lymph nodes and initiates the production of cellular antibodies. These antibodies in turn reach the graft by way of the blood and bring about rejection of the homograft (Fig. 30). The intercellular antibody-like substances are the only ones with a firmly established role in rejection of transplants; however, increasing evidence shows that serum antibodies also function in the mechanism of rejection.

Nature provides at least five exceptions to the concept that skin grafts between individuals are invariably destroyed. (1) Identical twins accept grafts. Inbred animal strains develop such a high degree of genetic similarity so as to behave as identical twins and thus accept grafts. (2) Embryos accept grafts from each other. (3) Patients with certain disease states, such as diminished gamma globulin, will tolerate skin grafts (see Chapter Ten). (4) Chimeras (organisms with two genetically different types of tissue) will accept skin grafts. The phenomenon of natural tolerance (chimerism) occurs in cattle twins and has been reported in non-identical human twins. The possibility of tolerance to grafts between a

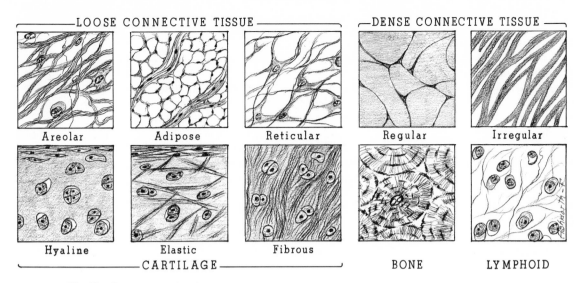

Fig. 28. *Loose connective tissue:*

Areolar: loosely arranged fibro-elastic connective tissue.

Adipose: regions of connective tissue dominated by aggregations of fat cells.

Reticular: makes delicate connecting and supporting frameworks, enters into the composition of basement membranes, produces lymphocytes and macrophages, and plays important roles as scavanger and agent of defense against bacteria.

Dense connective tissue:

Regular: fibers that are oriented so as to withstand tension exerted in one direction.

Irregular: fibers that are arranged so as to withstand tensions exerted from different directions.

Cartilage:

Hyaline: the most fundamental kind of cartilage, consisting of a seemingly homogeneous matrix permeated with fine white fibers.

Elastic: specialized cartilage with elastic fibers in the matrix.

Fibrous: specialized cartilage emphasizing collagenous fibers in its matrix.

Bone: a tissue consisting of cells, fibers, and a ground substance, the distinguishing feature of which is the presence of a ground substance of inorganic salts.

Lymphoid tissue: a tissue consisting of two primary tissue elements—reticular tissue and cells, chiefly lymphocytes—intermingling in intimate association in the reticular interstices.

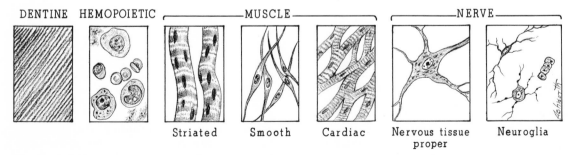

Fig. 29. *Dentine*, like bone, consists of a collagenous mesh and calcified ground substance; unlike bone, it contains neither vessels nor total cells. *Hematopoietic tissue:* blood-forming tissues; i.e., lymphoid organs, bone marrow, and spleen. *Muscle tissue* has the property of contractility and excitability (see Chapter Seven). *Nervous tissue* has the property of excitability and conductivity (see Chapter Eight).

43

TABLE 2.   Tissues.

TISSUE	LOCATION
Epithelial tissue	
Simple squamous	Body cavities (mesothelium), cardiovascular and lymphatic vessels (endothelium), terminal respiratory ducts, alveoli
Simple cuboidal	Many glands; pigmented epithelium of the retina
Simple columnar	Digestive tract from the lower esophagus to the anus, uterus, uterine tubes, bronchioles, gallbladder
Pseudostratified columnar	Nasal cavity, trachea, bronchi
Stratified squamous	Epidermis (skin), mouth and tongue, esophagus, anus, vagina, cornea, conjunctiva
Stratified cuboidal	Tubules of testis, graafian follicles of ovary, ducts of sweat glands, sebaceous glands
Stratified columnar	Pharynx and larynx
Transitional epithelium	Urinary tract
Connective tissue proper	
Loose connective tissue	
Areolar	Loosely arranged fibroelastic tissue between organs and muscles; supports blood vessels and nerves
Adipose	Subcutaneous fat, breast, bone marrow
Reticular	Framework of liver, lymphoid tissues, marrow, gastrointestinal tract, respiratory mucous membranes
Dense connective tissue	
Regular	Tendons, aponeuroses, ligaments
Irregular	Fasciae, capsules, sheaths, septae
Specialized connective tissue	
Cartilage	
Hyaline	Articular surfaces of bones, costal cartilages, trachea, tip of nose, larynx, fetal skeleton
Fibrous	Discs between vertebrae; symphysis pubis; knee and hip joints
Elastic	Auricle of external ear, auditory tube, epiglottis, cartilages of larynx
Bone	Skeleton
Dentine	Teeth
Hematopoietic (marrow) and bone	Marrow spaces of bones and vascular system
Lymphoid	Lymph nodes, thymus, spleen, tonsils, adenoids
Muscular tissue	
Striated skeletal (voluntary)	Skeletal muscles; muscles of the tongue, pharynx, larynx; extrinsic muscles of the eye
Smooth (involuntary)	Muscular walls of the digestive and urinary tracts, blood vessels
Cardiac	Heart
Nervous tissue	
Nervous tissue proper	Neurons and nerve fibers
Neuroglia	Supportive tissue in central nervous system

mother and a child has been reported. (5) Embryonic tissue—that is, tissue taken during the first trimester of pregnancy from the embryo— is accepted when grafted to adults. This has been accomplished in experimental animals.

In general, three approaches are being evaluated to prolong the life of homografts: (1) alter-

ing the antigenic *propensity* of the graft by irradiation; (2) transplanting the graft to a privileged site, such as the anterior chamber of the eye, in which not only the cornea will be accepted but other tissues as well; and (3) eliminating or lessening host resistance. Currently, x-rays and drugs suppressing antibody produc-

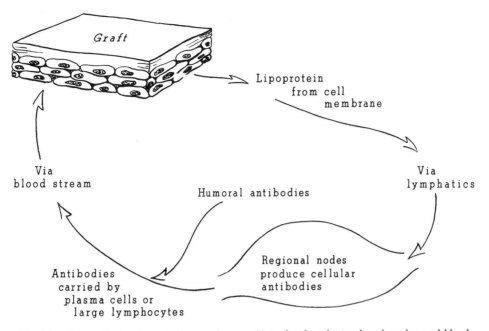

Fig. 30. Skin graft showing rejection mechanism. Note that lymphatics, lymph nodes, and blood vessels are necessary in graft rejection.

tion are being employed. The approach of lowering host resistance offers the greatest promise.

GRAFTING OF SPECIFIC TISSUES

Blood vessels. Homografts of arteries can be transplanted. This type of graft degenerates over a period of several years; however, the homologous arterial transplant functions as a so-called "homostatic" tissue. This means that viability is not necessary for successful transplantation, but the tissue acts as a foundation around which the individual's own cells can produce tissue. Today, the trend is toward the use of plastics for replacement of arteries.

Bone. Osteocytes in autologous bone grafts survive as living entities. Osteocytes in homologous or heterologous grafts die after transfer. Homologous and heterologous bone form a foundation for bone cells from the host to grow inward and replace the grafted tissue.

Cartilage. Both autologous and homologous cartilage survive transplantation. Possible explanations for survival of homografts of cartilage include the lack of blood vessels in the graft itself and the fact that the mucopolysaccharide matrix can act as a barrier against host cell infiltration.

Endocrine tissues. An impressive group of studies indicates that homotransplants of certain endocrine tissues do not provoke the usual rejection reaction. Endocrine tissue is less highly antigenic than other tissues.

Teeth. Dental reimplantation is the procedure of reinserting into the alveolar socket a tooth accidentally extracted or dislodged. Homologous transplantation of teeth is not successful.

PRESERVATION OF TISSUES

There are three general methods of tissue preservation: preservation in a nutrient medium at temperatures above freezing; preservation in a non-viable state by freeze-drying or chemical fixation (applicable to homologous grafts of blood vessels, since they do not have to remain alive to provide satisfactory function); and preservation by freezing or depressing the freezing point with the tissue remaining viable. The best long-term method of preservation is probably freezing. Cells like spermatozoa and red blood cells will survive freezing with the use of protective agents such as glycerol. To date this has not been possible with an entire organ or whole animal.

SUMMARY: TISSUES

SURVEY

1. **Function:** Tissues form a framework for all organs and, in turn, all organ systems of the body.

2. **Composition:** The basic unit of tissues is the cell.

3. **Types:**
    a. Epithelial
    b. Connective
    c. Muscular
    d. Nervous

EMBRYOLOGICAL DEVELOPMENT

1. The fertilized egg cleaves and the cells differentiate, forming different germ layers and tissues.

EPITHELIAL TISSUE

1. Functions in protection, absorption, secretion, and excretion. Cells of the epithelial tissue are classified according to shape or number of layers of cells.

2. **Cell classification:**
    a. Cell classes according to shape:
        (1) Squamous: Flat cells, functioning as a protective layer.
        (2) Cuboidal: Small, cube-shaped cells serving five functions:
            (a) Lining tissue for the ducts.
            (b) Formations of acini in external secretory glands.
            (c) An absorptive unit in kidney tubules.
            (d) Germinal coverings for ovaries.
            (e) Pigmented layer of the retina of the eye.
        (3) Columnar: Tall, rectangular-shaped cells line the ducts and are found in most mucus-secreting tissues.
    b. Cell classes according to arrangement:
        (1) Simple layer: One cell thick.
        (2) Stratified: Several layers.
        (3) Pseudostratified: Appears to be several layers thick, but actually all cells attach to the basement membrane.
        (4) Transitional epithelium: Several layers of closely packed cells which are soft, pliable, and easily stretched are attached, lining pelvis, kidney, ureters, urinary bladder, and upper part of urethra.

3. **Mucous membrane:** Lines digestive, respiratory, urinary, and reproductive tracts.

    a. Mucous membranes have four functions: protection, support for associated structures, absorption of nutrients into the body, and secretion of mucous enzymes and salts.

4. **Glandular epithelium:** Glands are involutions of epithelial cells, specializing in synthesizing and secreting certain special compounds; these glands can be divided into endocrine and exocrine.

5. **Endothelium:** The endothelial division of epithelial tissue consists of the lining of the heart, blood vessels, and lymphatics.

6. **Mesothelium or serous tissue:** Lined with simple squamous cells overlying a sheet of connective tissue; includes the lining membranes of the great cavities of the body and serves to protect and lubricate.

CONNECTIVE TISSUE

1. **General description:**

    a. Characterized by an abundance of intercellular material; provides support and leverage for muscle.
    b. Embryology: Develops in the embryo as mesenchyme; each mesenchymal cell will develop into different connective tissue cells.

2. **Loose connective tissue:**

    a. Areolar tissue: The most widely dispersed connective tissue—fine, pliable, resistant, elastic; contains fibroblasts, histiocytes, and mast cells. Areolar tissue is the basic supporting substance around organs, muscles, blood vessels, and nerves. It forms membranes around the brain and spinal cord; it comprises superficial fascia.
    b. Adipose tissue: Specialized areolar tissue with many fat-containing cells; 95 per cent of the fat in a fat cell breaks down into fatty acids and glycerol; adipose tissue acts as a firm, resilient packing around and between organs and between bundles of muscle fibers. In its subcutaneous location, it protects the body from excessive heat loss or excessive increases in temperature.
    c. Reticular tissue: A framework of fine-branching fibrils, found in lymphoid organs, bone marrow, gastrointestinal tract, and respiratory mucous membranes.

3. **Dense connective tissue:**

    a. Composed of closely arranged collagen and elastic fibers.

4. **Specialized connective tissue:**

    a. Cartilage: Produced by condensation of mesenchyme; cartilage yields a firm matrix between cells consisting of protein and mucopolysaccharides; cells of cartilage are called chondrocytes. Three types of cartilage exist.
        (1) Hyaline: The precursor of the skeletal system; during embryonic development much of it is gradually replaced by bone through the process of ossification.
        (2) Fibrous: Contains dense masses of inbranching collagenous fibers lying in bundles; it is dense and resistant to stretching; these cells are located in rows between the bundles of matrix.
        (3) Elastic: The most resilient type of cartilage; found in the auricles of the ear, auditory tube, epiglottis, and larynx.
    b. Bone: Firm structure of living tissue formed by impregnation of the intercellular material with inorganic salts. Bone is constantly being remodeled.
    c. Dentine: Dentine of the teeth is similar to bone. It is covered by enamel.
    d. Blood: A fluid tissue circulating through the body, carrying nutrients to cells, and removing waste products.
    e. Hematopoietic tissue: Marrow is the blood-forming (hematopoietic) tissue located in the shafts of bones.
    f. Lymphoid tissue: Found in lymph nodes, thymus, spleen, tonsils, and adenoids; functions in antibody production and in the production of certain leukocytes.
    g. Reticulo-endothelial system: Composed of connective tissue cells carrying on the process of phagocytosis. The reticulo-endothelial system is the body's first line of defense against infection.

MUSCLE TISSUE

1. Three types of muscle:

   a. Involuntary or smooth
   b. Voluntary or striated
   c. Cardiac

NERVOUS TISSUE

1. Types:

   a. Nervous tissue proper
   b. Interstitial connective tissue (containing neuroglia)

2. The most highly organized tissue of the body; initiates, controls, and coordinates the body's ability to adapt to its environment.

TISSUE TRANSPLANTATION

1. Types of transplants:

   a. Autotransplant
   b. Isotransplant
   c. Homotransplant
   d. Heterotransplant

2. Transplanted tissues are usually rejected because of the development of "actively acquired immunity." This occurs when the lipoprotein of the transplanted cell leaves the cell as an antigen, travels to lymph nodes, and stimulates the production of antibodies.

3. Nature provides at least five exceptions to the concept that the skin grafts between individuals are invariably destroyed: identical twins accept grafts; grafts between embryos are accepted; patients with certain diseases accept grafts from each other; chimeras accept grafts; and embryonic tissues are frequently accepted when grafted to adults.

4. Three approaches are being evaluated to prolong the life of homografts:

   a. Altering antigenic propensity of the graft by irradiation.
   b. Transplanting the graft to a privileged site.
   c. Eliminating or lessening host resistance by immuno-suppressive agents.

5. Grafting of specific tissues.

   a. Homografts of arteries can be transplanted; osteocytes in autologous bone grafts survive transplantation. Possibly certain endocrine tissues do not elicit rejection. A tooth which has been accidentally extracted or dislodged can be reinserted into the alveolar socket.

PRESERVATION OF TISSUE (THREE GENERAL METHODS)

1. Preservation of the life of the tissue in a nutrient medium at a temperature above freezing.

2. Preservation in a non-viable state by freeze-drying or chemical fixation.

3. Preservation by freezing or by depressing the freezing point with the tissue remaining viable.

STUDY QUESTIONS: TISSUES

1. List the four major categories of tissues.
2. Discuss the functions of epithelial tissue.
3. Explain the classification of epithelial cells according to shape and arrangement.
4. Review the locations of mucous membrane.
5. Explain the function of areolar tissue.
6. In what way is bone formed?
7. Discuss the function of the reticulo-endothelial system.
8. Compare: autotransplant, isotransplant, homotransplant, heterotransplant.
9. Review three approaches being evaluated to prolong the life of homografts.
10. Explain three general methods of tissue preservation.

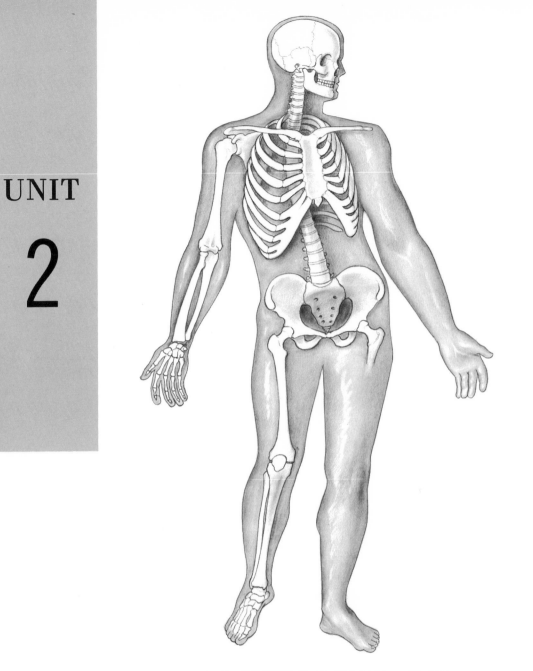

FRAMEWORK OF
THE BODY

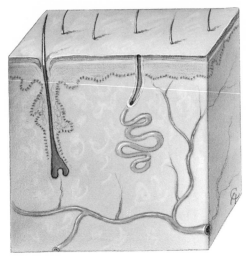

SKIN

IMPORTANCE

The skin of an average adult covers over 3000 square inches of surface area, weighs approximately 6 pounds (nearly twice the weight of the liver or brain) and receives about one-third of all blood circulating through the body. It is elastic, rugged, and, under ordinary conditions, self-regenerating. The skin is almost entirely waterproof, providing an efficient, closely regulated thermal barrier and participating in the dissipation of water and in the temperature-regulatory functions of the body. It is of ectodermal origin and derives its support from mesodermal connective tissue.

EMBRYOLOGY

Development of the skin and its appendages in utero begins with the formation of a single layer of cuboidal cells. By the sixth month of fetal life, this layer has divided into two layers, the epidermis and the dermis (corium or true skin) (Fig. 31).

LAYERS

Epidermis

The outer or epidermal layer is composed of stratified squamous epithelial cells. The epithelial cells of the epidermis are held together in large part by highly convoluted interdigitations (desmosomes) which are responsible for the

53

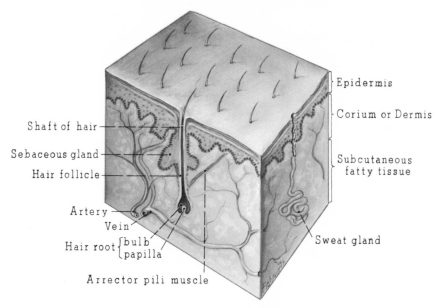

Shaft of hair

Sebaceous gland

Hair follicle

Artery

Vein

Hair root { bulb
            papilla

Arrector pili muscle

Epidermis

Corium or Dermis

Subcutaneous fatty tissue

Sweat gland

Fig. 31.   Three-dimensional view of the skin.

unique integrity of the skin. The epidermis is thickest as it encloses the palms and soles and becomes thinner over the ventral surface of the trunk.

The epidermis is composed of five layers, from superficial to deep (Fig. 32): stratum corneum (horny layer); stratum lucidum (clear layer); stratum granulosum (granular layer); stratum spinosum (prickly layer); and stratum germinativum (regenerative layer).

The *stratum corneum* forms the outermost layer of the epidermis and consists of keratinized cells which are continuously shed requiring replacement. It consists of 20 per cent water, as compared to 70 per cent water in the stratum germinativum. The stratum corneum is composed of flattened cells resembling scales, serving as a physical barrier to light and heat waves; microorganisms; and most chemicals. The thickness of this layer is determined by the amount of stimulation of the surface by abrasion and weight bearing—hence thick palms and soles and the development of calluses.

The *stratum lucidum,* lying deep in the stratum corneum, is present in all parts of the skin but is difficult to see in thinner skin. It is a layer one or two cells thick, consisting of transparent, flattened cells of little-known physiologic importance.

The *stratum granulosum,* two or three layers of flattened cells, provides a transition into the stratum germinativum. Granules accumulate in the cells, giving the layer its name; however, they do not contribute to skin color. The stratum granulosum is thought to be active in keratiniza-

tion, a process in which cells lose their nuclei, becoming more compact and brittle.

The *stratum spinosum* consists of several rows of "prickly" cells, polygonal in shape. The "prickles" are the desmosomes and special extracellular rods known as tonofibrils, which extend out to the cell membranes of the desmosomes. In some classifications this layer is included with the stratum germinativum.

The *stratum germinativum* (malpighian layer), the deepest and most important layer of the skin, contains the only cells in the skin capable of mitotic division. When new cells are formed, they undergo morphologic and nuclear changes as they move toward the most superficial layer. Simultaneously, these cells give rise to all outer layers of the epidermis. The epidermis will regenerate only so long as the stratum germinativum remains intact. The basal layer of these generative cells rests on a basement membrane which offers further protection from the environment.

Melanin, the principal pigment of the skin, is formed in the stratum germinativum by cells called *melanocytes.* The darker color of the skin is due to melanin; the pink tint is caused by vessels in the dermis (there are no vessels in the epidermis). The strongest factor in increasing pigmentation is the sun's stimulating effect on melanocytes. Melanin is capable of crosslinking with protein to form a tough, resistant compound; hence, heavily pigmented skin is more resistant to external irritation.

A variation in melanin content is the principal factor responsible for color differences among

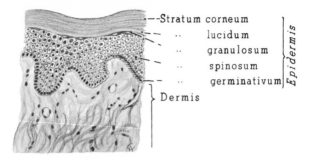

Stratum corneum
lucidum
granulosum
spinosum
germinativum

Epidermis

Dermis

Fig. 32. The epidermis (consisting of five distinct layers) and the dermis comprise the protective covering of the body.

races. Certain population groups have more active melanocytes in their skin. This causes black, yellow, brown, and white races. Darkly pigmented skin does not necessarily contain a greater number of melanocytes, but the melanocytes present are more active.

Dermis (Corium)

The dermis or corium, lying directly beneath the epidermis, is often called the true skin. It consists of connective tissue containing white collagenous and yellow elastic fibers. Blood vessels, nerves, lymph vessels, hair follicles, and sweat glands are embedded in the dermis. The dermis is divided into the papillary portion adjacent to the epidermis and the reticular portion lying between the papillary layer and the subcutaneous tissue. A sheet of areolar tissue, usually containing fat known as subcutaneous tissue or superficial fascia, attaches the dermis to the underlying structures.

APPENDAGES OF THE SKIN

The appendages associated with the skin include hair, nails, sebaceous glands, and sweat glands (Fig. 33).

Hair

Hair covers the entire body except the palms, soles, and portions of the genitalia; each unit of hair is composed of three parts—the cuticle, cortex, and medulla. The *cuticle,* the outermost portion, contains a single layer of overlapping scale-like cells. The *cortex,* or principal portion of the shaft, consists of elongated cells united to make flattened fibers. In dark hair, the fibers contain pigment granules. The central axis of the hair, known as the *medulla,* is composed of many-sided cells frequently containing air

spaces. The visible portion of the hair is the *shaft;* the embedded portion, the *root.* The hair follicle includes the root and its covering membrane (an outer connective tissue sheath and an inner epithelial membrane continuous with the stratum germinativum). When the arrector pili muscles (bundles of smooth muscle fibers attached to the hair follicles) contract, the skin assumes a so-called "goose flesh" appearance where hair is sparse and results in a certain degree of "hair standing on its ends" where the hair is prominent.

Hair growth is similar to growth of the epidermis, with the deeper cell layers responsible for production of new cells. The epithelial cells of the hair follicle divide mitotically. Daughter cells move upward, keratinize, and form the horny layer of the shaft.

The keratin of the cortex is polymerized and crosslinked in a characteristic folded configuration (alpha keratin) rendering the fibers elastic. When stretched, the keratin chain is drawn out into a more linear form (beta keratin). Unless it is greatly distended or altered by chemical agents, it returns immediately to its normal configuration. When hair is wet, it can be elongated to one and one-half times its normal length. This is possible because keratin can be readily stretched in the direction of the long axis of the molecular chains of amino acids. Permanent wave sets act on this principle. After the hair has been stretched and molded into a desired wave, reducing agents rupture the disulfide bonds of the hair. Oxidizing agents are then applied, reestablishing the stabilizing crosslinks in a new position.

Hair color. Hair color is determined by complex genetic factors. Gray hair occurs when pigment is absent. White hair results from an absence of pigment plus the formation of air bubbles in the hair shaft. Heredity and other unknown factors determine the graying of hair. The hair of a black cat will turn gray from a diet deficient in pantothenic acid. Restoring this substance to the diet causes the hair to return to its

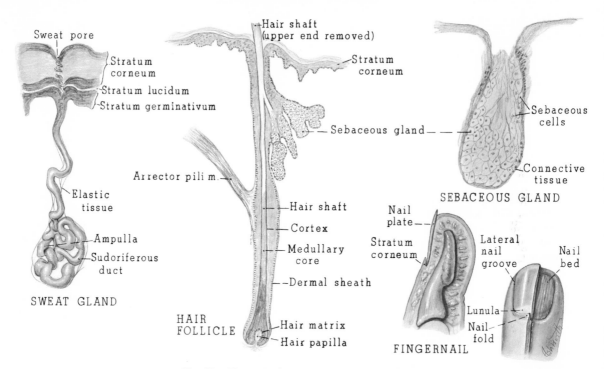

Fig. 33. The appendages associated with the skin.

normal color. This fact is of considerable interest but has not proved to be of importance in man.

Nails

The nails, a modification of the horny epidermal cells, are composed of hard keratin. Air mixed in the keratin matrix forms the white crescent, the *lunula*, at the proximal end of each nail. The nail plate arising from the proximal nail fold and attached to the nail bed grows approximately 1 mm. per week unless inhibited by disease. Regeneration of a lost fingernail occurs in 3½ to 5½ months; regeneration of a lost toenail occurs in 6 to 8 months.

Glands

SEBACEOUS GLANDS. *Sebaceous glands* arise from the walls of hair follicles and produce sebum, the oily substance primarily responsible for lubrication of the surface of the skin. Sebaceous secretion consists of entire cells containing sebum. When the cell disintegrates, sebum is secreted along the hair shaft onto the surface of the skin, providing a cosmetic gloss.

Sebaceous secretion is under the control of the endocrine system, increasing at puberty and in late pregnancy and decreasing with advancing age. The pubertal increase contributes to the

problem of acne in adolescents, and diminution in later life is responsible for the relative dryness of the skin.

The orifice of the sebaceous gland can become discolored as a result of oxidation of fatty material by the air, producing a "blackhead." Secretions retained in the gland provide a medium for the growth of pus-producing bacteria responsible for pimples and boils.

SWEAT GLANDS. *Sweat glands* are simple tubular glands found in most parts of the skin except the margins of the lips and the glans penis. They are most numerous in the palms and soles. It has been estimated that there are 3000 sweat glands per square inch on the palm. Each consists of a secretory portion and an excretory duct. The secretory portion, located below the dermis in the subcutaneous tissue, is a blind tube twisted and coiled on itself. From the coiled secretory portion, the excretory duct spirals through the dermis toward the surface. Each glandular tube is lined with secretory epithelium continuous with the epidermis.

Pure sweat contains the same inorganic constituents as blood but in lower concentration. The chief salt is sodium chloride. Organic constituents in sweat include urea, uric acid, amino acids, ammonia, sugar, lactic acid, and ascorbic acid. Sweat itself is practically odorless. The odor is produced by the action of bacteria on sweat. Ceruminous glands in the outer parts of the external auditory meatus and ciliary glands of the eyelids are modified sweat glands.

Each gram of sweat requires about 0.5 calorie for evaporation. This heat comes mostly from within the body. Sweating helps to lower the body temperature. It begins with a rise in body temperature of 0.2 to 0.5° F., and is initiated by the effect of elevated blood temperature on cerebral centers. Denervated skin (without nerves) does not respond to temperature changes by sweating. Some individuals have congenital absence of sweat glands. Such persons can die of heat stroke if exposed to high temperatures even for brief periods.

FUNCTIONS

The skin functions in *sensation, protection, thermoregulation,* and *secretion.* Four basic sensations—pain, temperature, touch, and pressure—are perceived in the skin. The concept that special receptors serve a specific sensory function is no longer held to be valid. The ability to discriminate between sensations is a result of the pattern presented to the cerebral cortex of the brain rather than the type of nerve ending stimulated. The skin forms an elastic, resistant covering, protecting man from his complex environment. It prevents the passage of harmful physical and chemical agents and inhibits excessive loss of water and electrolytes.

The acid mantle of the skin helps protect its surface from irritants and bacteria. Some skin diseases destroy the acidity of certain areas, impairing the self-sterilizing ability of the skin. In this condition, the skin is prone to bacterial invasion.

Experimental evidence indicates that the normal intact human skin is usually impermeable to water, carbohydrate, fat, and protein. All true gases and many volatile substances will pass through the epidermis. For example, many deaths have resulted from absorption of large quantities of organic pesticide sprays through the skin. Sex hormones are readily absorbed when applied in a proper vehicle. Mercury, lead, and copper penetrate the skin under certain conditions. The numerous follicular orifices serve as channels for absorption. Substances passing through normal skin are soluble in fat and water.

Heat is lost from the body by conduction, convection, radiation, and evaporation. These processes are regulated by nervous and chemical activation of sweat glands and by dilation and constriction of the capillary vessels (see Chapter Thirteen). As the body needs to dissipate heat, blood vessels of the skin dilate, allowing more blood to come to the surface with a resulting heat loss.

The skin plays a part in the secretory functions of the body. Sebum secreted by sebaceous glands has antifungal and antibacterial properties and helps maintain the texture of the skin. Sweat is a secretion.

TRANSPLANTATION OF SKIN

The skin has a great capacity for regeneration and repair. If the epidermis is removed, the skin will regenerate, provided that isolated patches of the stratum germinativum remain. In a deeper wound, a new covering of epidermis is formed over the denuded area by active division of epidermal cells at the margin. In some cases, this natural process of repair is inadequate to secure

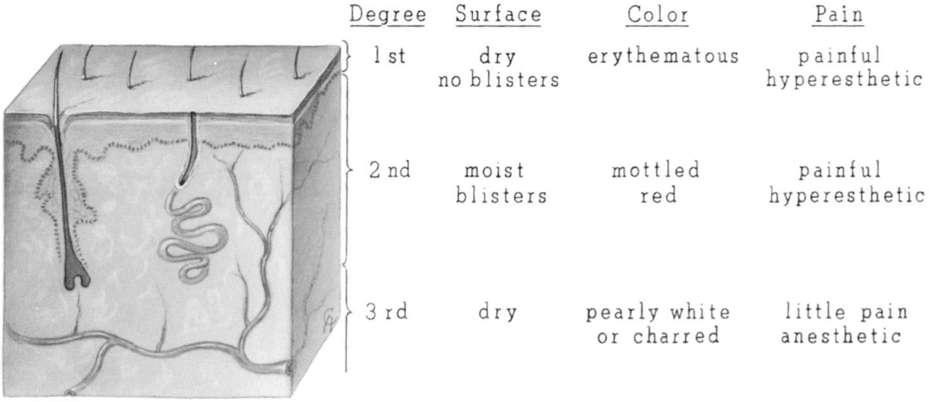

Fig. 34. Extent of burn injury—first, second, and third degree. In a first degree burn only the epidermis is injured (as in sunburn); a second degree burn extends into the dermis; a third degree burn involves the full thickness of skin, epidermis and dermis. (Courtesy of Parke, Davis.)

an efficient return of function to the damaged tissue, as in third degree burns (Fig. 34), and transplantation of the skin offers a solution.

WOUND HEALING

Wound healing involves the reaction of the entire body to trauma, as well as local changes in the wound itself. The body responds *clinically* to injury by a temporary elevation of temperature and pulse rate. Chemically, loss of nitrogen and potassium is followed by nitrogen and potassium retention.

During wound healing, bleeding into the wound results in clot formation, and vasodilation permits circulating cells, oxygen, and nutrients to be carried to the wound area. Debris in the wound is removed by phagocytes, and endothelial capillary buds appear in the clot by the second day. Fibrin trabeculae in the clot provide a framework for cellular migration.

Fibroblasts multiply in the wound and migrate from the periphery to combine with endothelial tissue and young blood vessels. These comprise *granulation tissue.* Fibroblasts release precursors of collagen into the interstitial spaces which form collagen fibers in the wound itself.

The *epidermis* is capable of rapid regeneration. Cell migration begins a few hours after an epidermal incision. A small defect will be covered completely after about 48 hours.

Factors interfering with wound healing. Many factors interfere with wound healing, including inadequate nutrition; necrotic tissue (dead or dying tissue); foreign bodies; bacteria; interference with blood supply; blockage of lymphatics; a systemic disease, such as diabetes mellitus; and psychological factors.

Abnormalities. Figure 35 illustrates various abnormalities of the skin.

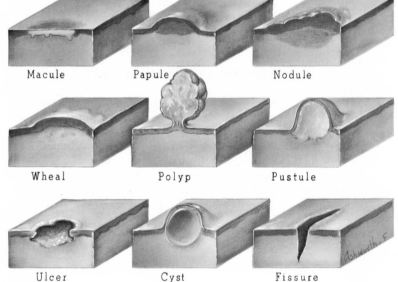

Macule   Papule   Nodule

Wheal   Polyp   Pustule

Ulcer   Cyst   Fissure

Fig. 35. Terms used in connection with abnormalities of the skin. *Macule:* a discolored, unelevated spot, especially reddened, on the skin. *Papule:* a solid elevation of the skin. *Nodule:* a small node which is solid and irregular in form. *Wheal:* a flat edematous elevation of the skin, frequently accompanied by itching. *Polyp:* a pedunculated or sessile growth extending into the lumen of a body cavity or appearing on the skin. *Pustule:* an elevation filled with pus. *Ulcer:* a loss of substance on a cutaneous or mucous surface. *Cyst:* any sac, normal or otherwise, especially one which contains a liquid or semisolid substance without pus. *Fissure:* any cleft or groove.

SUMMARY: SKIN

IMPORTANCE

1. **The skin receives one-third of the blood circulating through the body. It is elastic, regenerates, and functions in sensation, protection, thermoregulation, and secretion.**

EMBRYOLOGY

1. **The two layers of the skin, epidermis and dermis, develop by the sixth month of fetal life from a layer of cuboidal cells.**

LAYERS

1. **Epidermis:**
   a. Structure: Covering for the body—about 3000 square inches of surface area in an adult.
   b. Composition: Stratified squamous epithelial cells; thickest on palms and soles.
   c. Epidermal layers (beginning with the outermost):
      (1) Stratum corneum
      (2) Stratum lucidum
      (3) Stratum granulosum
      (4) Stratum spinosum
      (5) Stratum germinativum
   d. Pigmentation:
      (1) Principal pigment is melanin formed in the melanocytes; melanin causes the darker color of the skin.
      (2) Vessels in the dermis cause the pink tint of the skin.
      (3) The sun stimulates melanocytes and increases pigmentation.
2. **Dermis or corium:**
   a. Structure: Divided into the papillary segment close to epidermis and reticular portion between the papillary layer and subcutaneous tissue.

APPENDAGES OF THE SKIN

1. **Hair:**
   a. Covers body excluding palms and soles; thickest on scalp.
   b. Each unit of hair composed of cuticle, cortex, and medulla.
   c. Keratin of the cortex causes elasticity in the hair fibers.
   d. Color determined by complex genetic factors; gray hair, absence of pigment; white hair contains air bubbles.
   e. Arrector pili muscles are bundles of smooth fibers attached to hair follicles.
2. **Nails:**
   a. Composed of hard keratin, modification of the horny epidermal cells.
   b. Arise from proximal nail fold and are adherent to nail beds.
   c. Grow at the rate of approximately 1 mm. per week.
3. **Glands:**
   a. Sebaceous: Produce sebum for lubrication of skin's surface; secretion increases at puberty and late in pregnancy, declining with advancing age.
   b. Sweat glands: Simple tubular glands, consisting of a secretory portion and an excretory duct; pure sweat contains the same inorganic constituents as the blood, but in lower concentration. Ceruminous glands in outer parts of the external auditory meatus and ciliary glands of the eyelids are modified sweat glands.

FUNCTIONS

1. **Sensation:**
   a. Four basic sensations: pain, temperature, touch, and pressure.
   b. Ability to discriminate between sensations is a result of the pattern presented to the cerebral cortex of the brain.
2. **Protection:**
   a. Skin forms an elastic, resistant covering for protection against the external environment.
   b. Inhibits excessive loss of water and essential electrolytes.
   c. Acid mantle of the skin protects surface from irritants and bacterial onslaughts.
   d. Skin is water repellent; all substances passing through are soluble in fat or water.

3. **Thermoregulation:**
   a. Heat is lost from the body by processes of conduction, convection, radiation, and evaporation.
   b. The dermis is a better heat conductor than the epidermis or subcutaneous tissue.
   c. Evaporation may occur as either insensible water loss or visual water loss (perspiration).
4. **Secretion: The skin has a minor secretory function; it secretes sebum and sweat.**

Transplantation of Skin

1. **Skin may be transplanted to secure an efficient return of function to damaged tissue.**

Wound Healing

1. **Body reactions to wound healing:**
   a. The entire body reacts to trauma.
   b. Local changes occur in the wound itself.

2. **Physiologic process:**
   a. Clinically: The body responds by a temporary elevation of temperature and pulse rate.
   b. Chemically: Body adjustment in nitrogen and potassium balance.

3. **Local changes:**
   a. Bleeding results in clot formation.
   b. Fibrin trabeculae provide a framework for cellular migration.
   c. Fibroblasts multiply and combine with endothelial tissue (granulation tissue).
   d. Fibroblasts release precursors of collagen which form collagen fibers.

4. **Factors interfering with wound healing:**
   a. Inadequate nutrition.
   b. Necrotic tissue.
   c. Foreign bodies.
   d. Blockage of lymphatics.
   e. Interference with blood supply.
   f. Systemic disease.
   g. Psychologic factors.

STUDY QUESTIONS: SKIN

1. Discuss the functions of the epidermis and its five secondary layers.
2. Outline the structure and composition of the dermis.
3. Which factor is responsible for dark skin color? For the pinkish tint of the skin?
4. Discuss the reason for color differences among races.
5. List three appendages of the skin.
6. Describe the composition of the hair.
7. Explain the function of keratin in the hair.
8. Discuss the conditions causing brown hair, gray hair, and white hair.
9. Describe the composition of the nail.
10. Discuss the cause of "blackheads."
11. List four functions of the skin.
12. Discuss the role of the skin in secretory function of the body.
13. Outline the clinical and chemical reactions of the body during wound healing.
14. List the factors involved in wound healing; the factors interfering with wound healing.

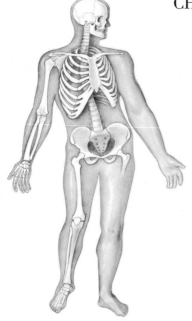

THE

SKELETAL

SYSTEM

FUNCTIONS

The supporting structure of the body is a joined framework of bones called the *skeleton*. It enables man to stand erect and to accomplish extraordinary feats of artistic grace, athletic endeavor, and physical endurance.

Contrary to appearance, the individual bones of the skeleton are indeed living tissues. Five general functions are ascribed to the skeleton as a whole.

1. It assists in *body movement,* giving attachment to the muscles and providing leverage.

2. It *supports* the surrounding tissues, including the teeth.

3. It *protects* vital organs and other soft tissues of the body.

4. It manufactures blood cells. This *hematopoietic* function occurs in the red bone marrow.

5. It provides a *storage* area for mineral salts, especially phosphorus and calcium, to supply body needs.

There are 206 bones in the skeleton. The *axial part* consists of the *skull* (28 bones, including those of the face), the *hyoid bone,* the *vertebrae* (26 bones), the *ribs* (24 bones), and the *sternum.* The *appendicular part* of the skeleton consists of the *arms* or *upper extremities* (64 bones, including the *shoulder girdle*), and the *legs* or *lower extremities* (62 bones, including the *pelvic girdle*).

62 FRAMEWORK OF THE BODY

Leonardo da Vinci is credited with being the first anatomist to correctly illustrate the skeleton. The Belgian physician, Andreas Vesalius (1514–1564), reconstructed a human skeleton that is still in existence today as the oldest anatomic specimen. Current investigation centers around actual function of the cells of bone in health and disease.

EMBRYOLOGY

The bones of the skeleton are derived from the middle germ layer, or mesoderm. This activity begins during the first month of intra-uterine life when the embryonic shield is a little more than 2 mm. in diameter. The "cartilage" skeleton is completely formed at the end of 3 months. During the subsequent months of gestation, ossification and growth occur (Fig. 36).

Longitudinal growth of bones continues in a definite sequence until approximately 15 years of age in the female and 16 in the male. Longitudinal growth should not be confused with bone maturation and modeling, which are proc-

esses continuing until the age of 21 in both the male and female. This pattern of maturation is so regular that an individual's age can be determined with amazing accuracy from radiologic examination of his bones.

Bone develops from spindle-shaped cells called *osteoblasts*. These are found beneath the periosteum and in the endosteal region "inside" the bone, but they remain dormant until stimulated to become *osteocytes*. The nature of the stimulus triggering this change is not well understood. The osteoblast then produces a matrix. The osteocyte and matrix formed from the osteoblast calcify into the typical pattern of bone. Calcification is the initial mineralization of the uncalcified matrix or osteoid tissue. Ossification, on the other hand, is the actual formation of the crystalline structure of bone.

Ossification begins with the formation of crystals similar to hydroxyapatite—$3Ca_3(PO_4)_2 \cdot Ca(OH)_2$. These crystals are laid down in a lattice pattern, creating a large surface area for exchange of minerals.

It is sometimes stated that bone is preformed in the cartilage, since the majority of embryonic bones do resemble the future skeleton in shape

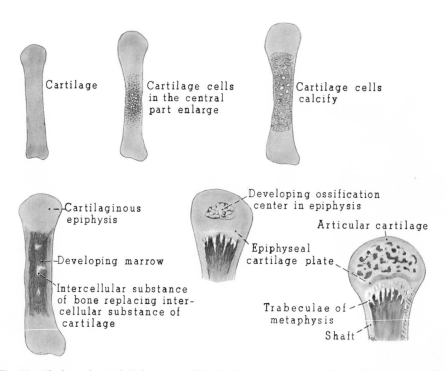

Fig. 36. The bony deposit laid down around the diaphysis spreads toward the epiphysis, where ossification is also occurring. Gradual replacement of cartilage by bone occurs, and an increase in lengthwise direction of the bone accompanies this process. Growth in diameter of the bone occurs primarily with the deposit of bony tissue beneath the periosteum.

and composition; however, it is incorrect to state that cartilage actually turns into bone. Cartilage merely represents the environment in which the bone develops.

Intramembranous Ossification

Only the bones of the cranium (skull) form completely by a process known as *intramembranous ossification*—that is, by a process in which the inorganic calcuim salts are deposited between the cells of the embryonic membrane. The membrane itself becomes the *periosteum* (around bone), while immediately within the periosteum can be found compact bone with an inner core of *spongy* or *cancellous bone.*

Enchondral Ossification

Most bones form by the process of *enchondral ossification,* referring to bone formation in the preformed cartilage models. Growth in length of a bone occurs at the growth plate, which consists of a number of layers of cartilage cells lying between the epiphysis and metaphysis. The basal layer of cells is abundantly supplied with blood, and this layer proliferates, producing an increased number of cells adding to the length of the bone. The upper layers of cells are thus lifted away from the source of blood and nutrients, the surrounding matrix calcifies, and the cells die. From the metaphyseal side, other blood vessels invade this calcified mass and connect it to the already formed bone.

Initially, a longitudinal cylinder of newly formed bone is laid down around the *diaphysis,* the shaft or central portion of each cartilage bone. This bony deposit spreads toward each end of the bone, or *epiphysis,* where ossification is also occurring. The result is a gradual replacement of cartilage and growth of the bone in a lengthwise direction.

Longitudinal growth is dependent, then, on the growth plate at the junction of the metaphysis and epiphysis. Growth in the diameter of bone occurs primarily by the deposit of bony tissue beneath the periosteum. In a short time, only two thin strips of tissue, the growth plates, remain between the end of the bone (epiphysis) and the shaft (diaphysis). When these two final sites have filled with osseous tissue, longitudinal growth is complete and growth is no longer possible. The initial shape assumed by a bone during its formation is genetically determined. Extrinsic factors such as muscle strength, mechanical stress, and biochemical environment assume a

function in determining the shape of a bone. Wolff's law reflects the role of mechanical forces acting on bone and, briefly stated, suggests that the structure of a bone is dependent on its function.

HISTOLOGY OF BONE

There are two types of bone, compact and cancellous (Fig. 37). In both, the osteocytes are the same but the arrangement of the blood supply is different, since the two varieties serve different purposes. In both compact and cancellous bone, the functional unit is the osteon, which consists of the osteoblast with its surrounding matrix. Compact bone is dense and strong. Cancellous bone, on the other hand, has many open spaces, giving the tissue a spongy appearance even without the aid of a microscope.

The Haversian System

The haversian system, the system of vessels in compact bone, is a prominent histologic feature of compact bone; it is named for the English anatomist who first described it. This system permits effective metabolism of bone cells and includes several components. The lamellae of compact bone surround small haversian canals running parallel to the surface of the bone. Contained within these canals are blood vessels nourishing the entire system. These canals bring in oxygen and food and remove waste products. Between each lamella of compact bone are several tiny cavities called *lacunae.* The lacunae are connected to each other and ultimately to the larger haversian canals by small canals, or *canaliculi.*

Each lacuna consists of an osteocyte, or mature bone-forming cell suspended in tissue fluid. It is this fluid that circulates through compact bone via the haversian system. The haversian system functions to keep osteocytes alive and healthy as "bone builders" during growth or during repair following fractures. In summary, the entire haversian system consists of a lacuna and its contained osteocytes, the canaliculi, a central canal with blood vessels, and the surrounding lamellae.

Marrow

The many spaces within cancellous bone are filled with *red bone marrow*. This marrow is

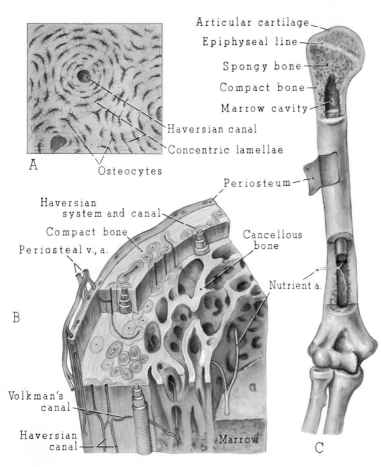

Fig. 37. *A.* Cross section of bone showing relation of osteocytes to haversian system. *B.* This section has been magnified out of proportion to show haversian system and lamellae. (Note communication between periosteal vessels and marrow vessels by way of Volkmann's canals.) *C.* Diagram of the structure of a long bone. (After Lockhart.)

richly supplied with blood and consists of fatty tissue admixed with blood cells and their precursors. The red bone marrow is the site of both red and white blood cell production; therefore, cells in all stages of development are found within it.

In the normal adult, the ribs, vertebrae, sternum, and bones of the pelvis contain red marrow in cancellous tissue. Red marrow within the ends of the humerus and femur is plentiful at birth but gradually decreases in amount through the years. Red blood cells (*erythrocytes*) and white blood cells (*leukocytes*) are the primary constituents of bone marrow.

Yellow marrow is connective tissue consisting chiefly of fat cells, and is found primarily in the shafts of long bones and within the *medullary canals* (the central canal of the bone shaft). Yellow marrow extends into the haversian systems, replacing red marrow when it becomes depleted.

The *osteoclast*, a type of cell found in bone tissue by light microscopy, should not be confused with the osteoblast, which has a smaller diameter and a different function. Osteoclasts are larger, contain several nuclei, and are associated with the breakdown of bone.

Summary of embryology and histology. Bone develops in two environments—preformed cartilage or fibrous membrane, termed endochondral and intramembranous respectively. Bones may be cancellous or compact, depending primarily on their structural form. In compact bone, the haversian system is the means by which the bone tissue receives its nourishment. Two types of marrow are found in bone—yellow and red. Red marrow has a hematopoietic function.

GROWTH OF BONE

Reabsorption and Deposition

Reabsorption of bone is a constant process and is counterbalanced by *osteoblastic deposition* of newly formed bone. This means that the strength and, in some instances, the size of skeletal bone will depend on the comparative activity of the two processes. For example, it is obvious that during the growth period deposition is more active than reabsorption. The role of the osteoclast has not been definitely established, but it is known that it is associated with the removal of dead bone from the inner side during remodeling. As a result, the medullary cavity enlarges, and the bone itself is prevented from becoming overly thick and heavy. Osteoblastic deposition continues to counteract the never-ending process of reabsorption, even when the bones are no longer capable of growth.

Physiology of Calcium

Calcium has several functions concerned with the maintenance of homeostasis (see Chapter Fifteen). These are best understood by viewing the effects of a severe calcium deficiency. Lack of calcium results in:

1. Depolarization of nerve fiber membranes with transmission of uncontrolled impulses. Under these conditions, *tetany*, or spasm of the skeletal musculature, occurs.

2. Weakness of cardiac muscle with a consequent inadequate supply of blood to the total body circulation.

3. Interference with the process of blood coagulation. (see Chapter Ten).

Ninety-nine per cent of the total calcium of the body exists in the bone. The small but important remainder is present in the blood plasma and in the interstitial fluid, where the ionized form of calcium participates in vital chemical reactions.

The exchange of calcium between the bones and body fluids occurs through a process of reabsorption and simple diffusion. In health, balance exists between calcium in the bones, calcium excretion by the kidneys and via the bowel, and calcium in the blood. The proper calcium ion concentration of the blood is controlled and maintained by the parathyroid glands. When the calcium concentration in the blood is reduced to one-half its normal level, nerve and muscle irritability ensue and death results. Excessive production of parathyroid hormone will elevate the blood calcium level. The significant point here is that additional calcium can be withdrawn from the bones, which are thus weakened by the loss of calcium and subject to the formation of cysts. This is only one of many illustrations of the fact that each system of the body is vitally dependent upon every other system. The skeleton is no exception to this rule.

Rickets. One of the common diseases resulting in physiologic changes in the bone is rickets, a manifestation of vitamin D deficiency. This condition causes changes in bone known as *rickets* in children and as *osteomalacia* in adults. Deficiency of two factors—vitamin D and sunlight—has to be considered. Vitamin D facilitates the absorption of calcium and phosphorus from the intestine. Short wave ultraviolet rays activate specific sterol precursors in the skin which are then converted into vitamin D. In actual practice, rickets is a disease of the slums, most common in countries with poor nutrition. If a child is fed a balanced diet and exposed to sufficient sunlight, cod liver oil or other sources of vitamin D are not necessary. The essential defect in rickets, failure of the bone to ossify, produces soft bones. When a baby with this condition begins to walk, the bones bend in response to mechanical stresses; various deformities, such as bow-legs, are noted.

Fractures

Fracture of bone. The breaking of bone or cartilage is known as a fracture. A fracture is usually accompanied by soft tissue injury. The resultant injury can be comparatively minor—for example, torn skin or bruised muscles; however, it can be even more serious than the fracture itself, as when the broken bone is associated with a divided artery or punctured lung.

The various types of fractures are given proper descriptive terms. A fracture can be open (compound) or closed (simple), depending on whether or not a communication occurs between the fracture site and a wound or opening in the skin. Because of the greater possibility of infection, a compound fracture is the more dangerous of the two.

Types of fractures:

A fracture is either *incomplete* or *complete*, depending on whether or not the fracture line extends partially or entirely through the substance of the bone. Fractures are classified according to the location or direction of the fracture line in the bone, and are then named *transverse, oblique, longitudinal,* or *spiral.*

In addition to the above general terms, several familiar and specific types of fractures are defined here.

Greenstick fracture—the bone is crumpled as a result of bending of pliable bones of children.

Fatigue fracture—the bone shows an incomplete break caused by stress; this is commonly seen in the metatarsals of soldiers who walk long distances.

Comminuted fracture—the bone is divided into more than two fragments by more than one fracture line.

Compression fracture—the opposite surfaces of bone are crushed more closely together, usually after comminution.

Pathologic fracture—the bone is broken down at a diseased site, with or without any external trauma.

Healing of fractures:

1. *Stage of the hematoma.* At the time of injury, bleeding occurs from damaged structures and a blood clot or hematoma forms between and around the bone fragments.

2. *Stage of granulation tissue.* The clot is invaded by cells and new capillaries. The proliferating cells or osteoblasts are derived from the deeper layers of the periosteum or the invading blood vessels.

3. *Callus formation.* A large mass of loosely woven bone forms, subsequently remodeling in accordance with Wolff's law.

4. *Ossification.* Bone is finally laid down. At this stage, the fractured ends are knit together by rigid bone.

Prompt medical attention is required even in the most simple of fractures to prevent serious complications. Bone healing occurs optimally when there is close and accurate approximation of the fracture ends. Provision for this by applying a splint or cast or by inserting a bone pin so that the structures are effectively immobilized and properly aligned is usually necessary for optimal repair.

CLASSIFICATION OF BONES

Individual bones of the skeleton are divided according to shape into five types: long, short, flat, irregular, and sesamoid (a small, rounded bone).

1. *Long bones* (for example, humerus, radius, tibia, and fibula) consist of a shaft and two extremities referred to by their anatomic names, the *diaphysis* and the *epiphysis*. The shaft is formed primarily by compact tissue, which is thickest in the middle of the bone where strain on it is the greatest. Strength of a long bone is further insured by a slight curvature of the shaft. The interior of the shaft is the *medullary canal*, filled for the most part with yellow marrow. The extremities of long bones have a long, thin covering of compact tissue overlying the cancellous tissue, which normally contains red marrow. The extremities are generally broad and expanded as compared to the shaft to facilitate articulation with other bones and provide a larger surface for muscle attachment.

2. *Short bones,* exemplified by the *carpal* bones of the wrist and *tarsal* bones of the ankle, have a somewhat irregular shape and are not merely a shorter version of a long bone type. Only a thin layer of compact tissue covers the spongy or cancellous tissue of a typical short bone.

3. *Flat bones* are found wherever there is a need for protection of soft body parts or a provision for extensive muscle attachment. Thus, the *ribs*, the *scapula*, parts of the *pelvic girdle*, and the bones of the *skull* are all examples of the flat bone group. These bones consist of two flat plates of compact tissue enclosing a layer of spongy bone.

4. *Irregular bones* have the same basic composition and structure as other groups of bones; however, this last group comprises bones of peculiar and differing shape, such as the vertebrae and ossicles of the ear.

5. *Sesamoid bones* are generally considered a separate type, since they consist of small, rounded bones. Sesamoid bones enter into the formation of joints, or are closely associated with another bone, cartilage, or ligament. The patella, or kneecap, is included among the 206 bones of the skeleton. It is the largest and most definitive of the sesamoid bones.

BONE MARKINGS

The surface of a typical bone exhibits certain projections (*processes*) or depressions (*fossae*). These markings are functional in the sense that they help to join one bone to another or serve as a passageway for blood vessels and nerves. They also provide attachment for muscles. The following terms will often be encountered in any discussion of bone.

process: any marked, bony prominence

spine: any sharp, slender projection, such as a spinous process

condyle: a rounded or knuckle-like prominence, usually found at the point of articulation with another bone

tubercle: a small, rounded process

tuberosity: a large, rounded process

trochanter: a large process for attachment of muscle, such as the trochanter of the femur

trochlea: a process shaped like a pulley

crest: a narrow ridge of bone

line: a less prominent ridge of bone than the crest

head: a terminal enlargement
aditus: the entrance to a cavity
alveolus: a deep pit or socket
fossa: a depression or cavity in or on a bone
fissure: a narrow slit, often between two bones
foramen: an orifice through which blood vessels, nerves, and ligaments pass
meatus or *canal:* a long, tube-like passage

sinus or *antrum:* a cavity within a bone
sulcus: a furrow or groove

DIVISIONS OF THE SKELETON
(Figs. 38 to 41)

The human skeleton is subdivided into the *axial* division, forming the supporting axis of the

Text continued on page 71.

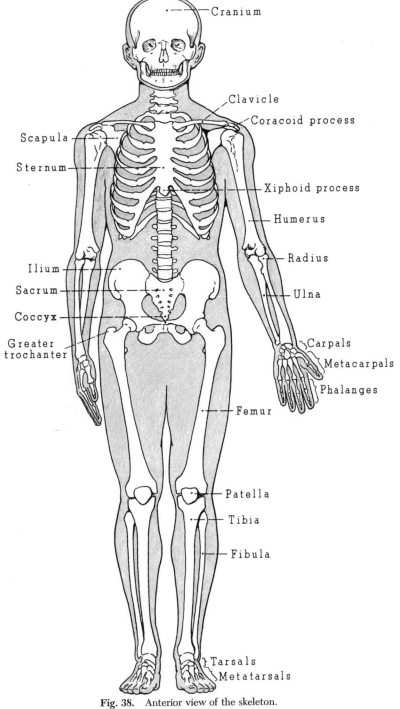

Fig. 38. Anterior view of the skeleton.

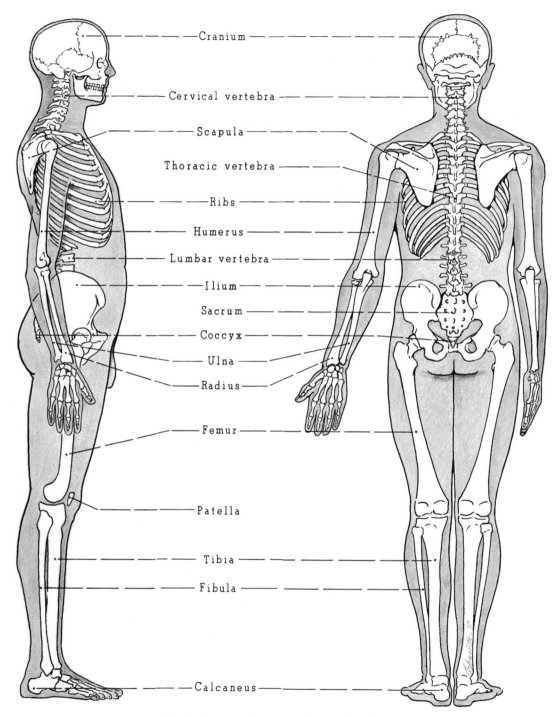

Cranium

Cervical vertebra

Scapula

Thoracic vertebra

Ribs

Humerus

Lumbar vertebra

Ilium

Sacrum

Coccyx

Ulna

Radius

Femur

Patella

Tibia

Fibula

Calcaneus

Fig. 39. Lateral and posterior views of the skeleton.

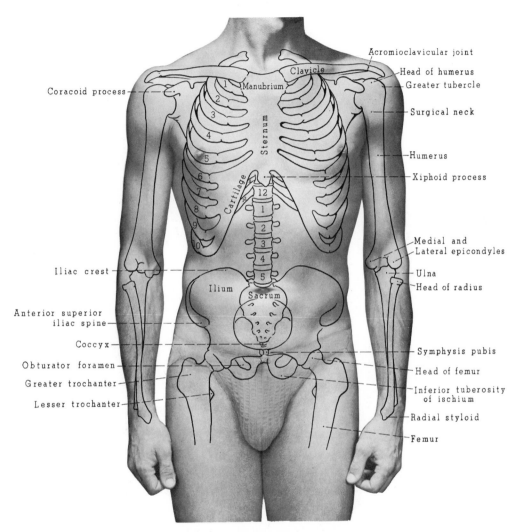

Fig. 40. The skeleton in relation to surface markings, anterior view.

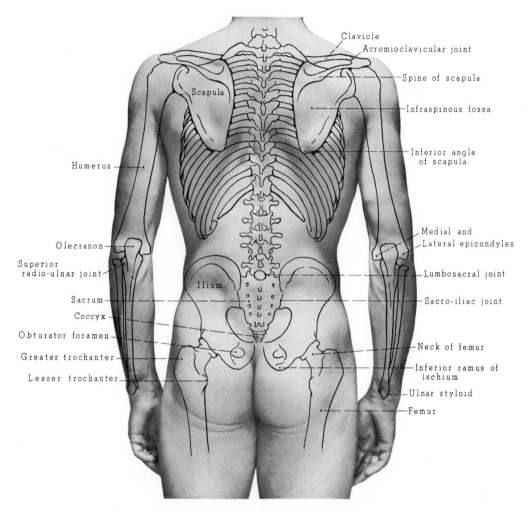

Clavicle

Acromioclavicular joint

Spine of scapula

Scapula

Infraspinous fossa

Inferior angle of scapula

Humerus

Medial and Lateral epicondyles

Olecranon

Lumbosacral joint

Superior radio-ulnar joint

Ilium

Sacro-iliac joint

Sacrum

Coccyx

Obturator foramen

Neck of femur

Greater trochanter

Inferior ramus of ischium

Lesser trochanter

Ulnar styloid

Femur

Fig. 41.   The skeleton in relation to surface markings, posterior view.

Continued from page 67.

body, and the *appendicular* division, consisting of the appendages and their surrounding bones. Components of the axial skeleton will be discussed first.

Axial Skeleton

CRANIAL BONES. The skull, in the proper use of the term, includes both the *facial* and *cranial* bones (Figs. 42 to 49). The bones of the cranium enclose and protect the brain and its associated structures, the special sense organs. The muscles of mastication as well as the muscles for head movements are attached to the cranium. At certain locations within the cranium, cavities or *air sinuses* are present (Fig. 50). These communicate with the nasal cavity.

The individual bones of the cranium are immovably united at *sutures*, or juncture lines. During infancy and early childhood, the articulation is formed by sheets of fibrocartilagenous tissue which gradually ossify. Union of the cranial bones continues as the bone itself grows by increments at its outside edges; thus, the bones grow toward each other, so to speak, and eventually meet at suture lines.

Frontal bone. The frontal bone forms the "forehead" and roof of the nasal cavity and orbits. It develops in two halves which have fused by the end of the second year of life. Paired cavities, the *frontal sinuses,* are present above the orbits near the midline. The notable markings of the frontal bone are the *orbital margin,* a definite ridge above each orbit, and the *supraorbital ridge,* a prominence overlying the frontal sinus. The two frontal sinuses act as sounding chambers to provide resonance to the voice.

Parietal bone. The two parietal bones form the sides and roof of the cranium and are joined at the *sagittal suture* in the midline. The line of articulation between the frontal bone and the two parietal bones is called the *coronal suture.* Like other parts of the cranium, the parietal bones exhibit a variety of grooves and depressions on their inner surfaces, lodging the venous sinuses and convolutions of the brain.

Occipital bone. The occipital bone forms the back and base of the cranium and joins the parietal bones anteriorly at the *lambdoidal suture.* The inferior portion of the bone has a large opening, the *foramen magnum* (literally, great opening), through which the spinal cord passes. It is at the level of the foramen magnum that the spinal cord joins the medulla oblongata of the brain. On each lower side of the occipital bone is a process called the *occipital condyle* for articulation with the first vertebra. Other obvious pro-

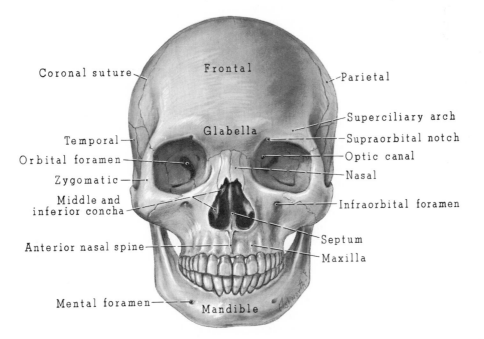

Fig. 42. Frontal aspect of skull.

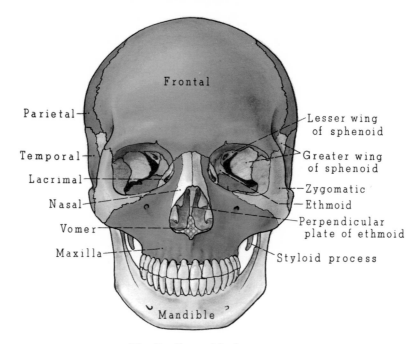

Fig. 43. Bones of the face.

jections are the *external occipital crest* and the *external occipital protuberance*. These can be felt through the scalp at the base of the neck. Several ligaments and muscles are attached in this region.

Temporal bone. The paired temporal bones help to form the sides and base of the cranium. Each encloses an ear and bears a fossa for articulation with the lower jaw. The temporal bone is irregular in shape and consists of the *squamous, petrous, mastoid,* and *tympanic* parts. The *squamous* portion is the largest and most superior of the four. It is a thin, flat plate of bone forming the temple. Projecting forward from the lower part of the squamous is the *zygomatic process*, forming the lateral part of the zygomatic arch or cheek bone. The *petrous* part, shaped roughly like a three-sided pyramid with its apex directed medially, is located deep within the base of the skull between the sphenoid and occipital bones. The petrous contains the inner ear within its complexly fashioned cavities and also bounds a part of the middle ear. The *mastoid* portion is located behind and below the meatus or opening of the ear. In the adult, it contains a number of air spaces called *mastoid cells* or *sinuses*, separated from the brain only by thin, bony partitions. Inflammation of the cells of the mastoid (mastoiditis) is not uncommon and is a potentially dangerous source of infection which may invade the brain or its outer membranes.

The *mastoid process* is a rounded projection of the temporal bone easily found behind the external ear. Several muscles of the neck are attached to the mastoid process. The *tympanic* plate forms the floor and anterior wall of the *external auditory meatus* and lies below the squamous portion anterior to the mastoid process. The long, slender *styloid process* is seen extending from the under surface of the tympanic plate, but is attached for the most part to the petrous portion of the temporal bone.

Sphenoid bone. The sphenoid bone forms the anterior portion of the base of the cranium. It is a single, wedge-shaped bone having a central body and two expanded wings that articulate with the temporal bones on either side. The sphenoid is joined anteriorly to both the ethmoid and frontal bones and posteriorly to the occipital bone. Thus, it serves as a kind of anchor, binding the cranial bones together. A septum projects downward from the body of the sphenoid bone toward the nasal cavity and divides the two sphenoidal sinuses. Superiorly, there is a marked depression, the *sella turcica*, which is occupied by the *hypophysis* (pituitary gland). Medial and lateral pterygoid plates extend from the base of the sphenoid to form a part of the walls and floor of the orbit. These are perforated by several foramina transmitting important nerves and blood vessels.

Ethmoid bone. The ethmoid is the principal supporting structure of the nasal cavity and contributes to the formation of the orbits. It is the

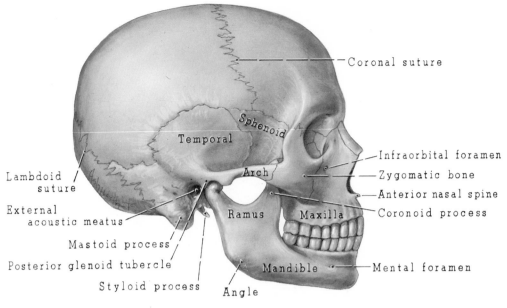

Fig. 44. Right side of skull.

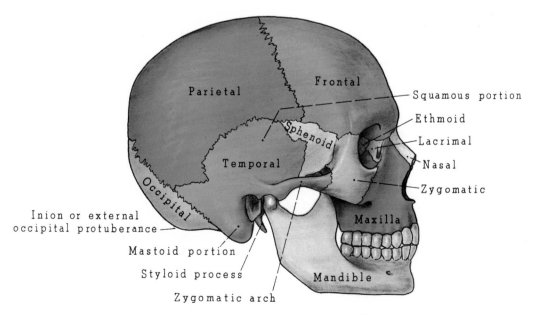

Fig. 45. Bones of the right side of the skull.

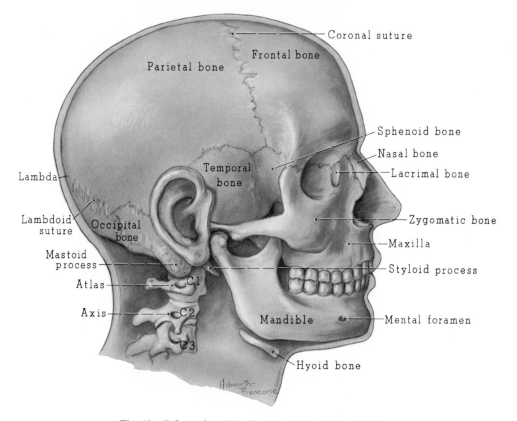

Fig. 46.   Relationship of skull and cervical vertebrae to face.

lightest of the cranial bones and consists pre-dominantly of *cancellous tissue*. The horizontal or *cribriform plate* of the ethmoid forms the roof of the nasal cavity and unites the two lateral masses of air cells, the *ethmoidal labyrinths*. (The outer walls of these small air spaces are completed by various bones of the face.) Each labyrinth exhibits two or three bony plates, the nasal conchae or *turbinate bones*, which project into the nasal cavity and allow for circulation and filtration of inhaled air before it passes to the lungs. The *perpendicular plate* of the ethmoid forms the upper part of the nasal septum.

AUDITORY OSSICLES.   Three bones of the ear —the *malleus, incus,* and *stapes*—are highly specialized in both structure and function. They will be discussed in detail in Chapter Nine.

The so-called *wormian bones* are located within the sutures of the cranium. These wor-mian bones are inconstant in number. They are small and irregular in shape, and are not in-cluded in the total number of bones in the body. In summary, then, the cranial portion of the skull consists of the following bones:

1 frontal	1 sphenoid
2 parietal	1 ethmoid
1 occipital	6 auditory ossicles
2 temporal	wormian bones
	(variable number)

FACIAL BONES.   Like those of the cranium, the bones of the face are immovably united by sutures, with a single exception—the mandible. The lower jaw is capable of movement in several directions and can be depressed or elevated, as in talking. It can also protrude or retract and move from side to side, as in chewing.

Nasal bone.   The paired nasal bones join to form the bridge of the nose. Superiorly, these flat bones articulate with the frontal bone and constitute a small portion of the *nasal septum*.

Palatine bone.   The two palatine bones form the posterior part of the roof of the mouth, or *hard palate*. This area is the same as the floor of the nose. Extensions of the palatine bones extend upward and help to form the outer wall of the nasal cavity. Each palatine bone is somewhat L-shaped with *perpendicular* and *horizontal plates.* The horizontal plate contributes to the palate and joins the maxillary bone anteriorly.

Maxillary bone. The two maxillae constitute the upper jaw. Between the ages of 7 and 12, maxillary growth is responsible for vertical elongation of the face. Each maxillary bone consists of a *body,* a *zygomatic process,* a *frontal process,* a *palatine process,* and an *alveolar process.*

The massive body of the maxilla forms part of the floor and outer wall of the nasal cavity, the greater part of the floor of the orbit, and much of the anterior face below the temple. This part of the bone, covered by several facial muscles, also contains a large maxillary sinus located lateral to the nose.

The *zygomatic process* extends laterally to participate in the formation of the cheek. The *frontal process* extends superiorly to the forehead. The *palatine process* passes posteriorly in a horizontal plane to articulate with the palatine bone and to form the greater portion of the bony palate anteriorly.

The *alveolar process* bears the teeth of the upper jaw. Each tooth is embedded in a socket, or alveolus. In a preserved *edentulous* (without teeth) maxilla, vertical ridges may be seen on the more anterior (external) surface corresponding to the roots of the teeth.

The two maxillary bones are joined at the *intermaxillary suture* in the median plane. This fusion is normally completed before birth. When the two bones do not unite to form a continuous bone, the resulting defect is known as a *cleft palate* and is usually associated with a *cleft lip.*

Zygomatic bone. The two bones forming the prominence of the cheek are also called *malar* bones and rest upon the maxillae articulating with their zygomatic processes. The *orbital surface* of the zygomatic bone forms part of the lateral wall and floor of the orbit. The *malar surface* of each bone is broad and flat and is seen from both lateral and anterior views of the face. The zygomatic bone has a *frontal process* extending upward to articulate with the frontal bone and a smaller *temporal process* articulating laterally with the temporal bone, thus forming the easily identified zygomatic arch.

Lacrimal bone. The paired lacrimal bones make up part of the orbit at the inner angle of the eye. These small, thin bones lie directly behind the frontal process of the maxilla. The lateral surface of the bone presents a *fossa* which lodges the *lacrimal sac* and provides a groove or canal for the passage of the *lacrimal duct.* One side of this groove is formed by a portion of the maxilla. Tears are directed from this point to the inferior meatus of the nasal cavity after having cleansed the eye.

Inferior turbinate bone. The two nasal conchae, or turbinate bones, are similar to those described with the ethmoid; the conchae of the ethmoid, however, occupy superior and middle portions. The *inferior turbinate* bones are larger,

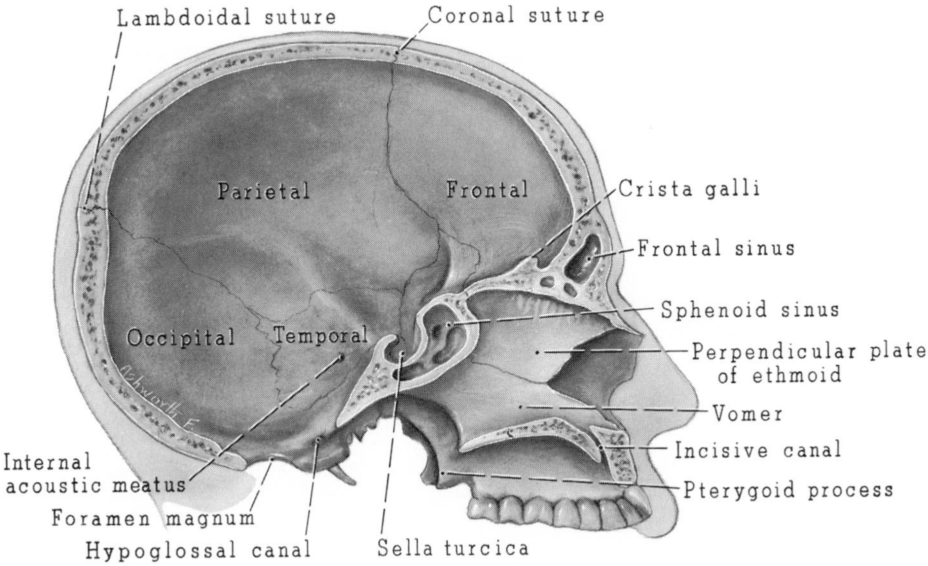

Fig. 47. Longitudinal section of skull.

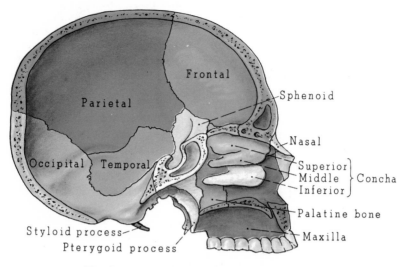

Fig. 48. Longitudinal view showing bones of skull.

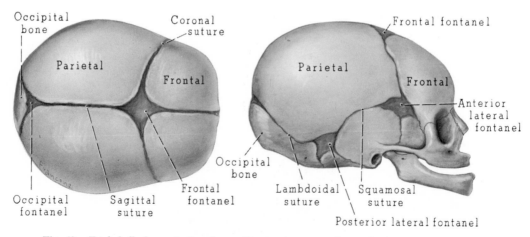

Fig. 49. Fetal skull, demonstrating that ossification is not complete at birth. The frontal fontanel closes at about 18 months of age; the posterior fontanel closes about 6 to 8 weeks after birth.

76

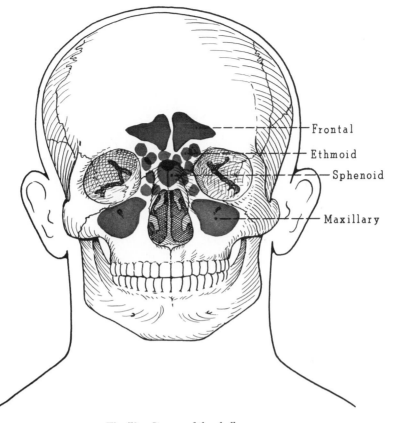

Fig. 50. Sinuses of the skull.

individual bones lying immediately below—one in each nostril on the lateral side. They are thin and fragile and consist of cancellous tissue in a scroll-like shape.

Vomer. The single, flat vomer constitutes the lower posterior portion of the nasal septum. The superior part of the bone has two lips, called *alae*, which articulate with the sphenoid superiorly. The word vomer is Latin for "plough-share," to which the bone presumably bears a resemblance.

Mandible (Fig. 51). Although the mandible develops in two parts, the intervening cartilage ossifies in early childhood and the bone becomes fused into a single continuous structure. This is called the *inferior maxillary bone.* The lower jaw is the strongest and longest bone of the face. In the U-shaped *body* of the mandible are the alveoli containing the lower teeth. This alveolar portion is covered by the mucous membrane of the mouth. On either side of the body are the *rami* which extend perpendicularly upward.

Each ramus presents a *condyle* or condyloid process for articulation with the mandibular fossa of the temporal bone. Also at the upper end of the ramus just anterior to the condyle is a *coronoid process* for attachment of the temporal muscle. The angle of the jaw is the area where the ramus meets the body of the mandible, rather than the region where the mandible articulates with the cranium.

The maxilla articulates with the cranium by way of the frontal bone and with the mandible by way of the temporal bone; thus, the upper and lower jaws are not connected to each other. In the elderly, the alveolar portion of the mandible ceases to grow. When the teeth are finally lost, the alveoli become absorbed by the body of the bone, and the chin develops an angle and appears more prominent.

ORBITS (Fig. 52). The two deep cavities in the upper portion of the face for protection of the eye are complexly formed. To summarize, the orbit consists of the following bones:

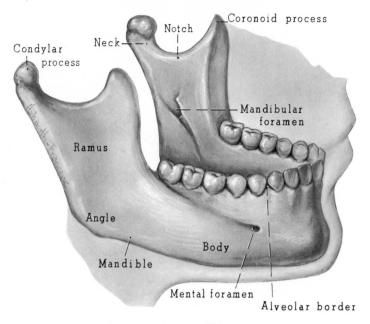

Fig. 51. Mandible.

Area of Orbit	Participating Bones
roof	frontal (primary bone)
	sphenoid
floor	maxilla
	zygoma
lateral wall	zygoma
	greater wing of sphenoid
medial wall	maxilla
	lacrimal
	ethmoid
	lesser wing of sphenoid
upper margin	frontal
lateral margin	zygoma
medial margin	maxilla

NASAL CAVITIES. The bony framework of the nose bounding the two nasal fossae is located in the middle of the face between the palate inferiorly and the frontal bone above. To summarize, the *nose* is formed by the following bones:

Area of Nose	Participating Bones
roof	ethmoid
floor	maxilla
	palatine
lateral wall	maxilla
	palatine
septum or medial wall	ethmoid
	vomer (primary bone)
	nasal bone
bridge	nasal bone

FORAMINA OF THE SKULL. The mastoid cells or sinuses communicate with the tympanic bone, whereas all the other cavities are referred to as the paranasal (accessory) sinuses—the frontal, maxillary, ethmoid, and sphenoid. Their mucous secretions aid in moistening the nasal cavity.

When viewing the floor of the cranial cavity from above, one observes the large foramen magnum and a number of considerably smaller foramina penetrating the individual bones. These openings are passageways for blood vessels and nerves (Figs. 53 to 56 and Table 3).

THE HYOID BONE. The single hyoid bone is the unique component of the axial skeleton since it has no articulations. Rather, it is suspended from the styloid process of the temporal bone by two *stylohyoid ligaments*. Externally, its position is noted in the neck, between the mandible and the larynx. It is shaped like a horseshoe, consisting of a central *body* with two lateral projections, the *greater* and *lesser cornua*. The hyoid bone functions as a primary support for the tongue and its numerous muscles.

THE TORSO OR TRUNK. The vertebrae, sternum, and ribs are the *trunk portion* of the axial skeleton. The *vertebral column* displays a remarkable combination of structural qualities, making it a highly versatile mechanism (Figs. 57 and 58). It is rigid enough to provide adequate support for the body, yet the discs between the vertebrae permit a high degree of flexibility.

The vertebral column provides *protection* for the delicate and vital spinal cord contained within its articulated channel.

The spinal column is formed by a series of 26 vertebrae separated and cushioned by intervertebral discs, or cartilages. The inner canal is formed by successive foramina of the individual vertebrae and by the ligaments and discs connecting them.

VERTEBRAE. All the vertebrae are constructed on the same basic plan, although they do exhibit characteristic specializations in the different anatomic regions. A typical vertebra is characterized by the following features.

1. A *body*—the thick, disc-shaped anterior portion. The upper and lower surfaces are roughened for attachment of intervening discs of fibrocartilage, and the anterior edge is pierced by small holes for vessels nurturing the bone.

2. An *arch* projects backward from the body and encloses a space (the *neural canal*) for passage of the spinal cord. The arch bears three processes for muscle attachment: a *spinous process*, directed backward, and two *transverse processes*, one on either side.

3. *Articular processes*—four in number (two superior and two inferior) with smooth, slightly curved surfaces for articulation with the vertebrae immediately above and below.

4. The arch itself consists of *two pedicles* originating from the vertebral body. Both are notched above and below, so that the articulated column has an opening, the *intervertebral foramen*, on each side. These foramina permit passage of nerves to and from the spinal cord.

5. The *laminae* form the remainder of the arch, completing the canal and forming the posterior wall of the vertebral column. Frequently, several of the laminae must be removed surgically after injuries to the vertebral column to relieve pressure on the spinal cord.

The vertebrae are named and numbered regionally from above downward. There are seven *cervical,* twelve *thoracic,* and five *lumbar* vertebrae (Fig. 58). These remain separate throughout life and are called movable vertebrae. In addition, there are five sacral vertebrae which become fused by adult life to form the single sacrum, and four coccygeal vertebrae which unite firmly into the single coccyx. These last two are called *fixed* vertebrae; consequently, the vertebrae are referred to as being 26 in number, rather than 33. Regardless of the individual's body height, the adult vertebral column measures approximately 60 to 70 cm. in length (24 to 28 inches).

Cervical vertebrae. The cervical vertebrae are the smallest vertebrae, having somewhat oblong bodies and being broader from side to side than from front to back. The spinous processes of the third, fourth, and fifth cervical vertebrae are *bifid,* or forked, to cradle the strong ligaments supporting the head. The transverse process is pierced by a foramen to allow passage of the vertebral artery (Fig. 59).

The first two cervical vertebrae are unique. The *atlas* supports the head by articulation with the condyles of the occipital bone. There is no typical body in the atlas, since it is a complete ring of bone having anterior and posterior arches and two lateral masses. The transverse processes, although present, are short and rounded, since they do not articulate with the ribs.

The axis (second vertebra) does have a body, from which the *odontoid process* projects up through the ring of the atlas to make a pivot on which the atlas and head rotate. There are *flattened articular facets* on each lateral mass of the axis for articulation with corresponding facets on the atlas.

Cervical vertebrae numbers 3, 4, 5, and 6 follow the typical patterns previously described. The seventh differs in that it has a long, undivided spinous process with a tubercle at its tip. The bone is called the *vertebra prominens,* since it can be seen and felt at the base of the neck.

Thoracic vertebrae. The bodies of the thoracic vertebrae are longer and more rounded than those of the cervical region. The thoracic vertebrae have two distinguishing characteristics —the long *spinous process,* pointed and directed downward; and six *facets,* three on either side for articulation with the ribs. The transverse processes of all but the eleventh and twelfth vertebrae carry a facet for the tubercle of the rib.

Lumbar vertebrae. The lumbar vertebrae are the largest and strongest of the different types. Their various projections are short and thick, and the spinous processes are modified for attachment of the powerful back muscles.

Sacrum (Fig. 60). The sacrum is a triangular, slightly curved bone positioned at the base of the pelvic cavity between the two innominate bones. Its base articulates above with the fifth lumbar vertebra, and the anterior surface of this broad base forms the *sacral prominence.* The sacrum has a cavity which is a continuation of the spinal canal.

Coccyx. The coccyx articulates with the tip or apex of the sacrum. Slight movement is possible at this joint, serving to increase the size of the birth canal during delivery.

VERTEBRAL COLUMN AS A WHOLE. In the embryo, the vertebral column shows a single

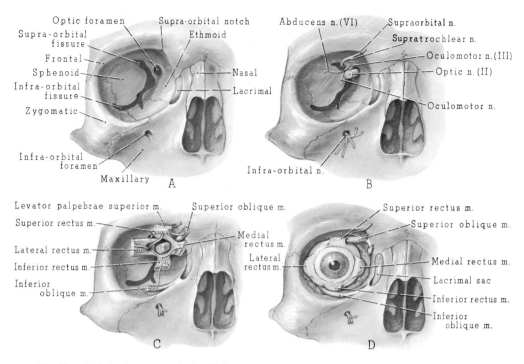

Fig. 52. *A.* Skeletal structure of orbit. *B.* Innervation to eye muscles. *C.* Muscles of the eye with associated nerves. *D.* Attachment of muscles to eye.

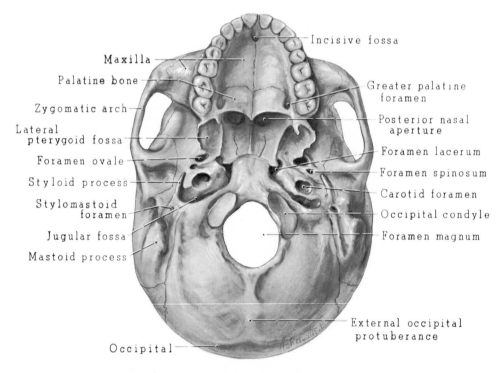

Fig. 53. Inferior surface of the skull.

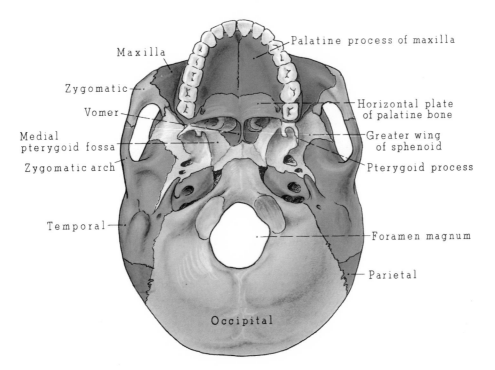

Fig. 54. Inferior surface of skull, showing various bones comprising it.

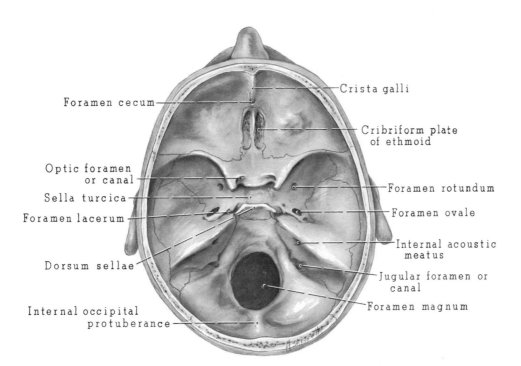

Fig. 55. Floor of cranial cavity.

TABLE 3.

FORAMEN	LOCATION	TRANSMITTED STRUCTURE(S)
Carotid canal or carotid foramen	Petrous portion, temporal bone	Internal carotid artery
Infraorbital foramen	Maxillary bone at lower rim of orbit	Maxillary division of fifth cranial nerve
Jugular foramen	Suture between petrous portion of temporal and occipital bones	Ninth, tenth, and eleventh cranial nerves
Mandibular foramen of mandible	Inner ramus of mandible	Nerves and vessels to lower teeth
Mental foramen of mandible	Outer body of mandible	Terminal branches of nerves from mandibular foramen
Optic foramen	Lesser wing of sphenoid	Second cranial nerve (optic)
Foramen ovale	Greater wing of sphenoid	Mandibular division of fifth cranial nerve
Foramen rotundum	Greater wing of sphenoid	Maxillary division of fifth cranial nerve
Superior orbital fissure	Within sphenoid, opening into orbital cavity	Third, fourth, and part of fifth cranial nerve
Stylomastoid foramen	Between styloid and mastoid processes of temporal bone	Facial nerve (seventh cranial) leaves cranial cavity
Supraorbital foramen	Frontal bone at orbital margin	Supraorbital nerve and blood vessels

C-shaped curve with the convex surface of the curve directed posteriorly. After birth, raising of the head creates an anteriorly directed curve in the neck; simultaneously the assumption of an erect posture creates an anteriorly directed curve in the lumbar area.

The normal curves of the spine can become exaggerated as a result of injury, poor body posture, or disease. When the posterior curvature is accentuated in the thoracic area, the condition is called *kyphosis*. When the anterior curvature in the lumbar region is accentuated, it is known as *lordosis*. When there is a lateral curvature associated with rotation of the vertebrae, it is termed *scoliosis*.

In addition to its functions of body support and movement, as well as protection of the spinal cord, the vertebral column is built to withstand forces of compression many times the weight of the body. The intervertebral discs of cartilage act as cushions, so that landing on the feet after a jump or fall will be less likely to fracture the vertebrae. The discs also act as shock absorbers to reduce a transmitted jarring or pressure on the brain.

INJURIES TO THE SPINAL COLUMN. When the spinal column is subjected to violence, fractures or dislocations can result. The most frequent fracture is a crush injury to the vertebral body. Sometimes a combined flexion and hyperexten-sion injury dislocates one vertebra on another, causing locking of the articular processes. This occurs most frequently in diving accidents.

HERNIATED INTERVERTEBRAL DISC. The intervertebral disc acts as a cushion between adjacent vertebral bodies. It is a fibrocartilaginous structure with a tough outer layer called the *annulus fibrosus* and a soft resilient interior remnant of the notochord, the *nucleus pulposus*. It thus resembles the structure of a golf ball. If the annulus becomes injured, the pressure within the disc is decreased and the nucleus can protrude (Fig. 61). The herniated portion sometimes causes pressure on a spinal nerve, resulting in nerve root irritation, a frequent cause of leg pain. Disc pathology can result from injury but is most commonly (80 per cent of the instances) due to attrition caused by a lack of blood supply during adult life.

THE THORAX (Figs. 62 and 63).   That portion of the trunk consisting of the *sternum*, the *costal cartilages*, the *ribs*, and the bodies of the *thoracic vertebrae* is properly called the thorax. This bony cage encloses and protects the lungs and other structures of the chest cavity. The thorax also provides support for the bones of the shoulder girdle and upper extremities. In adult life, it is cone shaped with a broad base.

Sternum (Fig. 62).   The "breastbone" develops in three parts—from above downward, the

Text continued on page 89.

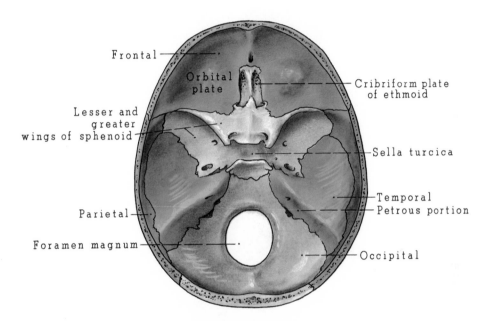

Frontal

Orbital plate

Cribriform plate of ethmoid

Lesser and greater wings of sphenoid

Sella turcica

Parietal

Temporal
Petrous portion

Foramen magnum

Occipital

Fig. 56. Floor of cranial cavity and its separate bones.

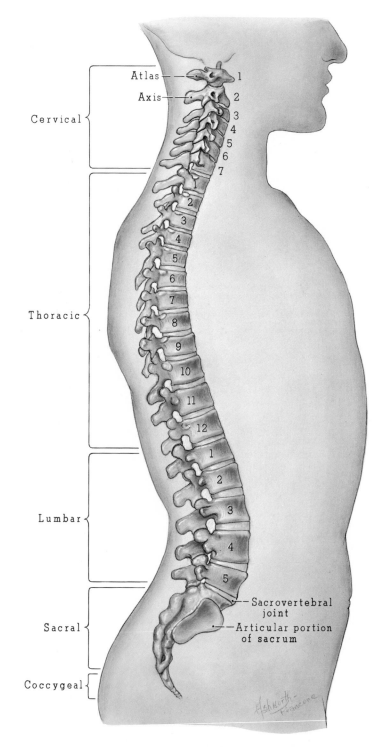

Cervical

Atlas —— 1
Axis —— 2
3
4
5
6
7

Thoracic

1
2
3
4
5
6
7
8
9
10
11
12

Lumbar

1
2
3
4
5

Sacral

—— Sacrovertebral joint
—— Articular portion of sacrum

Coccygeal

Fig. 57. Vertebral column in relation to body outline.

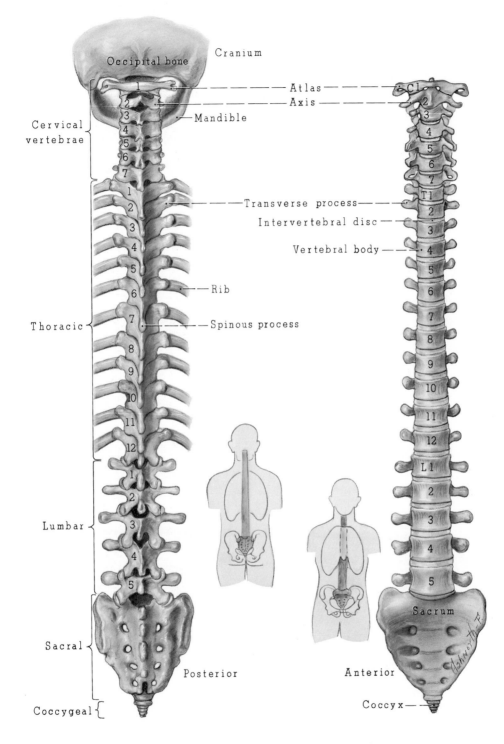

Cranium

Occipital bone

Atlas

Axis

Mandible

Cervical vertebrae

Transverse process

Intervertebral disc

Vertebral body

Rib

Thoracic

Spinous process

Lumbar

Sacral

Posterior

Anterior

Sacrum

Coccyx

Coccygeal

Fig. 58. Posterior and anterior views of vertebral column.

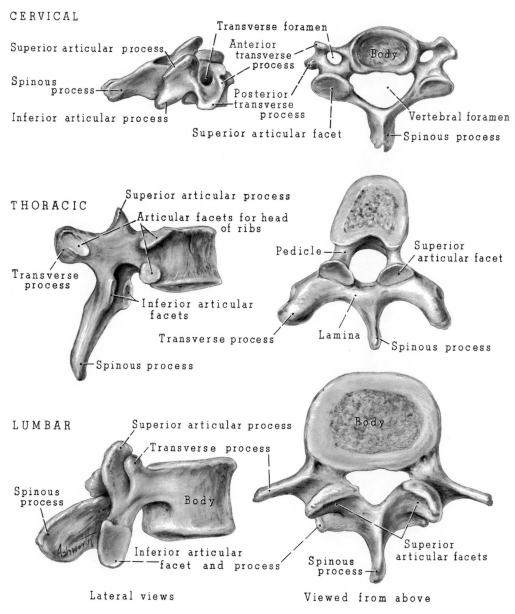

CERVICAL

Superior articular process

Spinous process

Inferior articular process

Transverse foramen

Anterior transverse process

Posterior transverse process

Superior articular facet

Body

Vertebral foramen

Spinous process

THORACIC

Superior articular process

Articular facets for head of ribs

Transverse process

Inferior articular facets

Transverse process

Spinous process

Pedicle

Superior articular facet

Lamina

Spinous process

LUMBAR

Superior articular process

Transverse process

Spinous process

Body

Inferior articular facet and process

Body

Spinous process

Superior articular facets

Lateral views

Viewed from above

Fig. 59. Lateral and top views of three different levels of vertebrae.

86

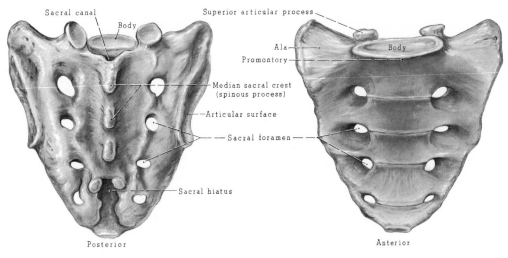

Fig. 60. Posterior and anterior views of sacrum.

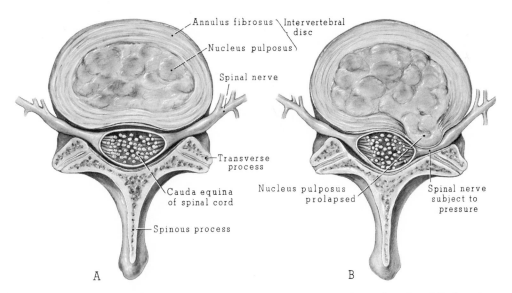

Fig. 61. *A.* Normal relations of intervertebral disc to the spinal cord and nerve branches. *B.* Prolapsed pulposus of intervertebral disc impinging on the nerve. (After Netter.)

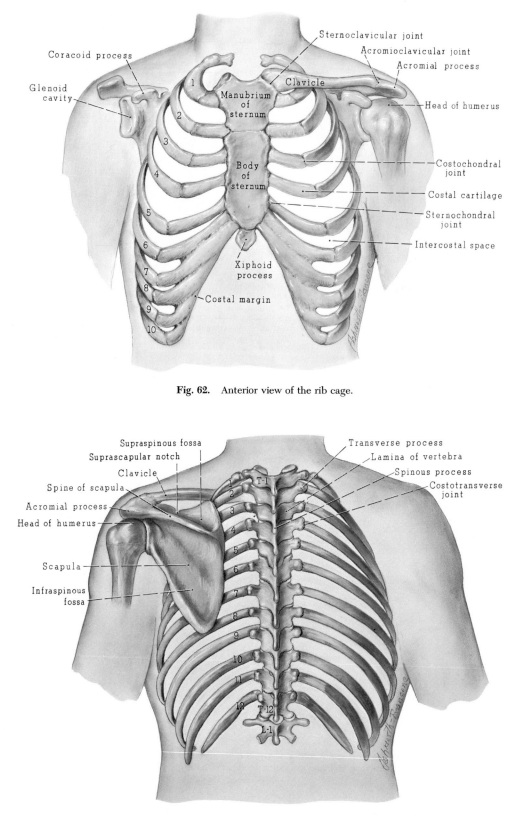

Fig. 62. Anterior view of the rib cage.

Fig. 63. Posterior view of the rib cage and scapula.

Continued from page 82.

manubrium, the *gladiolus,* and the *xiphoid.* The first two of these are named for their resemblance to the handle of a sword. There are no ribs attached to the xiphoid, but the manubrium and gladiolus exhibit notches on either side for attachment of the first seven costal cartilages. At the upper and outer aspects, the manubrium of the sternum articulates with the clavicle. Between the two points of articulation is the *suprasternal* or *jugular notch,* easily felt through the skin. The diaphragm, linea alba, and rectus abdominis muscle are attached to the xiphoid.

Ribs. The 12 pairs of ribs (costae) are named according to their anterior attachments. The upper seven pairs articulate directly with the sternum and are called *true ribs.* The lower five pairs join with the sternum only indirectly and are called *false ribs.* The *costal cartilages* of the eighth, ninth, and tenth rib pairs are attached to the cartilages of the rib above. The eleventh and twelfth "false" ribs have a second name, *floating ribs,* since their anterior ends are completely unattached. The posterior extremity of a typical rib presents a rounded *head* portion for attachment to facets on the body of the thoracic vertebrae. Ribs numbered 2 through 9 each articulate between the adjacent bodies of two vertebrae. The heads of ribs numbered 1, 10, 11, and 12 articulate with a single vertebral body.

A lateral bulge or tubercle is located below the *head* and *neck* of the rib extremity. Each tubercle rests on the facet of a single thoracic transverse process. From their posterior vertebral attachments, the curved ribs slope downward as well as outward, thus increasing the size of the thoracic cavity; however, the cavity's anterior margin is considerably higher than the posterior margin, because the lower edge of the sternum is at the level of the tenth thoracic vertebra rather than the twelfth, and because the costal cartilages of the false ribs are necessarily directed upward toward the sternum.

Appendicular Skeleton

BONES OF THE UPPER EXTREMITY. Included are the bones of the shoulder girdle, arm, forearm, wrist, hand, and fingers.

The clavicle (collar bone) is a long, slim bone located at the root of the neck just below the skin and anterior to the first rib (Fig. 64). The medial two-thirds of the clavicle is bowed forward, while the lateral one-third is bowed backward. The medial end articulates with the *manubrium* of the sternum and the lateral end with the *acromial process* of the scapula. The joint between the clavicle and the sternum is the only bony articulation between the upper extremity and the thorax.

The *scapula* is a large, flat, triangular bone located on the dorsal portion of the thorax, covering the area from the second to the seventh rib (Fig. 65). The *coracoid process* of the scapula is a projection originating from the anterior surface of the superior border. It serves as the origin for some muscles that move the arm. The acromial process (acromion) is the point of the shoulder articulating with the lateral end of the clavicle.

The *humerus* is the long bone of the upper arm. Its head is rounded and joined to the rest of the body by the *anatomic neck.* The upper part of the bone has two prominences, the *greater* and *lesser tubercles,* serving as insertions for many of the muscles of the upper extremity. The *bicipital groove* is located between the tubercles and contains the tendons of part of the biceps muscle.

The surgical neck of the humerus—so called because it is the site of the most common fracture in the elderly—lies below the tubercles. Inferior to the neck on the shaft is the *deltoid tuberosity* on the lateral side. Fractures of the humerus are occasionally associated with radial nerve injury.

The distal end of the bone becomes flattened and terminates in the *medial* and *lateral epicondyles.* The articular surface of the distal end of the humerus is formed by the *capitulum,* a smooth knob articulating with the radius, and the *trochlea,* a pulley-shaped area articulating with the ulna. The anterior surface of the distal end is the *coronoid fossa;* the posterior surface of the distal end is the *olecranon fossa.* Both fossae serve to receive the processes of the same name on the ulna.

The *ulna* is the longer, medial bone of the forearm (Figs. 66 and 67). Its shaft is triangular and the lower (distal) end of the bone is known as the *head.* The head articulates with the triangular articular disc of the wrist, and posterior to the head can be found the *styloid process.*

The *radius* joins with the ulna by an interosseus membrane traversing the area between the shafts of the two bones. It is shorter and located lateral to the ulna. The radial head articulates with the capitulum of the humerus. The shaft has a tuberosity on the medial side which serves for insertion of the biceps. The head of the ulna fits into the *ulnar notch* at the distal end of the radius. The styloid process of the radius is larger

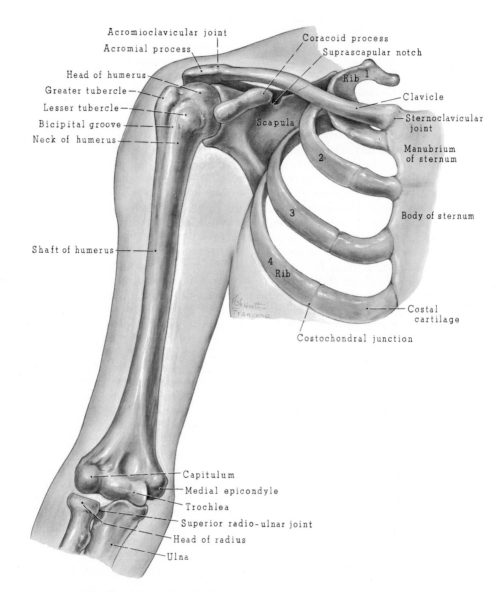

Acromioclavicular joint

Acromial process

Coracoid process

Suprascapular notch

Head of humerus

Greater tubercle

Lesser tubercle

Bicipital groove

Neck of humerus

Rib 1

Clavicle

Scapula

Sternoclavicular joint

Manubrium of sternum

2

3

Body of sternum

Shaft of humerus

4

Rib

Costal cartilage

Costochondral junction

Capitulum

Medial epicondyle

Trochlea

Superior radio-ulnar joint

Head of radius

Ulna

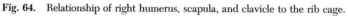

Fig. 64. Relationship of right humerus, scapula, and clavicle to the rib cage.

90

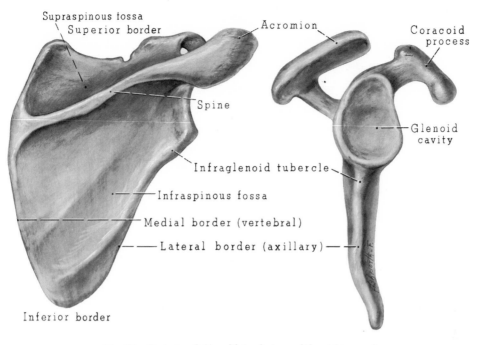

Fig. 65. Posterior *(left)* and lateral views of the right scapula.

than the styloid process of the ulna and articulates with the bones of the wrist.

The bones of the wrist are called carpals, and are situated in two rows of four each. In the proximal row from medial to lateral are the *pisiform, triquetrum, lunate,* and *scaphoid.* In the distal row from medial to lateral are the *hamate, capitate, trapezoid,* and *trapezium.*

The palm of the hand consists of five *metacarpal* bones, each with a base, shaft, and head. The metacarpals radiate from the wrist like spokes from a wheel, rather than being parallel, and articulate with the proximal phalanges of the fingers. Each finger (excluding the thumb) has three *phalanges*—a *proximal,* a *middle,* and a *terminal* or *distal phalanx.* The thumb has only two phalanges.

BONES OF THE LOWER EXTREMITY (Fig. 68). The pelvic girdle supports the trunk and provides attachment for the legs. The paired os coxae (pelvic bone or "hipbone") originally consists of three separate bones, the *ilium, ischium,* and *pubis.* These names are retained as descriptive regions for areas of the fused adult pelvic bone.

The *femur* is the bone of the thigh. It is the longest and heaviest bone in the body. The *patella,* or "kneecap" is the largest sesamoid

bone. Forming the lower portion of the leg are the *tibia* ("shinbone") and *fibula* ("calfbone"). The ankle and foot are composed of the *tarsal* and *metatarsal* bones, as well as the *phalanges.*

Pelvic bone (Fig. 69). The two "hipbones" articulate with each other anteriorly and at the pubic symphysis. Posteriorly, they articulate with the sacrum. The ring of bone thus formed is known as the pelvis; in adults the pelvic cavity within contains part of the sigmoid colon, the rectum, the bladder, and some of the reproductive organs. The pelvis of the female shows characteristic differences relating to adaptations for pregnancy and parturition.

Ilium. The uppermost and largest portion of the pelvic bone is the ilium, forming the expanded prominence of the hip. Its crest is projected into the *anterior superior iliac spine* and the *anterior inferior iliac spine.* The former is used as a convenient anatomic and surgical landmark, and both provide attachment to the muscles of the abdominal wall.

Ischium. The strongest portion of the pelvic bone is the *ischium,* directed slightly posteriorly. Its curved edge is seen from the front as the lowermost margin of the pelvis. It bears the rounded ischial tuberosity which takes the weight of the body in the sitting position.

Text continued on page 95.

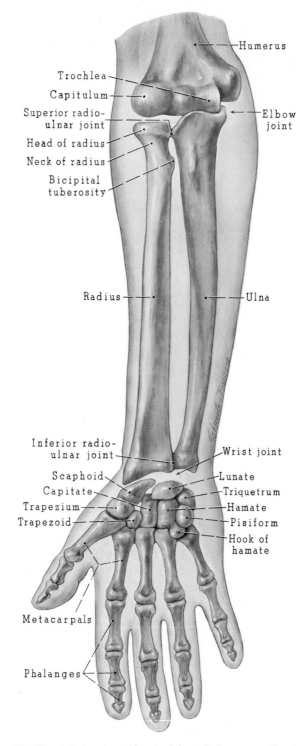

Fig. 66. Anterior view of bones of the right forearm and hand.

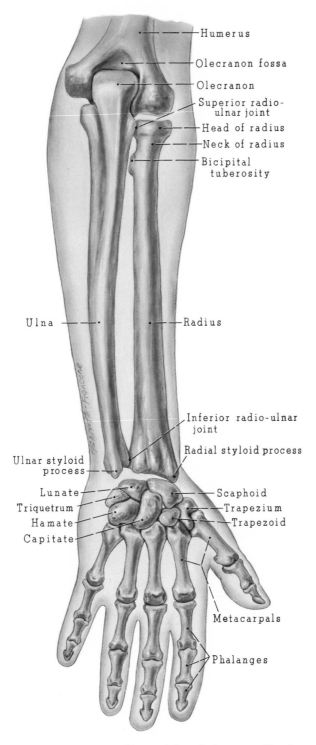

Humerus

Olecranon fossa

Olecranon

Superior radio-
ulnar joint

Head of radius

Neck of radius

Bicipital
tuberosity

Ulna

Radius

Inferior radio-ulnar
joint

Radial styloid process

Ulnar styloid
process

Scaphoid

Lunate

Trapezium

Triquetrum

Trapezoid

Hamate

Capitate

Metacarpals

Phalanges

Fig. 67. Posterior view of bones of the right forearm and hand.

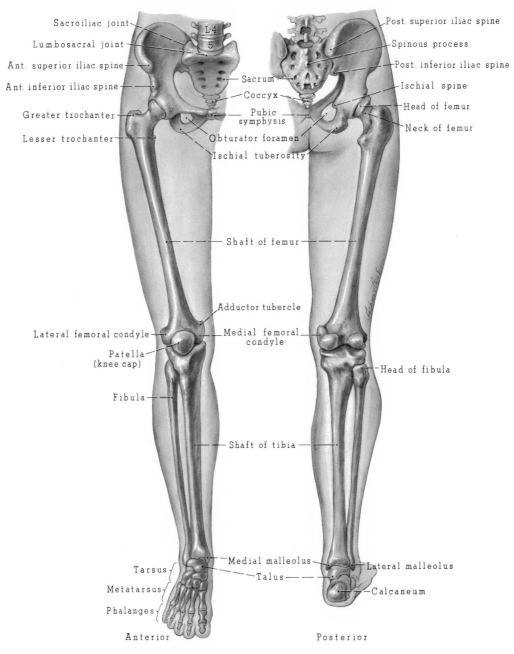

Sacroiliac joint
Lumbosacral joint
Ant. superior iliac spine
Ant. inferior iliac spine
Greater trochanter
Lesser trochanter

Post. superior iliac spine
Spinous process
Post. inferior iliac spine
Ischial spine
Head of femur
Neck of femur

L4
5

Sacrum
Coccyx
Pubic symphysis
Obturator foramen
Ischial tuberosity

Shaft of femur

Adductor tubercle
Lateral femoral condyle
Medial femoral condyle
Patella (knee cap)
Fibula

Head of fibula

Shaft of tibia

Tarsus
Metatarsus
Phalanges

Medial malleolus
Talus

Lateral malleolus
Calcaneum

Anterior

Posterior

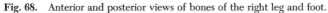

Fig. 68. Anterior and posterior views of bones of the right leg and foot.

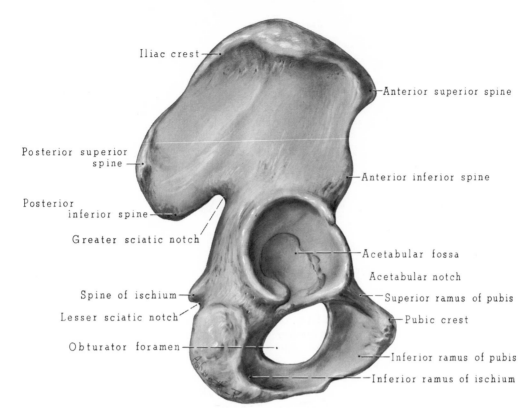

Iliac crest

Anterior superior spine

Posterior superior spine

Anterior inferior spine

Posterior inferior spine

Greater sciatic notch

Acetabular fossa

Acetabular notch

Spine of ischium

Superior ramus of pubis

Lesser sciatic notch

Pubic crest

Obturator foramen

Inferior ramus of pubis

Inferior ramus of ischium

Fig. 69. Lateral view of the right pelvic bone.

Continued from page 91.

Pubis. The pubis is superior and slightly anterior to the ischium. Between the pubis and ischium is the large *obturator foramen,* the largest foramen in the body. It is filled with fibrous areolar tissue, nerves, and blood vessels, and is functional only in the sense that it lightens the weight of the "hipbone." The pubis consists of a *body,* a *ridge,* a *crest,* and two branches or *rami* (pubic rami).

Acetabulum. On the lateral aspect of the "hipbone," just above the obturator foramen, is a deep socket called the acetabulum. All three portions of the pelvic bone meet and unite in this depression. The acetabulum receives the head of the femur to form the hip joint.

Pelvic cavity (Fig. 70). The pelvic cavity is bounded by the two "hipbones" laterally and anteriorly, and by the sacrum and coccyx posteriorly. The massive bony ring is divided into the *greater pelvis* and the *lesser pelvis* by the *pelvic brim.* Above the brim, the greater or "false" pelvis is formed by the concavities of the expanded iliac bones. Below and behind the brim, the lesser or "true" pelvis is continued as the pelvic cavity. The floor of the pelvic cavity is formed by muscles.

Male and female pelvic cavities are compared in Table 4.

Femur. The Latin word for "thigh" is femur. This single large bone of the upper leg is *not* in a vertical line with the axis of the erect body. Rather, it is positioned at an angle, slanting downward and inward. From the point of view of the skeleton, the two femurs appear as a "V." Because of the greater pelvic breadth, the angle of inclination of the femurs is greater in the female than in the male.

The upper extremity of the femur bears a rounded *head,* which projects medially upward to rest in the acetabulum, forming the hip joint. Below this is a constricted neck with greater and lesser trochanters. On the posterior aspect of the long shaft is a ridge called the *linea aspera,* the area of attachment for several muscles of the hip and leg.

The lower extremity of the femur is widened into massive *lateral* and *medial condyles,* separated by the *intercondyloid fossa.* The femur articulates distally with the tibia. The knee joint thus formed approximates the line of gravity of the body.

Patella. The "kneecap" is a small, flat, some-

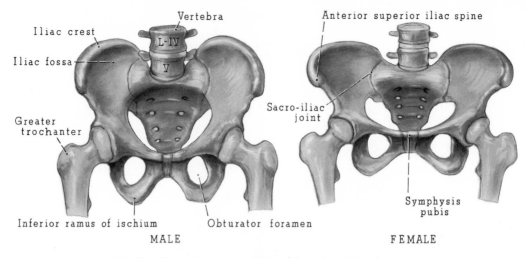

Iliac crest

Vertebra

Anterior superior iliac spine

Iliac fossa

L-IV

V

Sacro-iliac
joint

Greater
trochanter

Symphysis
pubis

Inferior ramus of ischium   Obturator foramen

MALE   FEMALE

Fig. 70. Comparison in proportions of the male and female pelves.

what triangular sesamoid bone lying in front of the knee joint and developed within the tendon of the quadriceps femoris muscle. The only articulation is with the femur. The patella is movable and serves to increase leverage of muscles that straighten the knee.

Tibia. The tibia is the larger of the two bones forming the lower leg. The upper end consists of two broad eminences, the *medial* and *lateral condyles.* Their concave surface articulates with the respective condyles of the femur. The lower extremity is smaller and prolonged as the *medial malleolus* which forms the inner ankle bone. Slightly lateral to this projection is the surface for articulation with the talus forming the ankle joint. The tibia also articulates with the fibula laterally at both upper and lower extremities.

Fibula. In proportion to its length, the fibula is the most slender bone in the body, lying parallel with and on the lateral side of the tibia.

Its upper extremity does not reach the knee joint but articulates by means of an expanded head with the tibia. The lower extremity terminates in a pointed process, the *lateral malleolus* or "outer ankle bone." The fibula articulates distally with both the tibia and the talus.

Tarsus (Fig. 71). The bones of the tarsus consist of a group of seven short bones which resemble the carpal bones of the wrist but are larger. Tarsal bones are arranged in the *hindfoot* and *forefoot.* The hindfoot consists of the calcaneum and the talus, navicular, and cuboid bones. The calcaneum is the largest bone of the group and forms the prominence of the heel. The *talus,* or *astragalus,* lies above the calcaneum obliquely. Its head projects forward and medially in the general direction of the great toe. The head of the talus articulates with the *navicular joint* or medial compartment of the midtarsal joint. The forefoot consists of the *medial cunei-*

TABLE 4.   Comparison of Male and Female Pelves.

	MALE (ANDROID)	FEMALE (GYNECOID)
Bone of pelvis	Heavy and rough	Small and slender
Sacrum	Narrow and curved	Broad, with a lesser curvature
False pelvis	Narrow	Wide
True pelvis	Deep but narrow, with less capacity	Shallow, wide, with greater capacity
Aperture of pelvic cavity	Heart-shaped	Oval
Greater sciatic notch	Narrow	Wide
Obturator foramen	Oval	Triangular
Pubic angle	Narrow, pointed	Wide, rounded
Direction	Tilted backward	Tilted forward

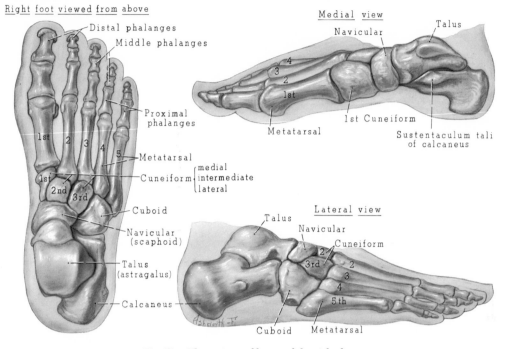

Fig. 71. Three views of bones of the right foot.

form (first), the *intermediate cuneiform* (second), the *lateral cuneiform* (third), the *metatarsals*, and the *phalanges*.

Metatarsal bones. There are five metatarsal bones in the foot. Each is a long bone with a base, shaft, and head. The *bases* of the first, second, and third metatarsals articulate with the three cuneiforms; the fourth and fifth metatarsals articulate with the cuboid. These joints are named the *tarsometatarsal* joints. The intrinsic muscles of the toes are attached to the shafts of the metatarsals. The heads articulate with the proximal row of the phalanges of the toe at the metatarsophalangeal joints. The first metatarsal is larger than the others, owing to its weight-bearing function.

Phalanges of the toes. Bones of the toes are classified as long bones in spite of their being short in length. Like the bones of the fingers, they are called phalanges. There are two phalanges in the great toe and three in each of the four lesser toes—a total of 14.

ARCHES OF THE FOOT. The bones of the foot are arranged in a series of *arches* enabling the foot to provide *weight bearing* while standing and *leverage* while walking. The arches of the foot run longitudinally.

There are two *longitudinal arches*. The calcaneum, talus, navicular, cuneiform, and the first, second, and third metatarsals comprise the *medial longitudinal arch*. This arch is supported by the calcaneum posteriorly and by the heads of the three metatarsals anteriorly. The "keystone" of the longitudinal arch is the navicular.

The *lateral longitudinal arch* is shallower and consists of the calcaneus, cuboid, and fourth and fifth metatarsals. The "keystone" of the lateral arch is the cuboid.

FLATFOOT. The term *pes planus*, or flatfoot, indicates a decreased height of longitudinal arches. This can be inherited or can result from muscle imbalance in the foot. It is rarely a cause of pain.

TABLE 5. Bones.

BONE	NUMBER	LOCATION
1. *Skull*	28 bones	
Cranium	8 bones	
Occipital	1	Posterior cranial floor and walls
Parietal	2	Forms the greater part of the superior lateral aspect and roof of the skull between frontal and occipital bones
Frontal	1	Forms forehead, most of orbital roof, and anterior cranial floor
Temporal	2	Inferior lateral aspect and base of the skull, housing middle and inner ear structures
Sphenoid	1	Mid-anterior base of the skull; forms part of floor and sides of orbit
Ethmoid	1	Between nasal bones and sphenoid, forming part of anterior cranial floor, medial wall of orbits, part of nasal septum, and roof
Face	14 bones	
Nasal	2	Upper bridge of nose
Maxillary	2	Upper jaw
Zygomatic (malar)	2	Prominence of cheeks and part of the lateral wall and floor of the orbits
Mandible	1	Lower jaw
Lacrimal	2	Anterior medial wall of the orbit
Palatine	2	Posterior nasal cavity between maxillae and the pterygoid processes of sphenoid
Vomer	1	Posterior nasal cavity, forming a portion of the nasal septum
Inferior nasal conchae (inferior turbinates)	2	Lateral wall of nasal cavity
Auditory Ossicles	6 bones	
Malleus (hammer)	2	Small bones in inner ear in temporal bone, connecting the tympanic membrane to the inner ear and functioning in sound transmission
Incus (anvil)	2	
Stapes (stirrup)	2	
Hyoid	1 bone	Horseshoe-shaped, suspended from styloid process of temporal bone
2. *Trunk*	51 bones	
Vertebrae	26 bones	
Cervical	7	Neck
Thoracic	12	Thorax
Lumbar	5	Between thorax and pelvis
Sacrum	1 (5 fused)	Pelvis—fixed or false vertebrae
Coccyx	1 (5 fused)	Terminal vertebrae in pelvis—fixed or false vertebrae
Ribs	24	True ribs—upper seven pairs fastened to sternum by costal cartilages; false ribs—lower five pairs; eighth, ninth, and tenth pairs attached to the seventh rib by costal cartilages; last two pairs do not attach and are called floating ribs
Sternum	1	Flat, narrow bone situated in median line anteriorly in chest
3. *Upper Extremity*	64 bones	
Clavicle	2	Together, clavicles and scapulae form the shoulder girdle; the clavicle articulates with the sternum

TABLE 5. *Continued.*

BONE	NUMBER	LOCATION
Scapula	2	
Humerus	2	Long bone of upper arm
Ulna	2	The ulna is the longest bone of forearm, on medial side of radius
Radius	2	Lateral to ulna, shorter than ulna, but styloid process is larger
Carpals	16	Two rows of bones comprising the wrist
Scaphoid		
Lunate		
Triangular		
Pisiform		
Capitate		
Hamate		
Trapezium		
Trapezoid		
Metacarpals	10	Long bones of the palm of the hand
Phalanges	28	Three in each finger and two in each thumb
4. *Lower Extremity*	62 bones	
Pelvic	2	Fusion of ilium, ischium and pubis
Femur (thighbone)	2	Longest bone in body
Patella	2	Kneecap; located in quadriceps femoris tendon; a sesamoid bone
Tibia	2	Shinbone; antero-medial side of the leg
Fibula	2	Lateral to tibia
Tarsals	14	Form heel, ankle (with distal tibia and fibula), and proximal part of the foot
Calcaneum		
Talus		
Navicular		
Cuboid		
First cuneiform (medial)		
Second cuneiform (intermediate)		
Third cuneiform (lateral)		
Metatarsals	10	Long bones of the foot
Phalanges	28	Three in each lesser toe and two in each great toe

SUMMARY: THE SKELETAL SYSTEM

FUNCTIONS

1. The main supportive structure of the body is the skeleton, which is very much a living tissue.

2. The functions of the skeleton are:

   a. Assistance in accomplishing body movement.
   b. Support of other tissues.
   c. Protection of vital organs.
   d. Hematopoiesis.
   e. Provision of a storage area.

3. There are 206 bones in the skeleton.

   a. Axial skeleton consists of the skull, hyoid bone, vertebrae, ribs, and sternum.
   b. Appendicular skeleton consists of the upper and lower extremities.

EMBRYOLOGY

1. **Bone is derived from mesoderm, and the cartilage skeleton is formed in the embryo by the end of 3 months.**

2. **Vertical growth continues to 15 or 16 years, and modeling and shaping continues to about 21 years of age.**

3. **The bone-forming cells are osteoblasts which have been converted to osteocytes.**

4. **Calcification is the initial mineralization process, while ossification refers to the actual formation of the bone.**

5. **Cartilage does not turn into bone; it is the environment in which bone develops.**

6. **Intramembranous ossification is the process by which the bones of the face and skull are formed.**

7. **Enchondral ossification is the process by which the remaining bones of the body are formed.**

   a. The growth plate is the site of growth.
   b. The chondrocytes at the growth plate migrate away from this region, and lack of blood supply triggers calcification.

HISTOLOGY

1. **Two types of bone are seen: compact and cancellous.**

   a. Compact bone is dense and strong, and the lamellae (concentric layers of mineral deposits) are closely spaced.
   b. Cancellous bone has a spongy appearance, and the lamellae are much farther apart in this type of bone.

2. **The haversian system provides nourishment to the bone tissue.**

   a. The lamellae surround small haversian canals which run parallel to the long bone surface.
   b. Each canal has blood vessels traversing it.
   c. Between the layers in the lamellae are small cavities called lacunae.
   d. The lacunae are connected by small canals called canaliculi eventually leading into the haversian canal.
   e. In each lacuna there is an osteocyte actively forming new bone.

3. **Red and yellow marrow are found within the bone.**

   a. Red marrow is found in the spaces of cancellous bone manufacturing both white and red blood cells.
   b. Yellow marrow consists of fat cells and is found within the shafts of long bone extending into the haversian system.

4. **The osteoclast is also found in microscopic examination of bone.**

   a. Osteoclasts are larger than osteoblasts and contain several nuclei.
   b. They are found in the region of the breakdown of bone.

GROWTH OF BONE

1. **Reabsorption and deposition:**

   a. The thickness of bone is dependent on two processes: reabsorption and deposition. These two processes take place at different rates during different ages, so at times the bones may be relatively thicker than at other times.

2. **Physiology of calcium:**

   a. Lack of calcium results in the development of the following disorders:
      (1) Depolarization of nerve fibers resulting in muscle spasms.
      (2) Weakened cardiac muscle.
      (3) Interference with blood coagulation.
   b. The exchange of calcium between bones and body fluids takes place by diffusion and reabsorption.
   c. Rickets in the young or osteomalacia in the elderly is the result of vitamin D deficiency. In rickets, the bones fail to ossify.

3. **Fractures:**

   a. A break of bone or cartilage is termed a fracture.
   b. A fracture can be compound or simple, depending on whether or not the skin is broken.
   c. Incomplete fracture does not break through the entire bone, while a complete fracture indicates a break through the entire diameter of the bone.
   d. Types of fracture:
      (1) Greenstick fracture: bone crumpled from bending.
      (2) Fatigue fracture: incomplete break due to stress.
      (3) Comminuted fracture: bone is broken in several places.
      (4) Compression fracture: opposite surfaces of the bone are crushed more closely together.
      (5) Pathologic fracture: bone is broken without external trauma.
   e. Healing of fractures:
      (1) The first step is the hematoma in which blood clots in the injured area.
      (2) The clot becomes living tissue with the entry of new vessels and osteoblasts.
      (3) A large mass of loosely woven bone forms around the area.
      (4) Calcium and ossification occur.

CLASSIFICATION OF BONES

1. **Five types of bone can be seen:**

   a. Long bones consist of long shafts and two extremities.
   b. Short bones are irregularly shaped and are not a short version of long bones.
   c. Flat bones are for protection and consist of a layer of cancellous bone enclosed by layers of compact bones.
   d. Irregular bones are bones of peculiar shape.
   e. Sesamoid bones are bones associated with another bone, cartilage, tendon, or ligament.

BONE MARKINGS

1. **A projection is a process and a depression is a fossa. The following have been defined in the text:**

process	trochlea	fossa
spine	crest	fissure
condyle	line	foramen
tubercle	head	meatus
tuberosity	aditus	canal
trochanter	alveolus	antrum

DIVISIONS OF THE SKELETON

1. The axial skeleton:

    a. Skull: facial and cranial bones
    b. Vertebral column
    c. Ribs
    d. Sternum
    e. Hyoid bone

2. Appendicular skeleton:

    a. The upper extremity includes the scapula, shoulder, arm, and hand.
    b. The lower extremity includes the hipbone, femur, tibia, fibula, and foot.

3. Vertebral column injuries:

    a. Exaggerations of the spinal curvature are termed kyphosis when the posterior curvature is accentuated in the thoracic area; lordosis when the anterior curvature is accentuated in the lumbar region; and scoliosis when there is a lateral curvature and rotation of the vertebrae.
    b. The vertebral disc can become herniated when the outer covering (the annulus fibrosus) ruptures due to trauma and the inner core (the nucleus pulposus) protrudes.

4. The table of bones summarizes the nature of each bone of the body.

STUDY QUESTIONS: THE SKELETAL SYSTEM

1. List the functions of the skeletal system.
2. Describe the development of bone and discuss the differences between vertical growth and maturation.
3. Distinguish between intramembranous and enchondral ossification.
4. Define Wolff's law and discuss its importance to the growth of bone and the healing of fractures.
5. Compare and contrast compact and cancellous bone.
6. Discuss the anatomy and functional significance of the haversian system.
7. Describe the role of calcium in the skeletal system.
8. Enumerate the steps in the healing of a fracture.
9. List the various classes of bones and give several examples of each.
10. Define: condyle, tubercle, meatus, sulcus, aditus, tuberosity, fissure, and antrum.
11. Select one of the following: skull, thorax, upper extremity, or lower extremity, and discuss in terms of anatomy of the region, functions of the region, important muscles mentioned, disorders described, and differences, if any, between male and female in this area.

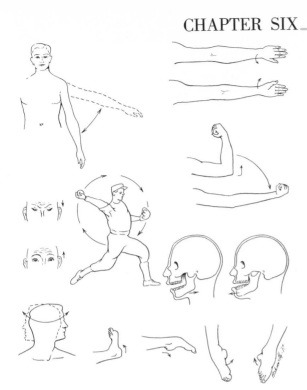

THE ARTICULAR SYSTEM

The first indication of bone in the embryo is a condensation of mesoderm which eventually becomes chondrified and ossified. The non-condensed portions of the mesoderm between the bones subsequently develop into the *joints*, or *articulations*. An articulation, by definition, occurs whenever two surfaces of bone join to-gether—regardless of the degree of movement permitted by this junction. Thus, the sutures be-tween the skull are considered as much a part of the articular system as is the elbow or the knee joint. Following a general discussion of the anatomy and physiology of joints, special con-sideration will be given to the largest and most complex joint in the body, the knee joint.

CLASSIFICATION OF JOINTS (Fig. 72)

Joints are categorized into three groups ac-cording to the degree of movement permitted. Subclasses are associated with each of the gen-eral categories based on the structural compo-nents of individual joints.

Synarthroses

Synarthroses are joints which do not permit movement.

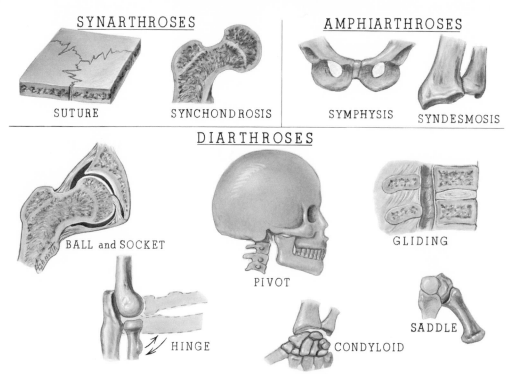

Fig. 72. Joints are categorized into three groups, according to the degree of movement permitted. Each of these groups is in turn subdivided with respect to the structural components of individual joints.

Suture. A suture is an articulation in which the bones are united by a thin layer of fibrous tissue. Examples are the suture joints of the skull.

Synchondroses. Synchondroses are joints in which two bony surfaces are connected by cartilage. This is a temporary joint, the cartilage being replaced by bone in later life. An example is the epiphysis in the body of a long bone.

Amphiarthroses

Amphiarthroses are slightly movable articulations.

Symphyses. Symphyses are joints in which the bones are connected by a disc of fibrocartilage. An example is the pubic symphysis.

Syndesmoses. Syndesmoses are joints in which the bones are connected by an interosseus ligament. An example is the radio-ulnar articulation.

Diarthroses (Synovial Joints)

Diarthroses are freely movable articulations. The bony surfaces of these joints are covered with articular cartilage connected by ligaments. Diarthrodial joints are lined with *synovial membrane*. The bone, articular cartilage, articular capsule, synovial membrane, synovial fluid, nerves, lymphatics, and blood vessels are included among the components of a diarthrodial joint.

Most joints in the body are of the diarthrodial type. These, in turn, are classified according to the shape of the articulating end of the involved bones. The shapes include the following.

1. *Ball and socket joint:* The ball-shaped head fits into a concave socket. This type of joint provides the widest range of motion, with movement in all planes in addition to rotation. An example of the ball and socket joint is the hip (Fig. 73).

2. *Hinge joint:* A convex surface fits into a concavity, and motion is limited to flexion and extension in a single plane. An example is the elbow joint.

3. *Pivot joint:* In the pivot joint, motion is limited to rotation; the joint is formed by a pivot-like process within a ring or by a ring or pivot. Examples are the atlas and axis.

4. *Condyloid:* An oval-shaped condyle fits

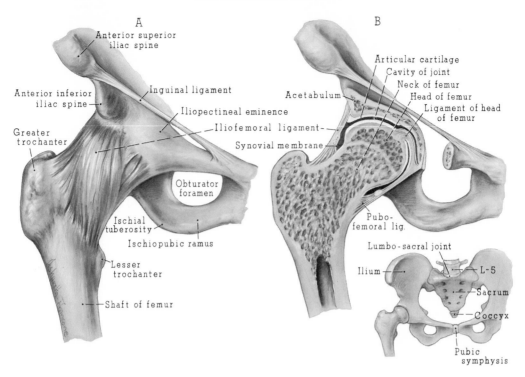

Fig. 73. Hip joint, showing ligaments between femur and pelvic bone; intact (*A*) and sectioned (*B*) to show attachments.

into an elliptical cavity. Motion is possible in two planes at right angles to each other. This type of joint does not permit radial rotation. An example is the wrist joint between the radius and carpal bones.

5. *Saddle joint:* In a saddle joint, the articular surface is concave in one direction and convex in the other; the other articular surface is reciprocally convex-concave so that the two bones fit together. Movement is possible in two planes at right angles to each other. This type of joint does not permit axial rotation. An example is the joint between the first metacarpal and the trapezium.

6. *Gliding joint:* A gliding joint is formed by the opposing plane surfaces or slightly convex and concave surfaces, permitting only gliding movement. An example is the intervertebral joint (Fig. 74).

MOVEMENTS OF SYNOVIAL JOINTS

The following movements occur at synovial joints (Fig. 75).

1. *Flexion:* bending or decreasing the angle between two bones.

2. *Extension:* increasing the angle between two bones.

3. *Abduction:* the bone moves away from the midline.

4. *Adduction:* the bone moves toward the midline.

5. *Rotation:* the bone moves around a central axis, and the plane of motion is perpendicular to the axis.

6. *Circumduction:* the bone describes the surface of a cone.

7. *Supination:* movement of the bones of the forearm permitting the palm to move inward, so that the radius and ulna are parallel (Fig. 76).

8. *Pronation:* movement of the forearm permitting the back of the hand to turn upward and forward, such as the crossing of the radius and ulna (Fig. 76).

9. *Eversion:* movement at the ankle joint permitting the sole of the foot to turn outward.

10. *Inversion:* movement at the ankle in which the sole of the foot turns inward.

11. *Protraction:* moving a part of the body forward.

12. *Retraction:* moving a part of the body backward.

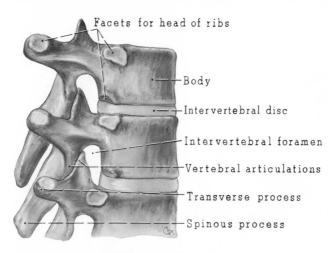

Fig. 74. Relationship of vertebral bodies and intervertebral discs. Note articulations between vertebrae.

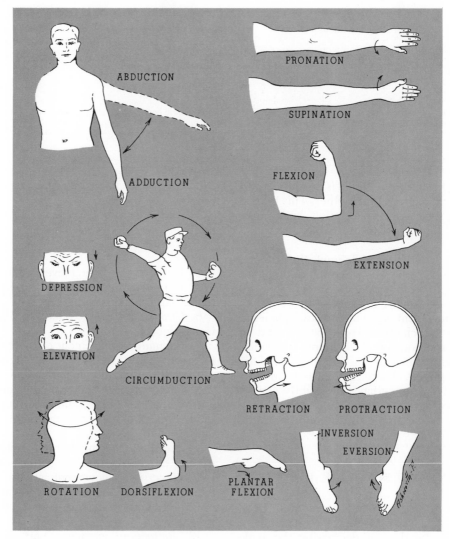

Fig. 75. Types of movement permitted by diarthrodial joints.

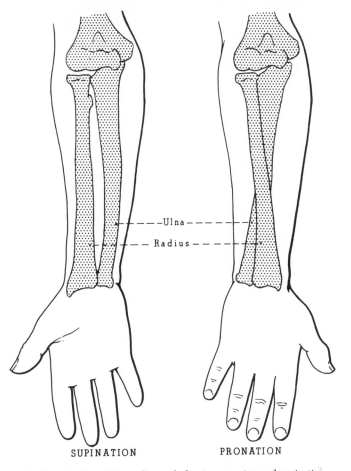

Ulna

Radius

SUPINATION   PRONATION

Fig. 76. Position of the radius and ulna in pronation and supination.

ANATOMY OF SYNOVIAL JOINTS

Cartilage provides a smooth, gliding surface for opposing bone. This smooth gliding surface is made possible because of lubrication by the synovial fluid.

Synovial fluid, containing a variable number of mononuclear cells with a pH of approximately 7.4, is 95 per cent water. The fluid has a total protein concentration varying from 1 to 2 per cent, and its electrolyte pattern is similar to that of a dialysate of plasma.

Articular cartilage has a limited blood supply. It receives its nourishment from the underlying bony surface via the synovial fluid, and from a small number of subsynovial vessels primarily at the junction of the cartilage with the joint capsule. Synovial fluid, however, is the major source of nutrition for the cartilage, and in itself is able to sustain the viability of cartilage.

Articular discs are located between the articular cartilages of synovial joints. The disc, composed of fibrocartilage, joins with the capsular ligament peripherally. It is thought that the articular disc functions as a buffer to minimize the impact of shock. Articular discs are supplied with nerve fibers providing sensory function and permitting the joints to respond more promptly and with precision to pressure changes within the joint cavity.

Collagenous fibers running directly from one bone to another comprise the fibrous capsule enclosing a diarthrodial joint. Well-defined bands of fibers are usually differentiated as local thickenings of the capsule to form intrinsic or capsular *ligaments* which further strengthen joints and play a part in restraining movements in certain directions (Fig. 77). Ligaments are usually arranged so that they remain taut while the joint is in the position of greatest stability.

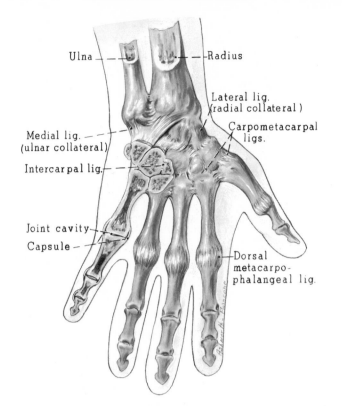

Fig. 77. Ligaments of the hand with cross-sectional view of a synovial joint showing the joint cavity and capsule.

The *capsule* of a hinge joint permits movements of flexion and extension. The range of joint motion is directly related to the laxity of the capsule. In the shoulder joint, for instance, which has the greatest range of motion in the body, the capsule is loose enough to permit the head of the humerus to be drawn away from the articular surface of the scapula. If one were actually to sever the muscles at the shoulder joint, while leaving the fibrous capsule still intact, the humerus would be drawn as much as 1 inch away from the scapula. On the other hand, in the hip joint, the range of motion is more limited in relation to the requirements of greater strength, and the capsule is thicker and shorter.

Muscles provide an important mechanism for maintaining the stability of joints. They possess many advantages over ligaments, particularly during relaxation and contraction in which the muscles maintain the articular surfaces in firm contact at every position of the joint. The importance of the musculature can be seen in paralysis, in which the related joints allow much greater range of motion than is normal.

In summary, joints serve the purposes of weight bearing and providing motion. They are so constructed as to afford stability. The joint capsule, ligaments, tendons, muscles, and articular discs provide stability. Viscous, synovial fluid aids in maintaining the proximity of articular components.

BURSAE

Bursae are closed sacs with a synovial membrane lining similar to that of a true joint. A bursa can be found in the spaces of connective tissue between tendons, ligaments, and bones. Bursae function to facilitate the gliding of muscles or tendons over bony or ligamentous surfaces. *Subcutaneous bursae* are found between the skin and underlying bony processes, such as the olecranon and patella. *Subfascial bursae* are located beneath the deep fascia. *Subtendinous bursae* are found in locations where one tendon overlies another or overlies a bony projection. The walls of subtendinous bursae may be continuous with the synovial membrane of a joint through an opening in the capsular wall (Fig. 78).

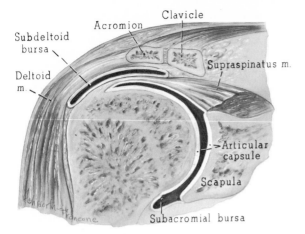

Fig. 78. Subdeltoid and subacromial bursae of the shoulder, cross sectioned to show attachments of muscles.

DISORDERS OF JOINTS

Bursitis

Bursitis is an inflammation of the synovial bursa which may result from excess stress or tension placed on the bursa, or from some local or systemic inflammatory process. It may occur in any of the periarticular bursae; the most frequent location is the subacromial bursa. The subacromial bursa lies close to the shoulder joint; consequently, in inflammation of this bursa, movement of the shoulder joint is limited and painful. Since the supraspinatus tendon forms the floor of the subacromial bursa, the patient with subacromial bursitis has limited abduction at the shoulder joint. Eventually, with inflammation, deposits of calcium occur in the supraspinatus tendon and further interfere with shoulder motion. If bursitis persists, the muscles eventually atrophy. With chronic bursitis, the shoulder can actually become stiff, even though the joint itself is not diseased. Inflammation of bursae located about the elbows, knees, ischial tuberosities, and attachment of the tendo calcaneus (Achilles tendon) causes similar changes.

Arthritis

Arthritis, an inflammation of joints, is one of the most common and painful abnormalities of the articular system. Fifty varieties of arthritis are known. Three common types are rheumatoid arthritis, osteoarthritis (degenerative arthritis), and gouty arthritis.

Rheumatoid arthritis. Rheumatoid arthritis is a systemic disease with widespread involvement of connective tissue. Its cause is unknown. The earliest stage in rheumatoid arthritis is an inflammation of the synovial membrane in which the tissue becomes thickened. This thickened synovial tissue (*pannus*) grows inward from the synovium along the surface of the articular cartilage. Growth of the pannus actually damages the cartilage. Next, the inflammatory tissue becomes invaded with tough fibrous material which is adherent and prevents motion of the joint. This stage is known as *fibrous ankylosis* (ankylosis means immobility of a joint). The fibrous tissue may ultimately become calcified and undergo changes to osseous tissue, resulting in a firm bony union, *bony ankylosis*. Rheumatoid arthritis, then, develops in four stages: inflammation of the synovium, formation of the pannus, fibrous ankylosis, and, finally, bony ankylosis.

Osteoarthritis (degenerative arthritis). Joints are subject to a great deal of wear and tear. After years of use, degenerative changes are to be expected. Some evidence of degenerative joint disease is found in many individuals over the age of 45. The weight-bearing joints of the lower extremities and spine are particularly subject to wear and tear and often show early degenerative changes. There is initially a softening of the cartilage, followed by a separation of fibers and, later, by an actual disintegration of the cartilage, which soon thins out. This thinning of the cartilage irritates both the perichondrium and periosteum and, in turn, stimulates cartilagenous and bony proliferation at the margins of the joint. As the cartilage wears thin, the bone beneath the cartilage becomes eburnated (eburnation: conversion of bone into an ivory-like mass). It is the presence of these marginal bony growths that has given the disease its outdated name "hypertrophic arthritis." Hypertrophy means thickening or increasing size without an increase in the number of cells.

Gouty arthritis. Gout is a metabolic disorder, the major clinical manifestation of which is arthritis. It is a disturbance of purine metabolism usually associated with an elevated uric acid in the blood. In an attack of acute gout, the synovium is inflamed. With repeated attacks of gouty arthritis, urates deposit in and about the joint structures and, together with inflammatory changes, produce severe damage to the articular cartilage.

Rheumatic Fever

The musculoskeletal system may be involved in rheumatic fever, a disease characterized by inflammation of the synovial tissues, tendons, and other connective tissues about joints. Rheumatic fever begins abruptly with an intense inflammatory reaction of joints and then tends to subside after a brief period. No pannus occurs in rheumatic fever, so the cartilage and bone are not damaged. The functional disturbances of rheumatic fever can be attributed to active inflammation similar to changes noted in the early stages of rheumatoid arthritis. When the disease subsides, the patient usually does not show any residual functional damage of the articular system, but frequently has permanent damage to the heart valves, which manifests itself in later life as rheumatic heart disease.

Primary Fibrositis

Primary fibrositis, sometimes called "rheumatism" by the layman, is a disease of fibrous connective tissue more than a disease of muscles. Fibrositis occurring in the low back is referred to in non-scientific circles as "lumbago." Chronic fibrositis either involves many structures simultaneously or migrates from one part of the body to another. The involved portions of the body are usually tender and stiff. Since movement of the joints depends on function of periarticular and connective tissue and muscles, irritation of these structures leads to limitation of movement. Since the joints themselves are healthy, no permanent damage occurs. As soon as the connective changes are relieved, the locomotor system again functions normally.

Tenosynovitis

Tendon sheaths may become inflamed, interfering with the free passage of the enclosed tendon. Function of joints moved by these tendons will then be impaired. If the inflammation occurs along the sheaths of the flexor tendons of the fingers, the finger frequently cannot be extended by the flexor apparatus without assistance—a so-called "trigger finger." In many instances, inflammation of the flexor tendon sheath and palmar fascia may cause adhesions so strong that movement of the fingers is completely prevented. The fingers then become deformed and remain in positions of flexion. Dupuytren's contracture is an inflammation of the palmar fascia resulting in flexional deformities of the third, fourth, and fifth fingers.

THE KNEE JOINT

Anatomy (Figs. 79 to 84)

There are two *semilunar cartilages* involved in the knee joint: the *medial semilunar cartilage* and the *lateral semilunar cartilage*. The medial semilunar cartilage attaches by short fibers to the tibia and is relatively fixed in position. It functions to deepen the socket for the medial femoral condyle. The lateral semilunar cartilage is semicircular and attached to the tibia, with its long fibers permitting gliding of the disc. It functions to insure smooth articulation.

Two sets of ligaments are involved in movement of the knee joint. These are the *anterior* and *posterior cruciate ligaments* and the *medial* and *lateral collateral ligaments*.

The anterior cruciate ligament limits extension and rotation. The posterior cruciate ligament prevents forward dislocation of the femur.

The collateral ligaments prevent lateral dislocation of the knee. These extend from the lateral epicondyle of the femur to the head of the tibia (*tibial ligament*), and from the medial epicondyle of the femur to the capsule and medial surface of the tibia (*medial ligament*). The synovial membrane of the knee is attached to the articular cartilage of the femur and tibia. The synovial membrane does not merely line the fibrous capsule as it does in other joints, but actually excludes the cruciate ligaments from the interior portion of the joint. This membrane has many fat-filled folds which assist in reducing the open spaces in the joint cavity during movement. Several subcutaneous bursae are associated with the knee joint. These are found between the patella and the skin. Inflammation of these bursae may be the cause of so-called "housemaid's knee."

Internal Derangement of the Knee

The knee joint depends on strong ligaments and strong muscles of the thigh for its stability. The condyles of the femur and tibia are held in contact by these structures during flexion and extension. An *internal* derangement is a mechanical derangement of the function of the joint

Text continued on page 115.

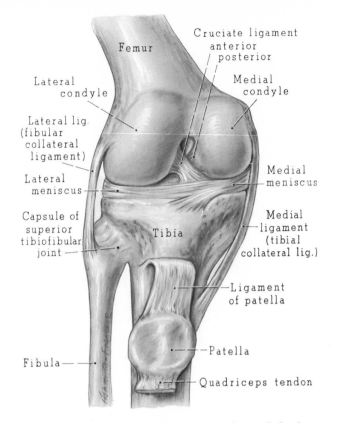

Fig. 79. Anterior view of the right knee joint, slightly flexed. The patella has been severed from the quadriceps muscle and pulled down, exposing the ligaments between the femur and tibia.

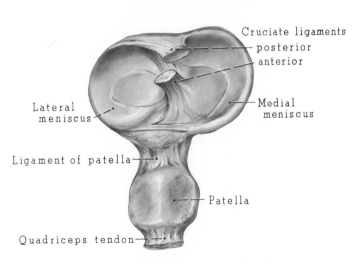

Fig. 80. Articular surface of the right tibia.

111

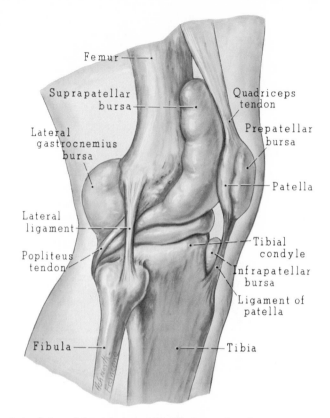

Fig. 81. Lateral view of the right knee joint. The bursae have been expanded for clarity.

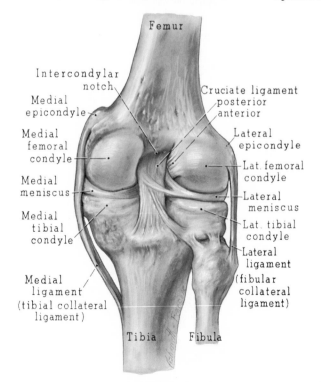

Fig. 82. Posterior view of the right knee joint.

112

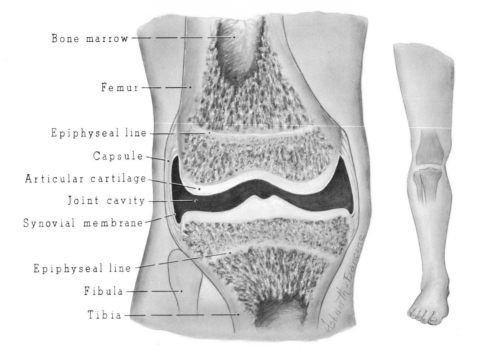

Bone marrow

Femur

Epiphyseal line

Capsule

Articular cartilage

Joint cavity

Synovial membrane

Epiphyseal line

Fibula

Tibia

Fig. 83. Frontal section through the right knee joint.

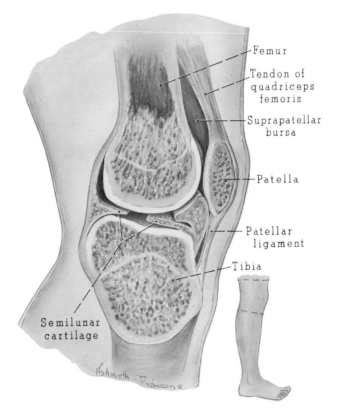

Femur

Tendon of quadriceps femoris

Suprapatellar bursa

Patella

Patellar ligament

Tibia

Semilunar cartilage

Fig. 84. Lateral view of the right knee joint in sagittal section.

TABLE 6. Joints.

JOINT	TYPE	MOVEMENT
Vertebral	Diarthrodial Gliding	Flexion and extension of the spine by gliding
Atlanto-epistropheal	Diarthrodial Pivot	Rotation of the atlas upon the axis
Temporomandibular	Diarthrodial Hinge and gliding	Opening and closing of the jaws; protrusion of the mandible; lateral displacement of the mandible
Costovertebral	Diarthrodial Gliding	Gliding
Sternocostal	Diarthrodial Gliding, except for first rib, which is synarthrodial (immovable)	Slight gliding
Sternoclavicular	Diarthrodial Gliding	Gliding
Acromioclavicular	Diarthrodial Gliding	Gliding of the clavicle on the acromion; rotation of the scapula upon the clavicle
Shoulder	Diarthrodial	Flexion, extension, abduction, adduction, rotation, circumduction
Elbow	Diarthrodial Hinge	Flexion, extension
Radioulnar	Diarthrodial Pivot	Pronation, supination (rotation)
Wrist (radiocarpal)	Diarthrodial Condyloid	All movements except rotation
Intercarpal	Diarthodial Gliding	Flexion, extension
Carpometacarpal	Diarthrodial Saddle	Flexion, extension, abduction, adduction
Metacarpophalangeal	Diarthrodial Condyloid	Flexion, extension, limited abduction, limited adduction, circumduction
Interphalangeal	Diarthrodial Hinge	Flexion, extension
Sacro-iliac	Amphiarthrodial Symphysis	Limited
Symphysis pubis	Amphiarthrodial Symphysis	Slight
Hip	Diarthrodial Ball and socket	Flexion, extension, adduction, abduction, rotation, circumduction
Knee	Diarthrodial Hinge	Flexion, extension
Tibiofibular	Diarthrodial Gliding	Gliding movement
Talocrural (ankle)	Diarthrodial Hinge	Dorsiflexion and plantar flexion
Intertarsal	Diarthrodial Gliding	Gliding—backward and forward from side to side
Tarsometatarsal	Diarthrodial Gliding	Slight gliding of the bones
Metatarsophalangeal	Diarthrodial Condyloid	Flexion, extension, adduction, abduction
Interphalangeal	Diarthrodial Gliding	Flexion, extension

Continued from page 110.

caused by some abnormality which eliminates the supporting strength of the major ligaments or prevents the contact and smooth gliding of the condyles during flexion and extension of the knee. The most common derangement of the knee is a tear of the semilunar cartilage which usually results from a twisting injury. Normally, the cartilage buffers rotary grinding action of the condyles of the femur on the tibia. When the medial semilunar cartilage is torn, the patient presents a history of a twisting injury with a snapping sensation on the inner side of the knee.

A torn lateral semilunar cartilage, on the other hand, also presents a history of a twisting injury, but with a snapping sensation on the outer side of the knee. The medial semilunar cartilage is more frequently damaged than the lateral one.

A patient with a torn semilunar cartilage experiences painful locking of the knee joint with tenderness at the site of injury. Usually a torn semilunar cartilage does not heal, since cartilage has a poor blood supply. Surgical removal of the torn cartilage or torn portion of the cartilage is the only definitive treatment of this condition.

SUMMARY: THE ARTICULAR SYSTEM

EMBRYOLOGY

1. Joints develop from non-condensed mesoderm between bones.

CLASSIFICATION OF JOINTS

1. There are three groups of joints:
    a. Synarthroses: no movement.
       (1) Suture: fibrous tissue unites bones.
       (2) Synchondroses: cartilage unites bones.
    b. Amphiarthroses: slightly movable joints.
       (1) Symphyses: fibrocartilage disc unites bones.
       (2) Syndesmoses: interosseus ligament connects bones.
    c. Diarthroses: freely movable joints.
       (1) Ball and socket
       (2) Hinge
       (3) Pivot
       (4) Condyloid
       (5) Saddle
       (6) Gliding

MOVEMENTS OF SYNOVIAL JOINTS

1. Flexion—decreasing angle between two bones.

2. Extension—increasing angle.

3. Abduction—bone moves away from the midline.

4. Adduction—bone moves toward the midline.

5. Rotation—bone moves around the central axis.

6. Circumduction—bone describes the surface of a cone.

7. Supination—the palm is upward.

8. Pronation—the palm is downward.

9. Eversion—the sole of the foot is turned outward.

10. Inversion—the sole of the foot is turned inward.

11. Protraction—a part of the body is moved forward.

12. Retraction—a part of the body is moved backward.

ANATOMY OF SYNOVIAL JOINTS

1. The synovial fluid is a viscous lubricant and is found in all synovial joint cavities.

2. The articular cartilage acts as a cushion providing a smooth gliding surface. Nourishment is obtained from the bony surfaces and synovial fluid.

3. Also present in synovial joints is the synovial membrane. This membrane surrounds the cavities and slips in and out of the openings caused by movement.

4. Articular discs are fibrocartilage which serve to buffer shock.

5. Ligaments help to maintain the relationships between bones and limit motion.

6. Articular muscles function to maintain the stability of joints by relaxation and contraction to insure firm contact throughout the articular surface.

BURSAE

1. Bursae are found in close proximity to joints and are usually associated with spaces between connective tissue.

2. Bursae are closed sacs with a synovial membrane lining.

DISORDERS OF JOINTS

1. Bursitis is the inflammation of the synovial bursa; it may result from excess stress, local inflammation, or systemic disease.

2. Arthritis is the general term for inflammation of joints.
   a. Rheumatoid arthritis is a disease of unknown cause and is systemic in its effects. The stages of rheumatoid arthritis are inflammation of the synovium, formation of the pannus, fibrous ankylosis, and bony ankylosis.
   b. Osteoarthritis: This type of arthritis comes from wear and tear on joints in old age. The articular cartilage begins to wear thin and the surfaces adhere, causing pain and inflammation.
   c. Gouty arthritis is a metabolic disorder in purine metabolism which causes uric acid to be deposited in the blood.

3. Rheumatic fever is a disease in which the synovial tissues become inflamed and then rapidly return to normal.

4. Primary fibrositis ("rheumatism" or "lumbago") in the lower back region is an inflammation of the fibrous connective tissue of joints.

5. Tenosynovitis: The tendon sheaths become inflamed and may deter movement of the involved joints.

THE KNEE JOINT

1. Anatomy:
   a. The knee joint is the largest and most complex joint in the body.
   b. Two semilunar cartilages are found in the knee joint.
   c. Two pairs of ligaments are found; the cruciate and collateral ligaments provide stability and necessary limitation of motion.

2. **Internal derangement of the knee:**

   a. The most common internal derangement of the knee is a tear of the medial semilunar cartilage. The torn part or the entire cartilage should be removed, since cartilage has a poor blood supply and will not heal.

STUDY QUESTIONS: THE ARTICULAR SYSTEM

1. List the classes and subclasses of joints, and discuss the basis for this classification.
2. Describe the different forms of diarthrodial joints and the actions of these joints.
3. Discuss the functional differences among articular cartilage, synovial membrane, and synovial fluid.
4. Describe three common forms of arthritis.
5. Discuss the anatomy and disorders of bursae.
6. Define the role played by ligaments in the maintenance of joint stability, and illustrate by a specific reference to the knee joint.

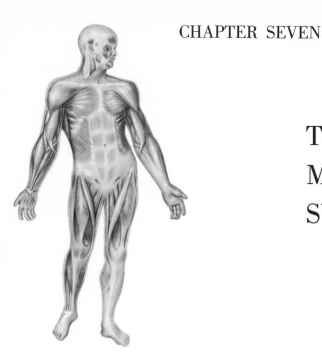

THE
MUSCULAR
SYSTEM

Knowledge of the anatomy and physiology of the muscular system was uncertain and vague through the Renaissance. A few attempts to theorize the nature of muscular action were made by Hippocrates and Galen, but no real progress occurred until the 17th century, when Anton van Leeuwenhoek made the initial observations of muscle under the microscope. These observations laid the foundation for today's knowledge of the structure and function of muscle.

Muscles comprise 40 to 50 per cent of the body's weight. When they contract, they effect movement of the body as a whole; of blood (circulation); of food through the digestive tract; of urine through the urinary tract; and of the chest, diaphragm, and abdomen during respiration. The two key words, then are *contraction* and *movement*.

TYPES OF MUSCLE

The three types of muscle tissue are *striated*, *smooth*, and *cardiac* (Fig. 85).

Striated Muscle

Striated muscle, or skeletal muscle, develops from the primitive myotomes. The mature cells

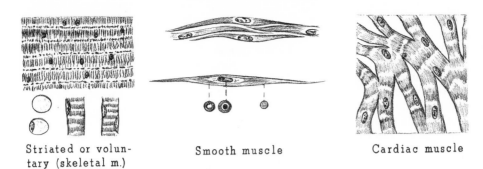

Striated or volun-
tary (skeletal m.)   Smooth muscle   Cardiac muscle

Fig. 85. Types of muscle cells.

are long and slender, ranging from 1 to 50 mm. in length, and from 40 to 50 microns in diameter. Since they have a preponderance of length as compared to width, these cells are called fibers. Each muscle cell is multinucleated and is surrounded by an electrically polarized membrane —the *sarcolemma.* The sarcolemma is bounded by delicate connective tissue called the *endomysium.*

The entire muscle consists of a number of skeletal muscle bundles known as *fasciculi.* Fasciculi are bound by a sheath called the perimysium, which forms the muscle *septae* visible to the naked eye. These septae are continuous with the coarse connective tissue investing the muscle, known as the *epimysium.* The *fascia,* composed of areolar tissue, forms a covering over the entire muscle trunk. When viewed under the microscope, the skeletal muscle cell is seen to have regular *striations.* These striations are fine, parallel filaments (*myofibrils*) embedded in the *sarcoplasm* (ground substance) of the muscle fiber (Fig. 86).

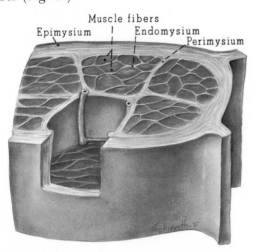

Muscle fibers

Epimysium | Endomysium
                              Perimysium

Fig. 86. Schematic drawing showing the general structure of a muscle.

Each myofibril consists, in cross striations, of alternating dark and light bands referred to as the *A-* and *I-bands* respectively. The dark band is an anisotropic (with abnormal refractive properties) protein, *myosin.* The light band is isotropic (with normal refractive properties), and consists chiefly of the protein *actin.* In addition, two other markings are of importance—the *Z-band,* a narrow, dark-staining band in the central region of the I-band, and the *H-band,* located in the central portion of each A-band, containing only the thick myosin fibrils (Fig. 87).

PHYSIOLOGY OF CONTRACTION. The basic unit of muscular contraction is the *motor unit.* This consists of a group of muscle fibers all innervated by the terminal branches of a single motor axon. A motor unit usually contains between 100 and 200 muscle fibers. The units are actually intermeshed, so that stimulation of a single nerve causes a weak contraction throughout the entire muscle body, rather than a strong contraction in a single area of the muscle.

Motor units are subject to the *all-or-none principle.* That is, the nerve fibers and associated muscle fibers respond entirely to a stimulus or do not respond at all. The individual motor unit, therefore, does not determine the strength of contraction; rather, the number of motor units stimulated plus the rapidity of the stimulus govern the magnitude of contraction.

The weakest stimulus from a nerve fiber that will initiate contraction is known as the *liminal stimulus.* If the stimulus is of lesser intensity, it is called *subliminal.* A muscle twitch occurs when the liminal stimulus is attained. After a period of latency, all muscle fibers associated with the stimulated nerve contract and then relax (Fig. 88). The duration of the muscle twitch is less than 0.1 second.

Two types of muscle twitches can be distinguished. The first is *isotonic,* in which the muscle changes in length while having the same tension applied to it throughout contraction. The second type, or *isometric*, occurs when the muscle remains at a constant length, even with a sudden increase in muscle tension.

The strength of muscle contraction is determined by the total number of motor units contracting and by the number of times per second each motor unit is stimulated. The latter process is referred to as a *summation of stimuli*, which simply means that rapid subliminal stimuli eventually are additive to give a twitch. The summation of contraction occurs when a second stimulus takes place at the apex of the preceding one. This phenomenon of increased strength of contraction under constant but rapid stimuli is known as *treppe*.

In contrast to the brief duration of the action potential, the contraction response of muscle

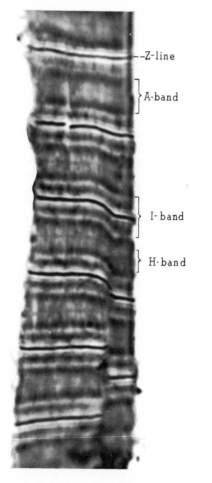

Fig. 87. Striated muscle, longitudinal section, as seen under a light microscope (magnification 4600×). (Courtesy of Dr. Wolf H. Fahrenbach, Oregon Regional Primate Research Center.)

lasts up to 0.1 second or more. When a repetitive series of stimuli is delivered and conducted along the sarcolemmal membrane, a smooth and sustained summated contraction occurs. This fused contraction is called *tetanus.*°

Muscle spasm is the involuntary contraction of a muscle or group of muscles caused by repetitive activation of entire motor units associated with repetitive firing of the motor nerve. It is seen in a variety of conditions, such as tetanus. In muscle cramp, there is a rapid, disordered firing of a portion of the motor unit, along with a tendency for the cramp to spread from one part of the unit to adjacent ones.

To insure the rapid reaction of muscle to external stimuli, muscles remain in a state of readiness and are said to possess *muscle tone*. Tone is due to a continuous flow of stimuli from the spinal cord to each motor unit; it can be increased or decreased, depending upon the level of activity of the nervous system. In states of anxiety there is an increase in tone; during periods of restfulness a decrease in tone occurs, along with a reduction in the actual number of stimuli reaching the muscle. The action potential is the electrical manifestation of the impulse.

MECHANISM OF CONTRACTION. In 1868, Kühne observed that a globulin-like protein called *myosin* could be extracted from muscle with a strong salt solution. In 1934, it was determined that myosin jells in the form of threads much like muscle fibers. Soon it was demonstrated that threads of myosin become more extensible under the influence of adenosine triphosphate.

In 1942, myosin was discovered to contain a heavy fraction which settles rapidly after centrifuging. In other words, it is not a homogenous substance. It was then observed that the gradual increase in viscosity is caused by a dissolution of another protein distinct from myosin in the muscle. This protein, *actin*, unites with myosin to form *actomyosin*. Actomyosin, in the presence of a high concentration of salt, dissociates into its component parts on the addition of ATP. The present-day concept of muscle contraction can be discussed under three headings: the neuro-electrical factors; the chemical interactions; and the energy sources.

Neuro-electrical factors. A muscle fiber has

° It should be emphasized that the term *tetanus* used in descriptions of muscle physiology is not the clinical disease of the same name; tetanus the disease is characterized by recurrent spasms and contractions of muscle caused by anaerobic bacterial infection.

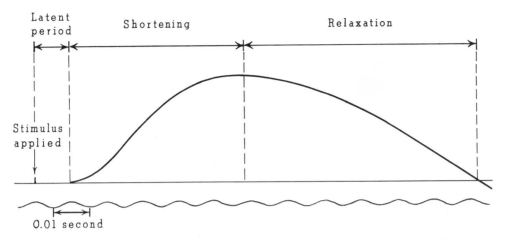

Fig. 88. The single twitch. A muscle twitch occurs when the minimal stimulus is attained. All of the muscle fibers associated with the stimulated nerve, after a period of latency, contract and then relax. The duration of this twitch is less than 0.1 second. Note that the period for relaxation is longer than the time needed for contraction. (After Carlson and Johnson.)

a resting potential, so that the inside of the fiber is negative to the outside by 90 millivolts. During excitation, depolarization occurs, tending to make this potential difference closer to zero. The excitation level is any stimulus above a minimal stimulus. The impulse travels along the motor nerve toward the muscle fiber. At the neuromuscular junction on the motor end plate, *acetylcholine,* a substance produced at the synapse, is released. Acetylcholine brings about muscular contraction, presumably by depolarizing the sarcolemma. The wave of depolarization travels down the muscle fiber at a rate of 1.9 to 2.9 meters per second, a special enzyme called *acetylcholinesterase* breaks down the acetylcholine, and the fiber is again ready for reactivation. Many compounds such as neostigmine (an excitor of the parasympathetic nerves) and curare inhibit the ability of acetylcholinesterase to hydrolyze acetylcholine and are clinically useful because of this action.

Chemical interactions. This series of electrical changes triggers a number of chemical alterations leading to actual contraction of the fiber. During contraction, actin fibrils slide into spaces between the myosin fibrils. The mechanism is incompletely understood. One theory holds that the calcium ions are responsible—that calcium diffuses into the membrane when acetylcholine causes the membrane to become more permeable to positive ions. These positive calcium ions then react to stimulate enzyme activity, catalyzing an energy-releasing reaction

which, in turn, brings on the sliding of the filaments. This picture of muscle contraction is incomplete, but it displaces the older concept that the myosin reacts with the actin during contraction. What occurs, then, is not a reaction but an *interaction* between the two during contraction.

Electron micrographs have led to the concept that, on contraction, the myosin fibers fold upon themselves to some extent. This comes about from the observed dimensions (Fig. 89).

Energy sources. Energy for muscle contraction is thought to come from the hydrolysis of ATP. Recall that the reaction then is: ATP → ADP + phosphate + energy for interaction when the breaking of the high energy phosphate bond makes energy available to the muscle. Recent studies have cast some doubt on the role of ATP as the energy source for muscular contraction. For the present, however, let us accept the concept of high energy phosphate and assume that in some way events leading to depolarization of the membrane also lead to ATP → ADP + phosphate + energy for interaction.

The energy yielded by the ATP breakdown is utilized when the myosin and actin filaments intermesh. ATP for further contraction is synthesized by means of anaerobic glycolysis, the Krebs cycle, and the breakdown of phosphocreatine.

Phosphocreatine is found only in muscle tissue and reacts with ADP to form ATP + creatine. Phosphocreatine + ADP → ATP + creatine. When muscles are at rest, the excess ATP not

RELAXED MUSCLE FIBER

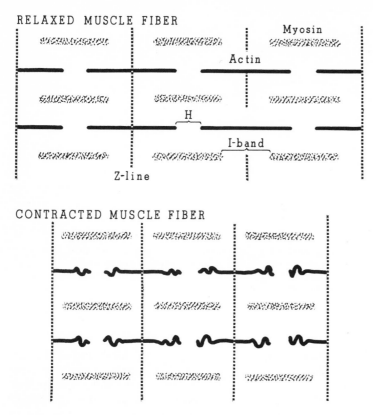

CONTRACTED MUSCLE FIBER

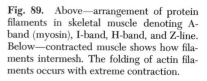

Fig. 89. Above—arrangement of protein filaments in skeletal muscle denoting A-band (myosin), I-band, H-band, and Z-line. Below—contracted muscle shows how filaments intermesh. The folding of actin filaments occurs with extreme contraction.

needed for the energy of contraction transfers phosphate to creatine to build up a reserve of phosphocreatine. The overall reaction then is: ATP + creatine $\rightleftharpoons$ phosphocreatine + ADP. The yielded products depend on whether or not the muscle is contracting.

RELAXING SYSTEM. After a muscle contracts, there must be some means for it to relax. A relaxing factor has recently been discovered in muscle. This presumably acts with the energizing substance of muscle (possibly ATP) and renders it inactive until the next stimulus reaches the particular fiber. The exact structure and function of the relaxing substance has not been elucidated.

In summary, then, it is currently believed that the muscle fiber is depolarized by a nerve impulse and that, during depolarization, a series of interactions is triggered including the breakdown of ATP to yield energy. The energy is utilized to move the actin and myosin fibrils past each other. A relaxing factor reacts with ATP to halt contraction. The ATP is resynthesized through the normal biochemistry of the cell plus the breakdown of phosphocreatine.

OXYGEN DEBT. During muscular contraction, energy is derived from anaerobic hydrolysis of high energy phosphate bonds. The energy for replenishment of these bonds can come from anaerobic glycolysis. This is phosphorylation and breakdown of glycogen to pyruvate and then conversion to lactic acid, rather than complete oxidation to carbon dioxide and water.

As exertion increases, the production of lactic acid also increases. An increase in oxygen flow to the tissue is necessary to oxidize the lactic acid back to pyruvic acid. After exercise, the oxygen flow above the basal oxygen consumption level is defined as the *oxygen debt*. This debt is repaired rapidly at first, and then at a slower rate as equilibrium is approached.

Smooth Muscle

Smooth muscle is found in the digestive tract and other hollow structures, such as the urinary bladder and blood vessels. It is under the control of the autonomic nervous system and cannot be influenced at will. Each smooth muscle cell contains a single large nucleus, and its fiber is more delicate than the fiber of striated muscle. These cells seem to be connected by fibrils extending from one cell to another. The banding or cross striation effect, noted on electron microscopy in skeletal muscle, is absent in the smooth muscle fiber.

The smooth muscle of hollow structures, such as the small intestine, is grouped into two layers, an inner circular and an outer longitudinal layer. Simultaneous contraction of the two layers results in a reduction in both the circumference and length of the tubular structure. In contrast to skeletal muscle, the arrangement of smooth muscle cells produces a slower contraction, but permits greater extensibility.

Smooth muscle cells are arranged into two patterns within the body. In the first, cells are found in rolled sheets. This pattern of rolled sheets is found in the organs of the intestinal tract and the urinary system. In the other arrangement, the smooth muscle pattern is less well organized and occurs where finer gradations of contractions occur, such as in the iris of the eye.

Actin and myosin fibers are not so regularly arranged in smooth muscle as in striated muscle. The contraction of smooth muscle occurs in a similar way to contraction in skeletal muscle but without the regularity of rearrangement of fibrils found in skeletal muscle. The fibrils, with their linear arrangement, slide together and rhythmically shorten the fiber. In contraction of smooth muscle, a nerve impulse reaches the fiber and is transmitted to the remainder of the fiber. A slow wave of contraction then passes over the entire muscle mass.

Cardiac Muscle

Cardiac muscle is involuntary muscle, possessing the striated appearance of voluntary muscle. It develops from primitive mesodermal cells. Fibers of cardiac muscle surround a close network of blood and lymph capillaries, and are roughly quadrangular in shape, forming a continuous protoplasmic sheet or *syncytium*. Thus, myocardial fibers intertwine to produce a continuous branching network, permitting the heart to contract en masse.

The rapid rhythm of cardiac muscle is the result of a special property of this type of muscle fiber to receive an impulse, contract, immediately relax, and receive another impulse. All these events occur about 75 times per minute. The period of an individual contraction is slower in cardiac than in skeletal muscle—about 0.3 second, compared to 0.09 second in skeletal muscle. Rapid contraction of cardiac muscle is called *fibrillation*.

Disorders of Muscle

Disease of muscle originates either in the nerve supply, the vascular supply, or the connective tissue sheaths. The major symptoms of muscular disorders are paralysis, weakness, pain, atrophy, spasm, and cramps.

A condition in which a muscle shortens its length in the resting state is known as a *contracture*. Contractures occur when an individual remains in bed for prolonged periods and the muscles are not properly exercised. Eventually, the muscles readjust to the resting length of a flexed arm or leg. Contractures are treated by the painful and slow procedure of exercising and relengthening the muscle. Contractures can be prevented by keeping the body in correct alignment when resting and by periodically exercising the muscles. Muscular exercise can either be active (by the patient himself), or passive (by someone else).

Myalgia refers to muscular pain; *myositis* is the term used to describe inflammation of muscular tissue. *Fibrositis* is an inflammation of the connective tissue within a muscle, particularly near a joint. Usually a combination of fibrositis and myositis, *fibromyositis*, is present. Such a condition is commonly known as rheumatism, lumbago, or charley horse.

Two other entities affecting the muscle are *muscular dystrophy* and *myasthenia gravis*. The cause and treatment of both are unknown. Muscular dystrophy occurs most often in males and is a slowly progressive disorder ending in complete helplessness. In muscular dystrophy, the child begins to walk clumsily and tends to fall. Examination reveals pseudohypertrophy of some muscle groups and wasting of others. The term pseudohypertrophy is employed because the muscles feel large because of the deposition of fat.

Myasthenia gravis is characterized by the easy fatiguability of muscles. It is caused by an impairment of conduction of the normal impulse at the myoneural junction of striated muscle. This is thought to be caused either by a lack of acetylcholine or an increase in cholinesterase at the junction. Neostigmine, a drug serving to interfere with cholinesterase, is given for therapy. Surgical removal of the thymus (if enlarged) has been beneficial, but the reason behind this relationship is unknown.

In *atrophy* the muscle fibers degenerate. Muscles can become a fraction of their normal size; within 6 months to 2 years the fibers are actually replaced by fibrous tissue. Stimulation

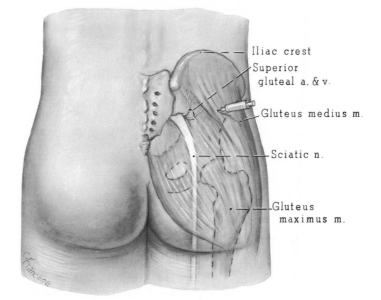

Fig. 90.　Intramuscular injection in the gluteal region should be in the upper outer quadrant.

of nerves with an electric current keeps muscular tissue viable until full muscular activity returns.

Muscles act in an orderly fashion. The performance of even the slightest movement demands the cooperative effort of many muscles. This effort is called *coordination;* the cerebellum of the brain is devoted largely to the maintenance of this function. If a muscle becomes paralyzed, the sequence for coordination is disrupted and other muscles are unable to act in sequence; thus, coordination is destroyed and atrophy occurs.

Intramuscular Injection

The importance of a proper site for intramuscular injection is recognized by those who have experienced the pain resulting when a poor site is selected for injection. The ideal site is deep within the muscle, and away from major nerves and arteries. The best sites are into the vastus lateralis, the deltoid, and the gluteal muscles.

The gluteal region has become the most common site for intramuscular injection. The area best suited is the upper and outer quadrant (Fig. 90). The student should remember that the gluteal region extends to the anterior superior iliac spine. This should be used as a landmark when defining the quadrants. When the upper outer quadrant is used, there is little danger of

the needle piercing the sciatic nerve or the superior gluteal artery.

The deltoid muscle is thick and extends from the clavicle, acromion, and spine of the scapula to the deltoid tuberosity of the humerus (Fig. 91). Owing to the non-yielding tendinous septae in the upper and lower regions of this muscle, only a small area in the center provides a satisfactory site for injection. This site is found 2 cm. below the acromion. The gluteal region is preferred, since it has a greater muscle mass permitting injections with larger volumes of fluid.

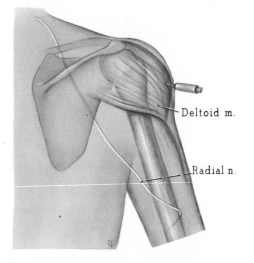

Fig. 91.　Intramuscular injection into the deltoid, two to three fingerbreadths below the acromion.

INTRODUCTION TO THE ANATOMY OF SKELETAL MUSCLES

The following tables include most of the important muscles of the body. Additionally, the origin and insertion of each muscle and its principal action and innervation are described. It should be remembered that muscles are named according to *action* (for example, adductor and extensor); according to *shape* (for example, quadratus); according to *origin* and *insertion* (for example, sternocleidomastoid); according to number of *divisions* (for example, quadriceps and triceps); according to *location* (for example, tibialis and radialis); and according to *direction of fibers* (for example, transversus).

The proximal attachment of muscle to bone (closer to the axial skeleton) is known as the *origin*, and the distal attachment (farther from the axial skeleton) represents the *insertion*. Most voluntary muscles are not inserted directly into bone, but rather through the medium of a strong, tough, non-elastic fibrous cord called a *tendon*. Tendons vary in length from a fraction of 1 inch to more than 1 foot. Muscles may have one of these closely packed bundles of white collagenous fibers attached to each of the extremities. If the tendon is wide, thin, and flat, it is called an *aponeurosis*.

Muscles are found in many sizes and shapes. The types include fusiform (spindle-shaped), quadrilateral (rhomboid), triangular, strap-like, and pennate (feather-like). A pennate arrangement in which fibers pass from either side to the central tendon to which they obliquely join, is the bipennate shape, while the unipennate shape has only one-half of a feather represented. In most muscles, the fibers pass in a line of pull from the origin to the insertion.

Muscles which bend a limb at a joint are called *flexors*. Muscles straightening a limb at a joint are called *extensors*. If the limb is moved away from the midline of the body, an *abductor* is at work; if the limb is brought toward the midline, *adductors* are responsible. There are also muscles *rotating* the involved limb. In movements of the ankle, muscles of *dorsiflexion* turn the foot upward, while muscles of *plantar flexion* bring the foot toward the ground. In movements of the hand, turning the forearm so that the palm of the hand faces upward is called *supination*, and turning it to bring the palm facing the ground is *pronation*. *Levators* raise a part of the body; *depressors* lower it.

In performing a given movement, such as bending the arm at the elbow, the muscles executing the actual movement are known as the *prime movers* or *agonists*. Muscles straightening the elbow are *extensors*, also called *antagonists*. The agonist muscle, or flexor, must relax for the extensor muscle or antagonist to perform. *Synergists* are muscles assisting the agonist. They hold a joint crossed by the tendon of the prime mover in the best possible position for effective action.

Muscles acting only on joints between their respective origin and insertion produce only movements at these joints. For instance, the *brachialis*, the muscle attached to the ulna and humerus, produces only movement at the elbow. Ability to bend the elbow is at first limited, because most of the energy is expended in attempting to pull the ulna upward in a straight direction. As the elbow bends, the angle of pull increases and the muscle becomes increasingly efficient. The optimal angle of pull for any muscle is a right angle. The system of levers also has an influence on the efficiency of muscular contraction.

Text continued on page 181.

TABLE 7. Muscles of Facial Expression.[*]

MUSCLE	ORIGIN	INSERTION	FUNCTION	INNERVATION
Epicranial (occipitofrontalis) Occipitalis	Occipital bone and mastoid portion of temporal bone	Galea aponeurotica, epicranial muscle	Draws scalp backward	Posterior auricular branch of facial
Frontalis	Galea aponeurotica	Frontal bone above supra-orbital line	Elevates eyebrows and wrinkles skin of forehead	Temporal branch of facial
Zygomaticus minor	Zygomatic bone	Greater alar cartilage and skin of nose, orbicularis oris	Draws upper lip upward and outward	Facial
Levator labii superioris	Maxilla below infra-orbital foramen	Orbicularis oris	Elevates upper lip	Facial
Buccinator	Alveolar processes of maxilla and mandible	Orbicularis oris at angle of mouth	Compresses cheek and retracts angle	Facial
Zygomaticus major	Zygomatic bone	Orbicularis oris	Pulls angle of mouth upward and backward when laughing	Facial
Mentalis	Incisive fossa of mandible	Skin of chin	Raises and protrudes lower lip, as in doubt or disdain	Facial
Orbicularis oris	Muscle fibers surrounding the opening of mouth	Angle of mouth	Closes lips	Facial

[*] See also Figures 92 and 93.

126

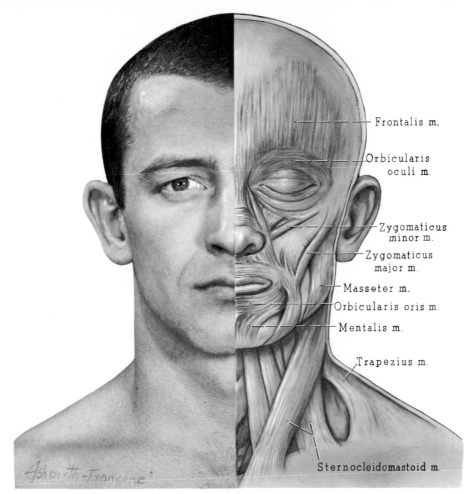

Frontalis m.

Orbicularis oculi m.

Zygomaticus minor m.

Zygomaticus major m.

Masseter m.

Orbicularis oris m.

Mentalis m.

Trapezius m.

Sternocleidomastoid m.

Fig. 92.   Muscles of the face, superficial layer.

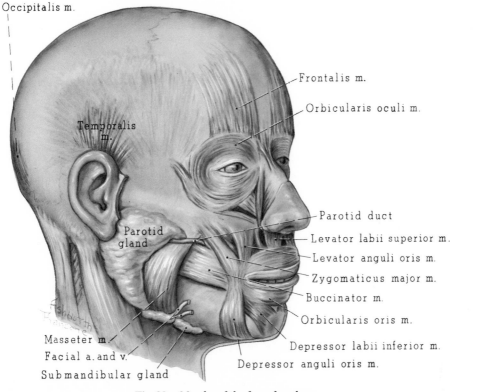

Occipitalis m.

Temporalis m.

Parotid gland

Masseter m.

Facial a. and v.

Submandibular gland

Frontalis m.

Orbicularis oculi m.

Parotid duct

Levator labii superior m.

Levator anguli oris m.

Zygomaticus major m.

Buccinator m.

Orbicularis oris m.

Depressor labii inferior m.

Depressor anguli oris m.

127

Fig. 93.   Muscles of the face, deep layer.

TABLE 8.   Muscles of Mastication.*

MUSCLE	ORIGIN	INSERTION	FUNCTION	INNERVATION
Masseter	Zygomatic process and adjacent portions of maxilla	Angle and lateral surface of ramus of mandible	Closes jaw	Trigeminal
Temporalis	Temporal fossa of skull and from deep surface of temporal fascia	Coronoid process of mandible	Raises mandible and closes mouth; draws mandible backward	Trigeminal
Medial pterygoid	Pterygoid fossa of sphenoid; tuberosity of maxilla	Ramus of mandible	Raises mandible; closes mouth	Trigeminal
Lateral pterygoid (two-headed)	Upper head from zygomatic surface of sphenoid; lower head from lateral surface of pterygoid plate	*Upper:* condyle of mandible *Lower:* articular disc of joint between temporal bone and mandible	Brings jaw forward	Trigeminal

* See also Figures 94 and 95.

TABLE 9.   Muscles of the Eye.*

MUSCLE	ORIGIN	INSERTION	FUNCTION	INNERVATION
Superior rectus	Apex of orbital cavity	Upper and central portion of eyeball	Rolls eyeball upward	Oculomotor
Inferior rectus	Apex of orbital cavity	Lower central portion of eyeball	Rolls eyeball downward	Oculomotor
Medial rectus	Apex of orbital cavity	Midway on medial side of eyeball	Rolls eyeball medially	Oculomotor
Lateral rectus	Apex of orbital cavity	Midway on lateral portion of eyeball	Rolls eyeball laterally	Abducens
Superior oblique	Apex of orbital cavity	Between superior and lateral recti of eyeball	Rotates eyeball on axis; directs cornea downward and laterally	Trochlear
Inferior oblique	Orbital plate of maxilla	Between superior and lateral recti of eyeball	Rotates eyeball on its axis; directs cornea upward and laterally	Oculomotor

* See also Figures 96 to 98.

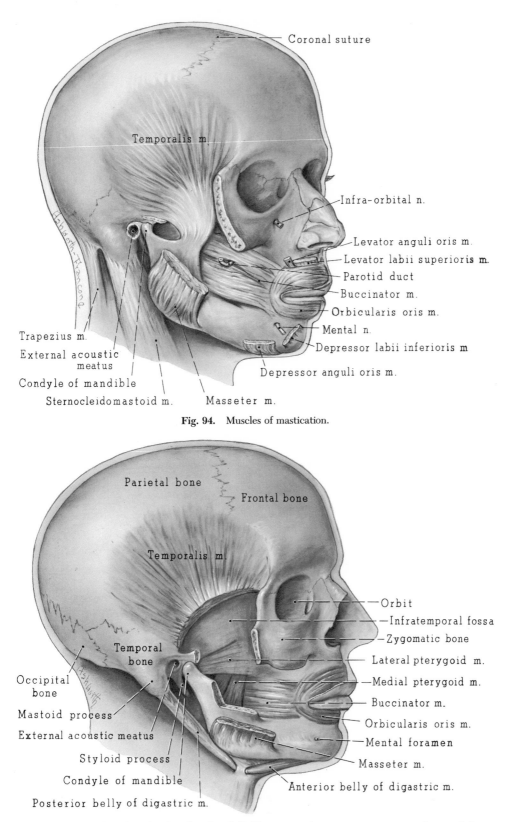

Coronal suture

Temporalis m.

Infra-orbital n.

Levator anguli oris m.

Levator labii superioris m.

Parotid duct

Buccinator m.

Orbicularis oris m.

Mental n.

Depressor labii inferioris m.

Depressor anguli oris m.

Trapezius m.

External acoustic meatus

Condyle of mandible

Sternocleidomastoid m.

Masseter m.

Fig. 94. Muscles of mastication.

Parietal bone

Frontal bone

Temporalis m.

Orbit

Infratemporal fossa

Zygomatic bone

Temporal bone

Lateral pterygoid m.

Medial pterygoid m.

Buccinator m.

Occipital bone

Orbicularis oris m.

Mastoid process

Mental foramen

External acoustic meatus

Masseter m.

Styloid process

Anterior belly of digastric m.

Condyle of mandible

Posterior belly of digastric m.

Fig. 95. Muscles of the head within the skull. The temporalis, masseter, zygoma, and part of the mandible have been removed.

129

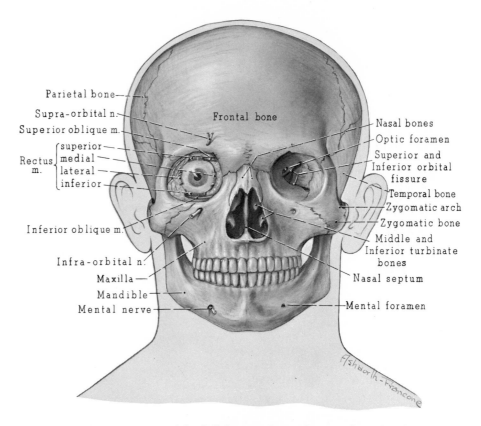

Fig. 96. Anterior view of the skull showing relation of eye muscles to the orbit.

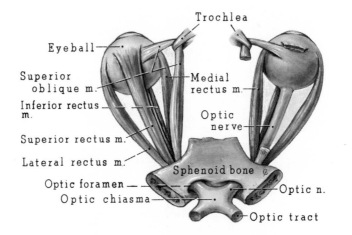

Fig. 97. Extrinsic muscles of the eye. (Inferior oblique m. not shown. See Fig. 52.)

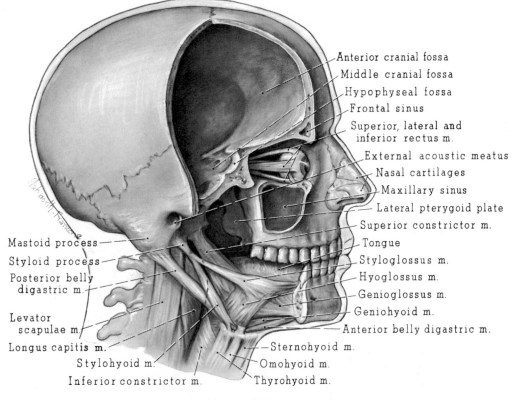

Anterior cranial fossa
Middle cranial fossa
Hypophyseal fossa
Frontal sinus
Superior, lateral and
inferior rectus m.
External acoustic meatus
Nasal cartilages
Maxillary sinus
Lateral pterygoid plate
Superior constrictor m.
Tongue
Styloglossus m.
Hyoglossus m.
Genioglossus m.
Geniohyoid m.
Anterior belly digastric m.
Sternohyoid m.
Omohyoid m.
Thyrohyoid m.

Mastoid process
Styloid process
Posterior belly
digastric m.
Levator
scapulae m.
Longus capitis m.
Stylohyoid m.
Inferior constrictor m.

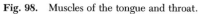

Fig. 98.   Muscles of the tongue and throat.

TABLE 10. Muscles Moving the Tongue.*

MUSCLE	ORIGIN	INSERTION	FUNCTION	INNERVATION
Genioglossus	Mental spine of mandible	Thin aponeurosis into hyoid bone	Depresses and thrusts tongue forward	Hypoglossal
Styloglossus	Styloid process of temporal bone	Entire length of and inferior surface of tongue	Draws tongue upward and backward	Hypoglossal

* See also Figure 98.

TABLE 11. Muscles Moving the Head.*

MUSCLE	ORIGIN	INSERTION	FUNCTION	INNERVATION
Sternocleidomastoid	Two heads from sternum and clavicle	Tendon into mastoid portion of temporal bone	Acting individually each draws head toward shoulder of same side; both muscles acting together push head forward	Spinal accessory

* See also Figures 99 to 101.

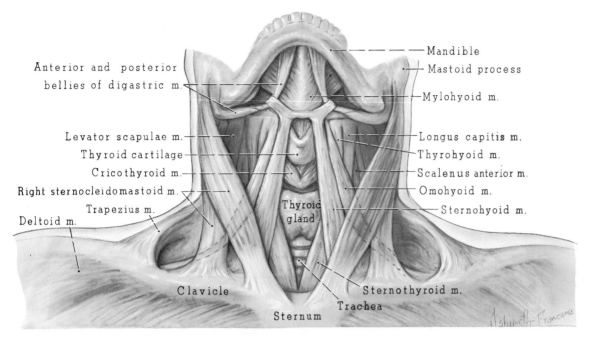

Anterior and posterior
bellies of digastric m.

Levator scapulae m.
Thyroid cartilage
Cricothyroid m.
Right sternocleidomastoid m.
Trapezius m.
Deltoid m.

Clavicle

Sternum

Mandible
Mastoid process
Mylohyoid m.

Longus capitis m.
Thyrohyoid m.
Scalenus anterior m.
Omohyoid m.
Sternohyoid m.

Thyroid
gland

Sternothyroid m.
Trachea

Fig. 99. Muscles of the neck, superficial layer.

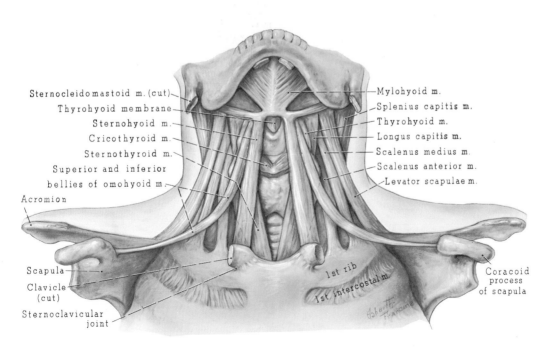

Sternocleidomastoid m. (cut)
Thyrohyoid membrane
Sternohyoid m.
Cricothyroid m.
Sternothyroid m.
Superior and inferior
bellies of omohyoid m.
Acromion

Scapula
Clavicle
(cut)
Sternoclavicular
joint

Mylohyoid m.
Splenius capitis m.
Thyrohyoid m.
Longus capitis m.
Scalenus medius m.
Scalenus anterior m.
Levator scapulae m.

Coracoid
process
of scapula

1st rib
1st intercostal m.

Fig. 100. Second layer of muscles of the neck.

133

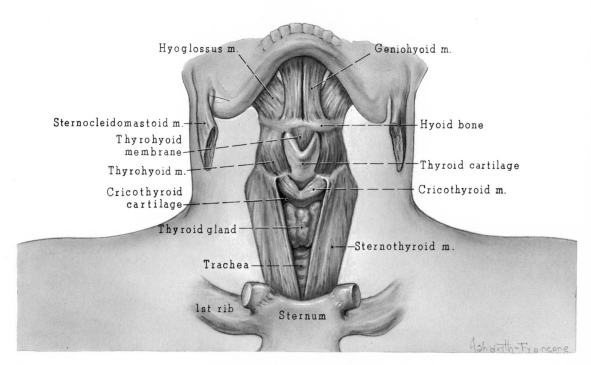

Hyoglossus m.

Geniohyoid m.

Sternocleidomastoid m.

Hyoid bone

Thyrohyoid membrane

Thyrohyoid m.

Thyroid cartilage

Cricothyroid cartilage

Cricothyroid m.

Thyroid gland

Sternothyroid m.

Trachea

1st rib

Sternum

Ashworth-Francone

Fig. 101. Deep muscles of the neck.

TABLE 12. Movement of Shoulder Girdle.[*]

MUSCLE	ORIGIN	INSERTION	FUNCTION	INNERVATION
Levator scapulae	Upper four or five cervical vertebrae	Vertebral border of scapula	Elevates scapula	Dorsal scapular
Rhomboid major	Spines of first four or five thoracic vertebrae	Vertebral border of scapula between root and inferior angle of spine of scapula	Moves scapula backward and upward, producing slight rotation	Dorsal scapular
Rhomboid minor	Lower part of ligamentum nuchae and anterior spinous processes of last cervical and first thoracic vertebrae	Vertebral border of scapula at root of spine	Elevates and retracts scapula	Dorsal scapular
Pectoralis minor[†]	Upper margins and outer surface of third, fourth, and fifth ribs from aponeurosis covering intercostals	Medial border of coracoid process of scapula	Depresses shoulder and rotates scapula downward	Anterior thoracic
Trapezius	Occipital bone; ligamentum nuchae and spinous processes of seventh cervical to twelfth thoracic vertebrae	Acromial process of clavicle and spine	Draws head to one side; rotates scapula	Spinal accessory
Serratus anterior	Outer surfaces and superior borders of the upper eighth or ninth rib; from intercostals between ribs	Ventral surface of vertebral border of scapula	Moves scapula forward away from spine and downward and inward toward chest wall	Long thoracic

[*] See also Figures 102 to 105.
[†] See Figure 120 for pectoralis minor.

135

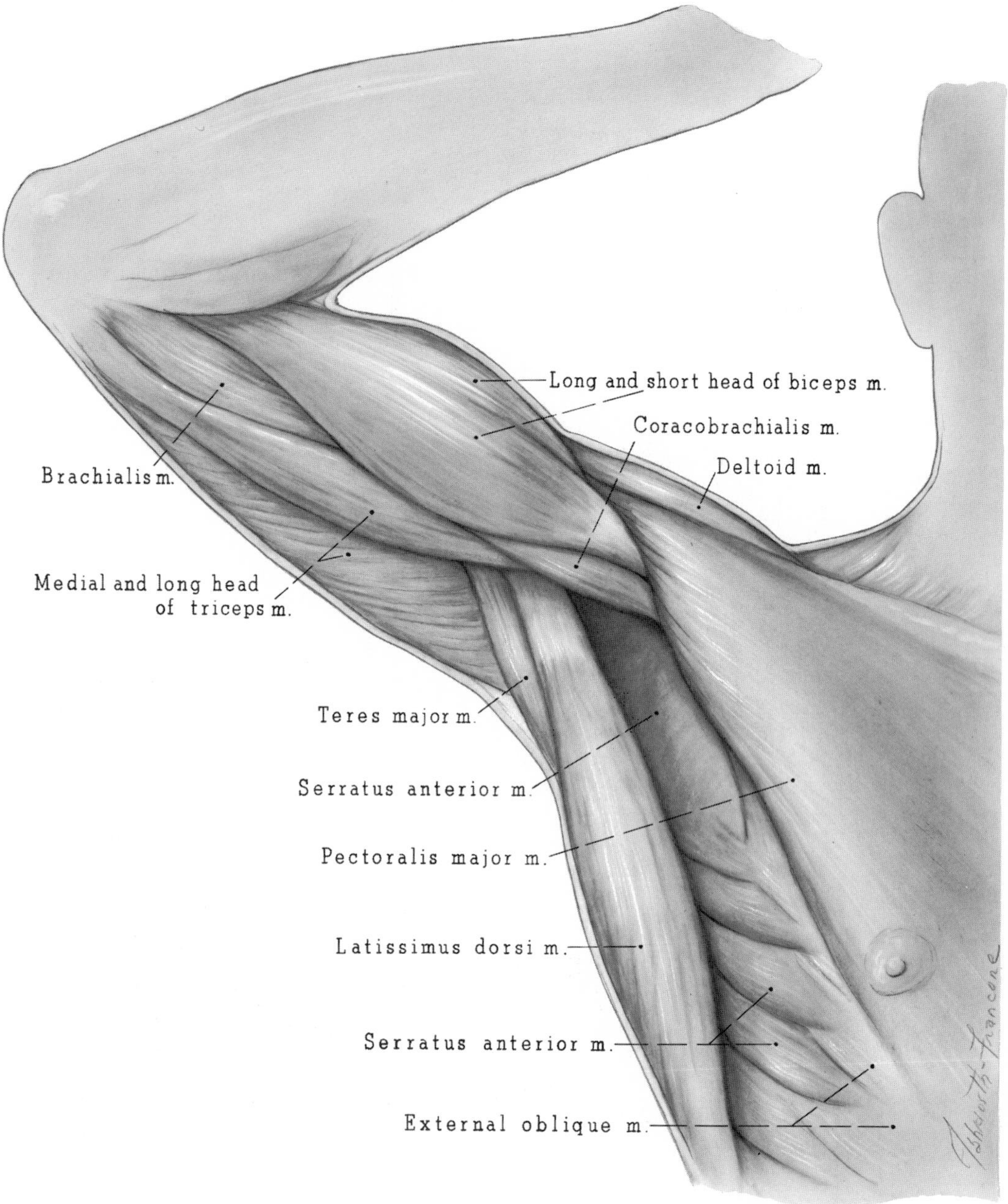

Long and short head of biceps m.

Coracobrachialis m.

Deltoid m.

Brachialis m.

Medial and long head
of triceps m.

Teres major m.

Serratus anterior m.

Pectoralis major m.

Latissimus dorsi m.

Serratus anterior m.

External oblique m.

Fig. 102. Muscles in the region of the axilla when the arm is raised.

136

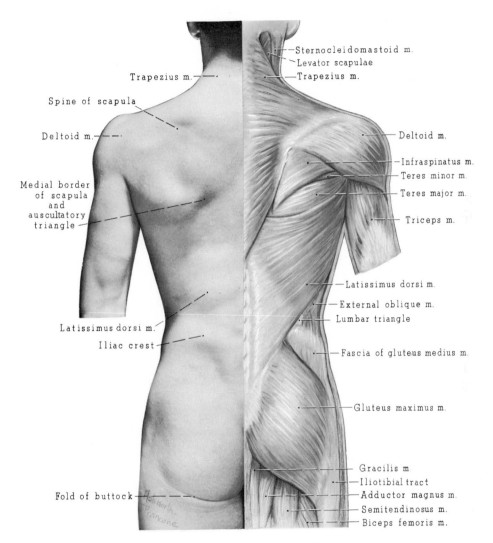

Fig. 103.　Muscles of the back.

Sternocleidomastoid m.
Levator scapulae
Trapezius m.
Trapezius m.
Spine of scapula
Deltoid m.
Deltoid m.
Infraspinatus m.
Teres minor m.
Medial border of scapula and auscultatory triangle
Teres major m.
Triceps m.
Latissimus dorsi m.
External oblique m.
Lumbar triangle
Latissimus dorsi m.
Iliac crest
Fascia of gluteus medius m.
Gluteus maximus m.
Gracilis m.
Iliotibial tract
Adductor magnus m.
Fold of buttock
Semitendinosus m.
Biceps femoris m.

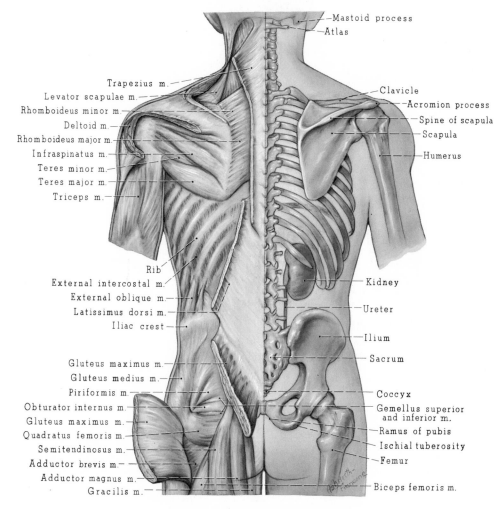

Mastoid process
Atlas

Trapezius m.

Levator scapulae m.
Rhomboideus minor m.
Deltoid m.
Rhomboideus major m.
Infraspinatus m.
Teres minor m.
Teres major m.
Triceps m.

Clavicle
Acromion process
Spine of scapula
Scapula
Humerus

Rib
External intercostal m.
External oblique m.
Latissimus dorsi m.
Iliac crest

Kidney
Ureter
Ilium
Sacrum

Gluteus maximus m.
Gluteus medius m.
Piriformis m.
Obturator internus m.
Gluteus maximus m.
Quadratus femoris m.
Semitendinosus m.
Adductor brevis m.
Adductor magnus m.
Gracilis m.

Coccyx
Gemellus superior
and inferior m.
Ramus of pubis
Ischial tuberosity
Femur
Biceps femoris m.

Fig. 104. Deep muscles of the back.

138

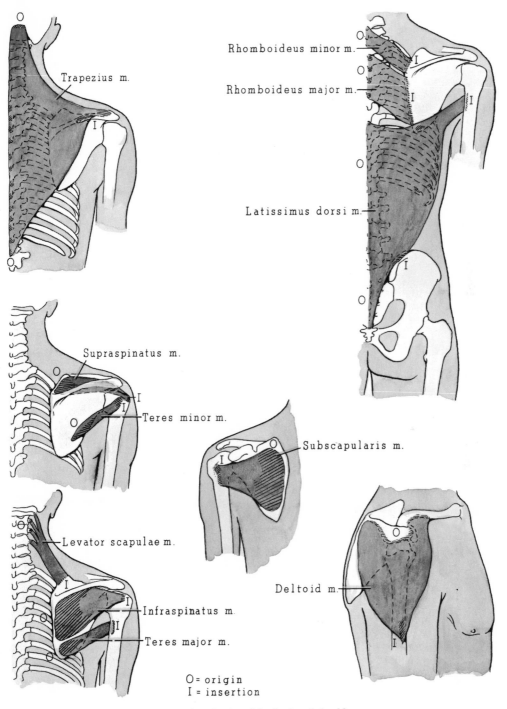

Rhomboideus minor m.

Rhomboideus major m.

Latissimus dorsi m.

Trapezius m.

Supraspinatus m.

Teres minor m.

Subscapularis m.

Levator scapulae m.

Deltoid m.

Infraspinatus m.

Teres major m.

O = origin
I = insertion

Fig. 105. Muscles of the back and shoulder.

TABLE 13. Muscles Moving the Humerus.*

MUSCLE	ORIGIN	INSERTION	FUNCTION	INNERVATION
Coracobrachialis	Coracoid process of scapula	Middle and medial surface of humerus	Flexes, adducts arm	Musculocutaneous
Pectoralis major	Anterior surface of sternal half of clavicle; sternum; aponeurosis of external oblique; six upper ribs	Crest and greater tubercle of humerus	Flexes, adducts, rotates arm medially	Anterior thoracic
Teres major	Posterior aspect of axillary border of scapula	Medial border of bicipital groove of humerus	Adducts, extends, rotates arm medially	Lower subscapular
Teres minor	Dorsal surface of axillary border of scapula	Greater tuberosity of humerus	Rotates arm laterally; adducts and draws humerus toward glenoid fossa	Branch of axillary
Deltoid	Clavicle; acromial process and posterior border of spine of scapula	Lateral surface of body of humerus	Abducts arm	Axillary
Supraspinatus	Fossa superior to spine of scapula	Greater tuberosity of humerus	Abducts arm	Suprascapular
Infraspinatus	Infraspinatus fossa on posterior aspect of scapula	Middle facet of greater tubercle of humerus	Rotates humerus outward	Suprascapular
Latissimus dorsi	Broad aponeurosis attached to the spinous process of lower six thoracic vertebrae, spinous process of lumbar vertebrae, spine of sacrum; posterior part of crest of ilium; outer surface of lower four ribs	Bicipital groove of humerus	Extends, adducts, rotates arm medially; draws shoulder downward and backward	Thoracodorsal

* See also Figures 102 to 105.

140

TABLE 14.   Muscles Moving the Elbow.*

MUSCLE	ORIGIN	INSERTION	FUNCTION	INNERVATION
Brachialis	Lower half of anterior surface of humerus	Tuberosity of the ulna and coronoid processes	Flexes forearm	Musculocutaneous and branch of radial
Triceps brachii (three-headed)		All heads insert into two aponeurotic laminae uniting above the elbow and in the olecranon of the ulna	Extends and adducts forearm (long head only); entire muscle extends forearm	Radial
Long head	Axillary border of scapula			
Lateral head	Lateral and posterior surfaces of body of humerus			
Medial head†	Posterior surface of body of humerus below lateral head			
Biceps brachii (two-headed)			Flexes arm; flexes forearm, supinates hand; long head draws humerus toward glenoid fossa and strengthens shoulder joint	Musculocutaneous
Long head	Supraglenoid tuberosity at upper margin of the glenoid cavity	Tuberosity of radius		
Short head	Coracoid process by tendon	Tuberosity of radius		

* See also Figures 106 to 108.
† Medial head of triceps not shown in figures.

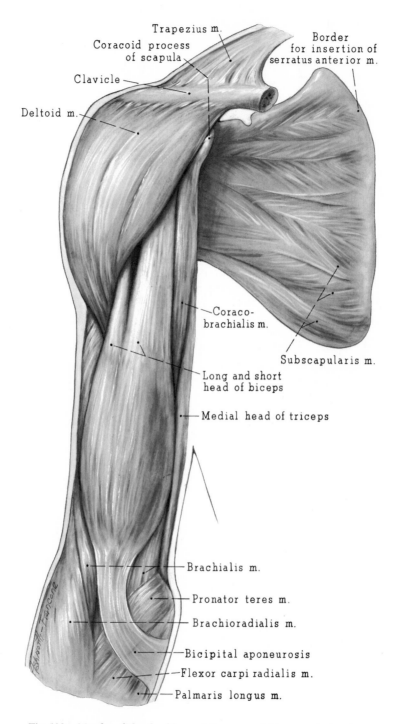

Fig. 106. Muscles of the shoulder and the upper right arm, anterior view.

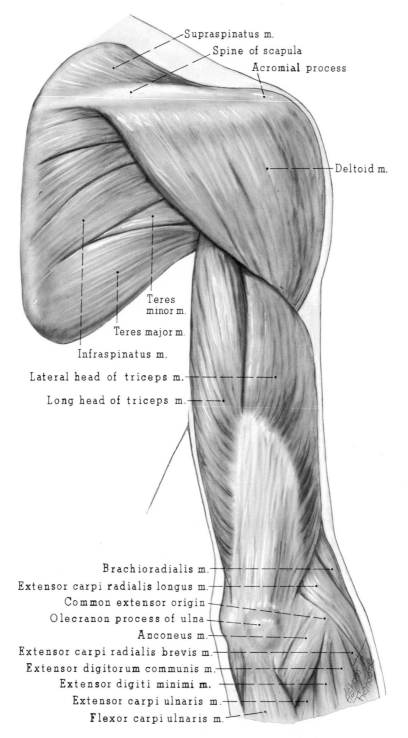

Supraspinatus m.

Spine of scapula

Acromial process

Deltoid m.

Teres minor m.

Teres major m.

Infraspinatus m.

Lateral head of triceps m.

Long head of triceps m.

Brachioradialis m.

Extensor carpi radialis longus m.

Common extensor origin

Olecranon process of ulna

Anconeus m.

Extensor carpi radialis brevis m.

Extensor digitorum communis m.

Extensor digiti minimi m.

Extensor carpi ulnaris m.

Flexor carpi ulnaris m.

Fig. 107. Muscles of the shoulder and upper arm, posterior view.

143

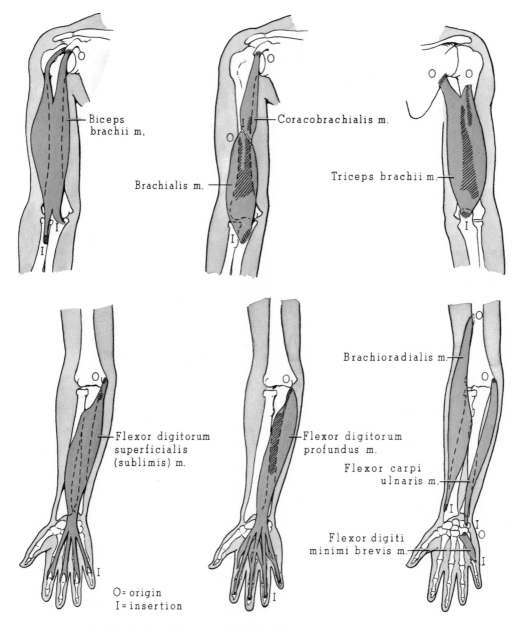

Biceps brachii m.

Coracobrachialis m.

Brachialis m.

Triceps brachii m.

Brachioradialis m.

Flexor digitorum superficialis (sublimis) m.

Flexor digitorum profundus m.

Flexor carpi ulnaris m.

Flexor digiti minimi brevis m.

O = origin
I = insertion

Fig. 108.   Origin and insertion of muscles of the upper arm, forearm, and hand.

TABLE 15.   Muscles Moving the Wrist.[*]

MUSCLE	ORIGIN	INSERTION	FUNCTION	INNERVATION
Flexor carpi radialis	Medial epicondyle of humerus	Base of second and third metacarpal	Flexes, abducts wrist	Median
Flexor carpi ulnaris	Medial epicondyle of humerus and upper two-thirds of dorsal border of ulna	Pisiform bone	Flexes, adducts wrist	Ulnar
Extensor carpi radialis longus	Lower third of lateral supracondylar ridge of humerus	Base of second metacarpal bone	Extends, abducts wrist	Radial
Extensor carpi ulnaris	Lateral epicondyle of humerus	Prominent tubercle on ulnar side of the base of fifth metacarpal bone	Extends, adducts wrist	Radial

[*] See also Figures 109 to 116.

TABLE 16.   Muscles Moving the Hand.[*]

MUSCLE	ORIGIN	INSERTION	FUNCTION	INNERVATION
Supinator	Lateral epicondyle of humerus; ridge on ulna; radial ligament of elbow	Anterior and lateral surfaces of body of radius	Supinates hand	Radial
Pronator teres	Medial epicondyle of humerus and coronoid process of ulna	Middle of lateral surface of body of radius	Pronates forearm	Median
Pronator quadratus	Lower part of volar surface of body of ulna	Volar surface of radius	Pronates forearm	Median (anterior interosseus branch)

[*] See also Figures 109 to 116.

145

TABLE 17.   Muscles Moving the Thumb.*

MUSCLE	ORIGIN	INSERTION	FUNCTION	INNERVATION
Flexor pollicis longus	Volar surface of body of radius	Base of distal phalanx of thumb	Flexes second phalanx of thumb	Posterior interosseus
Extensor pollicis longus	Lateral side of dorsal surface of ulna	Base of second phalanx of thumb	Extends terminal phalanx of thumb	Radial
Adductor pollicis	Trapezium, trapezoid, os magnum, shaft of third metacarpal	Ulnar side of base of first phalanx of thumb	Adducts thumb	Ulnar

* See also Figures 109 to 116.

TABLE 18.   Muscles Moving the Fingers.*

MUSCLE	ORIGIN	INSERTION	FUNCTION	INNERVATION
Flexor digitorum profundus	Anterior and medial surface of body of ulna; depression on medial side of coronoid process	Bases of terminal phalanges by four tendons	Flexes terminal phalanx of each finger	Ulnar and median

* See also Figures 109 to 116.

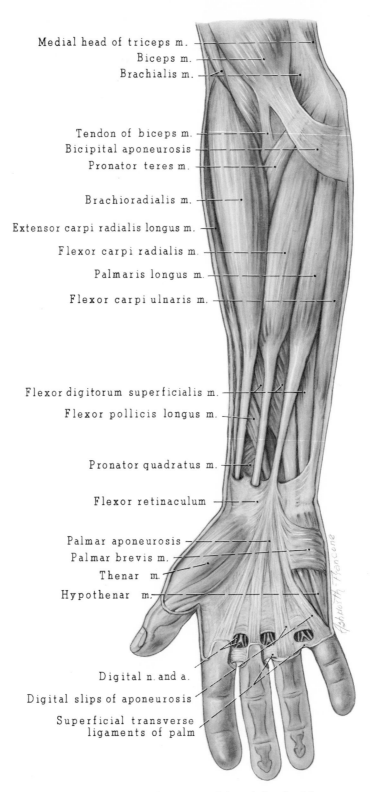

Medial head of triceps m.
Biceps m.
Brachialis m.

Tendon of biceps m.
Bicipital aponeurosis
Pronator teres m.

Brachioradialis m.

Extensor carpi radialis longus m.

Flexor carpi radialis m.

Palmaris longus m.

Flexor carpi ulnaris m.

Flexor digitorum superficialis m.
Flexor pollicis longus m.

Pronator quadratus m.

Flexor retinaculum

Palmar aponeurosis
Palmar brevis m.
Thenar m.
Hypothenar m.

Digital n. and a.
Digital slips of aponeurosis
Superficial transverse
ligaments of palm

Fig. 109.   Muscles of the palmar aspect of the right hand and forearm.

147

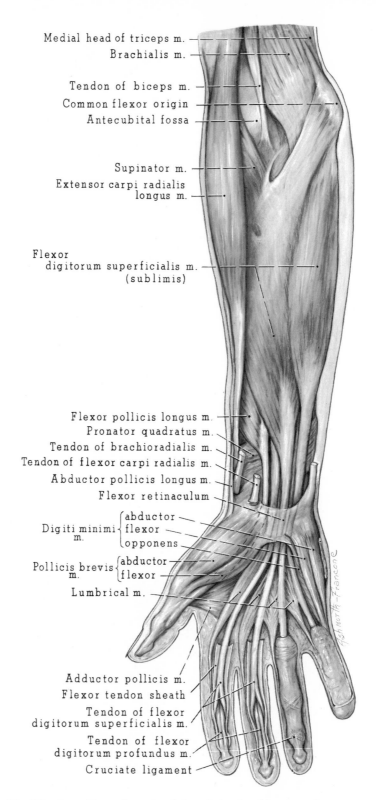

Medial head of triceps m. —
Brachialis m. —

Tendon of biceps m. —
Common flexor origin —
Antecubital fossa —

Supinator m. —
Extensor carpi radialis
longus m. —

Flexor
digitorum superficialis m. —
(sublimis)

Flexor pollicis longus m. —
Pronator quadratus m. —
Tendon of brachioradialis m. —
Tendon of flexor carpi radialis m. —
Abductor pollicis longus m. —
Flexor retinaculum —

Digiti minimi { abductor —
m. { flexor —
{ opponens —

Pollicis brevis { abductor —
m. { flexor —

Lumbrical m. —

Adductor pollicis m. —
Flexor tendon sheath —
Tendon of flexor
digitorum superficialis m. —
Tendon of flexor
digitorum profundus m. —
Cruciate ligament —

Fig. 110.   Second layer of muscles of the right hand and forearm, palmar aspect.

148

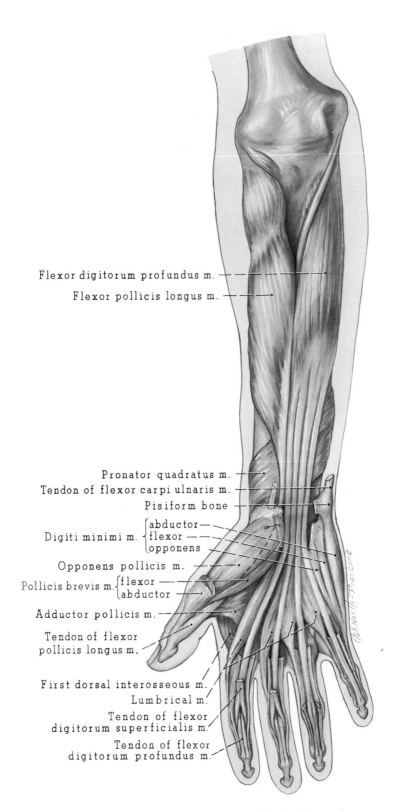

Flexor digitorum profundus m.

Flexor pollicis longus m.

Pronator quadratus m.

Tendon of flexor carpi ulnaris m.

Pisiform bone

Digiti minimi m. { abductor
flexor
opponens

Opponens pollicis m.

Pollicis brevis m. { flexor
abductor

Adductor pollicis m.

Tendon of flexor
pollicis longus m.

First dorsal interosseous m.

Lumbrical m.

Tendon of flexor
digitorum superficialis m.

Tendon of flexor
digitorum profundus m.

Fig. 111. Deep muscles of the right forearm and hand, palmar surface.

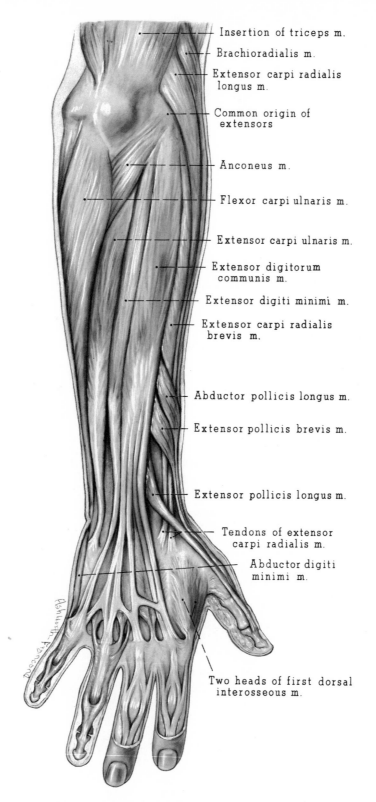

Insertion of triceps m.

Brachioradialis m.

Extensor carpi radialis
longus m.

Common origin of
extensors

Anconeus m.

Flexor carpi ulnaris m.

Extensor carpi ulnaris m.

Extensor digitorum
communis m.

Extensor digiti minimi m.

Extensor carpi radialis
brevis m.

Abductor pollicis longus m.

Extensor pollicis brevis m.

Extensor pollicis longus m.

Tendons of extensor
carpi radialis m.

Abductor digiti
minimi m.

Two heads of first dorsal
interosseous m.

Fig. 112. Posterior view of the right forearm and hand, showing the superficial muscles.

150

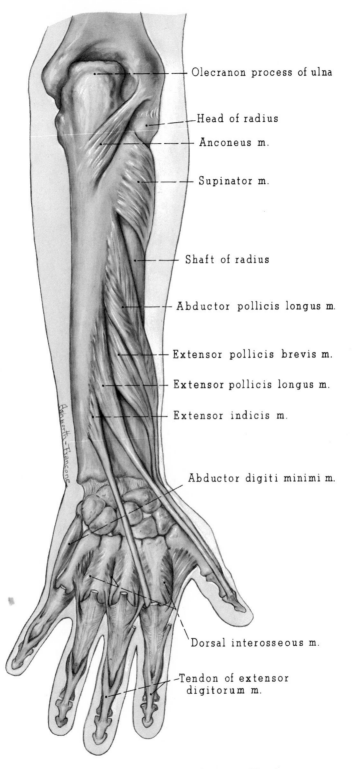

Olecranon process of ulna

Head of radius

Anconeus m.

Supinator m.

Shaft of radius

Abductor pollicis longus m.

Extensor pollicis brevis m.

Extensor pollicis longus m.

Extensor indicis m.

Abductor digiti minimi m.

Dorsal interosseous m.

Tendon of extensor
digitorum m.

Fig. 113. Deep layer of muscles of the right forearm and hand, posterior view.

151

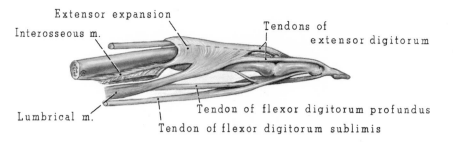

Fig. 114. Tendons of the finger, lateral view.

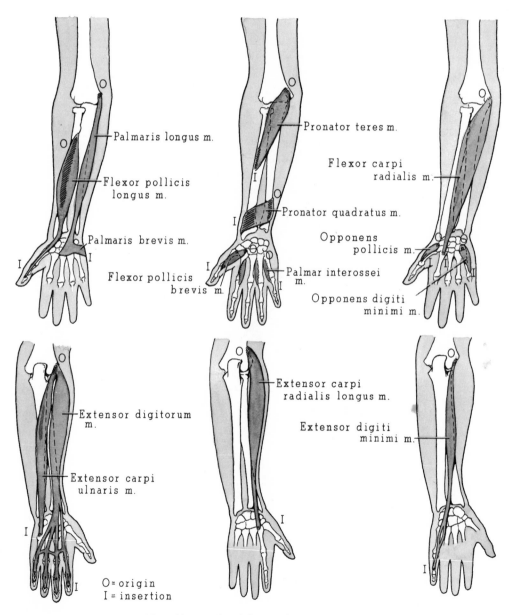

Fig. 115. Muscles of the right hand and forearm.

152

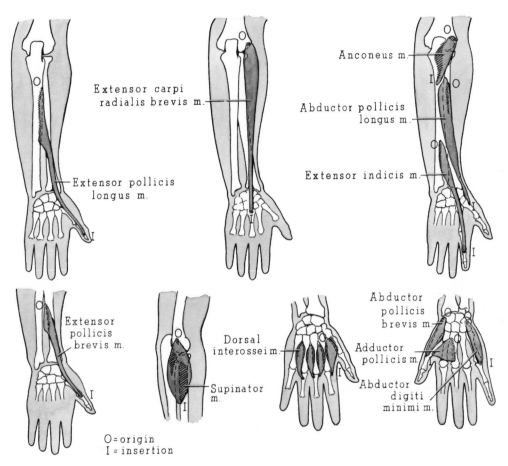

Extensor carpi
radialis brevis m.

Extensor pollicis
longus m.

Anconeus m.

Abductor pollicis
longus m.

Extensor indicis m.

Extensor
pollicis
brevis m.

Dorsal
interossei m.

Supinator
m.

Abductor
pollicis
brevis m.

Adductor
pollicis m.

Abductor
digiti
minimi m.

O = origin
I = insertion

Fig. 116.   Muscles of the right hand and forearm.

TABLE 19.   Muscles of the Abdominal Wall.*

MUSCLE	ORIGIN	INSERTION	FUNCTION	INNERVATION
External oblique	Lower eight ribs	Anterior half of outer lip of iliac crest; anterior rectus sheath	Compresses abdominal contents	Branches of eighth to twelfth intercostal; iliohypogastric, ilio-inguinal
Internal oblique	Inguinal ligament; iliac crest; lumbodorsal fascia	Costal cartilages of lower three or four ribs	Compresses abdominal contents	Branches of eighth to twelfth intercostal; iliohypogastric, ilio-inguinal
Transversus abdominis	Lateral third of inguinal ligament; anterior three-fourths of the inner lip of iliac crest; lumbodorsal fascia; inner surface of cartilages of lower six ribs	Xiphoid cartilage and linea alba	Constricts abdominal contents	Branches of seventh to twelfth intercostal; iliohypogastric, ilio-inguinal
Rectus abdominis	Crest of pubis and ligaments covering symphysis pubis	Cartilages of fifth, sixth, seventh ribs	Flexes vertebral column; assists in compressing abdominal wall	Branches of seventh to twelfth intercostal

* See also Figures 117 to 128.

TABLE 20.   Muscles of Respiration.*

MUSCLE	ORIGIN	INSERTION	FUNCTION	INNERVATION
Diaphragm	Xiphoid process; costal cartilages; lumbar vertebrae	Central tendon	Pulls central tendon downward to increase vertical diameter of thorax	Phrenic
External intercostals (11)	Lower border of rib	Upper border of rib below origin	Draws adjacent ribs together	Intercostal
Internal intercostals (11)	Ridge on inner surface of a rib	Upper border of rib below origin	Draws adjacent ribs together	Intercostal
Quadratus lumborum	Iliac crest; iliolumbar ligament	Last rib and upper four lumbar vertebrae	Flexes trunk laterally	Branches of twelfth thoracic and first lumbar

* See also Figures 120, 121, 123.

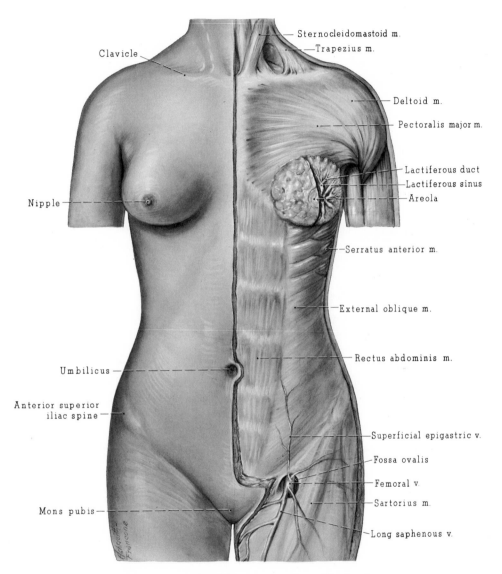

Clavicle

Sternocleidomastoid m.

Trapezius m.

Deltoid m.

Pectoralis major m.

Lactiferous duct

Lactiferous sinus

Nipple

Areola

Serratus anterior m.

External oblique m.

Rectus abdominis m.

Umbilicus

Anterior superior
iliac spine

Superficial epigastric v.

Fossa ovalis

Femoral v.

Sartorius m.

Mons pubis

Long saphenous v.

Fig. 117. Muscles of the anterior surface of the female.

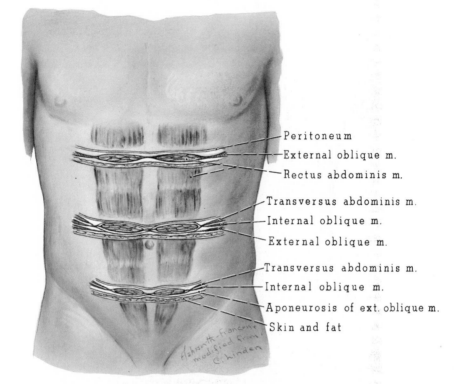

Peritoneum

External oblique m.

Rectus abdominis m.

Transversus abdominis m.

Internal oblique m.

External oblique m.

Transversus abdominis m.

Internal oblique m.

Aponeurosis of ext. oblique m.

Skin and fat

Fig. 118. Diagram of rectus muscles and sheaths of fascia enveloping them. The muscles have been cut to show the layers of fascia and peritoneum.

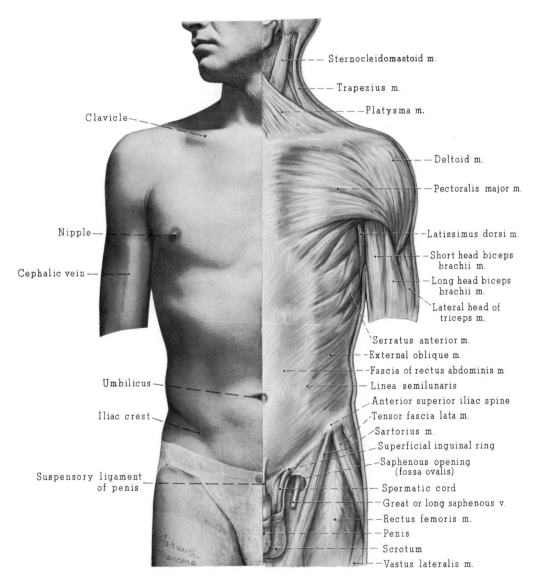

Fig. 119. Muscles of the anterior surface of the male.

Sternocleidomastoid m.

Trapezius m.

Platysma m.

Clavicle

Deltoid m.

Pectoralis major m.

Latissimus dorsi m.

Nipple

Short head biceps
brachii m.

Cephalic vein

Long head biceps
brachii m.

Lateral head of
triceps m.

Serratus anterior m.

External oblique m.

Fascia of rectus abdominis m.

Linea semilunaris

Anterior superior iliac spine

Umbilicus

Tensor fascia lata m.

Sartorius m.

Iliac crest

Superficial inguinal ring

Saphenous opening
(fossa ovalis)

Spermatic cord

Suspensory ligament
of penis

Great or long saphenous v.

Rectus femoris m.

Penis

Scrotum

Vastus lateralis m.

157

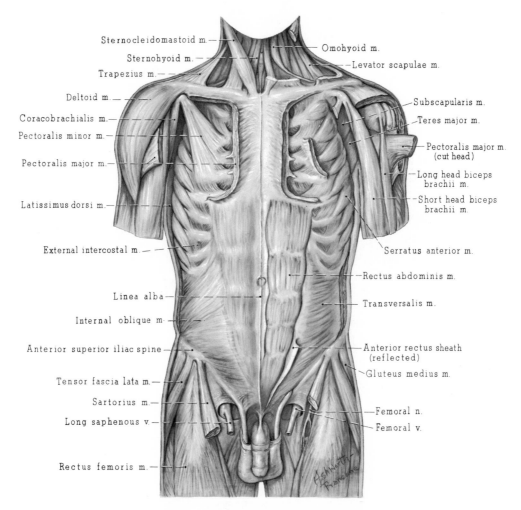

Sternocleidomastoid m.
Sternohyoid m.
Trapezius m.
Deltoid m.
Coracobrachialis m.
Pectoralis minor m.
Pectoralis major m.
Latissimus dorsi m.
External intercostal m.
Linea alba
Internal oblique m.
Anterior superior iliac spine
Tensor fascia lata m.
Sartorius m.
Long saphenous v.
Rectus femoris m.

Omohyoid m.
Levator scapulae m.
Subscapularis m.
Teres major m.
Pectoralis major m. (cut head)
Long head biceps brachii m.
Short head biceps brachii m.
Serratus anterior m.
Rectus abdominis m.
Transversalis m.
Anterior rectus sheath (reflected)
Gluteus medius m.
Femoral n.
Femoral v.

Fig. 120. Superficial musculature; skin and pectoralis major have been removed.

158

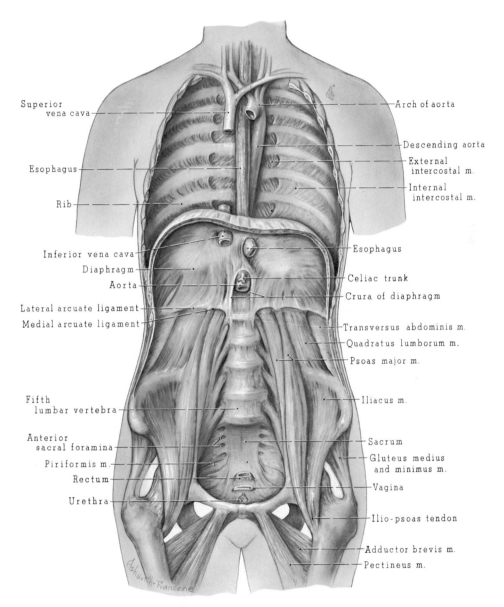

Superior
vena cava

Esophagus

Rib

Inferior vena cava

Diaphragm

Aorta

Lateral arcuate ligament

Medial arcuate ligament

Fifth
lumbar vertebra

Anterior
sacral foramina

Piriformis m.

Rectum

Urethra

Arch of aorta

Descending aorta

External
intercostal m.

Internal
intercostal m.

Esophagus

Celiac trunk

Crura of diaphragm

Transversus abdominis m.

Quadratus lumborum m.

Psoas major m.

Iliacus m.

Sacrum

Gluteus medius
and minimus m.

Vagina

Ilio-psoas tendon

Adductor brevis m.

Pectineus m.

Fig. 121.   Deep muscles of the thoracic, abdominal, and pelvic cavities.

159

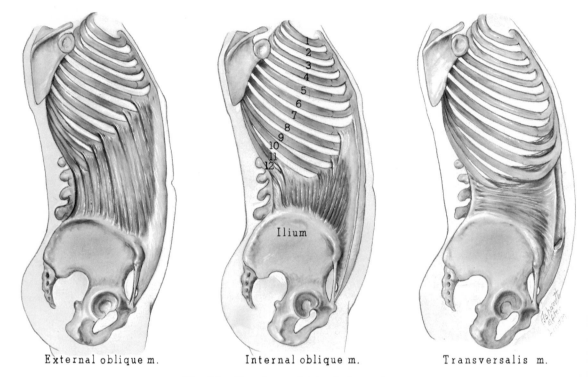

External oblique m.   Internal oblique m.   Transversalis m.

Fig. 122. Three layers of abdominal musculature.

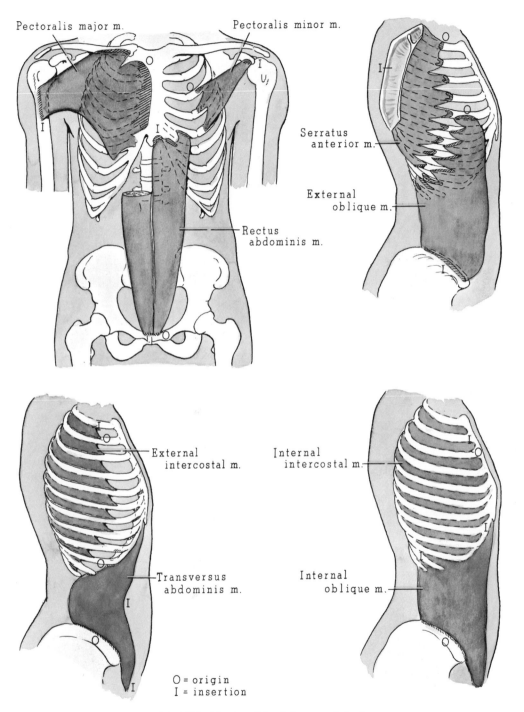

Pectoralis major m.

Pectoralis minor m.

Serratus
anterior m.

External
oblique m.

Rectus
abdominis m.

External
intercostal m.

Internal
intercostal m.

Transversus
abdominis m.

Internal
oblique m.

O = origin
I = insertion

Fig. 123. Muscles of the abdomen and chest.

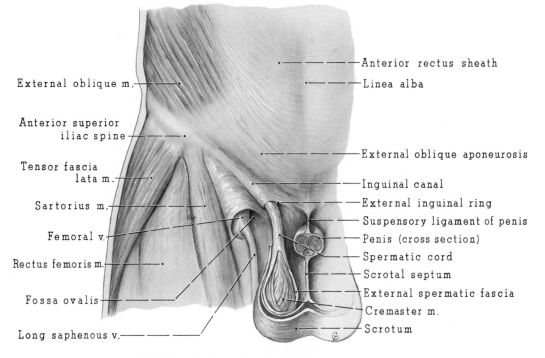

Fig. 124. Muscles of the inguinal region, superficial layer.

External oblique m.

Anterior superior
iliac spine

Tensor fascia
lata m.

Sartorius m.

Femoral v.

Rectus femoris m.

Fossa ovalis

Long saphenous v.

Anterior rectus sheath

Linea alba

External oblique aponeurosis

Inguinal canal

External inguinal ring

Suspensory ligament of penis

Penis (cross section)

Spermatic cord

Scrotal septum

External spermatic fascia

Cremaster m.

Scrotum

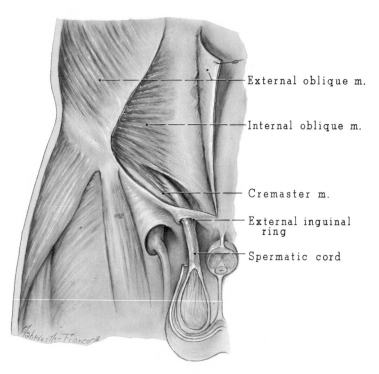

Fig. 125. Muscles of the inguinal region, middle layer.

External oblique m.

Internal oblique m.

Cremaster m.

External inguinal
ring

Spermatic cord

162

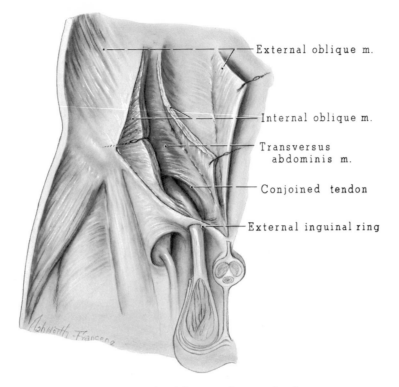

Fig. 126.   Muscles of the inguinal region, deep layer.

— External oblique m.

— Internal oblique m.

Transversus
   abdominis m.

— Conjoined tendon

— External inguinal ring

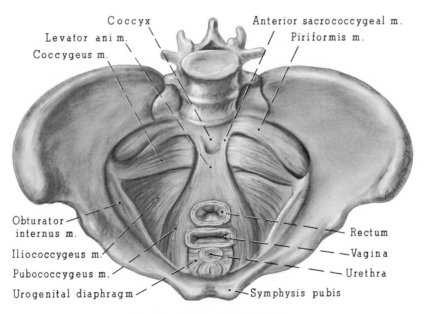

Coccyx   Anterior sacrococcygeal m.
Levator ani m.   Piriformis m.
Coccygeus m.

Obturator
   internus m.   — Rectum

Iliococcygeus m.   — Vagina

Pubococcygeus m.   — Urethra

Urogenital diaphragm   — Symphysis pubis

Fig. 127.   Muscles of the pelvic floor.

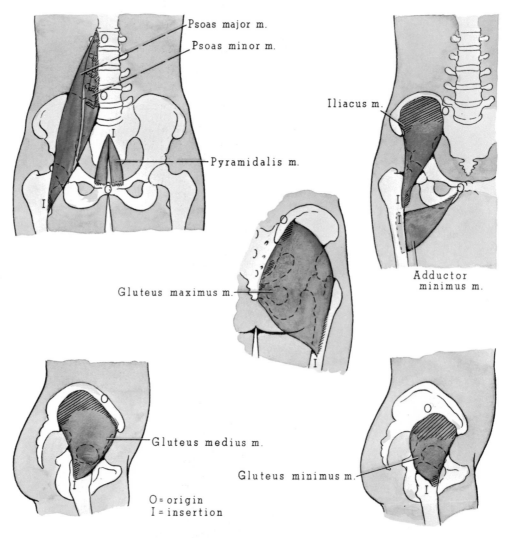

Psoas major m.

Psoas minor m.

Iliacus m.

Pyramidalis m.

Gluteus maximus m.

Adductor
minimus m.

Gluteus medius m.

Gluteus minimus m.

O = origin
I = insertion

Fig. 128. Muscles of the gluteal region.

164

TABLE 21. Muscles Moving the Femur.*

MUSCLE	ORIGIN	INSERTION	FUNCTION	INNERVATION
Iliopsoas				
Psoas major	Transverse processes of lumbar vertebrae	Lesser trochanter of femur	Flexes, rotates thigh medially	Second and third lumbar
Iliacus	Margin of iliac fossa	Lateral side of tendon of psoas major	Flexes, rotates thigh medially	Femoral
Gluteus maximus	Posterior gluteal line of ilium and posterior surface of sacrum and coccyx	Fascia lata, gluteal ridge	Extends, rotates thigh laterally	Inferior gluteal
Gluteus medius	Lateral surface of ilium	Strong tendon that runs into lateral surface	Abducts, rotates thigh medially	Superior gluteal
Gluteus minimus	Outer surface of ilium	Anterior border of greater trochanter	Abducts, rotates thigh medially	Superior gluteal
Tensor fascia lata†	Anterior part of iliac spine	Iliotibial band of fascia	Tenses fascia lata	Superior gluteal

* See also Figures 129 to 141.
† Sometimes spelled faciae latae.

TABLE 22. Muscles Moving the Knee Joint.[*]

MUSCLE	ORIGIN	INSERTION	FUNCTION	INNERVATION
Biceps femoris				
Long head	Tuberosity of ischium	Lateral side of head of the fibula and lateral condyle of tibia	Flexes leg; rotates laterally after flexed	Long head: tibial
Short head	Lateral lip of linea aspera of femur			Short head: peroneal
Semitendinosus	Tuberosity of ischium	Upper part of body of tibia	Flexes leg, extends thigh	Tibial
Semimembranosus	Tuberosity of ischium	Medial condyle of tibia	Flexes leg, extends thigh	Tibial
Popliteus	Lateral condyle of femur	Posterior surface of body of tibia	Flexes leg, rotates it medially	Tibial
Gracilis	Symphysis pubis and pubic arch	Medial surface of body of tibia	Adducts thigh, flexes leg	Obturator
Sartorius	Anterior superior spine of ilium	Medial border of tuberosity of tibia	Flexes thigh, rotates it laterally	Obturator
Quadriceps femoris (four heads)		Inserts into base of patella and condyles and tuberosity of tibia	Extends leg, flexes thigh	Femoral
Rectus femoris	Two tendons: one from anterior inferior iliac spine; other from groove above the acetabulum			
Vastus lateralis	Broad aponeurosis from greater trochanter and linea aspera of femur			
Vastus medialis	Medial lip of linea aspera; intertrochanteric line			
Vastus intermedius	Ventral and medial surfaces of body of femur			

[*] See also Figures 129 to 141.

166

TABLE 23. Muscles Moving the Foot.°

MUSCLE	ORIGIN	INSERTION	FUNCTION	INNERVATION
Gastrocnemius	Two heads from lateral and medial condyles of femur; adjacent part of capsule of knee	Tendo calcaneus	Plantar flexes foot (points toes); flexes leg; supinates foot	Tibial
Soleus	Posterior aspect head of fibula and medial border of tibia	Tendo calcaneus	Plantar flexes foot	Tibial
Tibialis posterior	Interosseus membrane between tibia and fibula	Three cuneiform; cuboid navicular bone; second, third, fourth, metatarsals	Plantar flexes foot	Tibial
Tibialis anterior	Lateral condyle and upper portion of lateral surface of body of tibia	Undersurface of medial cuneiform and base of first metatarsal	Dorsally flexes foot	Deep peroneal
Peroneus tertius	Lower third of medial surface of fibula	Dorsal surface of base of fifth metatarsal bone	Dorsally flexes foot	Deep peroneal
Peroneus longus	Head and lateral surface of body of fibula	Lateral side of first metatarsal and medial cuneiform bone	Everts; plantar flexes foot	Peroneal
Peroneus brevis	Lower two-thirds of lateral surface of body of fibula	Tuberosity at base of fifth metatarsal	Everts foot	Peroneal

° See also Figures 130 to 141.

167

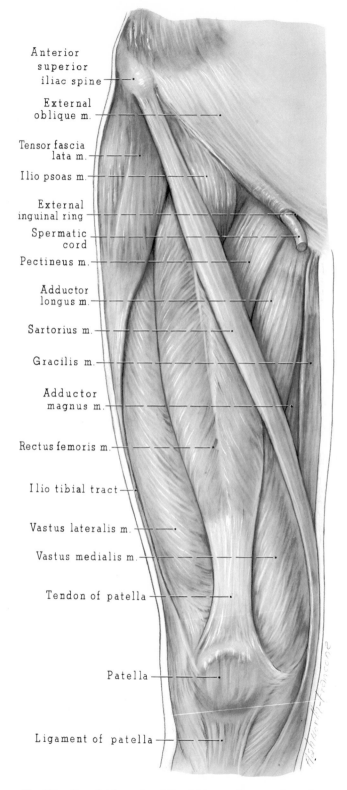

Anterior
superior
iliac spine

External
oblique m.

Tensor fascia
lata m.

Ilio psoas m.

External
inguinal ring

Spermatic
cord

Pectineus m.

Adductor
longus m.

Sartorius m.

Gracilis m.

Adductor
magnus m.

Rectus femoris m.

Ilio tibial tract

Vastus lateralis m.

Vastus medialis m.

Tendon of patella

Patella

Ligament of patella

Fig. 129. Superficial muscles of the right upper leg, anterior surface.

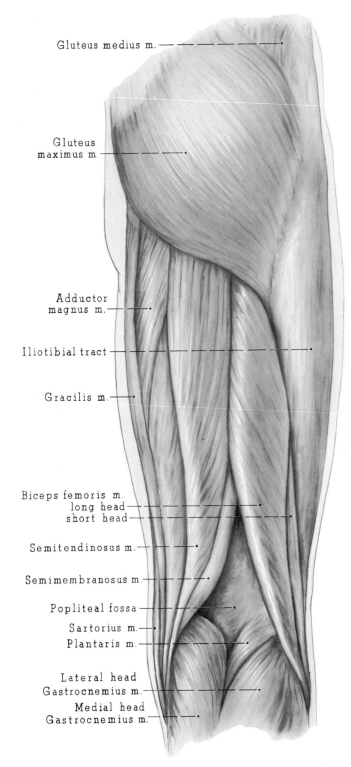

Gluteus medius m.

Gluteus maximus m.

Adductor magnus m.

Iliotibial tract

Gracilis m.

Biceps femoris m.
long head
short head

Semitendinosus m.

Semimembranosus m.

Popliteal fossa

Sartorius m.

Plantaris m.

Lateral head
Gastrocnemius m.

Medial head
Gastrocnemius m.

Fig. 130. Superficial muscles of the right upper leg, posterior surface.

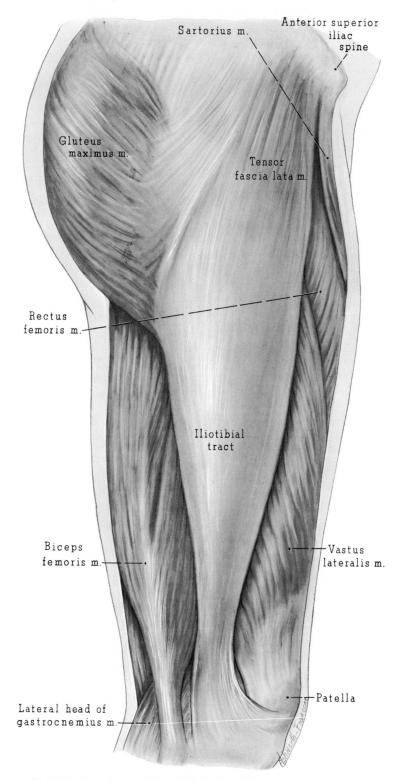

Fig. 131. Lateral view of superficial muscles of the right upper leg.

170

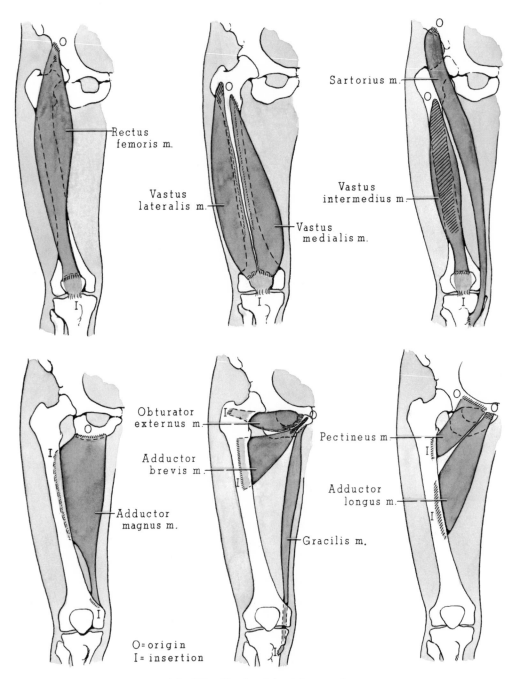

Rectus
femoris m.

Vastus
lateralis m.

Vastus
medialis m.

Sartorius m.

Vastus
intermedius m.

Obturator
externus m.

Adductor
brevis m.

Adductor
magnus m.

Pectineus m.

Adductor
longus m.

Gracilis m.

O= origin
I= insertion

Fig. 132. Muscles of the right upper leg.

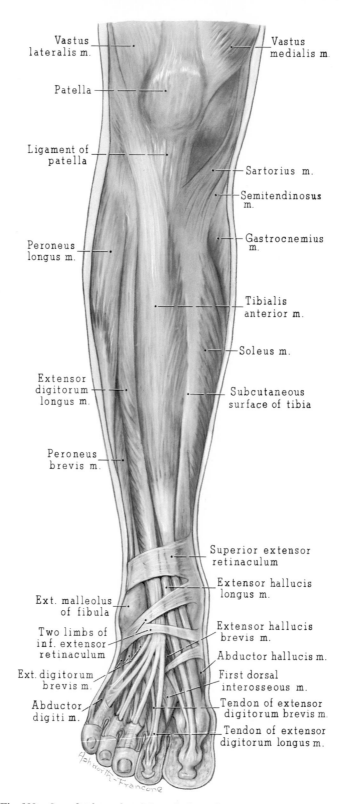

Vastus
lateralis m.

Vastus
medialis m.

Patella

Ligament of
patella

Sartorius m.

Semitendinosus
m.

Gastrocnemius
m.

Peroneus
longus m.

Tibialis
anterior m.

Soleus m.

Extensor
digitorum
longus m.

Subcutaneous
surface of tibia

Peroneus
brevis m.

Superior extensor
retinaculum

Extensor hallucis
longus m.

Ext. malleolus
of fibula

Two limbs of
inf. extensor
retinaculum

Extensor hallucis
brevis m.

Abductor hallucis m.

First dorsal
interosseous m.

Ext. digitorum
brevis m.

Abductor
digiti m.

Tendon of extensor
digitorum brevis m.

Tendon of extensor
digitorum longus m.

Fig. 133. Superficial muscles of the right lower leg and foot, anterior surface.

172

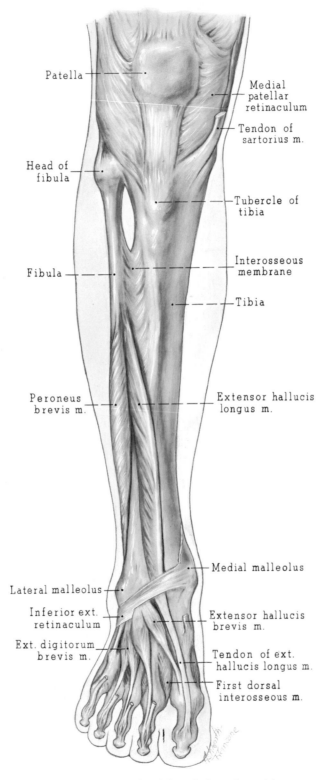

Patella

Medial patellar retinaculum

Tendon of sartorius m.

Head of fibula

Tubercle of tibia

Interosseous membrane

Fibula

Tibia

Peroneus brevis m.

Extensor hallucis longus m.

Medial malleolus

Lateral malleolus

Inferior ext. retinaculum

Extensor hallucis brevis m.

Ext. digitorum brevis m.

Tendon of ext. hallucis longus m.

First dorsal interosseous m.

Fig. 134. Deep muscles of the right lower leg and foot.

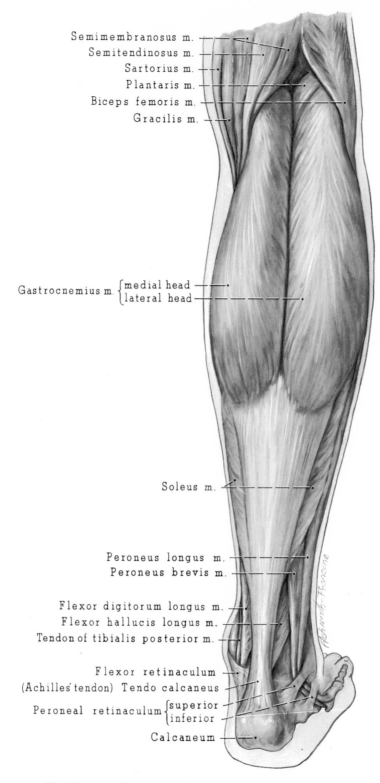

Semimembranosus m.
Semitendinosus m.
Sartorius m.
Plantaris m.
Biceps femoris m.
Gracilis m.

Gastrocnemius m. {medial head
                  {lateral head

Soleus m.

Peroneus longus m.
Peroneus brevis m.

Flexor digitorum longus m.
Flexor hallucis longus m.
Tendon of tibialis posterior m.

Flexor retinaculum
(Achilles' tendon) Tendo calcaneus
Peroneal retinaculum {superior
                     {inferior
Calcaneum

Fig. 135. Superficial muscles of the right lower leg, posterior view.

174

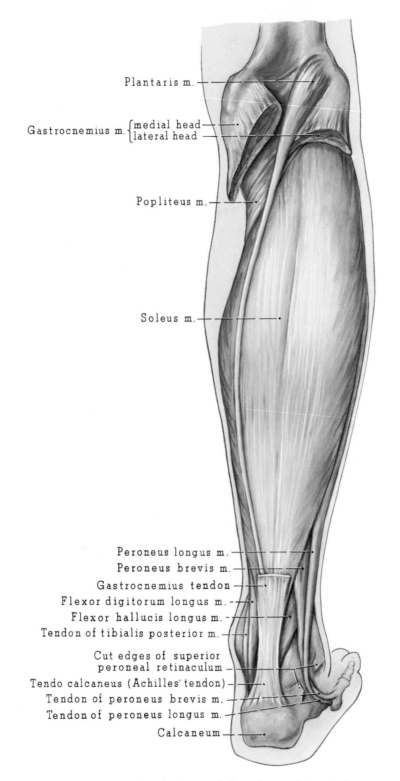

Plantaris m.

Gastrocnemius m. {medial head
lateral head

Popliteus m.

Soleus m.

Peroneus longus m.
Peroneus brevis m.
Gastrocnemius tendon
Flexor digitorum longus m.
Flexor hallucis longus m.
Tendon of tibialis posterior m.

Cut edges of superior
peroneal retinaculum
Tendo calcaneus (Achilles' tendon)
Tendon of peroneus brevis m.
Tendon of peroneus longus m.
Calcaneum

Fig. 136. Second layer of muscles of the right lower leg and foot, posterior view.

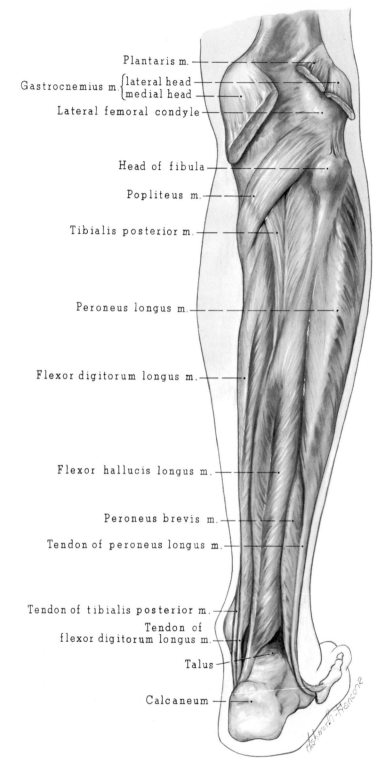

Plantaris m.

Gastrocnemius m. {lateral head
                  {medial head

Lateral femoral condyle

Head of fibula

Popliteus m.

Tibialis posterior m.

Peroneus longus m.

Flexor digitorum longus m.

Flexor hallucis longus m.

Peroneus brevis m.

Tendon of peroneus longus m.

Tendon of tibialis posterior m.

Tendon of
flexor digitorum longus m.

Talus

Calcaneum

Fig. 137. Deep muscles of the right lower leg and foot, posterior view.

176

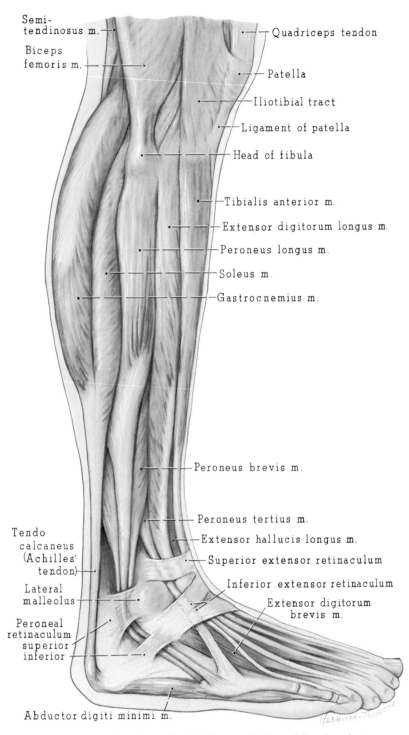

Semi-
tendinosus m.

Biceps
femoris m.

Quadriceps tendon

Patella

Iliotibial tract

Ligament of patella

Head of fibula

Tibialis anterior m.

Extensor digitorum longus m.

Peroneus longus m.

Soleus m.

Gastrocnemius m.

Peroneus brevis m.

Peroneus tertius m.

Extensor hallucis longus m.

Superior extensor retinaculum

Tendo
calcaneus
(Achilles'
tendon)

Inferior extensor retinaculum

Extensor digitorum
brevis m.

Lateral
malleolus

Peroneal
retinaculum
superior
inferior

Abductor digiti minimi m.

Fig. 138. Superficial muscles of the lower right leg and foot, lateral view.

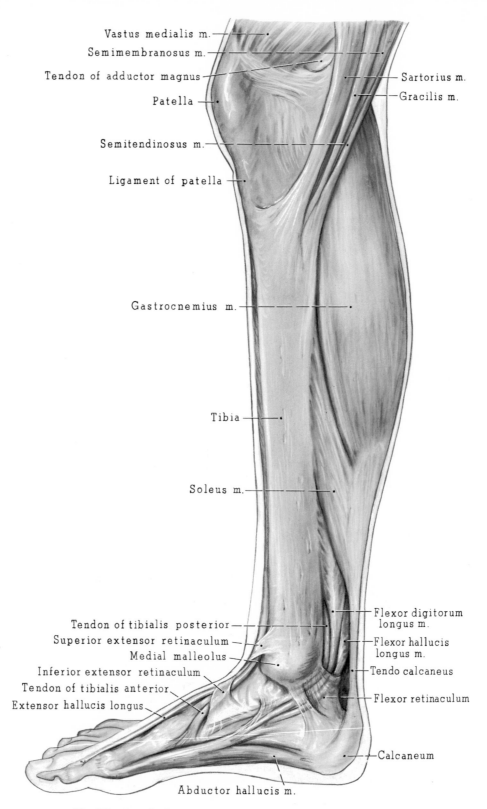

Vastus medialis m.

Semimembranosus m.

Tendon of adductor magnus

Patella

Semitendinosus m.

Ligament of patella

Sartorius m.

Gracilis m.

Gastrocnemius m.

Tibia

Soleus m.

Tendon of tibialis posterior

Superior extensor retinaculum

Medial malleolus

Inferior extensor retinaculum

Tendon of tibialis anterior

Extensor hallucis longus

Flexor digitorum longus m.

Flexor hallucis longus m.

Tendo calcaneus

Flexor retinaculum

Calcaneum

Abductor hallucis m.

Fig. 139. Superficial muscles of the lower right leg and foot, medial view.

178

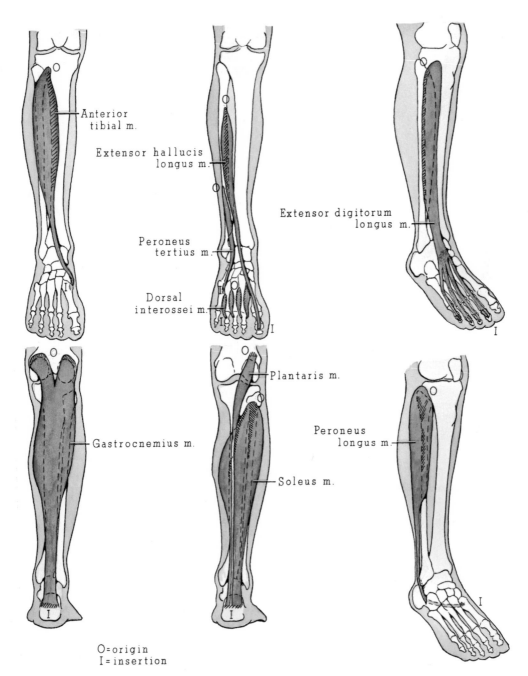

Anterior
tibial m.

Extensor hallucis
longus m.

Peroneus
tertius m.

Dorsal
interossei m.

Extensor digitorum
longus m.

Plantaris m.

Gastrocnemius m.

Peroneus
longus m.

Soleus m.

O = origin
I = insertion

Fig. 140. Origin and insertion of muscles of the foot and lower leg.

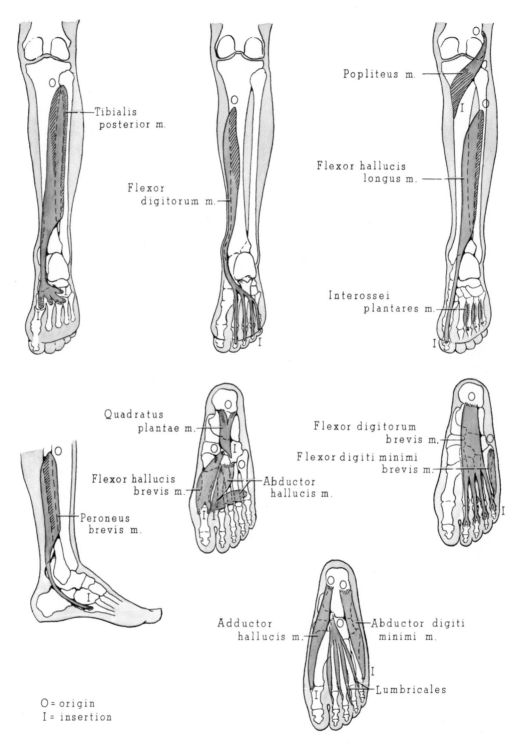

Tibialis
posterior m.

Flexor
digitorum m.

Populiteus m.

Flexor hallucis
longus m.

Interossei
plantares m.

Quadratus
plantae m.

Flexor hallucis
brevis m.

Peroneus
brevis m.

Abductor
hallucis m.

Flexor digitorum
brevis m.

Flexor digiti minimi
brevis m.

Adductor
hallucis m.

Abductor digiti
minimi m.

Lumbricales

O = origin
I = insertion

Fig. 141. Origin and insertion of muscles of the foot and lower leg.

Continued from page 125.

SUMMARY: THE MUSCULAR SYSTEM

GENERAL

1. The key words of the muscular system are *movement* and *contraction.*

2. Muscle can be differentiated into three types: striated, smooth, and cardiac.

TYPES OF MUSCLE

1. **Striated muscle:**
   a. The voluntary musculature of the skeletal system is striated muscle.
      (1) The sarcolemma surrounds each multinucleated cell.
      (2) The endomysium surrounds the sarcolemma.
      (3) Fasciculi are groups of muscle bundles ensheathed by the perimysium.
      (4) The entire muscle is invested by a coarse layer of connective tissue called the epimysium.
      (5) The striated appearance results from alternating light and dark bands of protein fibrils.
      (6) The proteins actin and myosin make up the I-band and the A-band respectively.
   b. Physiology of contraction:
      (1) The motor unit is the important entity in contraction.
      (2) A group of muscle fibers all innervated by the terminal branches of a motor axon constitutes a motor unit.
      (3) The all-or-none principle states that the entire motor unit responds to a single stimulus in the same manner each time it is stimulated. The strength of contraction is dependent on the rate of stimulation and the number of motor units stimulated.
      (4) Two types of contraction are defined. Isometric—the muscle remains at constant length and the tension is increased; isotonic—the muscle length changes with constant tension.
      (5) Prolonged contraction with *increase* in strength is called a tetanic contraction.
      (6) Muscles are kept in a state of readiness by a continuous flow of stimuli. This is called muscle tone.
   c. Mechanism of contraction:
      (1) The three factors considered are the neuro-electrical interactions, the chemical interactions, and the energy sources.
      (2) The resting potential of a muscle is 90 millivolts.
      (3) Acetylcholine is released at the nerve ending and causes the contraction.
      (4) Contraction occurs when the actin and myosin fibrils intermesh.
      (5) One of the more recent theories holds that calcium ions trigger this reaction.
      (6) Although questioned, ATP probably provides the energy for contraction. It is resynthesized by anaerobic glycolysis, the Kreb cycle, and the phosphocreatine metabolism.
   d. Relaxing system:
      (1) The muscle relaxes by means of a relaxing factor present in the muscle cell.
   e. Oxygen debt:
      (1) If, during exercise, oxygen cannot be delivered to the muscle tissues in great enough concentration to metabolize the accumulating lactic acid, the muscle has developed what is called "oxygen debt."

(2) The oxygen debt is relieved by increased oxygen consumption after exercise.

2. Smooth muscle:

a. Smooth muscle (involuntary) is found in the digestive system, urinary system, eye, blood vessels, and many other locations.
b. It is often arranged in longitudinal and circular layers.
c. The mechanisms of contraction are dependent on actin and myosin. The regular arrangement as found in skeletal muscle is not present.

3. Cardiac muscle:

a. Cardiac muscle is found only in the heart and has a combination of characteristics of both smooth and striated muscle. It is cross and longitudinally striated but is involuntary.
b. The fibers intertwine, permitting an en masse contraction of the entire muscle.
c. The important characteristic of heart muscle is the ability to contract and relax in rapid intervals.

4. Disorders of muscle:

a. Contracture is a disorder in which the muscle shortens its resting length.
b. Myalgia refers to muscular pain.
c. Myositis is inflammation of muscle.
d. Fibrositis is an inflammation of connective tissues within the muscle.
e. Muscular dystrophy and myasthenia gravis are two disorders which cripple muscle cells. The cause and cure of both are unknown.
f. Atrophy is a progressive degeneration of the muscle tissues.

5. Intramuscular injection:

a. The proper site for intramuscular injection is one which avoids major nerves and blood vessels.
b. The three areas best suited for intramuscular injection are the upper outer quadrant of the gluteal area; the vastus lateralis; and the deltoid muscle, at least 2 cm. below the acromion.

INTRODUCTION TO ANATOMY OF SKELETAL MUSCLE

1. **Muscles are named according to action, shape, origin and insertion, number of divisions, location, or direction of fibers.**

2. **Actions of muscles:**

a. Flexors decrease angle between joints.
b. Extensors increase angle between joints.
c. Abductors move limb away from midline.
d. Adductors move limb toward midline.
e. Rotators move limb around axis.
f. Dorsiflexors turn foot upward.
g. Plantar flexors point toes.
h. Supinators turn palm of hand upward.
i. Pronators turn palm downward.
j. Levators raise part of body.
k. Depressors lower part of body.

3. **Shapes of muscle: fusiform, quadrilateral, triangular, strap-like, or pennate.**

4. **The origin is the proximal attachment of the muscle to the skeleton. The insertion is the distal attachment of the muscle.**

5. Attachment of muscle to bone is usually indirect by means of tendons, consisting of strong inelastic fibrous tissue.

6. Muscles act only on the joint between the origin and insertion.

7. Prime movers execute any action, while antagonists must relax for the action to occur.

8. Synergists assist the prime movers and act to reduce excess and unnecessary motion.

STUDY QUESTIONS: THE MUSCULAR SYSTEM

1. Describe the characteristics of each of the three different types of muscular tissue.
2. Define a motor unit.
3. Outline the neuro-electrical, chemical, and energy factors in the contraction of skeletal muscle.
4. Describe five common disorders of skeletal muscle.
5. Discuss the anatomic basis for naming muscles.
6. Review the muscles in Tables 7 to 23 as to origin, insertion, function, and innervation.
7. Discuss the rationale and technique for giving intramuscular injections as described in the text.

INTEGRATION
AND METABOLISM

CHAPTER EIGHT.

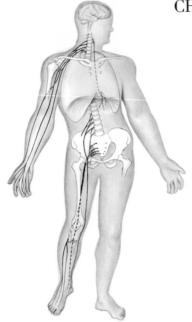

THE NERVOUS SYSTEM

Throughout history the complexities of the human body have stimulated the imagination of its possessor. Each mystery solved merely reveals multiple avenues of complex organizational patterns intimately involved in the function of the living, thinking human being. Perhaps even more fascinating than molecular biology itself is the knowledge of man's ability to comprehend, learn, and act as an individual organism—not only to grasp the wonder of the world, but to question and study it. Man's awareness of his environment is made possible by the integrated functioning of the nervous system, a group of tissues composed of highly specialized cells possessing the characteristics of excitability and conductivity. The nervous system, in association with the endocrine system, creates not only an awareness of the environment, but makes it possible for the human body to respond to environmental changes with the necessary precision.

DEVELOPMENT OF THE NERVOUS SYSTEM (Fig. 142)

At an early stage, the embryonic central nervous system is a hollow tube. This *neural tube* develops by a longitudinal process of elevation and fusion from a flat sheet of ectodermal cells, the *neural plate*. Even before the neural tube closes at its cephalad end, three primary brain vesicles can be recognized—the *forebrain*

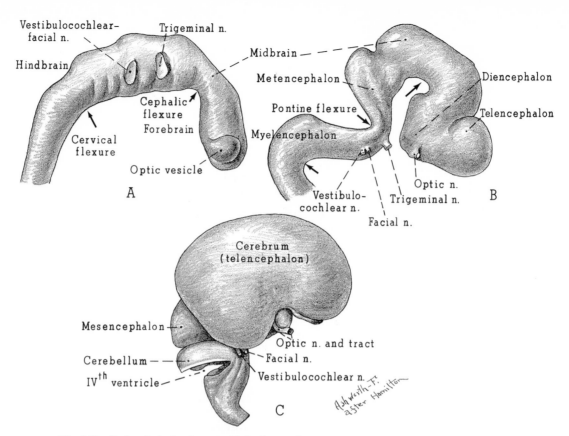

Fig. 142. Embryologic development of the brain. Three primary brain vesicles can be recognized: the forebrain (prosencephalon), the midbrain (mesencephalon), and the hindbrain (rhombencephalon). *A* and *B* show development at about 3 weeks and 6 weeks respectively. Ultimately the forebrain subdivides into the telencephalon and the diencephalon, the midbrain remains the mesencephalon, and the rhombencephalon becomes the metencephalon and myelencephalon. *C* shows the brain at approximately 11 weeks of development.

(*prosencephalon*), the *midbrain* (*mesencephalon*), and the *hindbrain* (*rhombencephalon*). Cellular migration and unequal growth rates result in flexures, thickenings, invaginations, and evaginations in the primary brain vesicles. Three to 4 weeks following fertilization of the ovum, a bend called the cephalic flexure appears in the portion of the neural tube destined to become the midbrain. The cavity of this part of the tube remains narrow and persists as the cerebral aqueduct of Sylvius, draining cerebrospinal fluid from the third to the fourth ventricle. Shortly after the cephalic flexure appears, the cervical flexure forms at the eventual junction of the medulla and the spinal cord.

The portion of the neural tube between the two flexures forms the hindbrain, from which develop the *pons, medulla,* and *cerebellum.* The cavity of the hindbrain becomes the fourth ventricle. Simultaneously, the *optic vesicle,* an evagination of the forebrain, is converted into the optic cup; this is destined to become the retina of the eye. Within a few days, the third or pontine flexure appears in the hindbrain in a dorsal position, subdividing the hindbrain

(rhombencephalon) into the *myelencephalon* and *metencephalon.* From the forebrain (prosencephalon), evaginating cerebral vesicles now constitute the *telencephalon,* while medially the remainder of the forebrain is the *diencephalon* and its cavity, the third ventricle. The midbrain has not undergone any subdivisions and is still referred to as the *mesencephalon.*

While the neural tube is closing, a differentiation of cells occurs along each lateral edge. These cells later send axon processes into the spinal cord and send dendrites peripherally to form the dorsal or sensory root ganglia of the spinal cord.

The newborn infant has few, if any, neurologic attributes. The autonomic centers of the newborn function incompletely. He is dependent on protection to maintain body temperature. His movements are futile and useless in terms of protecting himself. He responds to loud noises with a startle; the sense of cutaneous pain is poorly developed. As the years pass, the central nervous system continues to develop and the most highly integrated functions are added. In brain deterioration of advanced age, futile, use-

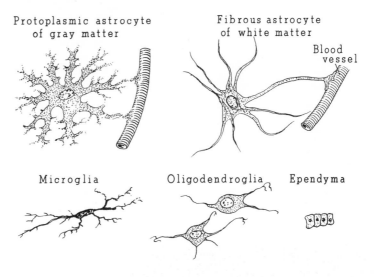

Protoplasmic astrocyte
of gray matter

Fibrous astrocyte
of white matter

Blood
vessel

Fig. 143. Neuroglial cells of central nervous system.

Microglia

Oligodendroglia

Ependyma

less movements recur similar to those noted in the newborn.

TYPES OF NERVE CELLS

The nervous system is composed of a special tissue containing two major types of cells: *neuroglia* (glial cells), the supporting elements; and *neurons* (nerve cells), the active conducting elements.

Neuroglia

The non-nervous elements consist of blood vessels, connective tissue, and supporting cells known collectively as neuroglia (from *glia*, meaning glue). Glial cells differ in size and shape and are recognized in four general categories (Fig. 143).

1. *Astrocytes* (from the Greek *astron*, meaning star)—so named because their processes are star-like in shape.

2. *Oligodendroglia*—cells with fewer and shorter processes.

3. *Microglia*—cells with a few processes.

4. *Ependyma*—a specialized type of neuroglial tissue lining the ventricles of the brain and the central canal of the spinal cord.

The glial cells function in supportive, reparative, and metabolic capacities. Most primary tumors of the brain and spinal cord, called "gliomas," affect these cell types.

Neurons

STRUCTURE.   The basic unit of the nervous system is the neuron, or nerve cell, which conducts an electrical impulse from one part of the body to another (page 195). The neuron itself consists of a cell body and various processes. The *cell body* consists of a mass of granular cytoplasm, the perikaryon, in which the mitochondria, Nissl substance, neurofibrils, Golgi apparatus, and centrally placed nucleus are located.

Neurons have two types of processes: *axons* and *dendrites*. An axon is a single, elongate cytoplasmic extension carrying nerve impulses *away* from the cell body. The dendrites are processes that carry impulses *toward* the cell body. The word dendrite means "tree-like," and denotes the manner in which the processes appear in motor neurons, as numerous short branches thickened at their point of origin. Sensory neurons have a single long dendrite, histologically similar to the axon with which it is fused near the cell body.

The axon substance, or axoplasm, is jelly-like. The axon itself has a smooth outline diminishing gradually in caliber as it gives off more minute branches known as *collaterals*. There is only one axon per neuron. In the spinal cord, many of the terminal axonal branches have swollen little button-like structures (boutons) in contact with cell bodies and dendrites of other neurons.

Microscopic structure of the axon. Axons consist of four parts: a central core, or *axis cylinder; a myelin sheath* (not always present); a *neurilemma;* and *Schwann cells* (Fig. 144). The myelin encompasses the entire axon, except at its termination and at periodic constrictions called *nodes of Ranvier.* Most peripheral nerves are surrounded by a myelin sheath. The *neuri-*

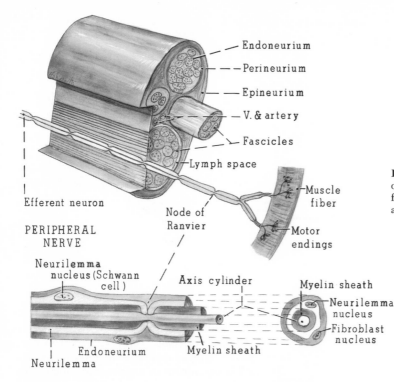

Endoneurium
Perineurium
Epineurium
V. & artery
Fascicles
Lymph space
Muscle fiber
Motor endings

Efferent neuron

PERIPHERAL NERVE

Node of Ranvier

Neurilemma nucleus (Schwann cell)

Axis cylinder

Myelin sheath

Neurilemma nucleus

Fibroblast nucleus

Endoneurium

Myelin sheath

Neurilemma

Fig. 144. Diagram showing components of a peripheral nerve and neuron. (Modified from J. Z. Young.) The myelin sheath actually winds in a spiral around the nerve fiber.

lemma is a thin membrane completely enveloping the nerve fiber and forming the outer covering. Schwann cells lie within the neurilemma. All fibers in peripheral nerves possess a neurilemma and Schwann cells, but fibers in the brain and spinal cord have neither. In the brain and spinal cord, oligodendrocytes take the place of the Schwann cells.

The *Nissl,* or *chromidial, substance* is a nucleoprotein usually found scattered through the perikaryon and dendritic cytoplasm. It has a high iron content which serves as a catalyst for oxidation reactions and which is believed to assist in the transmission of the nerve impulse. Nissl substance also assumes a role in the reaction to injury of nerve cells. When the axon is severed, the Nissl substance is reduced, first in the dendrites, then in the cytoplasm near the nucleus, and eventually in the periphery of the cell. It becomes diffuse and finally disappears. This reaction is called *chromatolysis.*

Neurofibrils appear to run through the nerve cell from the dendrites around the nucleus and into the axon. The function of the neurofibril is unknown.

The term *nerve fiber* includes an axon and its sheath. The myelinated nerve fiber is an axon with a myelin sheath. A non-myelinated fiber lacks a myelin sheath. Nerve fibers in the gray matter of the central nervous system are mainly non-myelinated. The white matter contains large numbers of myelinated fibers. Larger fibers with myelin sheaths conduct impulses faster than smaller ones lacking the myelin covering.

When a nerve fiber is crushed, the part of the fiber connected to the cell body continues to transmit impulses, but the part distal to the injury gradually disintegrates. If the nerve is protected by a neurilemmal sheath, parts of the damaged portion can regenerate. Damaged fibers of the optic and auditory nerves as well as fibers within the central nervous system cannot repair themselves by this method since they lack a protective sheath.

CLASSIFICATION

Neuron types according to structure. Neurons, structurally, fall into three groups: *unipolar, bipolar,* and *multipolar.* This classification depends on the number of processes extending from the cell body. A unipolar neuron has only one process, an axon; such neurons are rare except in the embryo. Bipolar neurons have only one dendrite and one axon and are found in the retina of the eye. Multipolar neurons have many dendrites but only one axon. The majority of neurons in the brain and spinal cord are multipolar.

Neuron types according to function. There are three types of neurons entering into the formation of nerve pathways. *Sensory* (afferent) neurons convey impulses from the skin or other sense organs to the spinal cord and brain. *Motor* (efferent) neurons carry impulses away from the brain and spinal cord to muscles and glands. Pyramidal cells, so named because the cell body is pyramidal, make up a high percentage of cortical motor neurons. *Internuncial* (intercalated) neurons conduct impulses from afferent to efferent neurons, forming links in the neural pathways and lying entirely within the central nervous system.

Physiology of Neurons

Neurons function to conduct signals from one part of the body to another by both electrical and chemical phenomena. When an impulse travels along an axon from one node of Ranvier to another, the characteristic transmission is *electrical.* When the impulse is transmitted from one neuron to another across a synapse, the characteristic transmission is typically *chemical.*

The capacity for selective permeability to ions is a function of the cell membrane (see Chapter Two). It is this property of the nerve cell which is involved in the transmission of the nerve impulse. Active transport of sodium from the axoplasm to the interstitial fluid, a process involving the "sodium pump," is the most important selective capacity of the nerve cell membrane.

This creates a membrane potential in the following manner. Sodium concentration in the axoplasm is maintained at a level of 1 milliequivalent, while the concentration of sodium in the interstitial fluid is approximately 142 milliequivalents. The difference creates a large deficit of positive sodium ions inside the membrane. On the other hand, potassium ions (K^+), free to diffuse through the cell membrane, would normally equilibrate across the membrane and reach equal concentrations on both sides of the membrane. However, the negative organic ions, which cannot diffuse through the membrane, have an attraction for available positive charges.

The sodium pump keeps sodium ions from entering the cell to help "neutralize" the negative charges, so instead the potassium ions are electrostatically compelled to concentrate within the cell. These ions only partially compensate for the deficit of positive charge. The net electronegative potential created within the fiber as a result of the action of the sodium pump is called the *membrane potential.* In the normal resting state of a nerve fiber, the charge is positive outside and negative inside the membrane.

A stimulus to a nerve cell is associated with an increased permeability to sodium ions. Due to the concentration gradient previously established by the sodium pump, the sodium ions then diffuse freely into the axoplasm and produce an abundance of positive ions. This results in a positive charge within the membrane and a relatively negative charge outside the membrane. The reversal of potential is called *depolarization.* Passage of the electrical current increases the permeability of the adjacent area of the membrane, and sodium ions pass through, thus propagating the current in both directions—up and down the length of the fiber. Conduction from one neuron to another, however, occurs in only one direction, because of the peculiar properties at the nerve synapse. The spread of increased permeability and electrical current along the membrane is called the wave of depolarization, or *nerve impulse* (Fig. 145).

The flow of sodium into the fiber continues until the inside of the fiber has been charged to a high positive level. This state of events causes the membrane to become impermeable to sodium again. Potassium next diffuses slowly back through the membrane, with the reestablishment of electronegativity inside and the positive state outside. This process is called repolarization. Repolarization begins at the point at which depolarization began.

The entire cycle involves only a fraction of a second and the fiber is then ready to transmit new impulses; however, the fiber must become repolarized before any new impulses can be

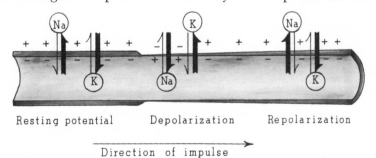

Fig. 145. Conduction of nerve impulse.

Resting potential   Depolarization   Repolarization

Direction of impulse

transmitted. The period of time elapsing between depolarization and repolarization is known as the *refractory period,* divisible into two parts—an absolute refractory period and a relative one. During the absolute refractory period, no response by the nerve occurs, irrespective of the strength of the stimulus. During the relative refractory period, it is possible to set up a response, but the stimulus required is greater than that required by the resting nerve. The duration of the refractory period varies for fibers of different size and structure. The fiber is said to be in a refractory state when subsequent stimuli no longer influence it. After repolarization, the sodium ions that have leaked into the neuron are pumped out again by the sodium pump, and the potassium ions move inside the cell to make up the charge deficit.

All-or-none principle. If the stimulus is strong enough to elicit a response by depolarization of the fiber, an impulse occurs. The strength of the impulse itself does not vary in any single nerve fiber. Once the impulse has been initiated by such a stimulus, it rises to a constant and maximum magnitude, independent of any further increase or intensity of the stimulus. Thus, the term *all-or-none* phenomenon.

Transmission of the impulse at the synapse. A nerve fiber terminates in a knob-like body, closely associated with the dendrite or body of another cell and forming a *synapse.* Whereas nerve impulse conduction is an electrical process, transmission at the synapse is a chemical process. An excitatory hormone stimulating the second cell is produced at the synapse. This substance is probably *acetylcholine,* which then acts on the cell membrane to increase its permeability to sodium ions. Subsequently, a leakage of sodium ions into the cell causes electric currents which flow along the surface in a wave of depolarization. In approximately 1/500 second the destruction of acetylcholine by the enzyme cholinesterase permits re-establishment of membrane potential.

When a nerve fiber is stimulated at any point, the nerve impulse generated travels in both directions—that is, up and down the length of the fiber. Only the axon termination, and not the dendrite, liberates acetylcholine at the synapse; thus, the synapse is a "one-way street," with impulse transmission occurring in only one direction—from axon to dendrite.

Neuromuscular junction. Acetylcholine is liberated at the junction of nerve and muscle fibers. This increases the sodium ion permeability of the sarcolemma and causes an electrical impulse to travel along the muscle fiber in both directions at approximately 3 meters per second. The action potential produced brings about an interaction of actin and myosin resulting in contraction of the muscle fiber (see Chapter Seven). In a disease known as myasthenia gravis, intermittent weakness of skeletal muscles occurs, because of inhibition of normal transmission at the myoneural junction. Myasthenia gravis is relieved by drugs which inhibit the action of the enzyme cholinesterase.

Rate of impulse conduction. The larger the nerve fiber and the thicker the myelin sheath, the more rapid the rate of conduction in the nerve. The largest nerve fibers are 20 microns in diameter, and these conduct at a rate of 100 meters per second. The smallest fibers are 0.5 micron in diameter, conducting at a rate of approximately 0.5 meter per second.

Reflex Arc

The basic unit of integrated neural activity is the reflex arc, consisting of five components: a sensory receptor, a sensory neuron, one or more internuncial neurons, a motor neuron, and an effector. Examples of spinal reflexes are stretch and flexor reflexes. The knee jerk is a stretch reflex demonstrated by light tapping of the tendon of the quadriceps femoris muscle. The leg extends. In this maneuver, the tendon is stretched, and impulses travel over dendrites in the femoral nerve to cell bodies in the dorsal root ganglion. They next travel over axons to synapses in the ventral horn of the gray matter. The stretch reflex involves a two-neuron circuit, so impulses travel to the dendrites of motor cell bodies in the ventral horn and then to the axons and muscle fibers of the quadriceps femoris, resulting in contraction (Figs. 146 and 147).

Three of the many types of reflexes evaluated clinically are *superficial, deep,* and *pathological* reflexes. Superficial reflexes are produced by cutaneous stimulation. An example is the abdominal reflex, in which cutaneous stimulation of a quadrant of the abdomen results in contraction of the muscles of the quadrant. Deep reflexes involve a stimulation of muscle tendons such as the patellar, achilles, biceps, or triceps. The best-known example, as we have seen, is the knee jerk or patellar reflex, an extension of the lower leg in response to tapping of the patellar tendon. If the skin of the sole of the foot is stimulated, the toes and feet may be withdrawn. If, upon plantar stimulation, dorsiflexion of the great toe and fanning of the remaining toes occur, a pathologic reflex called the *Babinski phenomenon* is present. Exaggerated deep reflexes are usually accompanied by diminished or absent superficial reflexes, or by pathologic reflexes such as the Babinski.

The normal activity of the reflex requires integration of both limbs of the arc, as well as integrity of the synaptic center. Destruction of either limb of the arc abolishes the reflex response, as does damage to the reflex center itself. An injury passing through a given cord segment abolishes the reflex having its center at that level. Below this injury the deep reflexes are increased, since the inhibitor influences from the higher centers have been removed. Above the level of injury, the deep reflexes are unchanged.

THE CENTRAL NERVOUS SYSTEM
(Fig. 148)

The *central nervous system* includes the brain and spinal cord. The *peripheral nervous system* includes the cranial and spinal nerves. The *autonomic nervous system* controls the smooth muscles of the gastrointestinal tract and cardiovascular system, as well as glandular secretions. The autonomic nervous system has two divisions: sympathetic and parasympathetic. In this discussion, the cranial nerves will be considered with the brain, and the spinal nerves with the spinal cord.

The Brain

The first mention of the term *brain* is found in the Egyptian scrolls of papyrus. Historically, the Greeks did not have a word for the brain. Due to rhythmic movements which seemed closely related with what occurred in the mind, they placed its location in the midriff, since the rhythm of breathing is closely related to mental states.

The word brain actually refers to "that part of the central nervous system contained within the skull." It is the most complex and largest mass of nervous tissue in the body and contains literally billions of nerve cells. It has been estimated that an electron tube computer would have to be the size of a New York City skyscraper to contain the equipment in the 3 pounds or so of the human brain.

The weight of the brain is an indication of growth which, in early life, depends on enlargement of cells and their processes, an increase in the neuroglial constituents, and myelinization of

the nerve fibers. The average weight of the human brain in the adult is approximately 1380 grams in the male and 1250 grams in the female. The brain grows rapidly up to the fifth year of life and stops growing after the age of 20. During old age, the weight of the brain decreases. When fully developed, the brain is a large organ filling the cranial cavity and applied closely to the inner wall of the skull. The brain is subdivided into three major areas, and in turn, into further subdivisions (Fig. 149).

The central nervous system is divided grossly into gray and white matter. *Gray matter* is so called because of its appearance and the preponderance of nerve cell bodies and non-myelinated fibers. *White matter,* on the other hand, is composed chiefly of myelinated nerve fibers—white in gross appearance—and few if any nerve cells.

The term nucleus, when applied to the nervous system, designates a mass of gray matter (i.e., nerve cells) in any part of the brain or spinal cord. *Ganglion* also means a cluster of nerve cells, but usually refers to those cells located outside the brain and spinal cord.

Nerve fibers of the brain and spinal cord with a common origin and destination constitute a *tract.* Although a tract occupies a regular position, it does not always form a compact bundle, because of some intermingling with fibers of neighboring tracts. There are a number of bundles of fibers in the brain which are so distinct anatomically that they have been given the names *fasciculus, brachium, peduncle, column,* and *lemniscus.* These may contain only a single fiber or may comprise several fibers running together in the same bundle. *Nerve, nerve root, nerve cord,* and *ramus* are appropriate anatomic terms for bundles of nerve fibers outside the brain and spinal cord.

Tracts are either ascending or descending, depending on whether they carry impulses to or from the brain.

A *commissure* is a band of fibers joining corresponding opposite parts of the brain and spinal cord.

The forebrain is divided into two portions: the telencephalon and the diencephalon. The telencephalon or cerebrum consists primarily of the two central hemispheres. The diencephalon consists of the thalamus and hypothalamus.

CEREBRUM (Figs. 150 to 152). The cerebrum is the largest portion of the brain, representing approximately seven-eighths of its total weight. Nerve centers governing all sensory and motor activities, as well as poorly defined areas which determine reason, memory, and intelligence, are located in the cerebrum.

With the increase in brain size occurring during embryonic development, the area of cortical gray matter expands out of all proportion and volume to the white matter upon which it rests. As a result, the surface rolls and folds upon itself. Each bulge produced in this manner is called a *gyrus,* or convolution. These gyri do not haphazardly occur, but are present in a distinguishable pattern. If the intervening furrow is shallow, it is called a *sulcus;* if it is deep, it is referred to as a *fissure.* The *longitudinal fissure* extends from the posterior aspect to the anterior border of the cerebrum, almost completely dividing it into two hemispheres.

The cerebral hemispheres with their coverings constitute the true brain. These hemispheres are "mirror twins," each with a full set of centers for sensory and motor activities of the body, and each associated for the most part with one side of the body. When one area of the cerebrum is damaged, the corresponding area of the other hemisphere can often develop control over the functions governed by the damaged region, illustrating great adaptability.

The *corpus callosum* is composed of nerve fibers which interconnect areas of the opposite hemispheres (Figs. 153 and 154). Its size and position suggest that its function is crucial in the proper performance of the cerebrum. If the corpus callosum is divided in two, an organism with two mental units is created, each with its own will competing for control over the whole. The corpus callosum allows the two hemispheres to share learning and memory.

Each hemisphere possesses five sulci of significance. Each sulcus serves to locate its corresponding gyrus of known function (Figs. 155 and 156).

The *lateral sulcus* (fissure of Sylvius) sweeps backward above the temporal lobe and continues over the superolateral surface almost horizontally backward. The lateral sulcus is associated with centers for speech and hearing.

The *central sulcus* (fissure of Rolando) commences at the midpoint of the superior border and extends inferiorly toward the lateral sulcus, separating the frontal and parietal lobes. The central sulcus is associated with centers for both motor and sensory function.

The *sulcus cinguli* is a prominent sulcus on the medial surface of the hemisphere, extending anteroposteriorly parallel to the corpus callosum. The cortex surrounding this sulcus functions in both olfactory and emotional responses.

The *calcarine sulcus* begins as the deep sulcus on the inferomedial surface above and adjacent to the corpus callosum. At the medial surface it divides into two smaller sulci, a lower horizontal one (postcalcarine) and an upper one (parietooccipital). These sulci include the visual areas.

The *collateral sulcus* runs parallel to the medial border and is closely associated with the center of smell.

CEREBRAL CORTEX (Figs. 157 to 159). Even before knowledge of the microscopic anatomy of the cortex was available, feeble attempts were made to discern the function of the cerebral cortex. During the Renaissance, for instance, physicians speculated as to the nature of the "seat of intelligence." An understanding of brain physiology, however, was delayed until it became possible to stimulate and remove portions of the central nervous system in the living animal. In the 19th century, many studies on cerebral localization were undertaken, particularly in attempts to localize speech to a given region. It was Broca in 1861 who correlated injury to the left frontal convolution with a loss of speech in a right-handed person; that is, a right-handed person will usually have a dominant left hemisphere. Recent studies have shown that most people have a dominant left hemisphere, whether or not they are right handed.

Brodmann divided the human cortex into 52 areas and employed numbers to designate each. The Brodmann scheme will be utilized in subsequent discussions to describe association and projection areas of the brain. Actual division of the cerebrum into lobes is a convenience, since these areas serve as reference points for discussion. These lobes bear the name of the overlying bones of the skull.

LOBES OF THE CEREBRAL CORTEX

Frontal lobe. The frontal lobe includes all the cortex lying anterior to the central sulcus and above the lateral sulcus. The precentral gyrus, or motor area, is area 4 of Brodmann. Immediately anterior to this is area 6. In front of area 6 can be found area 8.

Parietal lobe. This lobe extends from the central sulcus about four-fifths of the way around the cortex and joins the occipital lobe at the posterior aspect of the brain. The parietal lobe includes sensory areas 1, 2, and 3 of Brodmann, which lie in the postcentral gyrus. Sensory projection fibers in the medial lemniscus and spinothalamic tract converge on this sensory receptive area. These are concerned with light touch, two-point discrimination, pressure, and pain. Sensory cortical representation is similar in its distribution to that of the motor cortex but is not quite so definite. The parietal cortex is the receptive area for fine sensory stimuli, and the highest integration and coordination of sensory

Text continued on page 200.

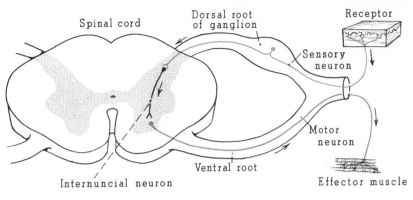

Fig. 146.   Simple reflex arc.

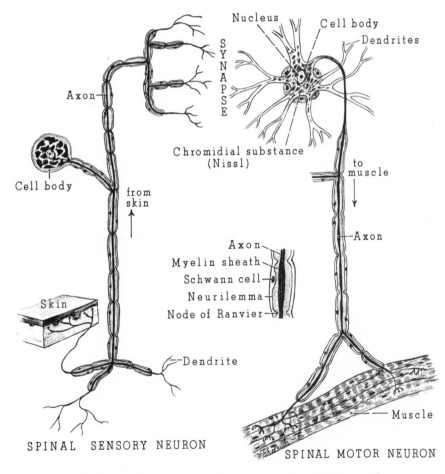

Fig. 147.   Motor and sensory neuron showing synapse in a two-neuron reflex arc.

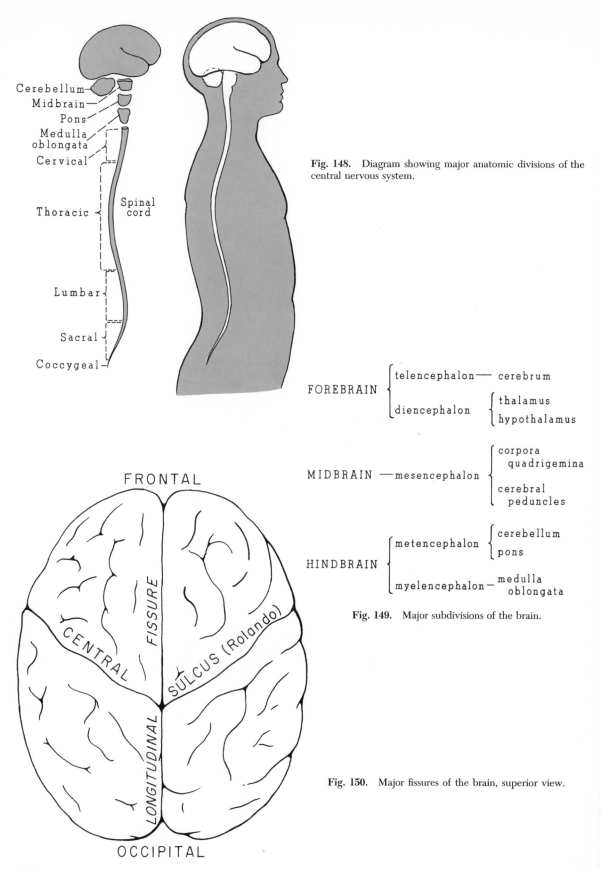

Cerebellum
Midbrain
Pons
Medulla
oblongata
Cervical

Thoracic

Spinal
cord

Lumbar

Sacral

Coccygeal

Fig. 148. Diagram showing major anatomic divisions of the central nervous system.

FOREBRAIN
{
telencephalon — cerebrum
diencephalon
{
thalamus
hypothalamus
}
}

MIDBRAIN — mesencephalon
{
corpora
quadrigemina
cerebral
peduncles
}

HINDBRAIN
{
metencephalon
{
cerebellum
pons
}
myelencephalon —
medulla
oblongata
}

Fig. 149. Major subdivisions of the brain.

FRONTAL

CENTRAL FISSURE

SULCUS (Rolando)

LONGITUDINAL

OCCIPITAL

Fig. 150. Major fissures of the brain, superior view.

196

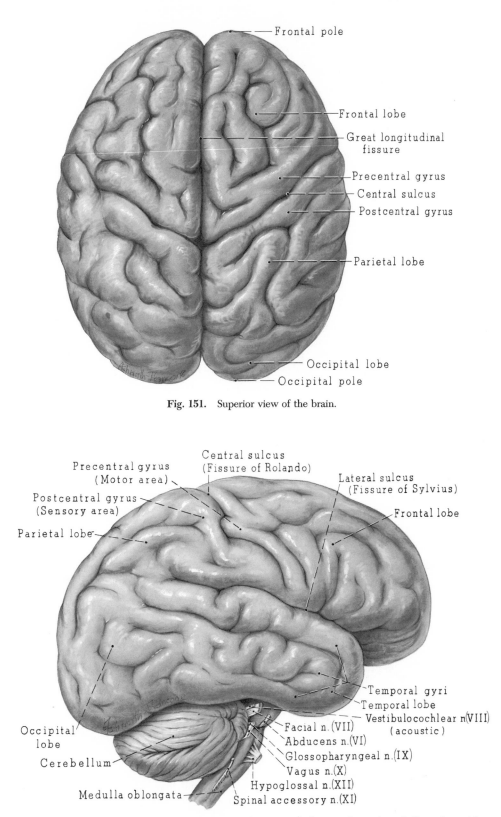

Frontal pole

Frontal lobe

Great longitudinal fissure

Precentral gyrus

Central sulcus

Postcentral gyrus

Parietal lobe

Occipital lobe

Occipital pole

Fig. 151. Superior view of the brain.

Precentral gyrus (Motor area)

Central sulcus (Fissure of Rolando)

Postcentral gyrus (Sensory area)

Lateral sulcus (Fissure of Sylvius)

Parietal lobe

Frontal lobe

Temporal gyri

Temporal lobe

Vestibulocochlear n(VIII) (acoustic)

Occipital lobe

Facial n. (VII)

Abducens n.(VI)

Glossopharyngeal n.(IX)

Cerebellum

Vagus n.(X)

Hypoglossal n.(XII)

Medulla oblongata

Spinal accessory n.(XI)

Fig. 152. Right side of the brain showing cerebrum, cerebellum, and spinal cord. Several cranial nerves are seen.

197

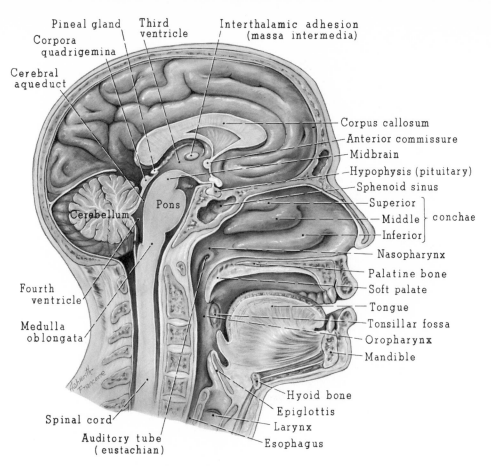

Fig. 153. Sagittal section through the head showing relationship of cerebellum, cerebrum, and spinal cord to other parts of the head and neck.

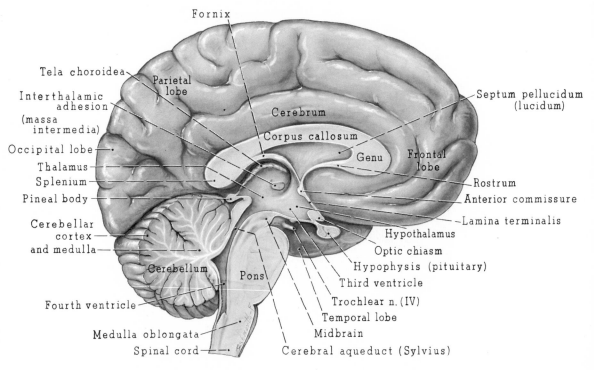

Fig. 154. Sagittal view of the left half of the brain and spinal cord.

198

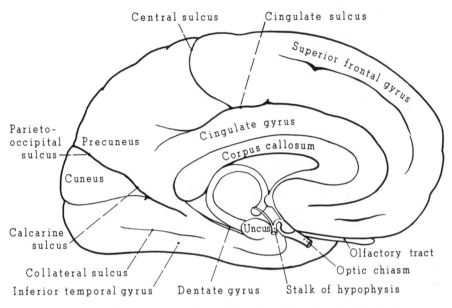

Fig. 155. Major landmarks of the medial portion of the left cerebral hemisphere.

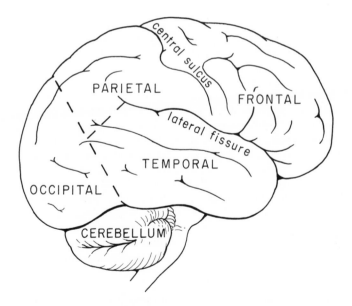

Fig. 156. Lobes of the cerebral cortex, lateral view, right side.

Continued from page 194.

information is carried on in this area. Damage to the parietal lobe can produce defects in the visual field and aphasia.

Temporal lobe. This lobe lies beneath the lateral sulcus. Area 41, the sensory receptive area for auditory impulses, and areas 41 and 42, the correlative centers for auditory impulses, are found in the temporal lobe. If one temporal lobe is injured or diseased, auditory disturbances do not occur, since auditory impulses from each side pass to both hemispheres.

Occipital lobe. The occipital lobe occupies the posterior segment of the cerebral hemisphere. Actually no true separation exists between the occipital lobe and the parietal and temporal lobes, although the parieto-occipital sulcus is considered the anterior margin. Area 17, the primary visual area, and areas 18 and 19, the correlation centers for visual impulses, are found in the occipital lobe.

PROJECTION AREAS. The meaning conveyed by a nerve message does not depend on its source alone. In addition to the receptor, the message must reach the appropriate synaptic endings in the brain. Portions of the cortex that have become specialized for dispatch of motor directives and for reception of sensory messages are known as *projection areas* (Fig. 159).

The centers for motor projection are located in the posterior portion of the frontal lobe or, more specifically, in the anterior wall of the central sulcus. The motor cortex controls all the voluntary musculature of the body. Groups of pyramidal cells in the cortex corresponding to motor controls of various parts of the body are referred to as *cerebral localization sites*. These motor areas are arranged in inverted order, commencing with the center for movement of the toes on the dorsal border of the hemisphere, and ending with the center for facial movements at the lower end of the gyrus. The area of the frontal lobe, the precentral motor cortex, is a major effector mechanism of the cerebral cortex. Stimulation of this area results in movement of skeletal muscle. In general, the amount of brain surface related to a specific part of the body is not proportionate to the size of the part, but to the extent of its use (Fig. 158).

Movements on the contralateral side of the body are represented in various regions of the cortex. The precentral or motor cortex is divided into Brodmann areas 4, 6, 8, and 44. Impulses from area 4 along the anterior lip of the central sulcus initiate voluntary movements for the opposite side of the body. Area 4 is desig-

nated as the cortical site from which pyramidal fibers originate; all other motor cortical areas in the animal are designated as extrapyramidal. Area 8 is not sharply differentiated from area 6, although it is found anterior to it. Stimulation of area 8 results in movement of the extrinsic muscles of the eye. The precentral motor cortex is a complex cortical region. Areas 4 and 6 receive afferent fibers from other regions of the cortex. Most of these afferent fibers arise from the sensory postcentral gyrus and the ventrolateral nucleus of the hypothalamus, the chief mechanism for controlling visceral (autonomic) functions of the body.

DYSFUNCTION OF THE CEREBRAL CORTEX

Frontal lobe. If the entire motor area is involved, hemiplegia or hemiparesis of the opposite side of the body results. Hemiplegia is a paralysis of one side of the body. Hemiparesis is a muscular weakness of one side. Involvement of area 6 of Brodmann results in spasticity of the opposite half of the body. If both areas 4 and 6 are injured, a greater degree of spasticity results than when area 6 only is disturbed. In addition to spastic paralysis, injury to the motor strip results in exaggerated tendon reflexes such as the knee jerk and ankle jerk. Abnormal reflexes including the Babinski also occur. The Babinski reflex is a dorsal flexion of the great toe on stimulation of the sole of the foot.

If the precentral gyrus is irritated, convulsive seizures of the jacksonian type occur. Jacksonian seizures are types of seizures beginning in a certain part of the body, extending from that part to remaining portions. When the attack is severe, there may be generalized convulsions accompanied by unconsciousness. Immediately after the seizure, the patient notes transitory weakness or actual paralysis of the affected part.

The prefrontal lobes lie anterior to the motor areas and are often spoken of as the "silent area" of the brain, since injury here does not produce paralysis. A patient with a prefrontal lobe tumor frequently exhibits a reversal of his personal habits. An individual who was neat becomes slovenly in dress. If the individual was meticulous as to his personal matters, he might become unconcerned with them. Patients with injuries or tumors of the frontal lobe fail to show interest when told of their physical condition and its possible implications. Due to this failure to exhibit interest, the operation of prefrontal lobotomy (severing the white matter in the frontal lobe) has been employed. In this procedure, a patient with pain secondary to cancer or some other disease is made less aware of this pain. The chief value of prefrontal lobotomy can be seen in patients who have only a short time to live. In these patients, the pain is widespread and control by other means is not practical. Lobotomy does not relieve pain in the usual sense, but the patient is relieved of many aspects of pain. A patient with a prefrontal lobotomy feels pain, but it no longer disturbs him. In exchange for relief from pain, however, he shows alterations in personality traits.

Hearing is a function of the temporal lobe; "word-seeing" is a function of the occipital lobe; and speech itself is a formulation of thought via the frontal lobe. Any deficiency in these three areas can result in *aphasia*. Motor aphasia, or loss of the ability to speak, is associated with injury to the inferior frontal gyrus of the dominant hemisphere (called Broca's area or Brodmann area 44). The lack of ability to comprehend the spoken or written word is *sensory* or *receptive aphasia*.

Injury to the posterior portion of the superior temporal gyrus produces an auditory receptive aphasia in which the patient has unimpaired hearing but still is unable to understand the significance of the spoken word. The parietal cortex (Brodmann area 39) of the dominant hemisphere is necessary for the higher interpretation of written symbols.

Temporal lobe. Disturbances resulting from involvement of the temporal lobe include auditory aphasia and "uncinate fits." Visual hallucinations may also occur. "Uncinate fits" are associated with bad odors and dreamy states. Temporal lobe tumors may involve the optic radiations, resulting in visual defects.

Occipital lobe. Injury or disease of the occipital lobe is associated with homonymous hemianopsia (blindness of the nasal half of one eye and the temporal half of the other). Visual hallucinations sometimes occur when the occipital lobes are damaged. These are characterized by flashes of light. Such hallucinations may be followed by generalized convulsive seizures. Area 17 of the cortex of the posterior portion of the calcarine sulcus is the primary visual center, whereas the adjoining areas, 18 and 19, are correlative centers for visual impulses.

SENSORY PROJECTION AREAS. The somatic sensory projection area (Brodmann areas 1, 2, and 3) face the motor region and stretch along the posterior slope of the central fissure to occupy the adjacent plateau of the parietal lobe. Sensations for touch from all parts of the body are received in this area. On the posterior aspect of the occipital lobe is a whitish stripe known as the striate cortex, or visual projection area (area 17 of Brodmann). The fibers of the optic radiations from lateral geniculate bodies terminate in this area, carrying impulses from the temporal side of the corresponding retina and the nasal side of the opposite retina. Consequently, the visual cortex of one cerebral hemisphere receives impressions from objects in the opposite field of vision. Ability to recognize and interpret visual stimuli is a function of areas 18 and 19 of the occipital cortex. These two areas act as a storehouse for visual memory.

The upper posterior aspect of the temporal lobe on the lower bank of the sylvian fissure is the auditory projection area. Areas 41 and 42 of Brodmann in the temporal lobe serve not only for the primary reception of sound, but also for its interpretation. The limbic lobe serves as the projection area for taste and smell.

ASSOCIATION AREAS. The brain must possess memory to relate information of the moment with that of the past and to recognize its significance. This involves functional correlation, repeated exchanges of data, and synthesis of data. Such elaborate functions of the cortex are performed by the association areas. More than three-fourths of the cerebral cortex is occupied by these areas. The portion of the frontal lobe anterior to the primary motor area is devoted to association patterns involved in writing and walking; for instance, in answering a question, the occipital lobe is the receptive area for visualizing words. The frontal lobe directs activities making possible the expression of an answer.

THE BASAL GANGLIA (Fig. 160). The basal ganglia are four paired masses of gray matter embedded in the white matter of the cerebral hemispheres. The basal ganglia belong to the extrapyramidal system and include the caudate nucleus, the lentiform nucleus (shaped like a biconvex lens, which, in turn, is composed of two parts, the putamen and the globus pallidus), the amygdaloid nuclei, and the claustrum. The caudate and lentiform nuclei, together with the white matter separating them, comprise the *corpus striatum* of the internal capsule. If a small blood vessel in this area ruptures, an interference with the efferent tracts descending from the cortex can occur, with resultant paralysis. The amygdaloid nuclei influence emotional behavior. Injury to the basal ganglia produces either unilateral or bilateral signs, including tremor, rigidity, disturbance of associated movements, and disturbance of gait and posture.

THE DIENCEPHALON. The thalamus and

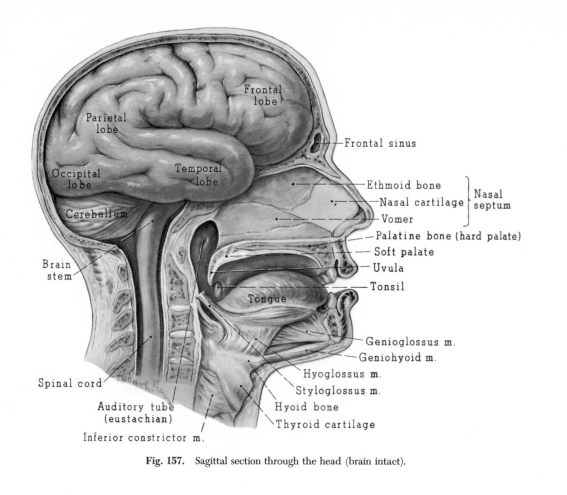

Fig. 157. Sagittal section through the head (brain intact).

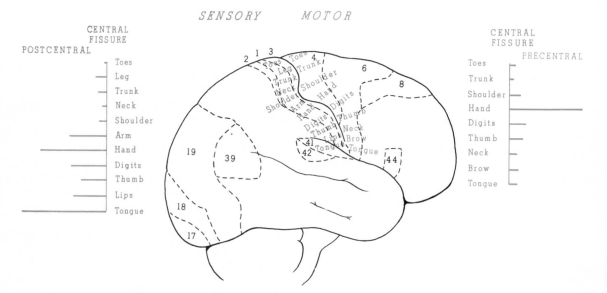

Fig. 158. Lateral view of the brain showing Brodmann areas and motor and sensory regions. The amount of brain surface related to a specific part of the body is not proportionate to the size of the part but to the extent of its use, as illustrated diagrammatically for the motor and sensory areas.

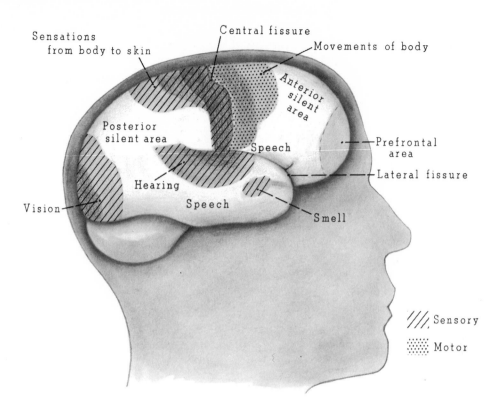

Fig. 159. Projection areas of the cerebral cortex.

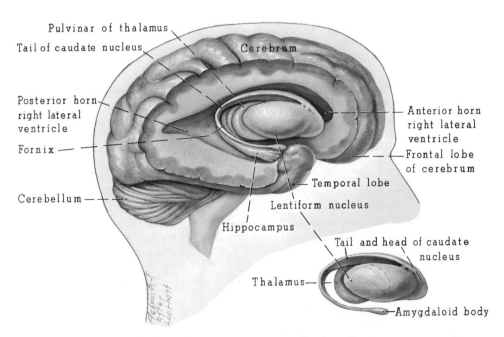

Fig. 160. Schematic representation of basal ganglia.

203

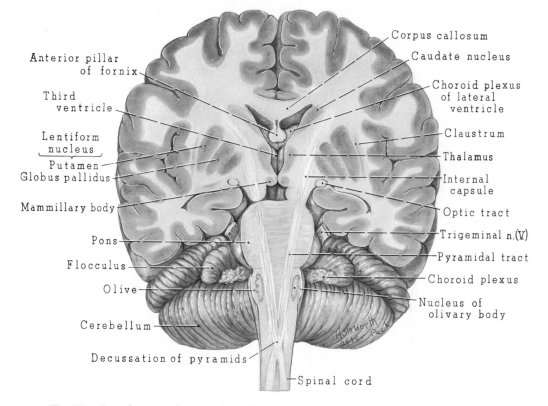

Fig. 161. Frontal or coronal section through the brain showing basal ganglia and brainstem. Note decussation of the corticospinal (pyramidal) tract just prior to entering the spinal cord.

hypothalamus constitute the diencephalon and are located in the forebrain along with the cerebrum. The *thalamus* is a large mass of gray matter located in the medioposterior aspect of each hemisphere. The pineal gland is found in the dorsomedial portion of the thalamus. The pineal gland is believed to be a sensitive biological "clock" converting cyclic nervous energy generated by light in the environment into endocrine information. The thalamus is an important relay station in which sensory pathways in the cord and brainstem form synapses on their way to the cerebral cortex. The *hypothalamus* lies beneath the thalamus. It contains temperature-controlling mechanisms and hunger-control centers, regulates some aspects of the functional activity of the hypophysis, and may assume a part in maintaining the waking state since sleepiness is found in hypothalamic disorders.

THE BRAINSTEM (Fig. 161). Collectively, the midbrain, pons, and medulla form the brainstem. The cerebral and cerebellar hemispheres sprout from the basic stem-like cranial enlargement of the spinal cord as a flower blooms from a stalk. The brainstem exerts a regulatory activity on many activities of the spinal cord. Cranial nerves emerge from the brainstem.

MESENCEPHALON (MIDBRAIN). The midbrain is found between the forebrain and hindbrain. It is concerned with motor coordination and is composed of several nuclear masses on its posterior surface. Four of these nuclear masses present as small elevations; the upper two, or *superior colliculi*, are involved in visual reflexes, and the lower two, or *inferior colliculi*, are associated with hearing. The four are known collectively as the *corpora quadrigemina*. (Two large diverging stalks emerge ventrally from each half of the cerebrum. The stalks are called cerebral peduncles; they constitute the main motor connection between the forebrain and hindbrain.) The mid-portion of the mesencephalon is known as the *tegmentum* and contains important efferent and afferent pathways. The tegmentum also contains the *red nucleus,* which is connected with the cerebellum by the superior cerebellar peduncle. This nucleus is important in motor movement and postural reflex patterns. A canal, the *cerebral aqueduct (of Sylvius),* passes lengthwise through the midbrain to connect the third and fourth ventricles. When the superior part of the midbrain is injured or diseased, an abnormality of conjugate movements of the eye results, particularly a paralysis of upward gaze.

CEREBELLUM. The cerebellum occupies the posterior cranial fossa. It is separated from the cerebral hemispheres by the *tentorium cerebelli*. Anteriorly, the fourth ventricle is interposed between the cerebellum and the pons and medulla oblongata.

The cerebellum is oval in shape with a central constriction and lateral expanded portions. The constricted central portion is called the *vermis* and the lateral expanded portions, the *hemispheres*. The cerebellum resembles the cerebrum in structure with the gray matter forming a layer of cortex placed on the surface rather than centrally located as in the spinal cord and brainstem. Cross section of the cerebellum reveals its patterns of folds and fissures which led anatomists of the medieval period to give it the name *arbor vitae* (tree of life).

The cerebellum is divided into lobes by deep and distinct fissures. These lobes include the anterior, posterior, and flocculonodular. The *anterior* and *posterior lobes* are concerned with the function of movement; the *flocculonodular lobe* is concerned with the function of equilibrium. The cerebellum is connected by afferent and efferent pathways with all other parts of the central nervous system. In general, tumors of the cerebellum are associated with an earlier increase in intercranial pressure than are neoplasms in other locations. Headaches, vomiting, and visual disturbances are common. Cerebellar tumors frequently involve neighboring structures, such as the cranial nerves and brainstem.

THE PONS. The pons lies anterior to the cerebellum and between the midbrain and medulla. On its ventral surface is a midline groove for the basilar artery. As the name implies, the pons is a bridge-like structure, consisting almost entirely of white matter linking the various parts of the brain and serving as a relay station from the medulla to the higher cortical centers. There are also several important nuclear groups for the cranial nerves.

MEDULLA OBLONGATA. The medulla oblongata is continuous with the spinal cord on one end and with the pons on the other. It lies ventral to the cerebellum, and its posterior aspect forms the floor of the fourth ventricle. On the ventral surface of the medulla are the pyramids, which, as the name implies, are pyramid-shaped tracts. The pyramids contain crossing upper motor neuron fibers, which ultimately synapse with the anterior horn neurons of the spinal cord. The pyramids extend to the lower margin of the pons. Two prominent nuclei, the *nucleus gracilis* and *nucleus cuneatus,* are located on the posterior portion of the medulla. It is in these nuclei that fibers from the corresponding tracts in the cord synapse with neurons whose axons extend to the thalamus and cerebellum. Externally, the medulla resembles the upper part of the spinal cord. Consequently it is often called the spinal bulb; but the medulla is thicker than the cord and consists of central gray matter broken into more or less distinct nests of cells or nuclear masses, with columns of white matter interwoven among the nuclei. All the afferent and efferent tracts of the spinal cord are represented in the medulla, and many of these decussate, or cross, from one side to the other, whereas others terminate. The medulla functions primarily as a relay station for passage of impulses between the cord and brain, and contains cardiac, vasoconstrictor, and respiratory centers, as well as many mechanisms for controlling reflex activities. The signs of medullary injury include cranial nerve defects on the same side of the body, paralysis and loss of sensation on the opposite side of the body, and irregularities of respiratory control.

RETICULAR FORMATION. Scattered throughout the entire brainstem are numerous large and small neurons related to each other by small processes. These neurons and their fibers constitute the reticular formation, an important part of the extrapyramidal pathway. They are not often collected into distinct nuclei; but the lateral reticular and inferior olivary nuclei are exceptions, in that they are readily identified as nuclear groups. The reticular formation is capable of modifying the reflex activity of the spinal neurons. It is believed essential for cortical activities such as initiating and maintaining wakefulness; hence, it is often called an activating system. Injury to this system can result in unconsciousness.

Vascular Supply to the Brain (Figs. 162 to 164)

The intracranial contents receive arterial blood from the internal carotid and vertebral arteries. Venous drainage is via the cerebral veins and dural venous sinuses. The diploic and emissary veins are communications between the intracranial and extracranial venous channels.

ARTERIAL SUPPLY. The *internal carotid arteries* arise from the common carotid arteries which bifurcate at the level of the thyroid cartilage, enter the carotid canal in the skull, pass along the anterior border of the tympanic cavity, and turn medially to pierce the dural lining on the side of the sphenoid bone. The internal carotid artery gives origin to the ophthalmic

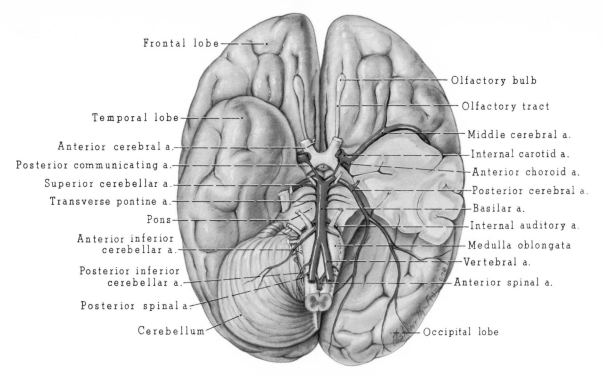

Frontal lobe

Olfactory bulb

Olfactory tract

Temporal lobe

Middle cerebral a.

Anterior cerebral a.

Internal carotid a.

Posterior communicating a.

Anterior choroid a.

Superior cerebellar a.

Posterior cerebral a.

Transverse pontine a.

Basilar a.

Pons

Internal auditory a.

Anterior inferior
cerebellar a.

Medulla oblongata

Vertebral a.

Posterior inferior
cerebellar a.

Anterior spinal a.

Posterior spinal a.

Cerebellum

Occipital lobe

Fig. 162. Arteries supplying the brain, ventral view.

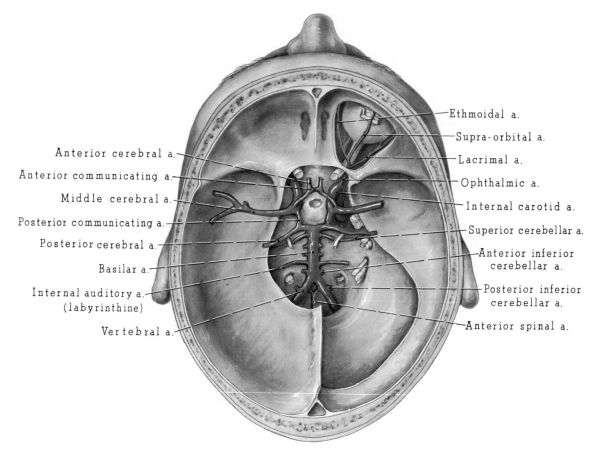

Ethmoidal a.

Supra-orbital a.

Anterior cerebral a.

Lacrimal a.

Anterior communicating a.

Ophthalmic a.

Middle cerebral a.

Internal carotid a.

Posterior communicating a.

Superior cerebellar a.

Posterior cerebral a.

Anterior inferior
cerebellar a.

Basilar a.

Posterior inferior
cerebellar a.

Internal auditory a.
(labyrinthine)

Anterior spinal a.

Vertebral a.

Fig. 163. Arterial supply of the brain as seen from above with the brain and right tentorium cerebelli removed.

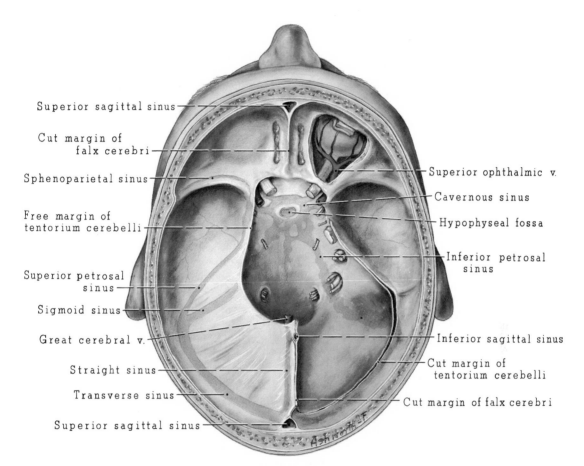

Superior sagittal sinus

Cut margin of falx cerebri

Sphenoparietal sinus

Free margin of tentorium cerebelli

Superior petrosal sinus

Sigmoid sinus

Great cerebral v.

Straight sinus

Transverse sinus

Superior sagittal sinus

Superior ophthalmic v.

Cavernous sinus

Hypophyseal fossa

Inferior petrosal sinus

Inferior sagittal sinus

Cut margin of tentorium cerebelli

Cut margin of falx cerebri

Fig. 164. Venous drainage of the brain and meninges with brain and right tentorium cerebelli removed.

artery, the anterior and middle cerebral arteries, and the posterior communicating arteries.

The *vertebral artery* arises from the subclavian, passes through the foramina in the cervical vertebrae, perforates the dura mater between the atlas and occipital bone and bends upward and medially in front of the medulla. Before uniting anteriorly at the lower margin of the pons to form the basilar artery, the vertebral arteries give rise to the posterior inferior cerebellar arteries. The anterior inferior cerebellar and superior cerebellar arteries arise from the basilar artery.

The *basilar artery*, in turn, bifurcates to form two posterior cerebral arteries. This system is connected to the internal carotids by the posterior communicating arteries, while the anterior communicating artery serves to join the anterior cerebral arteries. Thus, the circle of Willis, a site of aneurysms, is formed by the two posterior cerebral arteries, the two anterior cerebrals, the two internal carotid arteries, and the posterior and anterior communicating arteries.

Spontaneous subarachnoid hemorrhage from intracranial aneurysms can occur at any time from infancy to later life, although it is usually seen during the third and fourth decades. The death rate from rupture of an aneurysm in the circle of Willis region is as high as 50 per cent. The precise location of an aneurysm cannot always be determined by clinical features alone. Angiography, in which a substance opaque to x-ray is injected into the carotid arteries, helps in this identification. Treatment includes either ligation of the internal carotid artery in the neck or occlusion of the aneurysmal sac intracranially.

Cerebral hemorrhage and *thrombosis* usually occur after the age of 45. Both are more common in men than women and are generally secondary to atherosclerosis. The commonest site for thrombosis is the middle cerebral artery. An attack can occur without warning, or there may be some premonitory symptoms such as dizziness or disturbance in speech.

VENOUS DRAINAGE OF INTRACRANIAL STRUCTURES. The veins of the brain do not contain valves. They pierce the arachnoid and meningeal layers of the dura to open into the venous sinuses situated between the meningeal and endosteal layers of the dura. The larger sinuses tend to follow the course of the fissures of the brain; for example, the superior sagittal sinus lies in the convex margin of the falx cerebri. This network of sinuses eventually drains the venous blood of the brain into the internal jugular vein.

Ventricles, Cerebrospinal Fluid, and Meninges

VENTRICLES OF THE BRAIN (Figs. 165 and 166). Two lateral horns extend into each of the cerebral hemispheres. Each possesses a posterior, anterior, and inferior portion. The posterior portion extends into the occipital lobe, the anterior horn into the frontal lobe, and the inferior portion into the temporal lobe. Each lateral ventricle communicates with the third ventricle by way of the interventricular foramen (foramen of Monro). The third ventricle is a small, slit-like cavity in the center of the diencephalon continuous with the cerebral aqueduct which leads into the fourth ventricle. The fourth ventricle lies beneath the cerebellum on the superior surface of the pons and anterior half of the medulla. It communicates with the subarachnoid space via three openings or foramina—one medial aperture (foramen of Magendie), and two lateral apertures (foramina of Luschka). A tumor of the third ventricle can obstruct the flow of the cerebrospinal fluid and give rise to headaches and convulsive seizures, as well as to other signs of increased intracranial pressure.

CEREBROSPINAL FLUID (Fig. 166). Cerebrospinal fluid circulates within the ventricles and meshes of the subarachnoid space. It is colorless, with a composition similar to blood plasma. It consists of water with traces of protein, glucose, lymphocytes, and even some hormones.

The volume of cerebrospinal fluid ranges from 80 to 200 ml. Fifteen ml. are found in the ventricular cavities, and the remainder is in the subarachnoid spaces.

Actually, cerebrospinal fluid is a dialysate formed by the choroid plexus of the lateral, third, and fourth ventricles. Cerebrospinal fluid pressure is somewhat higher than venous pressure in the large sinuses of the dura. Since capillary pressure itself is usually higher than cerebrospinal fluid pressure, cerebrospinal fluid dialyzes from the capillaries of the choroid plexus into the ventricles and is probably absorbed into the venous system of the dural sinuses through the arachnoid villi. Cerebrospinal fluid can escape into the lymphatic system through the perineural lymphatic channels. Its only known function is *protection* serving as a water jacket to guard the brain and spinal cord against injury. There is no evidence that cerebrospinal fluid participates in metabolic activities of the brain.

Hydrocephalus (Fig. 167). Hydrocephalus is a condition occurring when blockage of circulation of cerebrospinal fluid increases pressure on the surface of the brain or cord. It is not common for an increased formation of fluid to be responsible for this condition, except in a tumor of the choroid plexus. Congenital hydrocephalus is spoken of as either communicating or noncommunicating, depending on whether or not there is transmission of fluid between the ventricles and subarachnoid spaces. Obstruction of the flow of fluid is probably the commonest cause of hydrocephalus. If this obstruction occurs before the time the sutures of the skull ordinarily close, the increased intracranial pressure produces an expansion of the brain and its coverings, with the entire head increasing progressively in size. The soft bones of the infant's skull are pushed apart and compression of the cortex results, until only a paper-thin ribbon of cerebral tissue remains. Despite marked depression of the cerebral cortex, the nerve cells frequently show a remarkable capacity for survival.

Following closure of the sutures, the brain can no longer yield to increasing hydrocephalus, and changes in brain tissue are then more destructive.

The signs and symptoms of hydrocephalus can be evident at the time of birth. The head enlarges, the anterior fontanelle bulges, and the suture lines of the skull separate. The veins of the scalp dilate, becoming prominent.

Surgical treatment consists of shunting the cerebrospinal fluid from one compartment into another in the normal fluid pathways, or from the cerebrospinal fluid compartments to some other area of the body where it can be absorbed. In hydrocephalus, the shunting procedure of choice is a catheter from the ventricles into the right atrium of the heart (Fig. 168).

MENINGES OF THE BRAIN (Fig. 169). Three membranes collectively known as the meninges provide protection to the brain and spinal cord. From outside in, these are the dura mater, arachnoid, and pia mater.

Dura mater. The dura mater is the outer tubular sheath of dense fibrous tissue. The term dura mater means literally "hard mother." There are two portions of the dura, cranial and spinal. The cranial dura is arranged in two layers, closely connected except where they separate to form sinuses for the passage of venous blood. The outer *endosteal layer* is adherent to the bones of the skull and forms the internal periosteum. This layer terminates at the foramen magnum, and its place is taken by the periosteal lining of the vertebral canal. The inner or *meningeal layer* covers the brain and sends numerous

prolongations inward for support and protection of the different lobes of the brain. The inner layer becomes continuous with the spinal dura mater.

Four extensions of the dura project into the cranial cavity: the falx cerebelli, the falx cerebri, the tentorium cerebelli, and the diaphragma sellae. These projections also form sinuses returning blood from the brain and sheaths surrounding the nerves as they pass out of the skull. The spinal dura mater extends from the foramen magnum to the second or third sacral vertebra posteriorly to the periosteum of the posterior aspect of the coccyx, forming a loose sheath around the spinal cord. The subdural cavity is a potential space between the spinal dura mater and the arachnoid, containing sufficient fluid to moisten the contiguous surfaces.

The arachnoid. The arachnoid is a delicate serous membrane located between the dura and pia. As the name implies, it has the microscopic appearance of a spider web. The cranial portion invests the brain loosely, with the exception of the longitudinal fissure, which passes over the various convolutions and sulci and does not dip down into them. The spinal portion is tubular and surrounds the cord loosely. The subarachnoid cavity between the arachnoid and the pia is occupied by thin trabeculae and intercommunicating channels in which the subarachnoid fluid is contained. Along the base of the brain, the pia and the arachnoid are separated to form the arachnoid cisternae.

The pia mater. The pia mater is a vascular membrane consisting of a plexus of fine blood vessels held together by areolar connective tissue. The cranial portion invests the surface of the brain and dips down between the convolutions; the spinal portion is thicker, less vascular, and closely adherent to the entire surface of the spinal cord, sending processes into the ventral fissure.

Meningitis. Meningitis is an infection of the meninges. The diagnosis depends on a history of infection, the so-called meningeal signs (such as stiffness of the neck), and abnormalities in the spinal fluid. In small infants, manifestations of mild meningitis are sometimes masked for several days, with the symptoms suggesting an upper respiratory infection.

Headache. Headache is one of the most common of all symptoms and can occur in the absence of definite pathology or as a manifestation of serious illness. Most headaches are transient, but a few are chronic, occurring over a

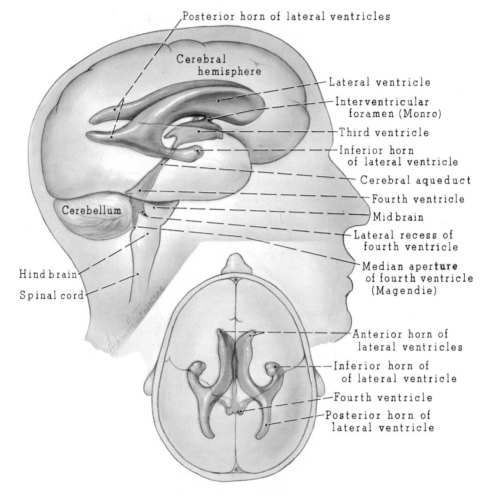

Posterior horn of lateral ventricles

Cerebral hemisphere

Lateral ventricle

Interventricular foramen (Monro)

Third ventricle

Inferior horn of lateral ventricle

Cerebral aqueduct

Fourth ventricle

Midbrain

Lateral recess of fourth ventricle

Median aperture of fourth ventricle (Magendie)

Cerebellum

Hindbrain

Spinal cord

Anterior horn of lateral ventricles

Inferior horn of of lateral ventricle

Fourth ventricle

Posterior horn of lateral ventricle

Fig. 165. Ventricular system, lateral and superior views.

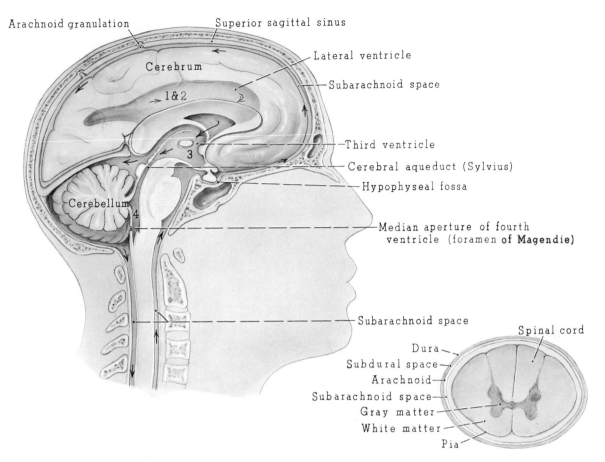

Arachnoid granulation   Superior sagittal sinus

Cerebrum

1 & 2

Cerebellum

4

Lateral ventricle

Subarachnoid space

Third ventricle

Cerebral aqueduct (Sylvius)

Hypophyseal fossa

Median aperture of fourth
ventricle (foramen of Magendie)

Subarachnoid space

Spinal cord

Dura

Subdural space

Arachnoid

Subarachnoid space

Gray matter

White matter

Pia

Fig. 166. Circulation of cerebrospinal fluid in brain and spinal cord.

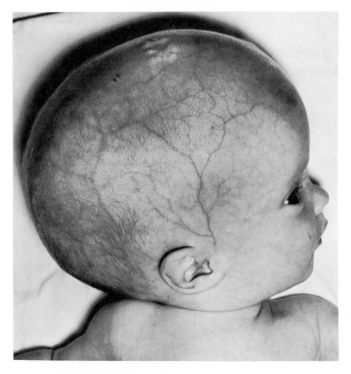

Fig. 167. Child, age 4 months, with hydrocephalus.

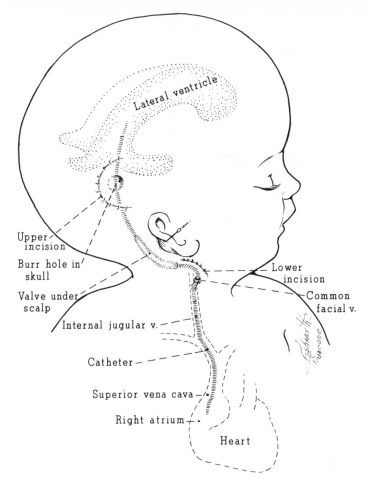

Fig. 168. Operative procedure for hydrocephalus in which a catheter drains the ventricular system into the right atrium.

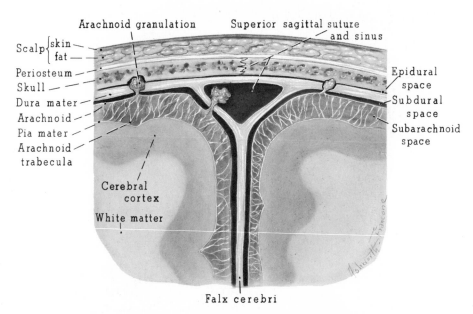

Fig. 169. Coronal section of skull, brain meninges, and superior sagittal sinus.

period of months or years. A headache can result from stimulation of any pain-sensitive structure in the head.

Headaches that occur only occasionally are caused by fatigue, eyestrain, or perhaps dietary indiscretion. Headaches persisting for weeks or months without relief, except in intensity, are often associated with psychologic abnormalities. When headaches occur with emotional tension, the pain commonly starts in the occipital region and spreads over the entire head. Often the patient describes it as a pressure sensation arising within the head.

Migraine. Migraine is a disorder characterized by recurrent attacks of headaches with or without associated visual or gastrointestinal disturbances. It occurs in 5 to 10 per cent of the population, usually in women, and is most frequently noted in the second or third decade of life. Headache in patients with migraine can be preceded by a period of depression or restlessness. The pain is usually generalized, but is sometimes sharply localized to one side of the head. In any given case, the symptoms seem to follow a pattern. Nausea and vomiting are common during the first attack. A patient with a migraine headache has abnormal sensitivity to light.

Concussion. The immediate unconscious state following an impact to the head is known as a *concussion*. It can be accompanied by pallor and even a shock-like state. At one time, it was thought that concussion was not associated with damage to the central nervous system; recent exacting techniques have shown that unconsciousness following head injuries, particularly closed head injuries, is due to actual damage of brainstem centers. This damage may be reversible.

Convulsive seizures. Convulsive disorders are more commonly known as epilepsy. If the attack is characterized by an only momentary suspension of consciousness, it is called petit mal; if there is an immediate loss of consciousness and a violent generalized convulsion, it is called grand mal.

CRANIAL NERVES (Figs. 170 to 172)

The cranial or cerebral nerves are 12 pairs of symmetrically arranged nerves attached to the brain. Each leaves the skull through a foramen at its base. The site where the fibers composing the nerve enter or leave the brain surface is usually termed the *superficial origin* of the nerve; the more deeply placed group of cells from which the fibers arise or around which they terminate is called the nucleus of origin or *deep origin* of the nerves. The cranial nerves include the olfactory, optic, oculomotor, trochlear, trigeminal, abducens, facial, vestibulocochlear (acoustic), glossopharyngeal, vagus, accessory, and hypoglossal nerves (Table 24).

The *olfactory nerve* (I) is formed by 20 small bundles of afferent visceral fibers (Fig. 173). These lead from the olfactory mucous membrane and almost immediately enter the olfactory bulb. The olfactory tract runs backward from the bulb and extends to the lateral and medial olfactory gyri. The olfactory nerve serves the function of smell. In testing for smell, each naris should be separately examined for the presence of the sense of smell. A complete absence of this sense is called *anosmia*.

The *optic nerve* (II) is composed of more than one million nerve fibers, or approximately 38 per cent of all the cranial nerve fibers (Fig. 174). Neither the olfactory nor the optic nerve is a cranial nerve in the proper sense; rather, they are tracts of fibers belonging to the central nervous system proper.

Visual impulses are received through the rods and cones—highly differentiated bipolar receptors of the retina—and are transmitted to the ganglionic cells. The optic nerves unite after their entrance into the cranial cavity to form the optic chiasm, where decussation occurs. Here, the fibers from the temporal half of the retina pass backward uncrossed, and the nasal fibers cross to the opposite side to unite with the temporal fibers of the other optic nerve to form the *optic tract*.

The optic tracts partially encircle the cerebral peduncles to reach the lateral geniculate body and the superior colliculus. From the lateral geniculate body, fibers arise passing through the posterior limb of the internal capsule and into the occipital lobe. These form the *optic radiations*. The visual cortical area lies on the medial aspect of each of the cerebral hemispheres and is divided by the calcarine fissure into upper and lower portions.

A *scotoma* is an area of varying size, shape, or intensity within the visual field in which stimuli are not perceived. The blind spot, or point of entrance of the optic nerve, is considered a physiologic scotoma. Injury to the optic tract behind the chiasm affects both optic nerves and produces blindness in the corresponding half of the retina. Injury in the central part of the chiasm produces blindness in the temporal half of both visual fields.

The *papilla*, or optic nerve head, is oval in

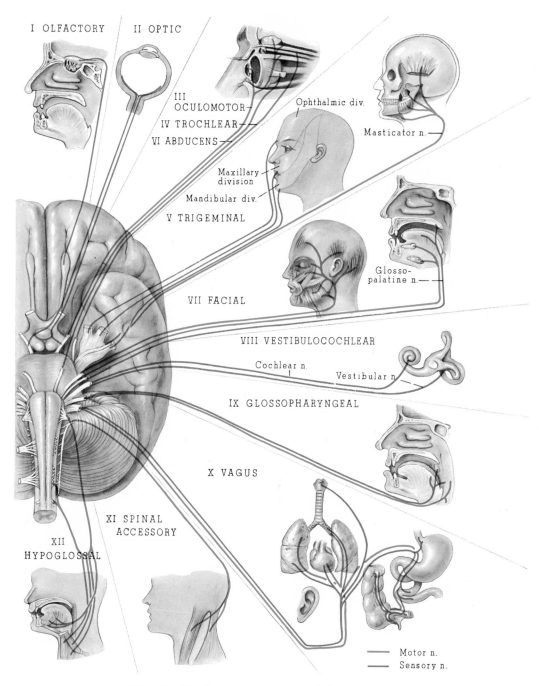

Fig. 170. Distribution of cranial nerves. (After Netter.)

I OLFACTORY   II OPTIC

III OCULOMOTOR

IV TROCHLEAR

VI ABDUCENS

Ophthalmic div.

Masticator n.

Maxillary division

Mandibular div.

V TRIGEMINAL

VII FACIAL

Glosso-palatine n.

VIII VESTIBULOCOCHLEAR

Cochlear n.   Vestibular n.

IX GLOSSOPHARYNGEAL

X VAGUS

XI SPINAL ACCESSORY

XII HYPOGLOSSAL

—— Motor n.

—— Sensory n.

TABLE 24. Cranial Nerves.

NUMBER	NAME	ORIGIN	EXIT FROM SKULL	FUNCTION
I	Olfactory	Cells of nasal mucosa	Cribriform plate of ethmoid	Sensory: olfactory (smell)
II	Optic	Ganglion cells in retina	Optic foramen	Sensory: vision
III	Oculomotor	Midbrain	Superior orbital fissure	Motor: external muscles of eyes except lateral rectus and superior oblique; levator palpebrae superioris. Parasympathetic: sphincter of pupil and ciliary muscle of lens
IV	Trochlear	Roof of midbrain	Superior orbital fissure	Motor: superior oblique muscle
V	Trigeminal	Lateral aspect of pons		
	Ophthalmic branch	Semilunar ganglion	Superior orbital fissure	Sensory: cornea; nasal mucous membrane: skin of face
	Maxillary branch	Semilunar ganglion	Foramen rotundum	Sensory: skin of face; oral cavity
	Mandibular branch	Semilunar ganglion	Foramen ovale	Motor: muscles of mastication; Sensory: skin of face
VI	Abducens	Lower margin of pons	Superior orbital fissure	Motor: lateral rectus muscle
VII	Facial	Lower margin of pons	Stylomastoid foramen	Parasympathetic: lacrimal, submandibular, and sublingual glands; Motor: muscles of facial expression; Sensory: taste, anterior two-thirds of tongue
VIII	Vestibulocochlear			
	Vestibular	Lower border of pons	Internal auditory meatus	Sensory: equilibrium
	Cochlear	Lower border of pons	Internal auditory meatus	Sensory: hearing
IX	Glossopharyngeal	Medulla oblongata	Jugular foramen	Motor: stylopharyngeus muscle; Sensory: tongue (posterior one-third), taste, pharynx; Branch to the carotid sinus
X	Vagus	Medulla oblongata	Jugular foramen	Sensory: external meatus, pharynx, and larynx; Motor: pharynx and larynx; Parasympathetic: thoracic and abdominal viscera
XI	Accessory	Medulla oblongata	Jugular foramen	Motor: trapezius and sternocleidomastoid muscles
XII	Hypoglossal	Anterior lateral sulcus between olive and pyramid	Hypoglossal canal	Motor: muscles of tongue

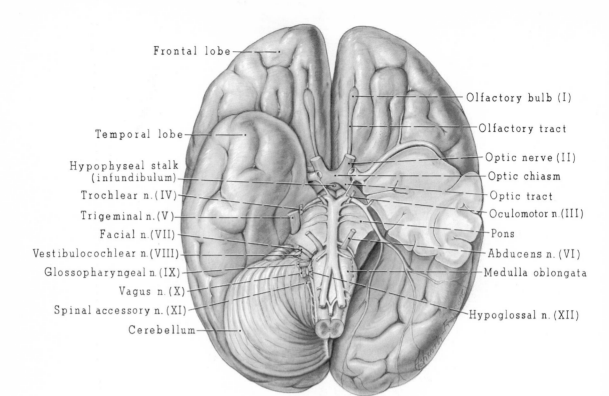

Fig. 171. Inferior surface of the brain showing sites of exit of the cranial nerves.

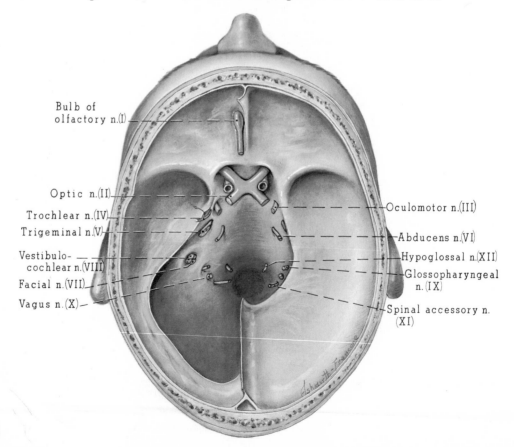

Fig. 172. Sites of exit of cranial nerves from the skull.

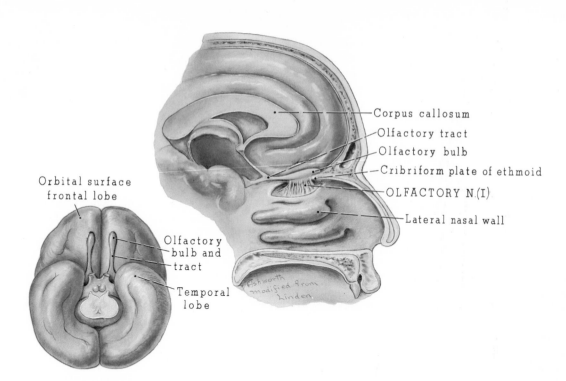

Fig. 173. Olfactory nerve (I).

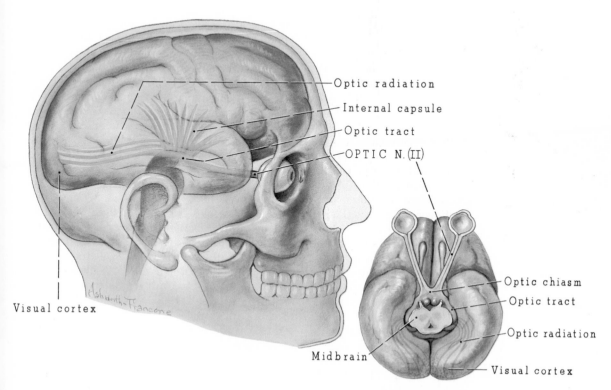

Fig. 174. Optic nerve (II).

shape and of a light gray color, in contrast to the red color of the remainder of the fundus or posterior part of the inner eye. Transmission of increased intracranial pressure to the optic nerve sheath may result in a swelling of the papilla, called *papilledema*. It seems probable that compression of the lymph spaces in the nerve itself causes swelling of the optic nerve head.

The *oculomotor nerve* (III), predominantly motor, is composed of somatic efferent nerves supplying superior, medial, and inferior recti, as well as the inferior oblique muscles of the eyeball (Fig. 175). It also supplies fibers to the levator palpebrae superioris muscle, which raises the eyelid. The patient with third nerve damage complains of blurred vision or of seeing two objects instead of one (diplopia). Weakness of the extraocular muscles is examined by the patient's holding his head without moving it and following the examiner's fingertips with his eyes.

The smallest of the cranial nerves, the *trochlear nerve* (IV) is composed of efferent fibers supplying the superior oblique muscle of the eye (Fig. 176). Its integrity is examined by checking movements of the eye.

The *trigeminal nerve* (V), the largest of the cranial nerves, consists of three divisions: ophthalmic, maxillary, and mandibular (Fig. 177). The trigeminal nerve conducts efferent fibers to the muscles of mastication via the mandibular branch. It is also composed of afferent fibers located in the skin of the face and anterior scalp, mucous membrane of the mouth, nasal cavities, and meninges. Injury to the trigeminal nerve produces a loss of sensation to light touch and temperature on the corresponding half of the face. In addition to this loss of sensation, the cornea and conjunctiva are insensitive, as are the mucous membranes of the corresponding side of the nose, mouth, and anterior two-thirds of the tongue. When the motor portion of the trigeminal nerve is affected, the masseter and other muscles of mastication are paralyzed and subsequently atrophy. The motor portion of the trigeminal nerve is tested by asking the patient to clench his teeth. The examiner feels the masseters to determine the strength of contraction. Examination of the sensory portion is conducted by evaluating the corneal reflex and sensation of the skin of the face.

Trigeminal neuralgia is perhaps the most agonizing of all benign afflictions of man. The maxillary and mandibular divisions of the fifth nerve are the usual sites of this disorder. The tic of trigeminal neuralgia is characteristic. Pain is excruciatingly explosive and stabbing in quality and is present over the area of distribution of the involved division. It is usually so severe that the facial muscles on the affected side develop a spasm; hence the term *tic douloureux*. Initially the attacks are brief, lasting from a few seconds to 2 minutes. Invariably, the patient becomes aware of trigger zones which, if touched, set off pain. These are usually located in the region of the mouth or upper lip. Eventually, the attacks may become more frequent, producing almost continuous paroxysms of pain. The cause of trigeminal neuralgia is unknown. Treatment includes division of the sensory root of the fifth nerve (see Fig. 206).

The *abducens nerve* (VI), composed of efferent fibers supplying the lateral rectus muscle of the eyeball, serves the function of lateral movement of the eye (Fig. 178).

The *facial nerve* (VII), essentially a motor nerve, is composed of efferent fibers found in the muscles of the face and scalp (Fig. 179). The facial nerve serves the function of facial expression and contains parasympathetic efferent fibers to the lacrimal, submandibular, and sublingual glands. It includes afferent fibers from the mucous membranes of the anterior two-thirds of the tongue, serving the function of taste.

When the seventh nerve is injured or diseased as it leaves the pons, the resulting paralysis gives the face a one-sided appearance, and the paralyzed side is flat and motionless. A loss of taste may occur in the anterior two-thirds of the tongue in the presence of damage to the facial nerve. In peripheral damage, such as occurs in Bell's palsy or injury to the facial nerve in the bony canal, all the muscles of facial expression are paralyzed. The patient cannot wrinkle his forehead or close his upper eyelid. In a central lesion, only the facial muscles below the eyelids are paralyzed.

The facial nerve is examined by asking the patient to wrinkle his forehead, to frown, to whistle, or to close his eyelids tightly. By these various simple maneuvers, muscles innervated by the facial nerve are tested and weakness or paralysis of the nerve is easily detected. The sensory function of the nerve is evaluated by asking the patient to protrude his tongue and by rubbing sugar, salt, or quinine onto the tongue to check for taste.

The *vestibulocochlear (acoustic) nerve* (VIII) is composed of afferent fibers found in the cochlea, utricle, saccule, and semicircular canal (Fig. 180). It serves the functions of hearing and equilibrium. There are two portions—the auditory or cochlear portion, concerned with hear-

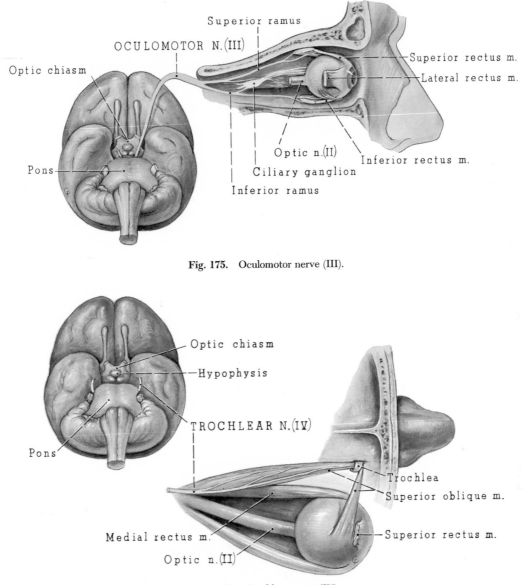

Fig. 175. Oculomotor nerve (III).

Fig. 176. Trochlear nerve (IV).

ing; and the vestibular portion, concerned with equilibrium. Injury to the vestibular portion of the acoustic nerve produces symptoms including vertigo (a sensation of whirling movement) and nystagmus (involuntary rapid eye movements). Both vertigo and nystagmus may be present in injury or disease of the vestibular apparatus.

Examination of the auditory nerve is carried out by testing the cochlear and vestibular portions. The cochlear portion is concerned with hearing, which can be evaluated by observing the patient's ability to hear the spoken voice or a whisper. For a more precise examination of hearing, the audiometer is employed. By means of this special instrument, the degree of hearing loss and frequency in which hearing losses occur can be measured (see Chapter Nine). The vestibular portion of the auditory nerve is tested by means of the past-pointing tests. The patient is asked to raise his arm and, with his arm outstretched, to bring his index finger down on the examiner's fingers. This is done first with the eyes open and then with the eyes closed. It is also carried out on the horizontal plane. Normally, the patient's finger touches the examiner's finger when the eyes are both opened and closed. In vestibular disease, the fingers consistently past-point to one side or the other. The

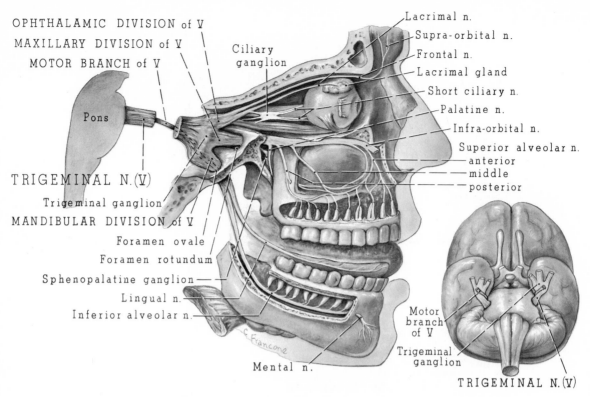

OPHTHALAMIC DIVISION of V
MAXILLARY DIVISION of V
MOTOR BRANCH of V

Ciliary ganglion

Lacrimal n.
Supra-orbital n.
Frontal n.
Lacrimal gland
Short ciliary n.
Palatine n.
Infra-orbital n.
Superior alveolar n.
anterior
middle
posterior

Pons

TRIGEMINAL N.(V)

Trigeminal ganglion

MANDIBULAR DIVISION of V

Foramen ovale
Foramen rotundum
Sphenopalatine ganglion
Lingual n.
Inferior alveolar n.

C. Francone

Mental n.

Motor branch of V
Trigeminal ganglion

TRIGEMINAL N.(V)

Fig. 177. Trigeminal nerve (V).

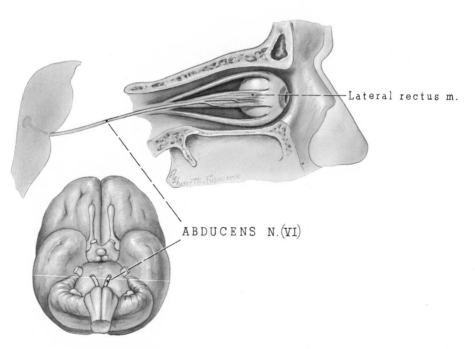

Lateral rectus m.

ABDUCENS N.(VI)

Fig. 178. Abducens nerve (VI).

220

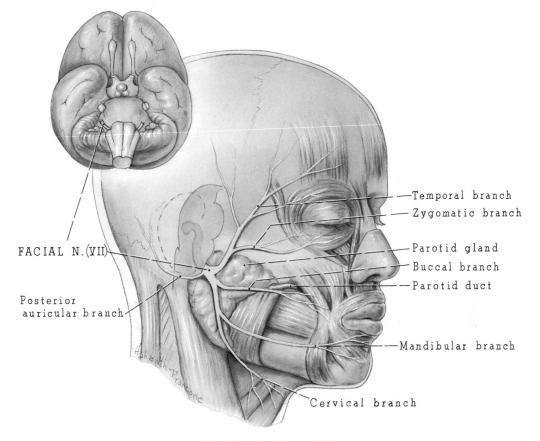

FACIAL N. (VII)

Posterior
auricular branch

Temporal branch
Zygomatic branch
Parotid gland
Buccal branch
Parotid duct

Mandibular branch

Cervical branch

Fig. 179. Facial nerve (VII).

vestibular portion of the auditory nerve is also examined by looking for *nystagmus*. Nystagmus consists of to and fro movements of the eyeballs in a horizontal or vertical plane, and occasionally in a rotary plane. It is elicited by asking the patient to focus on an object with the globe in various positions. Syringing the external auditory canal with hot or cold water sets up labyrinthine reactions such as nystagmus, past-pointing, and vertigo.

The *glossopharyngeal nerve* (IX) is formed by five or six small fibrous bundles emerging from the medulla oblongata (Fig. 181). Fibers are distributed to the parotid gland, the mucous membrane of the pharynx, the tongue, the carotid body, and the carotid sinus. The ninth nerve serves the function of general sensation and taste for the posterior one-third of the tongue. Its only motor function is innervation of the stylopharyngeus muscle, which aids in movement of the pharynx. The glossopharyngeal nerve supplies a branch to the carotid sinus.

The *vagus nerve* (X) is composed of fibers of all types (Fig. 182). The vagus innervates the pharyngeal muscles, the laryngeal muscles, and the smooth muscles of the esophagus, stomach, and intestine, and serves to give movement to these portions of the gastrointestinal tract. It

acts as a cardiac depressor and as a constrictor for the bronchial tree. The vagus nerve is routinely tested by observing pharyngeal muscles. This is accomplished by asking the patient to phonate and say "ah." Under normal circumstances, the soft palate and uvula will be pulled up in the midline. In the case of weakness of one side, the palate will be pulled to the healthy side upon phonation, while the diseased side droops.

The *accessory nerve* (XI) is a purely efferent nerve, arising as two groups of fibers and innervating the trapezius and sternocleidomastoid muscles (Fig. 183). It permits movement of the head and shoulders. Weakness of the trapezius muscle is determined by having the patient raise his shoulders against resistance. Weakness of the sternocleidomastoid muscle is ascertained by asking the patient to turn his head to the right and left against resistance of the examiner's hand.

The *hypoglossal nerve* (XII) is composed of efferent fibers. It supplies muscles to the tongue, allowing movement of the tongue (Fig. 184). The function of the hypoglossal nerve can be determined by having the patient protrude his tongue. When there is injury to this nerve, the tongue will deviate toward the side of the injury.

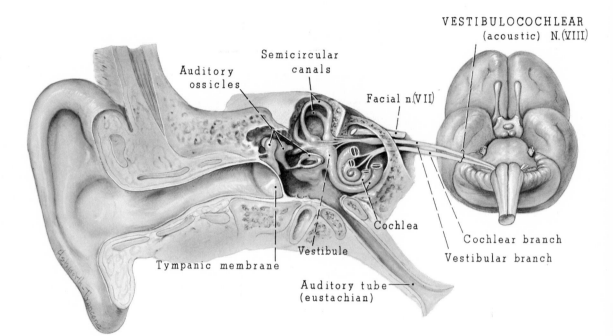

Auditory
ossicles

Semicircular
canals

Facial n.(VII)

VESTIBULOCOCHLEAR
(acoustic) N.(VIII)

Cochlea

Vestibule

Cochlear branch

Vestibular branch

Tympanic membrane

Auditory tube
(eustachian)

Fig. 180. Vestibulocochlear nerve (VIII).

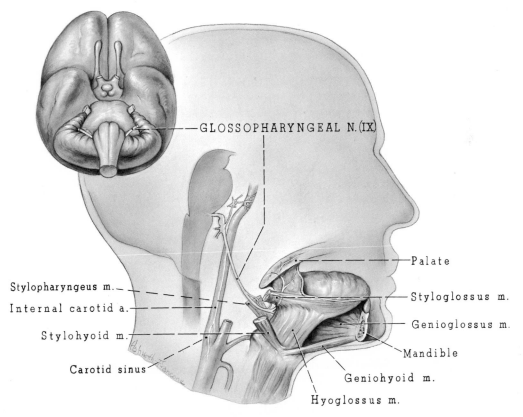

GLOSSOPHARYNGEAL N.(IX)

Palate

Stylopharyngeus m.

Styloglossus m.

Internal carotid a.

Genioglossus m.

Stylohyoid m.

Mandible

Carotid sinus

Geniohyoid m.

Hyoglossus m.

Fig. 181. Glossopharyngeal nerve (IX).

223

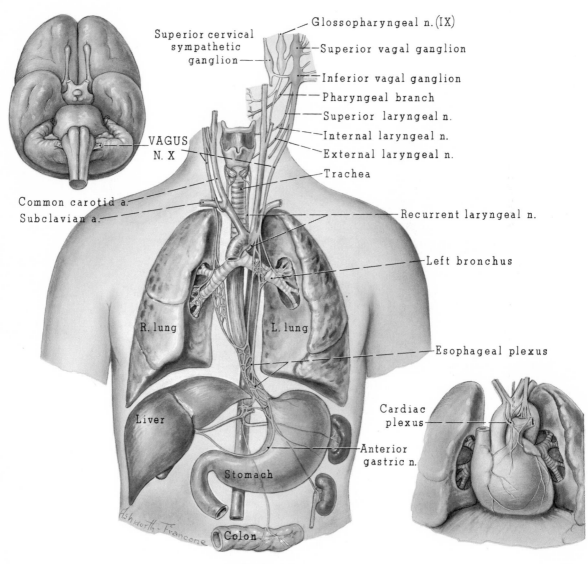

Superior cervical sympathetic ganglion

Glossopharyngeal n. (IX)

Superior vagal ganglion

Inferior vagal ganglion

Pharyngeal branch

Superior laryngeal n.

Internal laryngeal n.

External laryngeal n.

VAGUS N. X

Trachea

Common carotid a.

Subclavian a.

Recurrent laryngeal n.

Left bronchus

R. lung

L. lung

Esophageal plexus

Liver

Cardiac plexus

Anterior gastric n.

Stomach

Colon

Ashworth-Francone

Fig. 182. Vagus nerve (X).

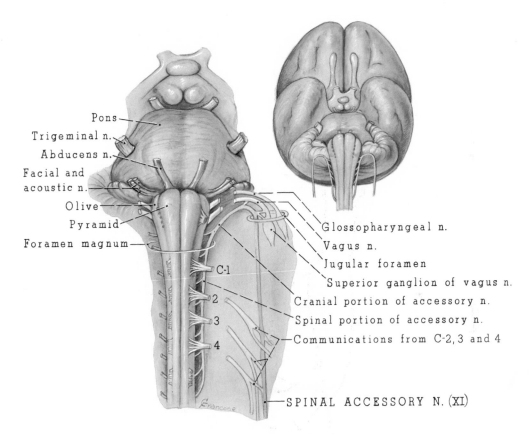

Pons

Trigeminal n.

Abducens n.

Facial and
acoustic n.

Olive

Pyramid

Foramen magnum

C-1

2

3

4

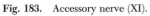

Glossopharyngeal n.

Vagus n.

Jugular foramen

Superior ganglion of vagus n.

Cranial portion of accessory n.

Spinal portion of accessory n.

Communications from C-2, 3 and 4

SPINAL ACCESSORY N. (XI)

Fig. 183.   Accessory nerve (XI).

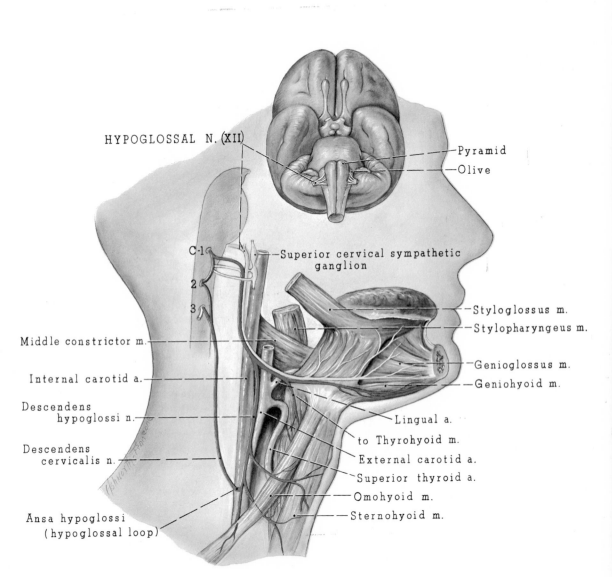

HYPOGLOSSAL N. (XII)

Pyramid

Olive

C-1

Superior cervical sympathetic ganglion

2

3

Middle constrictor m.

Internal carotid a.

Descendens hypoglossi n.

Descendens cervicalis n.

Ansa hypoglossi (hypoglossal loop)

Styloglossus m.

Stylopharyngeus m.

Genioglossus m.

Geniohyoid m.

Lingual a.

to Thyrohyoid m.

External carotid a.

Superior thyroid a.

Omohyoid m.

Sternohyoid m.

Fig. 184. Hypoglossal nerve (XII).

226

SPINAL CORD (Figs. 185 to 187)

The spinal cord, lodged within the spinal canal, is directly continuous superiorly with the medulla oblongata (see Fig. 153). It begins at the point of the uppermost rootlet of the first cervical nerve (the *foramen magnum*), and extends inferiorly to about the second lumbar vertebra, at which point it gives rise to a thread-like non-nervous portion, the *filum terminale*, a prolongation of the pia mater (Fig. 185).

The spinal cord is flattened dorsoventrally and exhibits two swellings along its length—the cervical and lumbar enlargements. These enlargements are produced by the greater number of nerve fibers entering from the brachial, lumbar, and sacral plexuses at these levels. In its growth, the spinal cord lags behind the growth of the vertebral column after the third embryonic month. As a result, the cord in the adult terminates at the junction of the first and second

Text continued on page 230.

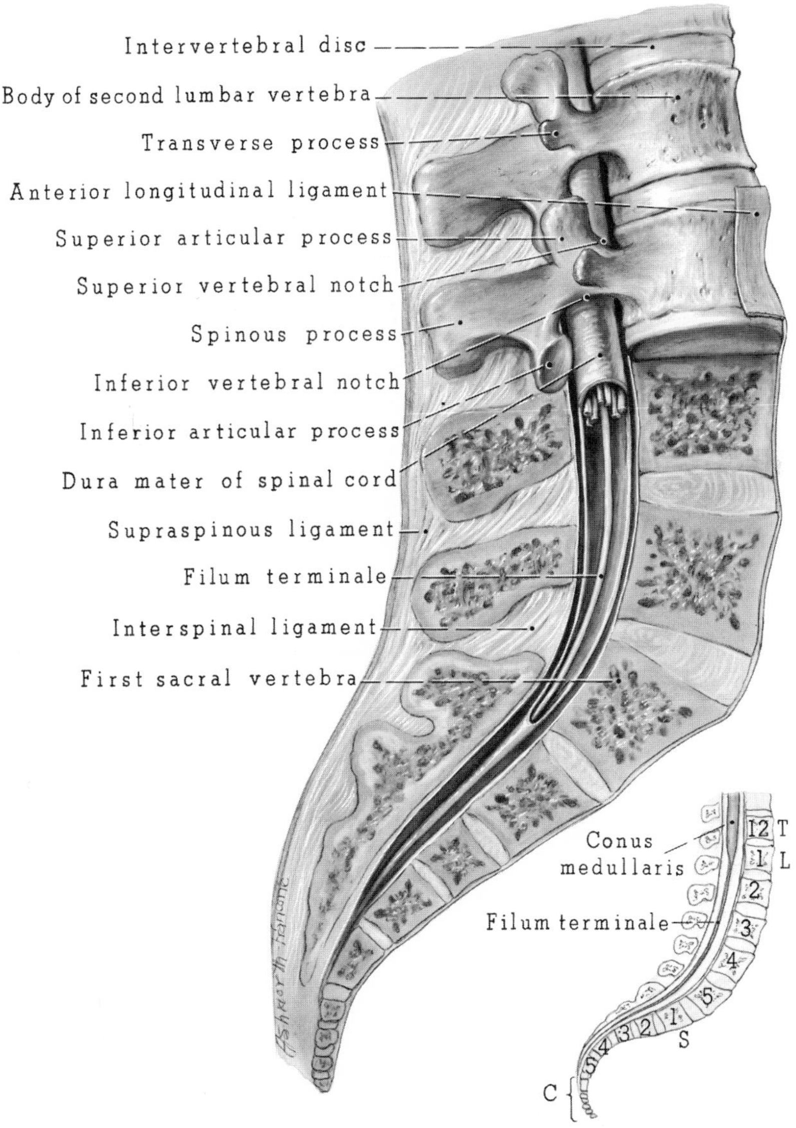

Fig. 185. Vertebral column, showing structure of vertebrae, filum terminale, and termination of dura mater.

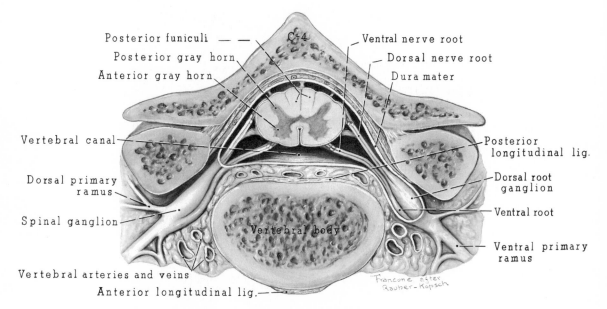

Posterior funiculi

Posterior gray horn

Anterior gray horn

Ventral nerve root

Dorsal nerve root

Dura mater

Vertebral canal

Posterior longitudinal lig.

Dorsal primary ramus

Dorsal root ganglion

Spinal ganglion

Ventral root

Vertebral arteries and veins

Ventral primary ramus

Anterior longitudinal lig.

C 4

Vertebral body

Francone after Rauber-Kopsch

Fig. 186.   Relation of spinal cord and nerves to vertebra.

228

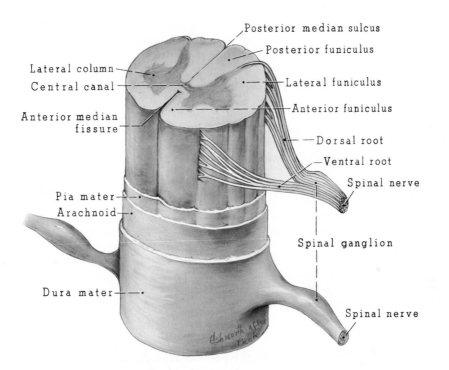

Fig. 187. Section of spinal cord illustrating formation of spinal nerve and layers of meninges.

lumbar vertebrae, and the spinal nerves arising from this terminal portion are drawn down into the shape of a horse's tail—thus, the term *cauda equina*. The *conus medullaris* is the tapered lower end of the spinal cord lying opposite the first segment of the lumbar region. Attached to it are the coccygeal and third, fourth, and fifth sacral nerves.

CROSS SECTION OF THE SPINAL CORD AND GENERAL FUNCTION OF TRACTS (Fig. 188). In cross section, the spinal cord reveals an outer covering of white matter and an inner gray mass arranged in the form of the letter *H*. There is a minute canal in the center of the cord—all that remains of the cavity of the neural tube. This opens into the fourth ventricle at its upper end and terminates blindly in the central canal of the filum terminale.

The transverse bar of the *H* is the *gray commissure* connecting the two lateral masses of gray matter. The portion of the gray substance dorsal to the central gray canal is called the *posterior gray commissure*, while the *anterior gray commissure* is that part of the substance found ventral to the canal.

Several longitudinal furrows groove the cord and serve as borders to tracts of nerve fibers traversing it. These furrows include the deep median anterior fissure, the shallow median posterior fissure, the posterior lateral sulcus, and the anterior lateral sulcus. Each serves as a reference point locating tracts known as anterior, lateral, and posterior funiculi. The funiculi, in turn, consist of smaller segments or fasciculi, which contain some ascending pathways to the brain from the cord and some descending pathways from the brain to the neurons in the spinal nerves (Fig. 189).

An anterior or ventral column and a posterior or dorsal column are found on each half of the gray matter. The anterior column contains cell bodies from which motor efferent fibers of the spinal nerves arise. The posterior column contains cell bodies from which afferent ascending fibers pass to the higher levels of the spinal cord into the brain after synapsing with sensory fibers from the spinal nerves. The gray matter also contains a great number of neurons connecting impulses from the dorsal to the ventral roots of the spinal nerves, from one side of the cord to the other, and from one level of the cord to another.

The white matter of the spinal cord is in the form of three longitudinal segments, the axons of which are myelinated and extend the length of the cord. Each column or funiculus consists of several different bundles of fibers or fiber tracts functionally distinct from one another. Some tracts are ascending or sensory and serve as pathways to the brain for impulses entering the cord via the afferent fibers of spinal nerves. Others are descending or motor and transfer impulses from the brain to the motor neurons of the spinal column. Still other tracts consist of short ascending and descending fibers beginning in one region of the spinal cord and terminating in another.

The spinal cord functions to convey messages

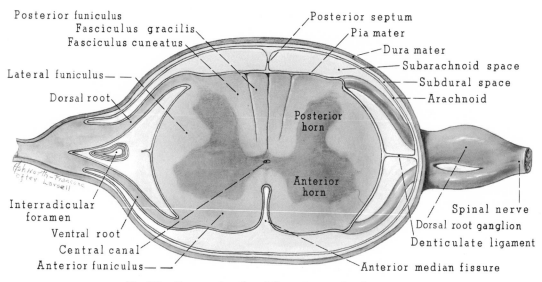

Posterior funiculus
Fasciculus gracilis
Fasciculus cuneatus
Lateral funiculus
Dorsal root
Posterior septum
Pia mater
Dura mater
Subarachnoid space
Subdural space
Arachnoid
Posterior horn
Anterior horn
Interradicular foramen
Ventral root
Central canal
Anterior funiculus
Spinal nerve
Dorsal root ganglion
Denticulate ligament
Anterior median fissure

Fig. 188. Cross section of cord illustrating meningeal coverings.

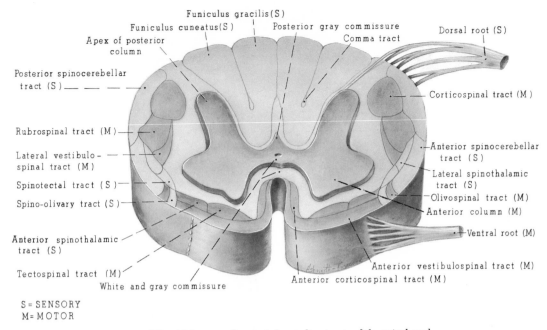

Fig. 189. Major ascending and descending tracts of the spinal cord.

to and from the brain and its periphery. This function is made possible via the ascending and descending tracts. The name of each tract is usually sufficiently descriptive to indicate the funiculus in which it travels, the location of its cells of origin, and the level of location of its axon termination. For example, it can be concluded that in the lateral spinothalamic tract fibers travel in the lateral funiculus of the cord, the cells of origin lie within the cord, and the terminal processes of the axon connect with other neurons at a thalamic level.

Since the spinothalamic tract extends from the lower level of the cord to the thalamus at a higher level, it is an ascending or afferent tract. The axon fibers of the ventral corticospinal tract lie in the ventral funiculus; its cells of origin are in the cortex, and its terminal connections in the spinal cord. It could be concluded, therefore, that the ventral corticospinal tract is an efferent or descending pathway.

Ascending tracts (Fig. 189). The ascending tracts of clinical importance are the following.

1. The *fasciculus gracilis* and *fasciculus cuneatus* are two major afferent tracts comprising the posterior funiculus (Fig. 190). These form the first link in the pathway for the sensations of motion, movement, touch, and pressure. The cells of origin are in the spinal root ganglia.

2. The *lateral spinothalamic tract* conveys stimuli of pain and temperature. It originates in the posterior portion of the posterior cell column,

crossing to the opposite side in the anterior commissure and then ascending to the thalamus in the lateral funiculus (Fig. 191). Injury to the lateral spinothalamic tract results in a loss of pain and temperature sensation on the opposite side of the body.

3. The *anterior spinothalamic tract* carries the stimuli of touch and pressure, arises in the posterior cell column, and crosses in the anterior region to the opposite side of the cord.

4. The *dorsal spinocerebellar tract* conveys impulses from the muscles of the legs and trunk between the sixth cervical and second lumbar segments. It is located on the lateral surface ventral to the posterior lateral sulcus and ascends to the cerebellum (Fig. 192).

5. The *anterior spinocerebellar tract* transmits impulses to the cerebellum through the medulla oblongata and pons.

6. The *spinotectal tract* originates in the cells of the *posterior gray column*. It crosses to the lateral funiculus and terminates in the corpora quadrigemina. The spinotectal tract acts as a correlation pathway of the spinal cord.

Descending tracts (Fig. 189). The second group of tracts originates in the brain and travels down the spinal cord to terminate in the gray substance. Most of the descending tracts are connected by one or more interrelated neurons. There are many descending tracts. Three will be considered.

1. The *rubrospinal tract* conveys impulses

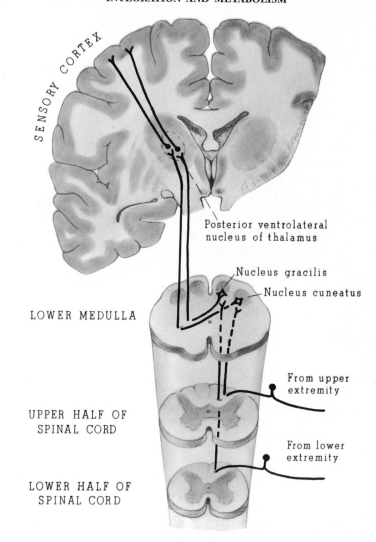

Fig. 190. Fasciculi gracilis and cuneatus of dorsal funiculus (pathway for position, movement, touch, and pressure).

from the cerebellum to the motor cells of the anterior column. It originates in the red nucleus of the midbrain, receives fibers from the cerebellum, and crosses over to descend near the center of the lateral funiculus.

2. The *corticospinal tract,* also called the *pyramidal tract,* forms the great motor pathways between the cerebral cortex and spinal nerves and carries impulses for voluntary movement. For the most part these impulses are concerned with skilled voluntary movements requiring participation by small numbers of muscle groups.

3. The *tectospinal tract* mediates the optic and auditory reflexes and originates in the superior colliculus. It then crosses to descend in the anterior funiculus to enter the motor cells of the anterior column.

INJURIES TO THE SPINAL CORD. The spinal cord may be either partially injured or transected. Partial injury produces paresthesias, weakness, increased deep reflexes, disturbances in urinary sphincter activity, and decreased ability to sense pain and temperature. Light touch may be retained. Complete transection of

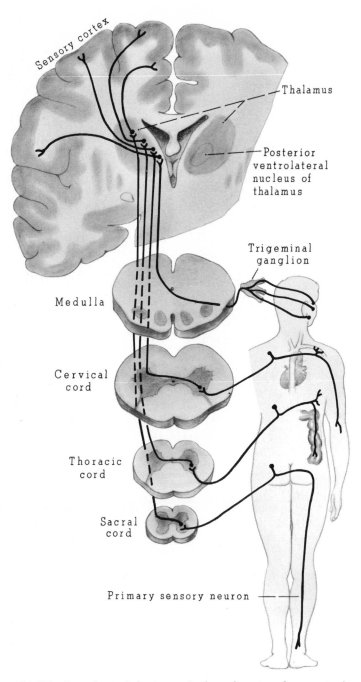

Fig. 191. Lateral spinothalamic tract (pathway for pain and temperature).

Sensory cortex

Thalamus

Posterior ventrolateral nucleus of thalamus

Trigeminal ganglion

Medulla

Cervical cord

Thoracic cord

Sacral cord

Primary sensory neuron

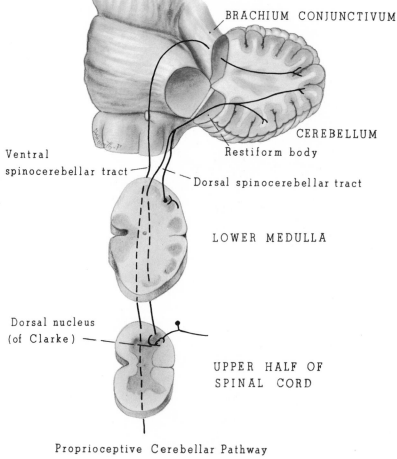

BRACHIUM CONJUNCTIVUM

CEREBELLUM

Restiform body

Ventral
spinocerebellar tract

Dorsal spinocerebellar tract

LOWER MEDULLA

Dorsal nucleus
(of Clarke)

UPPER HALF OF
SPINAL CORD

Proprioceptive Cerebellar Pathway
Muscle tension (stretch)
Position sense

Fig. 192.   Proprioceptive cerebellar pathway.

the cord results in drastic symptoms including a spastic paralysis, loss of all sensation, and loss of urinary and rectal sphincter control.

Spinal Nerves (Fig. 193)

A nerve is a bundle of nerve fibers outside the spinal cord or brain. In a transverse section of a spinal nerve, large numbers of closely packed fibers, some myelinated and some non-myelinated, can be seen by ordinary microscopy. These are grouped into small bundles called fascicles, each surrounded by a dense sheath, the *perineurium*. From the perineurium, strands of connective tissue called *endoneurium* extend into the spaces between the individual nerve fibers. The *epineurium* forms a protective covering for the entire nerve unit.

A pair of dorsal roots and a pair of ventral roots are attached to each segment of the spinal cord. Each dorsal root presents a spinal ganglion near or within the intervertebral foramen. Distal to the ganglion, the dorsal root combines with the corresponding ventral root to form a spinal nerve. The first cervical spinal nerve, which often lacks dorsal roots, emerges between the atlas and the skull. The second to seventh cervical nerves leave the vertebral canal above the corresponding vertebrae; the eighth nerve leaves the vertebral canal below the seventh cervical vertebra. Thereafter, the nerves exist below their corresponding vertebrae.

The 31 pairs of spinal nerves are named for the vertebrae anterior to their emergence. There are eight pairs of cervical spinal nerves, twelve thoracic, five lumbar, five sacral, and one coccygeal.

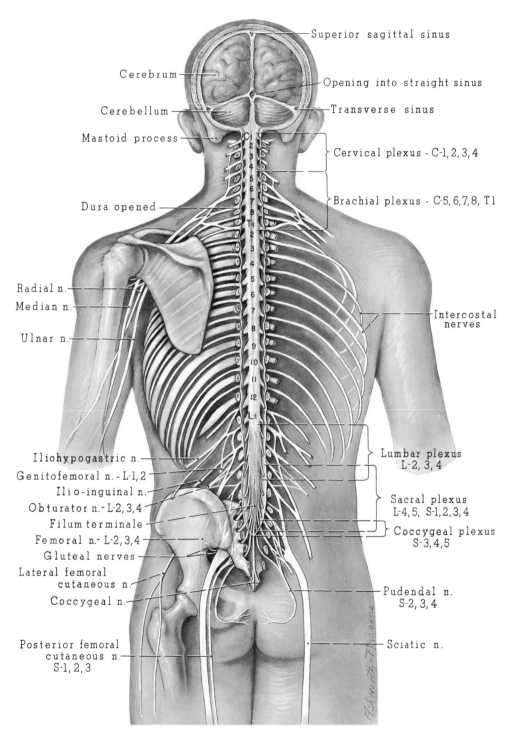

Superior sagittal sinus

Cerebrum

Opening into straight sinus

Cerebellum

Transverse sinus

Mastoid process

Dura opened

Cervical plexus - C-1, 2, 3, 4

Brachial plexus - C-5, 6, 7, 8, T1

Radial n.

Median n.

Ulnar n.

Intercostal nerves

Iliohypogastric n.

Genitofemoral n. - L-1, 2

Ilio-inguinal n.

Obturator n. - L-2, 3, 4

Filum terminale

Femoral n. - L-2, 3, 4

Gluteal nerves

Lateral femoral cutaneous n.

Coccygeal n.

Posterior femoral cutaneous n. S-1, 2, 3

Lumbar plexus L-2, 3, 4

Sacral plexus L-4, 5, S-1, 2, 3, 4

Coccygeal plexus S-3, 4, 5

Pudendal n. S-2, 3, 4

Sciatic n.

Fig. 193. Spinal cord and nerves emerging from it.

Many of the larger branches given off from the spinal nerves bear the same names as the artery they accompany or the part they supply. Thus, the radial nerve passes from the radial side of the forearm in company with the radial artery. The intercostal nerves pass between the ribs in company with the intercostal arteries. An exception to this rule is the sciatic nerve, which travels from the sacral plexus to the popliteal region, dividing into two large branches supplying the leg and foot.

Soon after a spinal nerve leaves the cord, it branches in four directions. The *meningeal branch* carries nerve fibers to and from the meninges of the spinal cord and the intervertebral ligaments. The *dorsal branch* carries nerve fibers serving the muscles and skin of the back of the head, neck, and trunk, while the ventral

parts of these structures are served by the *ventral branch*. The fourth branch, or *visceral branch*, belongs to the autonomic nervous system and has two portions, a *white* and a *gray ramus*.

The *white rami,* so designated because they are myelinated, consist of visceral afferent and preganglionic visceral efferent fibers connecting directly to the sympathetic ganglia. The cervical portions of the sympathetic trunk consist almost exclusively of ascending fibers. The lumbar and sacral portions of the trunk are composed largely of descending fibers from the white rami.

Upon separation from the ventral nerve root, the white rami can break up into more than one nerve strand; thus, there may be more than one white ramus at each segmental level. The preganglionic fibers, with the exception of those traveling through the splanchnic nerves, termi-

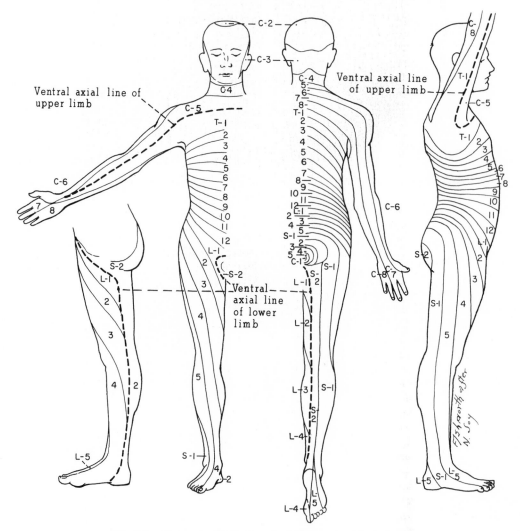

Fig. 194.   Cutaneous distribution of spinal nerves and dermatomes.

nate in ganglia of the sympathetic trunk where they enter into synaptic relationship with the postganglionic neurons. Most of the postganglionic neurons located in the ganglia of the sympathetic trunk send axons into the gray rami.

The *gray rami* consist of non-myelinated fibers that are axons of the cells in the sympathetic ganglia, serving to connect the sympathetic system with the peripheral nerves and distributed chiefly with the peripheral branches of spinal nerves. On entering the ganglion, the preganglionic fibers terminate near the sympathetic neuron, from which postganglionic fibers join the spinal nerves after passing down in the chain for some distance.

The *dorsal branch* extends backward through its transverse process to reach the muscular destination. Nerves in this area are segmentally arranged and located from the back of the head to the coccyx, usually between the posterior angles of the ribs on both sides. A strip of skin supplied by one pair of spinal nerves is called a dermatome (Fig. 194). C-1 supplies the muscles in the suboccipital region and is called the suboccipital nerve. C-2 helps form the suboccipital nerve, but deals mainly with the skin in the back of the head to the level of the vertex. This is called the greater occipital nerve.

The *ventral branches* are usually larger and more important, and supply the skin and muscles of the trunk, as well as the skin and muscles of the entire upper limbs.

PLEXUSES (Fig. 195 and Tables 25 to 28)

Cervical plexus. The first plexus formed is the cervical plexus, composed of the anterior (ventral) rami of C-1, 2, 3, and 4. It has three major branches—cutaneous, motor, and phrenic. The cutaneous branches extend in all directions from the posterior border of the sternocleidomastoid and supply the skin of the jaw, the back of the ear, the skin of the lateral and anterior sides of the neck, and the skin of the upper anterior thorax. The motor branches extend to supply the muscles of the neck along with the spinal accessory nerve. The phrenic nerve extends through the thorax to supply the large musculature of the diaphragm (Fig. 196).

The *brachial plexus* extends downward and laterally to pass over the first rib and behind the middle third of the clavicle to enter the axilla. It is composed of the anterior rami of nerves C-5, 6, 7, and 8, as well as T-1, and provides the entire nerve supply for the upper extremities. Important nerves arising from the brachial plexus are the following (Figs. 197 and 198).

1. The *circumflex (axillary) nerve* supplies the branch to the teres minor, and terminates by innervating the deltoid and the skin over it.

2. The *musculocutaneous nerve* supplies the biceps brachii, coracobrachialis, and brachialis. It is the sensory supply for the skin on the outer side of the forearm.

3. The *ulnar nerve* innervates the flexor carpi ulnaris and the medial half of the flexor digi-

TABLE 25. Cervical Plexus

NERVE	ORIGIN	INNERVATION
Cutaneous C-2,3,4		Skin, posterior region of sternocleidomastoid
Lesser occipital	C-2	Skin over lateral part of occipital region
Greater auricular	C-2,3	Skin over angle of jaw, parotid gland, posteroinferior half of lateral and medial aspects of auricle, skin over mastoid region
Anterior cutaneous	C-2,3	Supplies region about the hyoid bone and the thyroid cartilage (ventral and lateral parts of the neck from chin to sternum)
Supraclavicular	C-3,4	Shoulder, most lateral regions of the neck, upper part of breast
Phrenic	C-3,4,5	Diaphragm
Motor Segmental branches from ventral rami	Superficial branches	Lesser occipital, great auricular, ascending supraclavicular
	Deep branches	Anteriorly: muscles of the neck and jaw Posteriorly: sternocleidomastoid, levator scapulae, trapezius

TABLE 26. Brachial Plexus

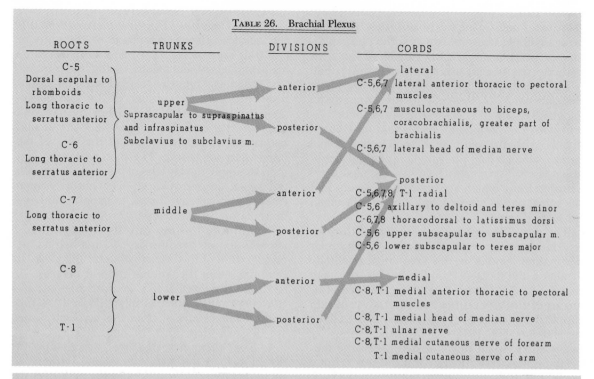

ROOTS

C-5
Dorsal scapular to rhomboids
Long thoracic to serratus anterior

C-6
Long thoracic to serratus anterior

C-7
Long thoracic to serratus anterior

C-8

T-1

TRUNKS

upper
Suprascapular to supraspinatus and infraspinatus
Subclavius to subclavius m.

middle

lower

DIVISIONS

anterior

posterior

anterior

posterior

anterior

posterior

CORDS

lateral
C-5,6,7 lateral anterior thoracic to pectoral muscles
C-5,6,7 musculocutaneous to biceps, coracobrachialis, greater part of brachialis
C-5,6,7 lateral head of median nerve

posterior
C-5,6,7,8, T-1 radial
C-5,6 axillary to deltoid and teres minor
C-6,7,8 thoracodorsal to latissimus dorsi
C-5,6 upper subscapular to subscapular m.
C-5,6 lower subscapular to teres major

medial
C-8, T-1 medial anterior thoracic to pectoral muscles
C-8, T-1 medial head of median nerve
C-8, T-1 ulnar nerve
C-8, T-1 medial cutaneous nerve of forearm
T-1 medial cutaneous nerve of arm

TABLE 27. Lumbar Plexus

NERVE	ORIGIN	INNERVATION
Iliohypogastric	T-12, L-1	Skin over pubis and lateral gluteal region.
Ilioinguinal	L-1	Muscles of abdominal wall, skin of pubis, inguinal region, upper thigh, and upper third of penis, anterior scrotum (labium majus in female).
Genitofemoral	L-1,2	Lateral half of thigh (dorsal and ventral) extending from lateral buttock to knee.
Lateral femoral cutaneous	L-2,3,4	Motor branches to extensors of the legs, the iliopsoas, the sartorius, and usually the pectineus. Cutaneous branches supply the ventral and ventromedial surface of the thigh, skin in the front of kneecap, medial side of leg, medial margin of foot.
Obturator	L-2,3,4	Supplies adductor muscles of thigh and gracilis. Cutaneous branch is distributed to the inner surface of the thigh.

TABLE 28. Sacral Plexus

NERVE	ORIGIN	INNERVATION
Sciatic Tibial	L-4 to S-3	Muscles of back of calf
Common peroneal	L-4 to S-2	Skin of back of calf and lateral side of foot; skin of upper side of knee and upper calf
Superior gluteal	L-4 to S-1	Gluteus medius and minimus
Inferior gluteal	L-5 to S-2	Gluteus maximus
Posterior femoral cutaneous	S-1,2,3	Skin of lateral part of perineum and lower buttock, back of thigh and leg

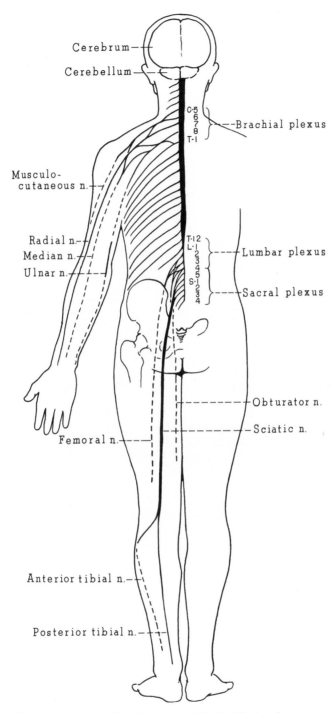

Fig. 195. Branches of spinal cord as seen on left side of body only, posterior view.

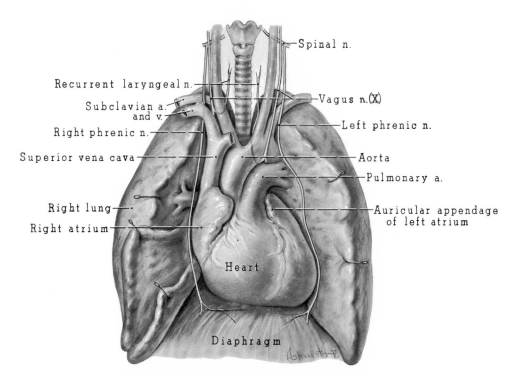

Fig. 196. Contents of thoracic cavity, illustrating positions of phrenic and recurrent laryngeal nerves. If, instead of the normal anatomy shown, an aortic aneurysm (dilatation) is present, the aorta could irritate the left recurrent laryngeal nerve innervating the vocal cords, causing hoarseness.

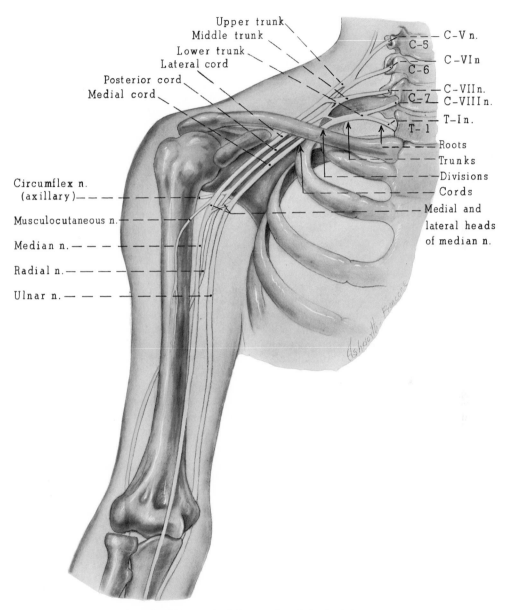

Upper trunk
Middle trunk
Lower trunk
Lateral cord
Posterior cord
Medial cord

C-5
C-6
C-7
T-1

C-V n.
C-VI n
C-VII n.
C-VIII n.
T-I n.

Roots
Trunks
Divisions
Cords
Medial and
lateral heads
of median n.

Circumflex n.
(axillary)
Musculocutaneous n.
Median n.
Radial n.
Ulnar n.

Fig. 197. Brachial plexus and its skeletal relations.

241

torum profundus in the forearm, as well as the muscles of the hand, except those supplied by the median nerve. If injured, it gives rise to a sensation of "pins and needles" in the area of its sensory distribution.

4. The *median nerve*, the great "flexor" nerve of the upper arm, supplies flexor muscles of the forearm, the three thenar muscles, and the two lateral lumbricals.

5. The *radial nerve* spirals around the back of the humerus supplying the triceps. It innervates all the muscles of the back of the forearm and receives sensory branches from the skin, the back of the forearm, and the hand. The radial nerve lies close to the humerus and can be seriously injured in fractures of the midshaft of the bone.

Lumbar plexus. The ventral rami of the lumbar segments 1, 2, 3, and 4 form the lumbar plexus. The lumbar plexus is situated on the inside of the posterior abdominal wall. There are three major branches in this plexus (Fig. 199).

1. The *lateral femoral cutaneous nerve* supplies the skin on the lateral half of the thigh.

2. The *femoral nerve*, the largest of the group, with the widest distribution, supplies the flexor muscles of the thigh and the skin of the anterior thigh, hip region, and lower leg.

3. The *genitofemoral nerve* supplies the scrotum and the skin of the thigh (not shown in Fig. 199).

Sacral plexus. The sacral plexus is formed on the anterior aspect of the sacrum by the rami of L-4 and 5 and S-1, 2, 3, and 4. It gives rise to the largest nerve in the body, the sciatic nerve. The branches of the sacral plexus include the following (Fig. 199).

1. The *sciatic nerve,* formed from L-4 and 5 and S-1, 2, and 3, is located deep to the gluteus maximus muscle and travels down the posterior aspect of the thigh, dividing into two terminal branches—the tibial and common peroneal nerves. The common peroneal innervates the skin on the anterior surface of the leg and the dorsum of the foot. The tibial innervates the posterior muscles of the leg.

2. The *pudendal nerve* is formed by the rami of S-2, 3, and 4, and supplies the muscles of the external genitalia, the skin of the perineum, and the anal sphincters.

The fifth sacral nerve and coccygeal nerves are unimportant in man. In animals, these two spinal nerves supply the tail.

SPECIAL EXAMINATIONS OF THE NERVOUS SYSTEM (Fig. 200). Examination of the spinal fluid is often necessary and is obtained with the patient lying on his side. The tap, or *lumbar puncture,* is best performed between the third and fourth lumbar vertebrae. If the puncture has been performed without trauma, clear fluid is obtained.

Intracranial tumors can produce a distortion of the ventricles of the brain. The ventricles are outlined by removing a small area of bone and then injecting air through a needle inserted into the posterior horn of the lateral ventricle (*ventriculography*), or by injecting air into the lumbar subarachnoid space (*encephalography*).

In cerebral angiography, visualization of the intracranial blood vessels is accomplished by injecting radiopaque media into the carotid or vertebral arteries. By proper timing, both the arterial and venous phases of circulation can be outlined.

The electroencephalogram (EEG) is a recording of the electrical activity of the brain made by means of electrodes applied to the scalp. A focal EEG abnormality may be indicative of focal abnormality of the brain.

The Motor Nervous System

Portions of the nervous system are known to be engaged primarily in bringing about movement. Functionally, the motor system can be divided into the lower motor neuron component, the upper motor neuron system, and the extrapyramidal system.

Lower motor axons arise from the cells of the anterior gray column of the spinal cord and from the cells of the motor nuclei of the cranial nerves. Axons from the spinal cord emerge through the anterior spinal routes and end in the skeletal muscles, while those from the brainstem are contained in the cranial nerves and terminate in the striated and smooth muscles. The lower motor axons are the "final common path" by which all nerve impulses subserving motor activity are transmitted to muscle.

The large motor cells of Betz, as well as other smaller cells, located mainly in the precentral gyrus of the cerebral cortex, are connected with the spinal motor neurons by a system of fibers known as the *pyramidal (corticospinal) tract* because of its shape in transverse section through the medulla. These neurons are the *upper motor neurons.* Many other parts of the cortex, including those involved in tactile, visual, and auditory sensation, as well as the anterior portions of the frontal lobes, are connected by fiber tracts with the motor cortex. These other portions of the cortex provide for sensory regulation of motor function and are the means of coordinating thought and action.

The *extrapyramidal system* includes all the pathways and involved nuclei mediating impulses between the motor cortex and anterior horn cells except the pyramidal tracts. This system includes the basal ganglia, parts of the thalamus, the red nuclei, the substantia nigra, and the reticular formation of the brainstem. Extrapyramidal tracts serve three general functions: facilitation, stimulation, and inhibition of anterior horn motor neurons.

In injury to the lower motor neuron, or in damage to the pyramidal tract alone, a flaccid paralysis results with muscle atrophy and an absence of deep tendon reflexes. Injury to the extrapyramidal system, on the other hand, results in spastic paralysis.

Abnormalities of the Central Nervous System

PARALYSIS.   Paralysis is a complete loss of motor function. *Paresis* means incomplete paralysis. Types of paralysis include *monoplegia*, paralysis of a single extremity; *hemiplegia*, paralysis of half the body along with corresponding limbs, such as the right arm and right leg; *paraplegia*, paralysis of both lower extremities; *diplegia*, paralysis of either both upper or both lower extremities; and *quadriplegia*, paralysis of all four extremities.

Paralysis may be either spastic or flaccid. Spastic paralysis follows damage to the extrapyramidal system, removing the controlling influence of the higher cerebral centers on the lower spinal reflex arcs. With spastic paralysis, there is increased muscle tone in the patient's limbs. The deep reflexes are increased and the superficial reflexes are diminished or absent (see page 192). There is no muscle atrophy. If tested electrically, muscles react normally to stimulation. With flaccid paralysis, there is a loss of both muscle tone and deep tendon reflexes. Muscle atrophy occurs. Flaccid paralysis results from damage to the pyramids or to the lower motor neurons.

DEGENERATION OF AREAS OF THE SPINAL CORD. *Tabes dorsalis.*   This is a disease caused by syphilis and characterized by progressive degeneration of the posterior funiculi and posterior roots of the spinal nerves. It results in ataxia and muscle weakness of the extremities.

Syringomyelia.   Syringomyelia is a condition of the spinal cord in which there is excessive multiplication of the neuroglia in the central gray substance accompanied by formation of cysts. The fibers which cross in the white substance in this entity undergo degeneration, interrupting the pain and temperature pathways of the lateral spinothalamic tract. Sensations of touch and pressure are not injured. Tumors and hemorrhage within the spinal cord destroy parts of the cord with similar dissociation effects.

Infantile paralysis (poliomyelitis).   Poliomyelitis is caused by a virus damaging the anterior horn cells of the cord and the motor nuclei of the cranial nerves. It is characterized by flaccid paralysis of the lower motor neuron type without sensory disturbances.

Multiple sclerosis.   Multiple sclerosis is a disease of the central nervous system characterized by a patchy demyelinization in multiple areas resulting in many symptoms involving both sensory and motor systems. These include virtually all the dysfunctions of the nervous system. There is no specific treatment. Multiple sclerosis is a chronic disease marked by periods of absence of symptoms sometimes lasting months or years.

Parkinsonism.   Paralysis agitans (parkinsonism) is a disease affecting the elderly. Although the cause is not completely understood, it appears to be a diffuse inflammation within the central nervous system, either infectious or toxic in origin, especially associated with degeneration of various parts of the basal ganglia and substantia nigra. Parkinsonism is characterized by rigidity without other evidence of corticospinal tract involvement, and by tremors of the extremities. Many patients with parkinsonism are considered candidates for surgery of the basal ganglia, particularly those who have had treatment for 5 to 10 years with various drug combinations. At present, surgery involves destruction of the ventrolateral nucleus of the thalamus by stereotaxic techniques.

DEGENERATION AND REGENERATION OF PERIPHERAL NERVES (Fig. 201).   When a peripheral nerve is injured, there may be an anatomic or physiologic interruption of function. The nerve distal to the point of division undergoes changes originally described by Waller in 1852 and collectively known as *wallerian degeneration*. Within the first few days, the axons become granular at the site of injury. This granularity spreads distally throughout the whole axon; simultaneously, the myelin sheath disintegrates. Within 24 hours after injury, the axons of the proximal stump begin to regenerate, first forming buds, and then filaments which branch and grow at the rate of 1.5 mm. per day.

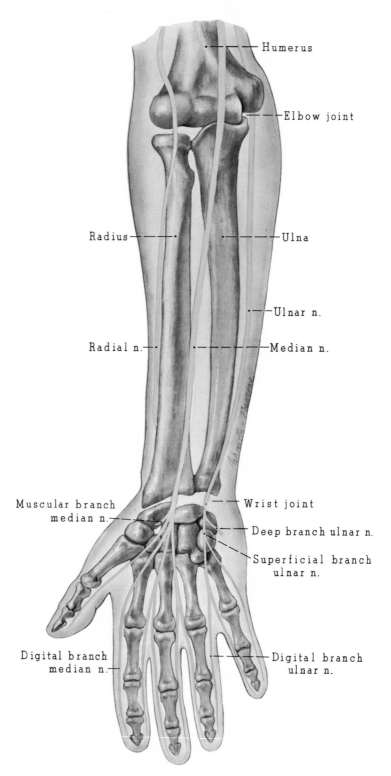

Fig. 198. Nerves of right forearm and hand (palmar view).

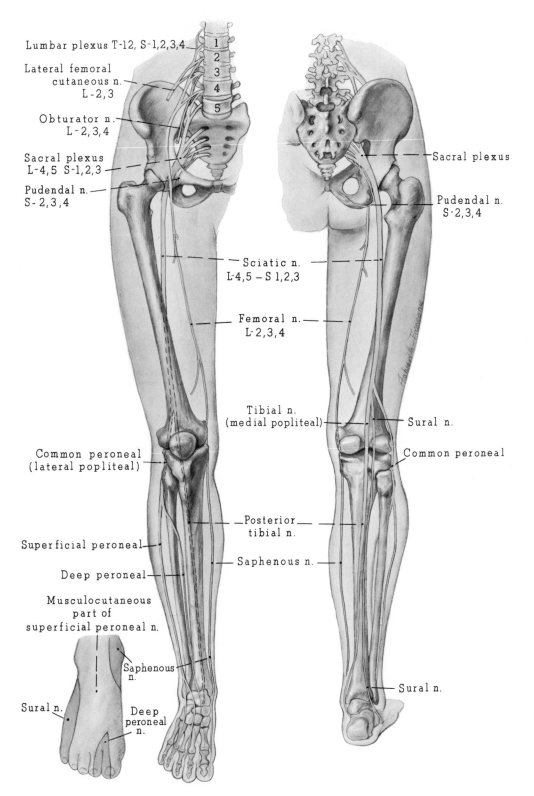

Lumbar plexus T-12, S-1,2,3,4

Lateral femoral
cutaneous n.
L-2,3

Obturator n.
L-2,3,4

Sacral plexus
L-4,5 S-1,2,3

Pudendal n.
S-2,3,4

Sacral plexus

Pudendal n.
S-2,3,4

Sciatic n.
L-4,5 – S 1,2,3

Femoral n.
L-2,3,4

Tibial n.
(medial popliteal)

Sural n.

Common peroneal
(lateral popliteal)

Common peroneal

Posterior
tibial n.

Superficial peroneal

Deep peroneal

Saphenous n.

Musculocutaneous
part of
superficial peroneal n.

Saphenous
n.

Sural n.

Sural n.

Deep
peroneal
n.

Fig. 199. Anterior and posterior view of the right leg and foot, showing lumbar and sacral plexuses and the regions supplied. Insert shows areas of the foot supplied by the nerves.

245

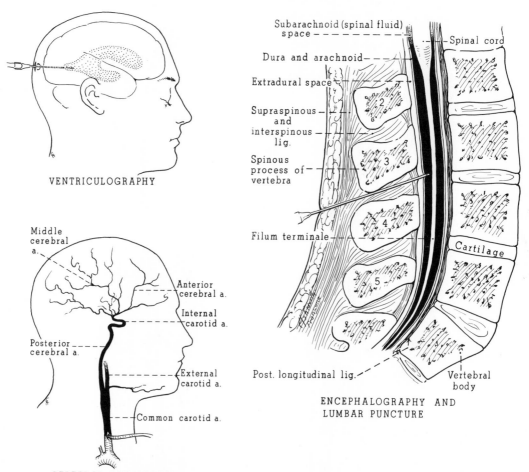

VENTRICULOGRAPHY

CEREBRAL ANGIOGRAPHY

Middle
cerebral
a.

Anterior
cerebral a.

Internal
carotid a.

Posterior
cerebral a.

External
carotid a.

Common carotid a.

Subarachnoid (spinal fluid)
space

Spinal cord

Dura and arachnoid

Extradural space

Supraspinous
and
interspinous
lig.

Spinous
process of
vertebra

Filum terminale

Cartilage

Post. longitudinal lig.

Vertebral
body

ENCEPHALOGRAPHY AND
LUMBAR PUNCTURE

Fig. 200. *Ventriculography:* An opening is made in the skull in the parieto-occipital region and a needle introduced into the lateral ventricle. The cerebrospinal fluid is slowly withdrawn and replaced by air and x-ray examinations are made.

Encephalography: X-ray examination of the brain is made following replacement of cerebrospinal fluid by air via the lumbar puncture route.

Lumbar puncture: Tapping of the subarachnoid space in the lumbar region, usually between the third and fourth lumbar vertebrae.

Cerebral angiography: X-ray examination of the vascular system of the brain is made after the injection of radiopaque material into the common carotid artery.

246

NERVE REGENERATION

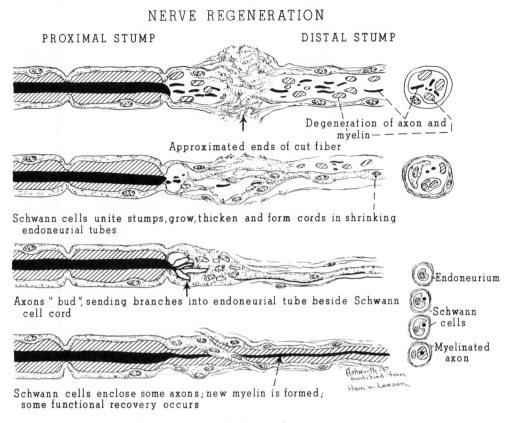

PROXIMAL STUMP

DISTAL STUMP

Degeneration of axon and myelin

Approximated ends of cut fiber

Schwann cells unite stumps, grow, thicken and form cords in shrinking endoneurial tubes

Axons " bud ", sending branches into endoneurial tube beside Schwann cell cord

Endoneurium

Schwann cells

Myelinated axon

Schwann cells enclose some axons; new myelin is formed; some functional recovery occurs

Fig. 201. Schematic drawing of nerve regeneration.

In the distal portion of the severed nerve, Schwann cells multiply and form a tube for reception of the regenerating nerve fibers. The fibers enter the tube in an orderly arrangement and follow this band of Schwann cells to reach their respective end organs. The nerve sheaths, bundles, and trunks are replaced by growth of these structures from the proximal end of the nerve.

The sympathetic fibers regenerate most rapidly. A return of function in peripheral nerve injury can be recognized initially by an improvement in color of the skin and evidences of vasomotor activity. The sensory function returns next. This is shown initially by sensitivity of the paralyzed muscle to pressure or pinching, and is followed by a return of protopathic sensitivity to pain, pressure, heat, and cold. Epicritic sensibility followed by sensitivity to joint movement and touch localization return next. The last function to return is the motor. Finally, actual muscle contraction occurs.

Peripheral nerve injury. The most accurate motor tests for injury to the median and ulnar nerves at the wrist are those involving the actions of the small muscles of the hand. If a patient is asked to oppose the tip of the thumb to the tip of the little finger without flexion of the distal phalanx of the thumb or little finger, a perfectly adequate and accurate test for median nerve function will have been employed. Function of the ulnar nerve distal to damage at the wrist can be tested by having the patient abduct and adduct the extended fingers. If the patient is unable to extend the wrist when the hand lies flat upon the table, the radial nerve has been injured.

AUTONOMIC NERVOUS SYSTEM
(Fig. 202)

The term autonomic means self-controlled and independent of outside influences. Thus, the autonomic nervous system is also called the involuntary nervous system; however, the autonomic system is not clearly separated from the central nervous system, functionally or anatomically. It is merely set apart for the convenience of study. The autonomic system is

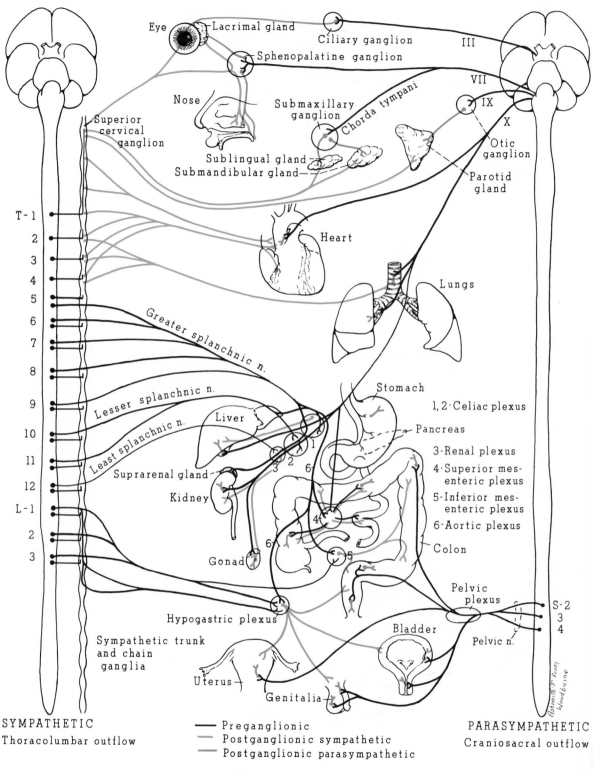

Eye
Lacrimal gland
Ciliary ganglion
III
Sphenopalatine ganglion
VII
Nose
Submaxillary ganglion
Chorda tympani
IX
X
Superior cervical ganglion
Otic ganglion
Sublingual gland
Submandibular gland
Parotid gland
T-1
2
3
4
5
Heart
6
7
Lungs
8
Greater splanchnic n.
9
Stomach
1, 2·Celiac plexus
Lesser splanchnic n.
10
Liver
Pancreas
11
Least splanchnic n.
3·Renal plexus
12
Suprarenal gland
4·Superior mes-enteric plexus
L-1
Kidney
5·Inferior mes-enteric plexus
2
6·Aortic plexus
3
Gonad
Colon
Pelvic plexus
S-2
3
4
Hypogastric plexus
Bladder
Sympathetic trunk and chain ganglia
Pelvic n.
Uterus
Genitalia

SYMPATHETIC
Thoracolumbar outflow

——— Preganglionic
——— Postganglionic sympathetic
——— Postganglionic parasympathetic

PARASYMPATHETIC
Craniosacral outflow

Fig. 202. Autonomic nervous system.

sometimes referred to as the visceral nervous system, in contradistinction to the central nervous system supplying all other areas of the body except the viscera.

Fibers of the autonomic nervous system are distributed to the smooth muscles of all parts of the body. The system can be separated into two divisions based on certain anatomic and pharmacologic differences of component fibers and their endings. These are the sympathetic, or adrenergic, and parasympathetic, or cholinergic, divisions respectively.

ANATOMIC DIVISIONS. The *sympathetic* or *thoracolumbar division* of the autonomic nervous system arises from all the thoracic and the first three lumbar segments of the spinal cord. The *parasympathetic* or *craniosacral division* of the autonomic nervous system arises from the third, seventh, ninth, and tenth cranial nerves, and from the second, third, and fourth sacral segments of the spinal cord. In general, it can be said that the sympathetic nervous system is involved in "fight" or "flight," while the parasympathetic system is involved in "repose" and "repair." The sympathetic system is the more primitive, exerting a mass action fortified by epinephrine from the medullary portion of the suprarenal gland. Its chief action is to constrict blood vessels. The parasympathetic system is more advanced structurally and functionally, and acts principally on smooth muscles and glands and in the gut.

PHARMACOLOGIC DIVISION. It has been found that the transmission of impulses by autonomic neurons and nerve fibers is associated with liberation of specific chemical substances at the ganglionic synapses and effector end organs. Preganglionic stimulation and postganglionic parasympathetic stimulation lead to the liberation of a substance resembling acetylcholine in the ganglion or parasympathetic end organ. Stimulation of the majority of the sympathetic ganglion cells or postganglionic fibers brings about liberation of the substance *sympathin*, resembling adrenalin. Stimulation of some sympathetic ganglion cells or their postganglionic fibers, however, leads to liberation of an acetylcholine-like substance. On the basis of the substance liberated, autonomic fibers are called cholinergic (forming acetylcholine) or adrenergic (forming sympathin).

Adrenergic nerve fibers exert a different physiologic effect from the cholinergic ones; thus, stimulation of the sympathetic nerves to the heart, which are adrenergic, causes an increased heart rate, while excitation of the parasympathetic nerves, which are cholinergic, causes a decrease in heart rate. In general, adrenergic fibers are excitatory, except in some regions such as the gastrointestinal tract where they exert an inhibitory effect. Cholinergic fibers are usually inhibitory, except in the gastrointestinal tract where they exert excitation.

GANGLIA OF THE AUTONOMIC NERVOUS SYSTEM. The ganglia of the autonomic nervous system can be divided into three groups: *vertebral, prevertebral,* and *terminal.* The vertebral group of ganglia is found on either side of the vertebral column, close to the bodies of the vertebrae. This group forms a series of 22 ganglia connected together in a chain or trunk, extending from the base of the skull to the coccyx. Prevertebral ganglia lie in the thorax, pelvis, and abdomen, near the aorta and its branches. Three large prevertebral ganglia, named according to their positions near their respective arteries, are the celiac, superior mesenteric, and inferior mesenteric. Terminal ganglia are small aggregates of ganglion cells lying upon or within the walls of the innervated organ.

Pre- and postganglionic neurons. The motor innervation of the visceral effector organ, in contrast to the innervation of the skeletal muscle in which a single neuron extends from the central nervous system to the muscle fiber, is by a two-neuron chain consisting of a preganglionic neuron and a postganglionic neuron with its cell body located in the autonomic ganglion. Thus, the preganglionic neuron conducts impulses from the spinal cord or brainstem to an autonomic ganglion, and the postganglionic neuron conducts from the ganglion to the visceral effector.

Sympathetic Nervous System (Fig. 203)

The sympathetic, or thoracolumbar preganglionic fibers, leave the spinal cord with the ventral roots. They then exit from these roots as rami communicantes, white or preganglionic, and enter ganglia of the sympathetic trunk. Some preganglionic fibers synapse in these ganglia; others continue to ganglia of the prevertebral plexuses, and still others reach and supply cells in the medullae of the suprarenal glands (Fig. 204).

Some of the postganglionic fibers return to the spinal nerves via the gray rami communicantes (postganglionic) and, by traveling with these nerves, reach blood vessels, smooth muscles, and sweat glands in the trunk and extremities. Other postganglionic fibers go directly to the adjacent viscera. There are three important branches in the thoracic portion of the sympathetic trunk,

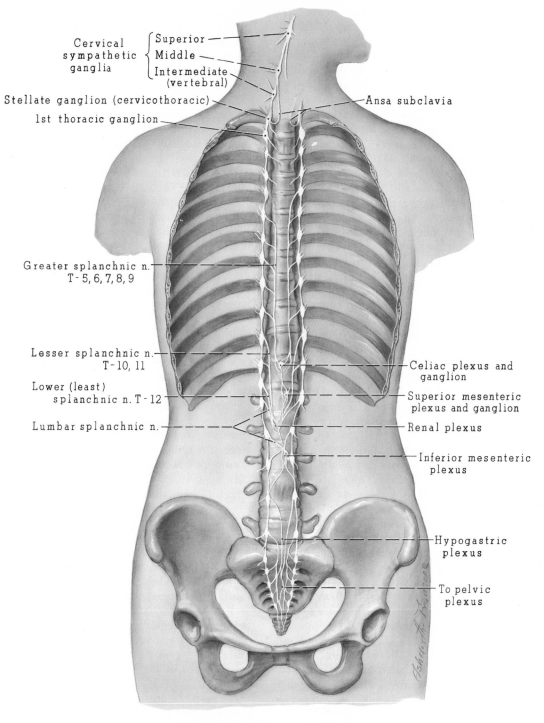

Cervical sympathetic ganglia
— Superior
— Middle
— Intermediate (vertebral)

Stellate ganglion (cervicothoracic)

1st thoracic ganglion

Ansa subclavia

Greater splanchnic n. T-5, 6, 7, 8, 9

Lesser splanchnic n. T-10, 11

Lower (least) splanchnic n. T-12

Lumbar splanchnic n.

Celiac plexus and ganglion

Superior mesenteric plexus and ganglion

Renal plexus

Inferior mesenteric plexus

Hypogastric plexus

To pelvic plexus

Fig. 203. Sympathetic nervous system.

termed the *greater, lesser,* and *least splanchnic nerves.* These travel through the diaphragm to the celiac and other ganglia and innervate the abdominal viscera.

PLEXUSES OF THE SYMPATHETIC SYSTEM. The great plexuses of the sympathetic system consist of ganglia and fibers derived from the lateral chain ganglia and spinal cord. These are located in the thoracic, abdominal, and pelvic cavities, and are given the names *cardiac, celiac,* and *hypogastric.* The cardiac plexus is situated at the base of the heart, lying on the arch and ascending portions of the aorta. The celiac plexus, also called the "solar plexus," is located in the abdomen in close relation to the celiac artery. The hypogastric plexus is situated anteriorly to the last lumbar vertebra and the sacrum.

Parasympathetic Nervous System

The parasympathetic, or craniosacral, part of the autonomic system consists of long preganglionic fibers arising from cells in the brainstem and sacral cord, and short postganglionic fibers arising in or near the organs innervated. Cranial fibers exist via the oculomotor, facial, glossopharyngeal, and vagus nerves. Their ganglion cells are in the walls of the thoracic and abdominal viscera and in four ganglia of the head: the ciliary, sphenopalatine, otic, and submandibular. The cells in the four cranial ganglia give origin to postganglionic fibers. The sacral fibers arising from the second, third, and fourth sacral segments leave the roots as pelvic nerves and are distributed to the pelvic viscera. Postganglionic fibers arise from the cells in the walls of the viscera.

Since sympathetic innervation to the head and neck comes from the white rami communicantes of T-1, 2, 3, and 4, it is obvious that division of the sympathetic trunk at a level between T-1 and C-8 results in an interruption of sympathetic supply to the head, neck, and most of the upper extremities. This produces Horner's syndrome, which includes narrowing of the palpebral fissure, small pupil, and the absence of sweating over the involved area (head, neck, and upper extremity).

The craniosacral or parasympathetic nervous system can be surgically altered in treatment of various disease states. The vagus nerves are divided for the treatment of duodenal ulcer. When the vagus nerves are divided, there is an important influence on hydrochloric acid secretion by the stomach. This results in the elimination of the cephalic phase of gastric secretion (see Chapter Thirteen) with diminished production of HCl by the parietal cells.

FUNCTIONS OF THE AUTONOMIC NERVOUS SYSTEM (Table 29). All the internal organs have a double nerve supply: one from the sympathetic, and one from the parasympathetic. Smooth muscle of hair, glands, and blood vessels and the suprarenal medullae are thought to have only sympathetic innervation. These two sets of nerves have opposing functions—one stimulates and the other inhibits the activity of a given organ. Thus, the heart rate is slowed by the parasympathetic division and accelerated by the sympathetic. On the other hand, the heart rate can be slowed by a decrease in sympathetic stimulation. In general, the parasympathetic system is concerned with restorative processes and the sympathetic with processes involving energy expenditure.

CONTROL OF THE AUTONOMIC NERVOUS SYSTEM. The hypothalamus is the major center for regulation and integration of both sympathetic and parasympathetic activity. It is connected with the cerebral cortex indirectly through the thalamus and also by direct afferent and efferent fibers with centers in the spinal cord. It joins with the peripheral and autonomic nervous systems, as well as with the hypophysis. Sympathetic control appears to reside in the posterior and lateral hypothalamic regions. Stimulation of these regions produces an increase in visceral and metabolic activities seen in emotional stress. Stimulation causes an increase in heartbeat, dilation of the pupils, a rise in blood pressure, increased rate and depth of respiration, and inhibition of the alimentary tract and urinary bladder.

Parasympathetic control apparently resides in the anterior and medial hypothalamus. If this region is stimulated, the cardiac rate is decreased and there is vasodilation of peripheral blood vessels, with increased motility and tone of muscles of the alimentary tract and the urinary bladder.

Anatomy and Physiology of Pain Pathways

ANATOMY. It is accepted that the epidermis and corium contain structures giving rise to sensations of touch, pain, heat, cold, or pressure when stimulated. Branching, non-myelinated, finely beaded nerve endings are found throughout the layers of the skin. Any given nerve fiber can convey impulses, but different stimuli set up different patterns of response. Recognition of the nature of the stimulus depends on the particular pattern of the *impulse as it is interpreted by the brain.*

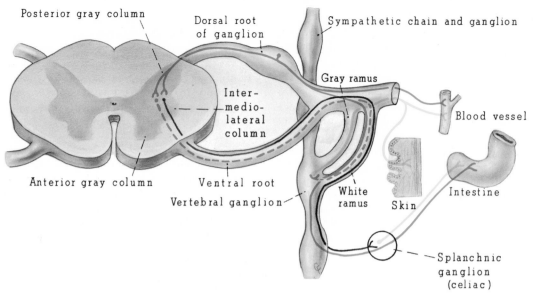

Fig. 204. Pathways for distribution of sympathetic fibers.

	TABLE 29. Functions of the Autonomic Nervous System.	
ORGAN	SYMPATHETIC STIMULATION	PARASYMPATHETIC STIMULATION
Eye		
Iris, ciliary muscle	Accommodates for far vision	Accommodates for near vision
Glands		
Lacrimal, parotid, submaxillary	Vasoconstriction	Stimulation of thin, copious secretion high in enzyme content
Sweat glands	Copious sweating (cholinergic)	None
Heart muscle	Increased rate	Decreased rate
Lungs		
Bronchi	Dilation	Constriction
Stomach		
Sphincter	Contraction	Inhibition
Glands	Inhibition	Secretion
Intestine		
Wall	Inhibition	Increased tone of musculature
Anal sphincter	Contraction	Decreased tone of musculature
Pancreas	Diminishes enzyme secretion	Stimulates secretion of pancreatic enzymes
Suprarenal gland		
Medulla	Secretion	No known effect
Kidney	Decreased output	No known effect
Urinary bladder		
Detrusor	Inhibition	Excitation
Trigone	Excitation	Inhibition
Penis	Ejaculation	Erection

PHYSIOLOGY OF PAIN. Painful stimuli are received at naked nerve endings scattered throughout the skin and viscera. Pain impulses are carried though myelinated and non-myelinated fibers either directly to the posterior root ganglia in somatic nerves and thence to the spinothalamic tract or indirectly, in sympathetic ganglia, to the posterior root by way of the white rami communicantes.

Stimuli effective in arousing the sensation of pain vary to some degree for each tissue. The very existence of pain impulses arising from the viscera was debated, until it was shown that adequate stimuli for pain originating in the heart or digestive tract, for example, were different from those producing pain in the skin. Skin is sensitive to cutting and burning, whereas this type of stimulation does not give rise to distress when applied to the stomach or intestine. Pain in the digestive tract is produced by distension or spasm of the smooth muscle, as well as by irritation of an inflamed mucosa. Severe pain can occur in skeletal muscle when the blood supply is reduced—the basis of a condition known as intermittent claudication (pain in the calf associated with arterial disease of the lower extremities).

Ischemia (reduction in oxygen supply), the only proved cause of pain in the heart muscle, is responsible for the pain of angina pectoris and myocardial infarction (blockage of the coronary artery to the heart with death of heart muscle).

Referred pain (Fig. 205). When pain is aroused by stimulation of afferent endings in the viscera, it is usually referred to some other skin area, a fact of great diagnostic importance.

Afferent nerves from the viscera terminate in the spinal cord segment which supplies the particular viscus involved. Those areas to which pain from various organs is referred have been mapped out; they indicate to the physician the internal source of irritation. For example, the sensory fibers from the heart terminate in the first through the fourth thoracic cord segments, and pain arising in the heart as a result of ischemia is not localized specifically to the region of the heart, but to those superficial and deep structures whose sensory nerves also terminate in the first through the fourth thoracic spinal segments. Thus, in heart pain in which sensory impulses enter mainly the left half of the first through the fourth thoracic cord segments, reference of pain to the arms is explained by the anatomic fact that the first thoracic segment supplies the inner

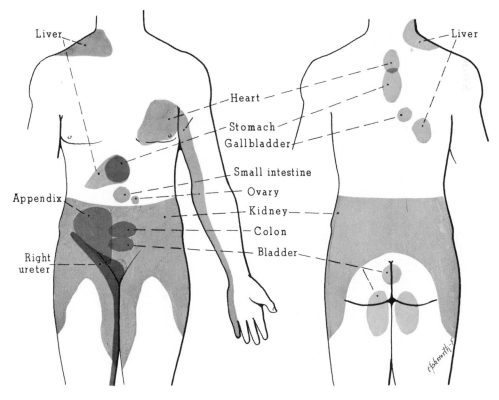

Fig. 205.   Areas of referred pain, anterior and posterior views.

segment of the arm as well as the thorax and heart. Thus, it is just as natural for heart pain to appear in the characteristic location in the left arm as in the anterior midchest.

Phantom limb pain. Following an amputation, the patient can retain the amputated limb as a part of his body image. This is a reflection of the association established between stimuli from the periphery and the cortical area of representation. Stimuli continue to arise from the severed sensory nerves and are interpreted centrally as arising, for example, from the hand. Yet the patient mistakenly feels that his pain is imaginary since he knows his hand was amputated. Pain of this kind places additional psychologic burdens on the patient who believes he is imagining things his reason tells him cannot exist. It is important to explain to this type of patient that the sensation of pain is real and not a figment of his imagination. The sensation can be defined clearly, and the patient will say that his arm is twisted or that his thumb is being pushed backward. The cortical image of the amputated extremity can remain fixed in the same position as when amputation occurred. This is particularly true in traumatic amputations.

The management of phantom limb pain is more effective if measures are taken to prevent it rather than treat it once the condition has been established. If pain is due to a surgical amputation, anesthetic infiltration of the nerve bundles at the site of amputation should be performed before surgery. In this way, the surgeon can probably minimize the locking or painful image in the patient's consciousness.

SURGERY OF PAIN (Fig. 206). Various methods have been employed to surgically relieve pain. In the majority of patients, however, medical measures are adequate. There remains, however, a group of people requiring surgical treatment. From a physiologic point of view, interruption of pain impulses has been carried out at three points: (1) the autonomic nervous system; (2) pathways in the peripheral nerves, spinal roots, and spinal cord; and (3) interruption of pathways within the brain. The various procedures performed on the autonomic nervous system consist of some form of sympathectomy. The most frequently employed operation on the parasympathetic system is interruption of the vagus nerves.

Division of the peripheral nerves or spinal pathways is sometimes undertaken for pain not

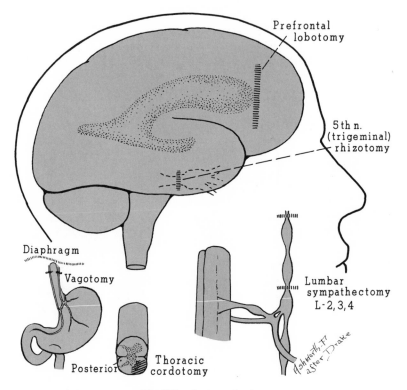

Fig. 206. Surgery of pain.

responsive to other means (intractable pain). The pathways within the spinal cord conveying pain impulses can be interrupted. The anterolateral, or spinothalamic tracts are sectioned in an operation known as anterolateral *cordotomy*. A cordotomy can be performed as high as the second cervical segment if pain relief in the arm is required. However, the optimal site for division of the spinothalamic tract is the upper thoracic region. Posterior cordotomy occasionally gives good results in patients with phantom limb pain of the lower extremities. The trigeminal root ganglion can be interrupted for tic douloureux.

A distinction must be drawn between the sensations of pain and the response of the patient to the pain. By means of operations on the frontal cortex, it is possible to alter the patient's reaction, so that, while pain is felt, the reaction is completely changed. As previously mentioned, operations on the frontal cortex are associated with personality changes (see Fig. 206 for location of this procedure).

SUMMARY

We have seen the development of the brain from the relatively undifferentiated arrangement of cells to the mass communication center of the complex human. It has been noted that the spinal cord evolves from the simple patterned neural tube and notochord to a conducting structure 40 to 45 cm. in length integrating all body functions. This is not the end. A greater knowledge of the brain in relation to the rest of the body has served merely as a stimulus to arouse more curiosity. For instance, how does one actually think? What really causes an epileptic seizure?

For hundreds of years, there were no tools sensitive enough to explore the consciousness of the human brain; consequently, the life-like

brain revealed little. In the past decade, many advances in mapping the brain have been made. Recent developments in pharmacology and electronics may solve many difficult problems of brain function. New improvements in anesthesia permit a patient to remain conscious during brain surgery so that he can discuss his reactions with his physicians. Tiny electrodes probe deeply into tissues. In fact, electrodes can be left connected to fine wires and plastic sockets within the brain for weeks or months. With probing has come also an increasingly accurate mapping of pinpoint areas in the midbrain, possibly to control hunger, sex, and other basic drives. With these techniques scientists are now learning how midbrain centers govern behavior and how they operate under stress.

Parkinson's syndrome, multiple sclerosis, and other diseases produce defective cells sometimes leading to tremors. Actual freezing and high frequency sound waves have been applied to the brain to block neuronal centers responsible for these tremors.

One of the most important discoveries in brain mapping is the actual localization of functional centers of the midbrain. Conceivably, penetration of the midbrain could lead to squelching of mammoth appetite and reduction in obesity. Stress is another area of study. It places abnormal demands on the thyroid and other glands regulated by the hypothalamus; thus, the exhausted cells break down and promote ulcers and abnormal behavior. Drugs are now being developed to diminish such errors or imbalance.

In summary, then, the nervous system not only controls physiologic responses, but also psychologic ones. Moods, in reality, are physiologic imbalances. Each time an individual senses his environment and reacts to it, the experience is mediated by the nervous system. This could be possible only in the most miraculous of all machines—the human body.

SUMMARY: THE NERVOUS SYSTEM

DEVELOPMENT OF THE NERVOUS SYSTEM

1. Surface ectoderm forms a neural plate, which then develops into the neural tube.

2. At the cephalic end of the neural tube, three primary vesicles form: the prosencephalon, mesencephalon, and rhombencephalon.

3. Three flexures form: the cephalic, cervical, and pontine flexures.

4. The optic vesicle evaginates from the forebrain.

5. The telencephalon or cerebral hemispheres form from the prosencephalon.

Types of Nerve Cells

1. **Neuroglia:**

   a. Non-nervous elements subserving functions of support, repair, and metabolism.
   b. Microglia—phagocytic cells in nervous tissue.

2. **Neurons:**

   a. Structure: contain nucleus, perikaryon, mitochondria, Nissl substance, neurofibrils and Golgi apparatus.
   b. Two types of processes: dendrites carrying impulses toward cell body and axons carrying impulses away from cell body.
   c. Microscopic structure of axon:
      (1) Consists of four parts: axis cylinder, myelin sheath, neurilemma, and Schwann cells.
      (2) Nodes of Ranvier: periodic constrictions in myelin sheath.
   d. Neuron types according to structure:
      (1) Multipolar: one axon, many dendrites.
      (2) Bipolar: one axon, one dendrite.
      (3) Unipolar: one axon, rare except in embryo.
   e. Neuron types according to function:
      (1) Sensory (afferent), convey impulses toward central nervous system.
      (2) Motor (efferent), convey impulses away from central nervous system.
      (3) Internuncial (intercalated), conduct impulses from sensory to motor neurons.
   f. Physiology of the neuron:
      (1) Conduction of nerve impulses: altered permeability of membrane results in sodium influx and potassium outflux, resulting in a self-propagating wave of negativity passing along neuron membrane.
      (2) All-or-none principle: once excited, a neuron will conduct impulses of constant and maximum magnitudes.
      (3) Transmission of impulse at the synapse: acetylcholine-like substance liberated by axon endings stimulates dendrite of postsynaptic neuron. Thus, an impulse travels in only one direction across a synapse.
      (4) Neuromuscular junction: acetycholine liberated by axon alters sarcolemma permeability to sodium ions, creating an impulse in muscle fiber.
      (5) Rate of impulse conduction: the larger the nerve fiber and the thicker the myelin, the faster the rate of conduction. Largest fibers conduct at 100 meters per second, the smallest at 0.5 per second.

3. **Divisions of the nervous system:**

   a. Central nervous system:
      (1) Brain.
      (2) Spinal cord.
   b. Peripheral nervous system:
      (1) Cranial nerves: 12 pairs.
      (2) Spinal nerves: 31 pairs.
      (3) Autonomic nervous system.

BRAIN

1. **Forebrain (prosencephalon):**

   a. Telencephalon (cerebrum).
   b. Diencephalon (thalamus, hypothalamus).

2. **Midbrain (mesencephalon):**

   a. Corpora quadrigemina.
   b. Cerebral peduncles.

3. **Hindbrain (rhombencephalon):**

   a. Metencephalon (cerebellum, pons).
   b. Myelencephalon (medulla oblongata).

CEREBRUM

1. **Description: largest portion of brain; partially divided by longitudinal fissure into two hemispheres (connected by corpus callosum); each hemisphere divided by fissures into four major lobes: frontal, parietal, temporal, and occipital.**

2. **Sulci.**

3. **Cortex: outer layer of gray matter arranged in convolutions or gyri; divided into 52 areas by Brodmann.**

4. **Projection areas: portions of cortex specialized for dispatch of motor directives and for reception of sensory messages.**

5. **Internal structures of the cerebrum:**

   a. Cerebral nuclei or basal ganglia influence normal movements.
   b. White matter in cerebrum: internal capsule and other tracts connecting the various lobes.

6. **Dysfunction of the cerebral cortex:**

   a. Motor area involvement results in hemiplegia or hemiparesis of the opposite half of the body.
   b. Epileptic seizures can originate from various foci in cortex.
   c. Other cerebral dysfunctions may result in altered behavior, visual defects, aphasias, etc.

DIENCEPHALON

1. **Thalamus:**

   a. Large mass of gray matter located in medioposterior aspect of each hemisphere.
   b. Relays afferent impulses to cerebral cortex.
   c. Lowest level of conscious recognition of sensation.

2. **Hypothalamus:**

   a. Involved in autonomic functions, sleep, appetite, and control of hypophysis.

MESENCEPHALON (MIDBRAIN)

1. **Connects cerebrum with pons and cerebellum.**

2. **Contains four nuclear masses: the corpora quadrigemina (superior and inferior colliculi).**

3. Fiber tracts: cerebral peduncles connect pons to cerebrum.

4. Canal, cerebral aqueduct of Sylvius, connects third and fourth ventricles.

5. Contains center for pupillary reflexes.

CEREBELLUM

1. Structure and location:

   a. Occupies posterior cranial fossa.
   b. Composed of constricted central portion (the vermis), and lateral expanded portions (the hemispheres).

2. Function:

   a. Anterior lobe: posture.
   b. Posterior lobe: coordination of movement.
   c. Flocculonodular lobe: equilibrium.

PONS

1. Structure and location:

   a. Lies anterior to cerebellum between midbrain and medulla.
   b. White matter with few nuclei.

2. Function:

   a. Bridge-like structure containing projection tracts between spinal cord and brain.

MEDULLA OBLONGATA

1. Structure and location:

   a. Continuous with spinal cord through foramen magnum.
   b. Ventrally are pyramids (corticospinal tracts).
   c. Contains mainly white matter.
   d. Nuclei: two most prominent nuclei, nucleus gracilis and nucleus cuneatus. Also inferior olivary nuclei and reticular formation.
   e. Various autonomic centers: e.g., respiratory, cardiac, vasomotor, vomiting, etc.

2. Function:

   a. Contains tracts from brain to cord and vice versa.
   b. Center for many reflexes (cough, etc.).
   c. Helps control heart, blood vessels, respiration.

RETICULAR FORMATION

1. Diffusely scattered neurons.

2. Part of extrapyramidal pathway.

3. Modifies (excites or inhibits) reflex activity of spinal anterior horn motor cells.

BRAINSTEM

1. Composed of midbrain, pons, and medulla.

2. Origin of some cranial nerves.

Blood Supply to Brain

1. Arterial supply:

   a. Circle of Willis formed from branches of internal carotid arteries and basilar artery. Basilar artery formed by vertebral arteries.

   b. Branches from this system go to all parts of brain.

2. Venous drainage:

   a. By venous sinuses in dura.

   b. Drainage ultimately into internal jugular vein.

Ventricles of the Brain

1. Four ventricles: two lateral ventricles, one in each hemisphere; one (third) ventricle in the diencephalon; one (fourth) beneath the cerebellum.

2. Lateral ventricles communicate with third via foramina of Monro. Third and fourth ventricles communicate via cerebral aqueduct of Sylvius.

Meninges of the Brain

1. Dura mater:

   a. Outer dense elastic tissue layer.

   b. Four extensions: falx cerebelli, falx cerebri, tentorium cerebelli, and diaphragma sellae.

2. Arachnoid:

   a. Middle delicate membrane.

   b. Between this and pia mater is subarachnoid space containing cerebrospinal fluid.

Cerebrospinal Fluid

1. Volume: 80 to 200 ml.

2. Formation: a dialysate formed by the choroid plexus of the ventricles.

3. Flows through ventricles and out foramina of Luschka and Magendie into subarachnoid space around spinal cord and brain. Reabsorbed into venous blood by arachnoid villi.

4. Function: protection.

5. Hydrocephalus: caused by blockage of cerebrospinal fluid circulation.

Cranial Nerves

1. Twelve pairs of symmetrically arranged nerves attached directly to the brain and leaving the skull through foramina.

2. Names in order from I to XII: olfactory, optic, oculomotor, trochlear, trigeminal, abducens, facial, vestibulocochlear (acoustic), glossopharyngeal, vagus, accessory, and hypoglossal.

3. For distribution and function see Table 24.

SPINAL CORD

1. Location and structure:
    a. Extends from foramen magnum to second lumbar vertebra.
    b. Terminates in filum terminale—an extension of the pia mater.
    c. Two swellings: cervical and lumbar enlargements.
    d. Contains butterfly-shaped core of gray matter.
    e. White matter arranged into anterior, posterior, and lateral funiculi.

2. Function:
    a. Contains all ascending and descending fiber tracts between peripheral nerves and brain.
    b. Center for segmental and intersegmental reflexes.

ASCENDING TRACTS (AFFERENT)

1. Fasciculus gracilis and fasciculus cuneatus convey sensations of position, movements, touch, and pressure.

2. Lateral spinothalamic tract conveys sensations of pain and temperature.

3. Ventral spinothalamic tract transmits stimuli of touch and pressure.

4. Dorsal spinocerebellar tract conveys sensory impulses from muscles and muscle tendons to cerebellum.

5. Ventral spinocerebellar tract: same as dorsal spinocerebellar tract.

6. Spinotectal tract: correlation pathway of spinal cord.

DESCENDING TRACTS (EFFERENT)

1. Corticospinal tract (pyramidal): major pathway from cortex to peripheral motor nerves for voluntary movements.

2. Tectospinal tract: originates in superior colliculus; mediates optic and auditory reflexes.

3. Rubrospinal tract: conveys impulses from cerebellum to anterior column motor cells; originates in red nucleus.

MOTOR NERVOUS SYSTEM

1. Composed of lower motor neurons, upper motor neurons.
    a. Lower motor neuron axons arise from anterior column of spinal cord and motor nuclei of cranial nerves to form the peripheral motor nerves.
    b. Upper motor neuron axons arise from pyramidal cells of Betz in precentral gyrus of cortex and terminate in the anterior column cells.
    c. Extrapyramidal system includes all motor pathways except corticospinal tracts.

REFLEXES

1. Reflex arc includes sense organ, afferent neuron, one or more synapses in a central integrating station, efferent neuron, effector.

2. Deep reflexes (e.g., knee jerk) consist of muscular contraction in response to the stretching of that muscle's tendon.

3. Superficial (cutaneous) reflexes (e.g., abdominal, cremasteric) consist of muscular contraction in response to cutaneous stimulation.

4. Pupillary reflex: pupil contracts in response to light or accommodation.

SPECIAL EXAMINATIONS OF CENTRAL NERVOUS SYSTEM

1. Lumbar puncture: withdrawal of spinal fluid for examination.

2. Encephalogram: cerebrospinal fluid replaced by air and x-rays taken to determine if fluid spaces are patent.

SPINAL NERVES

1. Structure: composed of large numbers of sensory dendrites and motor axons, grouped into fascicles each surrounded by perineurium. Epineurium covers entire nerve unit, while endoneurium extends between individual nerve fibers.

2. Formed from dorsal sensory root and ventral motor root of spinal cord.

3. Thirty-one pairs: 8 cervical, 12 thoracic, 5 lumbar, 5 sacral, and 1 coccygeal.

4. Four branches:

   a. Meningeal branch: to meninges of cord.
   b. Dorsal branch: to muscles and skin of back of head, neck, and trunk.
   c. Ventral branch: to muscles and skin of front of head, neck, and trunk.
   d. Visceral branch: two portions: white ramus is myelinated sympathetic fibers traveling to sympathetic ganglia. Gray ramus: non-myelinated sympathetic fibers from sympathetic ganglion back to peripheral nerve.

5. Plexuses:

   a. Cervical plexus: C-1, 2, 3, 4.
   b. Brachial plexus: C-5, 6, 7, 8, and T-1. Branches: axillary, musculocutaneous, ulnar, median, radial.
   c. Lumbar plexus: L-1, 2, 3, 4. Major branches: lateral femoral cutaneous, femoral, genitofemoral.
   d. Sciatic: L-4, 5, S-1, 2, 3.

6. Wallerian degeneration:

   a. Distal portion of severed nerve degenerates; proximal portion degenerates to first node of Ranvier.
   b. Distally, Schwann cells form tube, proximal portion regenerates and sends branches into tube.
   c. Rate of growth: 1.5 mm. per day.

AUTONOMIC NERVOUS SYSTEM

1. Involuntary part of nervous system that sends efferent fibers to smooth muscle of internal organs, blood vessels, glands, and ciliary muscle, and to cardiac muscle and gland cells. This system is concerned with maintaining homeostasis in the internal environment and with providing the "flight or fight" response.

2. Divisions:

   a. Sympathetic or thoracolumbar (mostly adrenergic).
   b. Parasympathetic or craniosacral (cholinergic).

3. Ganglia: vertebral, prevertebral, or terminal

4. Neurons:

   a. Preganglionic: from central nervous system to autonomic ganglia.
   b. Postganglionic: from autonomic ganglion to effector organ.

SYMPATHETIC SYSTEM

1. Postganglionic fibers issue from the 22 pairs of ganglia in sympathetic chain.

Some travel with spinal nerves, others reach the viscera via the three splanchnic nerves.

2. Functions—see Table 25.

PARASYMPATHETIC SYSTEM

1. Preganglionic fibers in vagus nerve (X) innervate viscera as far as left colic flexure. Remainder of viscera receive parasympathetic fibers from sacral division. Ganglion cells are in or near organs innervated.

2. Functions—see Table 25.

PAIN

1. Pain sensations transmitted by branching, non-myelinated, finely beaded naked nerve endings found throughout the layers of the skin.

2. Pain fibers travel in spinal or sympathetic nerves and then go to lateral spinothalamic tract of spinal cord.

3. Types of pain: referred, phantom limb.

STUDY QUESTIONS: NERVOUS SYSTEM

1. Name the three primary brain vesicles and the three flexures of the developing brain.
2. Briefly discuss the neuroglia. Name the different types and discuss their general functions.
3. Name the three types of neurons according to structure (number of processes) and the three types according to function.
4. Define a reflex arc. Name two deep superficial reflexes.
5. Briefly discuss the following: conduction of nerve impulses; all-or-none principle; synaptic transmission; and neuromuscular junction.
6. Name the lobes of the cerebrum.
7. Define: projection area.
8. What is white matter? Gray matter?
9. What is the general function of the thalamus?
10. What is the general function of the hypothalamus?
11. Name the canal in the mesencephalon and give its function.
12. Draw a diagram of the circle of Willis; include the arteries forming it and its major branches.
13. Give the location of each of the four ventricles of the brain.
14. Name the meninges of the brain in order from outside in. Where is the cerebrospinal fluid?
15. Trace the path of a drop of cerebrospinal fluid from the first (lateral) ventricle to the arachnoid villi.
16. Name the twelve cranial nerves. Which are sensory, which are motor, and which are mixed?
17. Diagram and label a cross section of the spinal cord.
18. Define ascending and descending tracts and name three examples of each.
19. Briefly discuss the structure and composition of a spinal nerve and name the four branches.
20. Name four major plexuses and give their levels of origin and major branches.
21. Briefly discuss wallerian degeneration.
22. Give a description of the autonomic nervous system.
23. Name the two divisions of the autonomic nervous system, and discuss the anatomic and functional differences between these two divisions.
24. What are pre- and postganglionic fibers?
25. Discuss the rationale behind referred pain.
26. Pain is transmitted by which tract of the spinal cord?

CHAPTER NINE.

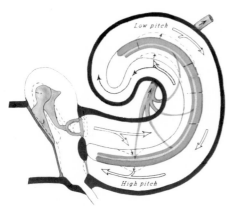

SPECIAL SENSES

PROCESS OF SENSATION

The sequence from stimulus to receptor to sensory nerve to central nervous system is the physical basis of sensation. In this sequence, there are many intricacies and mysteries. To understand the physical basis of sensation, the structure and function of the receptor for each of the senses must be studied.

A sensation will occur if all the following are present: a stimulus—that is, a physical event; a receptor—a specialized cell capable of responding to the stimulus and changing the physical event into a set of nerve impulses; and a central nervous system—to interpret impulses and bring about conscious sensation.

VISION

External Structures of the Eye

The external structures of the eye are the *orbital cavity*, the *extrinsic ocular muscles*, the *eyelids*, the *conjunctiva*, and the *lacrimal apparatus* (Fig. 207).

The orbital cavity. The orbital cavity contains the eyeball and is a bony, cone-shaped region in front of the skull lined with fatty tissue to cushion the eyeball. The bones forming the orbital cavity are fragile and thin. The bone at the rim of the orbit is thicker to protect the eye from injury (see Chapter Five).

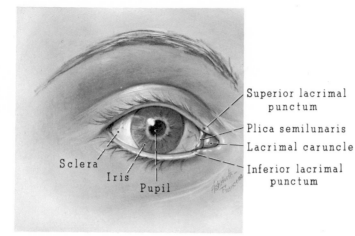

Fig. 207.   External appearance of the eye and surrounding structures.

Extrinsic ocular muscles.   Six extrinsic or external muscles connect the eyeball to the orbital cavity and provide rotary movement and support. These muscles are four straight (rectus) muscles (*superior, inferior, lateral,* and *medial*), and two oblique muscles (*superior* and *inferior*).

The eyelids.   The eyelids or palpebrae are two movable "curtains" located anterior to the eyeball; they protect the eye from dust, intense light, and impact. The *palpebral fissure* is the interval between the eyelids. The *canthus* is the corner or angle at which the lids meet. The free margins of the eyelids are surmounted by eyelashes, which protect the eye from dust and perspiration.

A plate of condensed fibrous tissue, the tarsus, is located at the free edge of each eyelid, giving the lid substance and shape. The tarsal plate contains tarsal (meibomian) glands opening onto the lid margin. These glands secrete an oily substance onto the eyelids.

Conjunctival membrane.   The conjunctiva, a thin layer of mucous membrane, lines the inner surface of each eyelid and is continuous with the surface cells at the margins of the cornea.

Lacrimal apparatus.   The eye is cleansed and lubricated by the lacrimal apparatus, which consists of four structures (Fig. 208):

1. *The lacrimal gland* is located in a depression of the frontal bone at the upper and outer angle of the orbit. Approximately 12 ducts lead from each gland to the surface of the conjunctiva of the upper lid, where they deposit lacrimal fluid (in excess, known as tears).

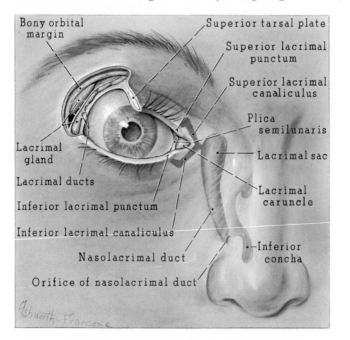

Fig. 208.   Lacrimal apparatus in relation to the eye.

2. The *lacrimal canals* (*canaliculi*) are ducts extending from the inner angle of the eyelid and emptying into the lacrimal sac. Two openings known as puncta, positioned at the inner canthus of the eye, open into these canals.

3. The *lacrimal sac* is located at the inner angle of the eyelids in grooves on the lacrimal bone. The lacrimal sac is an enlargement of the upper end of the nasolacrimal duct.

4. The *nasolacrimal duct* extends from the lacrimal sac to the inferior meatus of the nose, draining tears from the eye.

Fluid secreted by the lacrimal glands washes over the eyeball and is swept up by the blinking action of the eyelids. Muscles associated with the blinking reflex compress the lacrimal sac. When these muscles relax, the sac expands, pulling fluid from the edges of the lids along the lacrimal canals into the lacrimal sacs. Gravitational force, in turn, moves the fluid down the nasolacrimal duct into the inferior meatus of the nose. Thus, the eyeball is continually irrigated by a gentle stream of fluid which prevents it from becoming dry and inflamed.

Internal Structures of the Eye

LAYERS OF THE EYEBALL.   The wall of the eyeball is composed of three layers. The outer is the fibrous protective layer consisting of the *sclera* and *cornea*. The middle is the highly vascular pigmented layer composed of the *choroid*, *ciliary body*, and *iris*. The inner is the *retina*, a nervous layer containing nerve endings of the optic nerve (Fig. 209).

The outer, fibrous layer.   The sclera or "white of the eye" forms the fibrous external support of the eyeball. It covers the posterior three-fourths of the eyeball, joining with the transparent cornea covering the anterior portion of the eyeball. A ring-shaped sinus draining the anterior chamber of the eye, the sinus venosus sclerae (*canal of Schlemm*), is located within the sclera. If this canal becomes obstructed, glaucoma may result.

The cornea extends anteriorly from the sclera. It is approximately 10 to 11 mm. in diameter. The function of the cornea is similar to that of a photographic lens. Light rays coming to it are

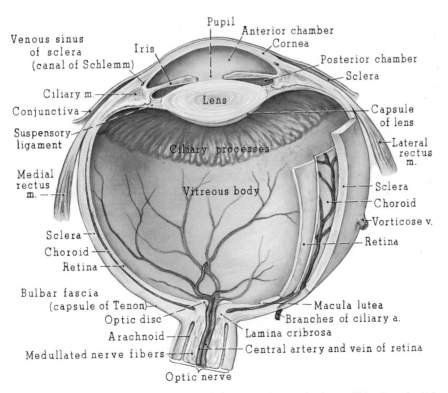

Fig. 209.   Mid-sagittal section through the eyeball showing layers of retina and blood supply. (After Lederle.)

focused slightly behind the retina. The crystalline lens of the eye sharpens the focus. The cornea might be compared to the coarse adjustment of a microscope, and the lens to the fine adjustment.

The middle, vascular layer. The *choroid*, the membranous lining inside the sclera, is highly vascular and darkly pigmented. This pigmentation prevents the internal reflection of light.

The *ciliary body* lies anterior to the choroid. It is located between the outer margin of the retina and the base of the iris. The ciliary body permits flexibility of the lens for clearer vision.

The *iris* is a diaphragm located anterior to the lens and posterior to the cornea. It has a circular opening in its center (the pupil) regulating the amount of light admitted to the interior of the eyeball. Circular and radiating pigmented muscle fibers are present in the iris. The circular fibers contract the pupil in strong light and near vision; the radiating fibers dilate the pupil in dim light and far vision.

The inner, nervous layer. The *retina* is the nervous layer of the eye. It translates light waves into neural impulses and is located anterior to the choroid, extending forward to the posterior part of the ciliary body. The structure and function of the separate layers of the retina are discussed in a subsequent paragraph.

REFRACTING MEDIA OF THE EYE. Besides the cornea, the refracting media of the eye are the aqueous humor, the lens, and the vitreous body. These media bend the light rays and help focus them on the retina.

The *aqueous humor* fills the anterior cavity of the eye (that portion of the eye in front of the lens). Aqueous humor is secreted by the ciliary processes and is absorbed from the anterior chamber at a rate comparable to its formation, thus maintaining constant pressure within the eyeball. Defective absorption of fluid increases the internal pressure and brings on glaucoma. Severe glaucoma may cause blindness. The aqueous humor nourishes the internal structures of the eye which do not possess a blood supply of their own.

The *lens*, lying immediately posterior to the iris, is a biconvex crystalline body enclosed in a transparent capsule. From this capsule, suspensory ligaments extend in laterally to the ciliary body supporting it. The tension of the suspensory ligaments attached to the lens adjusts its shape to keep the object continually focused on the retina. For distant vision, the lens thins; for near vision, the lens thickens.

The *vitreous humor*, a soft, jelly-like material, fills the posterior cavity of the eye (the portion behind the lens). If vitreous humor escapes from a wound, it is not reformed and blindness can result, since the retina loses its support and falls forward.

Physiology of Vision

For conscious reception of a visual image, the image must be formed on the retina and transformed into nerve impulses which are relayed to the brain.

The focusing of the image on the retina is called *accommodation*. This entails regulation of the amount of light admitted through the action of the iris, focusing the image by the cornea and lens, and aligning the visual axes of the two eyes.

FUNCTION OF THE RETINA. When the image is formed on the retina, the photosensitive cells of the retina (the rods and cones) translate the light energy into nervous impulses. Each eye contains approximately 6 million cones and 120 million rods. The majority of cones are massed together in a small area called the *macula lutea*, within which is a small region called the *fovea centralis* containing only cone cells. The concentration of cones diminishes away from the macula, whereas the concentration of rods reaches a maximum about 4 mm. from the fovea. The fovea is the central focusing point for the optic system of the eye. Since rods are absent in the fovea centralis, it is considered a "blind spot" in dim light (Fig. 210).

Rods are sensitive to dim light and function in night vision. They contain a photosensitive chemical called *rhodopsin* (visual purple). Light, acting as a stimulus on rhodopsin, initiates a chain reaction. The first product is lumi-rhodopsin, an unstable compound. This rapidly decays to form meta-rhodopsin which decomposes into retinene (visual yellow) and scotopsin. Rhodopsin is then reformed from retinene and scotopsin (Fig. 211). If a shortage of retinene exists, caused by a deficiency in its precursor vitamin A, rhodopsin cannot be formed and a condition known as night blindness results. It is currently believed that during the breakdown cycle of rhodopsin, scotopsin ionizes, attacks the nerve cell membrane, and produces a nerve impulse.

The photochemistry of color vision (daylight vision) is believed to involve cones rather than rods. Cones are more sensitive in light than rods because they can resynthesize their photosensitive chemical more quickly. Rods function better in dim light, since they are more sensitive to poor illumination.

NERVOUS PATHWAY FOR VISION (Fig. 212). The nervous pathway for vision through the retina involves the following steps.

1. Impulses are generated by the rods and cones.

2. Impulses pass through the outer nuclear and outer fibrous layers, forming the synaptic connections between receptor cells and bipolar cells.

3. Impulses are transformed in bipolar cells.

4. Impulses pass through the inner nuclear and inner fiber layers. These represent synaptic connections between the bipolar and ganglion cells.

5. Impulses are further coordinated within the ganglion cells.

The axons of ganglion cells form the optic nerve by perforating the sclera at the optic disc, creating a sieve-like structure, the *lamina cribrosa*. An absence of the visual end organs at this point accounts for the blind spot in the field of vision. The optic nerve extends from the disc to the optic chiasm, where the fibers undergo partial decussation. From the chiasm, the fibers (now called the optic tract) continue on each side of the midbrain, and the visual impulses are relayed by neurons to the occipital lobe of the brain (see Chapter Eight and Fig. 213).

BINOCULAR VISION. Man's eyes are arranged so that the image received by each eye is slightly different. Thus, man is said to have *binocular vision*. The points of the two retinas receiving identical images are termed corresponding points; however, corresponding points are different on each retina. The rays of light forming an image on the temporal half of the right retina form the same image on the nasal half of the left, and vice versa. Nerve pathways from corresponding points on each retina pass through the optic chiasm into the same visual area of the occipital lobe. One lobe receives the right-sided image of both the right and left eyes, and the other lobe receives the left-sided image. In the visual cortex images are fused, and a single visual sensation with a three-dimensional effect is experienced.

Binocular vision is maintained through nervous and muscular coordination of eye movements. If the muscles are not coordinated, *strabismus* results. In strabismus, the visual axes of the eyes are not parallel. Thus, the images of the two eyes do not fall upon corresponding retinal points, and double vision (diplopia) results.

Abnormalities of the Eye

The focusing properties of the eye are often imperfect, causing nearsightedness (myopia), farsightedness (hyperopia), oldsightedness (presbyopia), and uneven focusing in different planes (astigmatism). Other abnormalities of the eye include cataracts, opacities of the cornea, inflammations of the conjunctiva (conjunctivitis), and stye.

Myopia results from an abnormally long distance between the cornea and lens or lens and retina, and is a condition in which the image of a distant object focuses in front of the retina. By use of a concave lens of proper power, the position of the image is moved farther back to focus on the retina (Fig. 214). *Hyperopia* (farsightedness), is the opposite condition, resulting from an abnormally short distance between the cornea and lens; in hyperopia the image of an object focuses behind the retina. By use of a convex lens of proper power, the position of the image is moved forward to focus on the retina (Fig. 215). *Presbyopia* (oldsightedness) occurs with increasing age. In presbyopia, the lens gradually loses its elasticity, interfering with correct accommodation, so that the near point (i.e., the nearest point at which objects are seen distinctly) is a yard or more away from the eye; consequently, older individuals need a convex lens to clearly see objects less than a yard away.

Astigmatism is a visual defect resulting from distortion of the curvature of the cornea or lens of the eye. It is corrected by a cylindrical lens placed in the proper axial position (Fig. 216).

Senile cataract is an aging process in the lens. Actually, every opacity of the lens can be called a cataract; thus, there are few individuals over the age of 65 who do not have cataracts.

Injuries or infections of the cornea can lead to *corneal opacity*, causing blindness. A corneal transplant is a method of treatment. In a successful transplant, the transparency of the graft will persist. Homotransplants of the cornea are tolerated, since the anterior chamber of the eye lacks blood and lymph vessels (a sanctuary for a graft). Blood and lymph vessels are necessary for graft rejection. If corneal tissue is transplanted to another area, such as under the skin, it will be destroyed. If skin is transplanted to the anterior chamber of the eye, it will survive.

Conjunctivitis (inflammation of the conjunctiva) is the most common infection of the eye. It can be caused by any irritation from dust, pollen, bacteria, or viruses, and is characterized by inflammation and an increased flow of tears. The

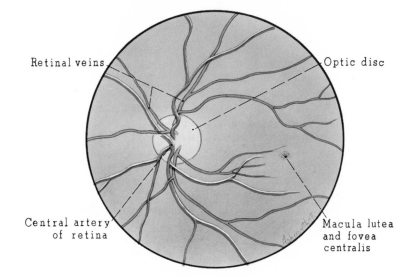

Retinal veins

Optic disc

Central artery
of retina

Macula lutea
and fovea
centralis

Fig. 210. Retina of the normal eye as seen through the ophthalmoscope.

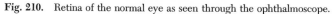

RHODOPSIN $\xrightarrow{\textit{light}}$ LUMI-RHODOPSIN

darkness

META-RHODOPSIN

SCOTOPSIN

RETINENE

VITAMIN A

Fig. 211. Rhodopsin cycle.

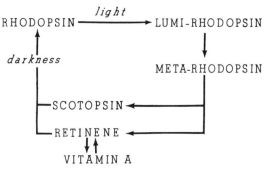

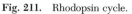

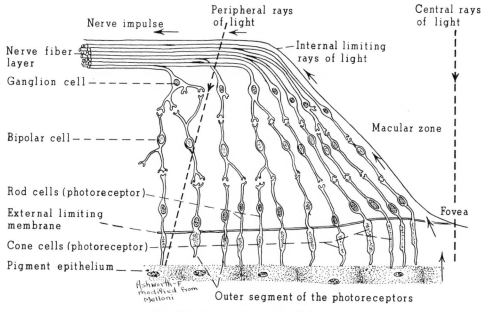

Nerve impulse

Peripheral rays
of light

Central rays
of light

Nerve fiber
layer

Internal limiting
rays of light

Ganglion cell

Bipolar cell

Macular zone

Rod cells (photoreceptor)

External limiting
membrane

Fovea

Cone cells (photoreceptor)

Pigment epithelium

Ashworth-F
modified from
Melloni

Outer segment of the photoreceptors

Fig. 212. Layers of the retina of the eye.

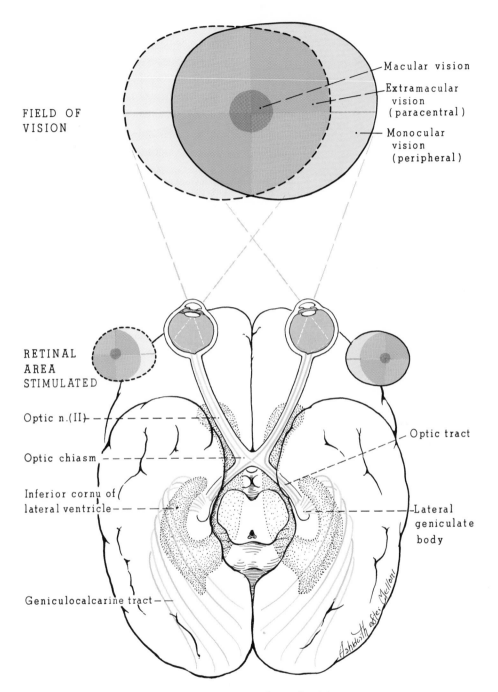

FIELD OF
VISION

Macular vision

Extramacular
vision
(paracentral)

Monocular
vision
(peripheral)

RETINAL
AREA
STIMULATED

Optic n.(II)

Optic chiasm

Inferior cornu of
lateral ventricle

Geniculocalcarine tract

Optic tract

Lateral
geniculate
body

Fig. 213.   Nervous pathways for vision.

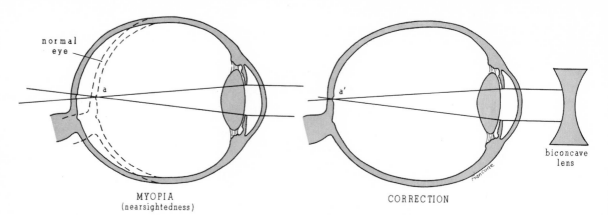

MYOPIA
(nearsightedness)

CORRECTION

biconcave
lens

Fig. 214. Myopia or nearsightedness; note how the image focuses in front of the retina. A biconcave lens is used as a corrective device for this condition. *a* indicates incorrect point of focus; *a'* indicates focus after correction.

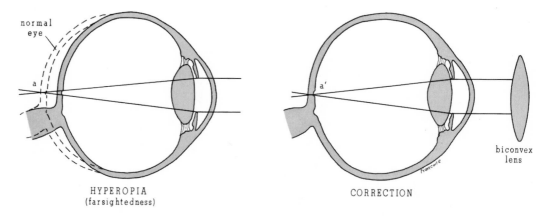

HYPEROPIA
(farsightedness)

CORRECTION

biconvex
lens

Fig. 215. Hyperopia or farsightedness; note how the image focuses behind the retina. A biconvex lens is used as a corrective device for this condition. *a* indicates incorrect point of focus; *a'* indicates focus after correction.

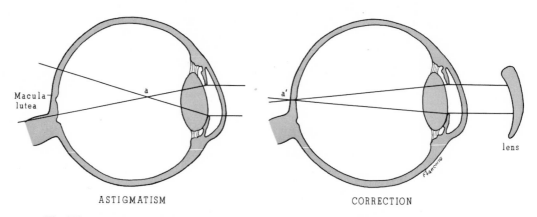

ASTIGMATISM

CORRECTION

lens

Fig. 216. Astigmatism: uneven focusing of the image resulting from distortion of the curvature of the lens or cornea. *a* indicates incorrect point of focus; *a'* indicates focus after correction.

conjunctival membrane takes on a pink or fiery red color. Mild cases will clear spontaneously if further irritation of the eye is prevented.

Stye is an inflammation of one or more of the sebaceous glands of the eyelid.

AUDITORY SENSE

The ear receives sound waves traveling in the air. Therefore, it is necessary to consider the properties of sound before studying the structure and function of the ear.

Physical Aspects of Sound

When sound is produced, the atmosphere is disturbed by sound waves radiating from the source. Sound waves impinge on the eardrum (tympanic membrane), and the membrane vibrates at the same frequency as the source creating the sound. Sound vibrations are carried from the tympanic membrane to the inner ear to be transformed into nerve impulses.

Structures of the Ear

The ear consists of three portions: an external, middle, and inner ear (Figs. 217 to 219).

EXTERNAL EAR. The auricle (ear flap) of the external ear collects sound waves and transmits them through the external acoustic meatus to the tympanic membrane. The external auditory canal is an S-shaped structure about 2½ cm. in length, lined with numerous glands secreting a yellow, waxy substance, *cerumen*. Cerumen lubricates and protects the ear.

MIDDLE EAR. The middle ear (tympanic cavity) is a tiny cavity in the temporal bone. Within it are the three auditory ossicles: the *malleus* (hammer), *incus* (anvil), and *stapes* (stirrup). Two small muscles, the *stapedius* and *tensor tympani*, are also found in the middle ear. The stapedius muscle is attached to the stapes, and the tensor tympani muscle to the handle of the malleus.

The middle ear has five openings—the opening covered by the tympanic membrane, the opening of the auditory tube, the opening into the mastoid cavity, and the openings into the inner ear (round and oval windows). Three functions have been ascribed to the middle ear. The first function is to transmit energy from sound vibrations in the air column of the external auditory meatus across the middle ear into the fluid contained within the *cochlea* (the central hearing apparatus). The bones of the middle ear pick up the vibrations from the tympanic membrane, and transmit them across the middle ear to the oval window (the opening to the inner ear). The second function of the middle ear is protective; it reduces the amplitude of vibrations accompanying intense sounds of low frequency. This function minimizes shock to the inner ear. The third function of the middle ear is to equalize air pressure on both sides of the membrane via the auditory tube to prevent the tympanum from rupturing.

THE INNER EAR. The inner ear consists of bony and membranous labyrinths. The bony labyrinth, composed of a series of canals hol-

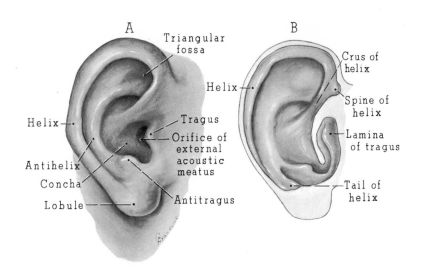

Fig. 217. *A.* External ear. *B.* Cartilage portion of ear.

A — Triangular fossa — Helix — Helix — Tragus — Orifice of external acoustic meatus — Antihelix — Concha — Lobule — Antitragus

B — Crus of helix — Spine of helix — Lamina of tragus — Tail of helix — Helix

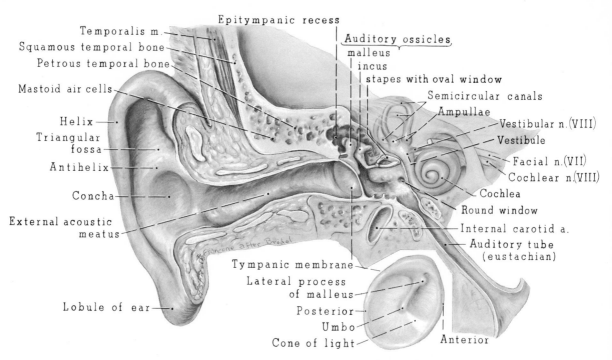

Fig. 218. Frontal section through the outer, middle, and internal ear.

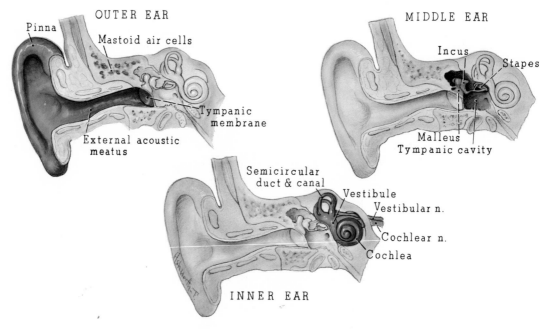

Fig. 219. Three divisions of the ear.

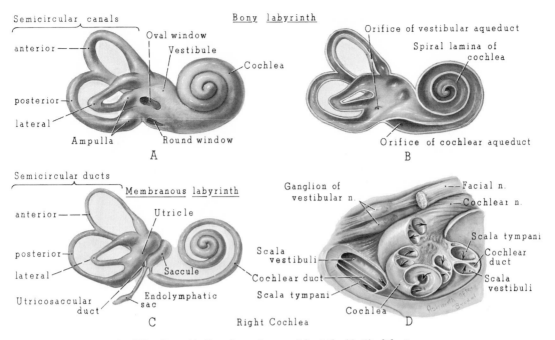

Fig. 220. Bony (*A, B*) and membranous labyrinths (*C, D*) of the inner ear.

lowed out of the temporal bone, is filled with perilymph. The membranous labyrinth, lying entirely within the bony labyrinth, is filled with endolymph. The bony labyrinth consists of the organ of hearing (the *cochlea*) and the organs of equilibrium (the *vestibule* and *semicircular canals*) (Fig. 220).

Equilibrium. The *saccule* and *utricle* are located within the vestibule. These are the portions of the membranous labyrinth containing sensory hairs with small calcium carbonate particles (*otoliths*) on the ends. Any movement of the head results in movement of the otoliths. Otolithic movement, in turn, stimulates the hairs, setting up neural impulses. These nerve impulses help in the maintenance of static equilibrium (the relationship of the body to the pull of gravity).

The semicircular ducts form the membranous portion of the semicircular canals. There are three semicircular canals in each ear at right angles to each other. A dilated portion called the *ampulla* is located at the base of each canal. With acceleration or deceleration of the body, the flow of endolymph in the ampulla and the ducts stimulates a number of hair cells. Stimulation of the hair cells sets up nerve impulses important in maintaining the dynamic equilibrium of the body. Other nerve impulses necessary in

maintaining the body's balance come from the vestibule, eyes, and proprioreceptors.

Hearing. The cochlea is coiled two and one-half times in the shape of a snail shell about a central axis of bone called the modiolus (Figs. 221 and 222). Three compartments comprise the hollow cochlea. The upper passage, or *scala vestibuli,* ends at the oval window; the lower passage, or *scala tympani,* ends at the round window. These two passages connect at the apex of the spiral; both contain perilymph. A third passage, the cochlear duct, filled with endolymph, lies between the scala vestibuli and the scala tympani.

The cochlear duct is bounded above by the vestibular membrane and below by the basilar membrane. The basilar membrane has tightly stretched fibers; the shorter fibers are located at the base, and the longer ones at the apex. The *organ of Corti,* the organ of hearing, lies on the basilar membrane; it consists of numerous receptor hair cells.

Physiology of Hearing

Sound waves, entering the acoustic meatus, create vibrations in the tympanic membrane. The ossicles of the middle ear, in turn, carry

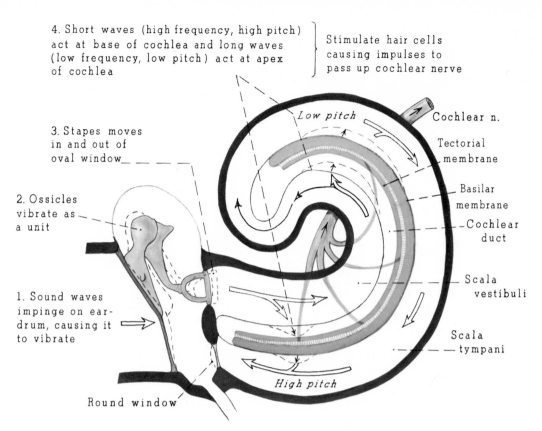

4. Short waves (high frequency, high pitch) act at base of cochlea and long waves (low frequency, low pitch) act at apex of cochlea } Stimulate hair cells causing impulses to pass up cochlear nerve

Cochlear n.

Low pitch

Tectorial membrane

Basilar membrane

Cochlear duct

3. Stapes moves in and out of oval window

Scala vestibuli

2. Ossicles vibrate as a unit

Scala tympani

1. Sound waves impinge on eardrum, causing it to vibrate

High pitch

Round window

Fig. 221. Diagram of the cochlea and sound waves.

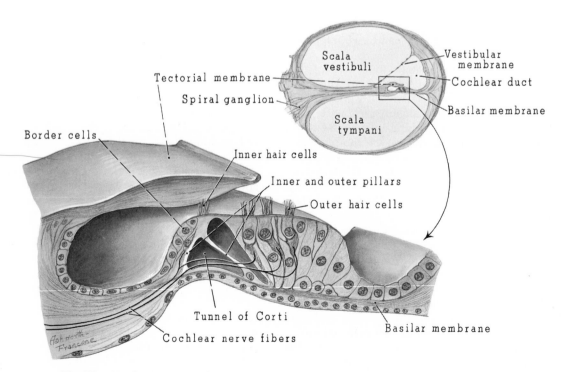

Scala vestibuli

Vestibular membrane

Cochlear duct

Tectorial membrane

Spiral ganglion

Basilar membrane

Scala tympani

Border cells

Inner hair cells

Inner and outer pillars

Outer hair cells

Tunnel of Corti

Cochlear nerve fibers

Basilar membrane

Fig. 222. Spiral organ of Corti. Insert of cross section of cochlea showing location of organ of Corti.

these vibrations to the oval window. Vibrations in the oval window set up sound waves in the perilymph traveling up the scala vestibuli, through the opening in the apex of the cochlea, and down the scala tympani. The waves are dissipated against the membrane of the round window. The sound waves, depending on the frequency of sound, set up sympathetic sound waves in various portions of the basilar membrane. Movement of the basilar membrane stimulates the hair cells of the organ of Corti to initiate the nerve impulses.

High frequency sounds stimulate hairs near the base of the cochlear duct; low frequency sound waves stimulate those near the apex. The loudness of sound is determined by the frequency and spread of nerve impulses ascending the cochlear nerve. Increased intensity of sound causes increased frequency of nerve impulses.

Nervous pathway for hearing. Neurons initiating the nerve impulses for sound have their endings scattered among the hair cells of the organ of Corti. The axons of these neurons, located in the cochlear division of the auditory (eighth) nerve, travel to the dorsal and ventral cochlear nuclei in the medulla, where they synapse. Some

of the neurons extend to the medial geniculate body, while others cross to the body of the opposite side. Thus, each ear sends impulses to both sides of the brain, and loss of temporal lobe function on one side does not interfere with hearing. Fibers pass from the medial geniculate body to the cortical center located in the upper part of the temporal lobe (see Chapter Eight).

Abnormalities of the Ear

DEAFNESS. Any portion of the auditory apparatus can be affected by disease or injury, leading to partial or total deafness. The extent of hearing loss at various frequencies can be determined with the aid of an audiogram (Fig. 223).

Conductive or transmission deafness. This condition is caused by interference in the transmission of sound vibrations through the external or middle ear. Vibrations may be blocked by wax or foreign bodies in the external or middle ear, or by adhesions of the bones of the middle ear. Transmission deafness is not characterized by damage to end organs or nerves; therefore, a person suffering from transmission deafness can

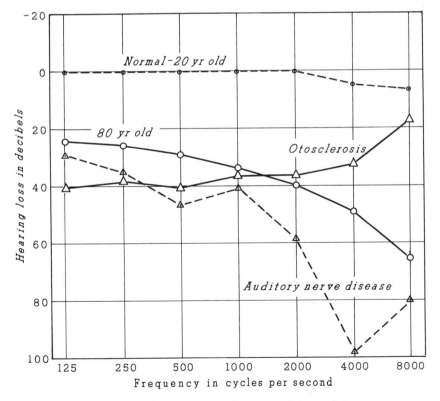

Fig. 223. Audiogram showing three types of abnormalities.

hear with a hearing aid. Ossification of the bones of the middle ear, or otosclerosis, is an example of transmission deafness.

Perceptive deafness. Perceptive deafness results from disease of the organ of Corti or of the auditory nerve. Hearing aids are not useful in this type of deafness.

Tinnitus. Tinnitus, ringing in the ear, can be caused by cerumen (wax in the ear), perforations of the tympanic membrane, fluid in the middle ear, or any disturbance of the auditory nerve, brainstem, or cortex. Tinnitus sometimes follows administration of drugs. Two of the most common offenders are aspirin and streptomycin. If the administration of streptomycin is discontinued when the tinnitus initially appears, ringing will cease. If streptomycin administration is maintained, tinnitus can be permanent.

Perforation of the tympanic membrane. Perforation of the tympanic membrane can impair hearing. The degree of hearing loss depends upon the size and location of the perforation. A patient with almost complete loss of the tympanic membrane can still hear slightly, since the vibrations by-pass the tympanum and travel to the inner ear by way of the bones of the skull.

OLFACTORY SENSE (SENSE OF SMELL)

Receptor Cells

Less is known about the sense of smell than about the more complex senses. Smell is perceived in the olfactory epithelium, an area about 2 cm. square, located on either side of the nasal passages. The olfactory epithelium contains two types of cells: supporting cells and actual olfactory cells.

Olfactory cells are neurons with dendrites reaching the surface of the mucosa. Dendrites pass between the supporting cells and divide into many fine hair-like processes (nerve endings). The nerve endings lie uncovered except for a thin layer of mucus; nowhere else in the body are nerve endings so exposed. The axons of the olfactory cell bodies pass through the *cribriform plate* of the *ethmoid bone* as fibers of the olfactory nerve. The exact route these axons follow is uncertain. They are believed to terminate in the rhinencephalon, the olfactory portion of the brain, located in the lower surface of the frontal lobe of the cerebral cortex.

Physiology of Smell

Many theories have been presented explaining the mechanism of smell. Three of the most widely accepted theories follow.

1. Substances readily detected by smell are generally fat soluble. Since the membrane of the nerve fiber consists largely of fat, it is possible that the substance detected is dissolved in the membrane. The dissolved substance could depolarize the membrane and establish a nerve impulse.

2. Olfactory receptors are thought to produce a variety of infrared wavelengths. Each type of molecule passing by the receptors absorbs a characteristic pattern of wavelengths; therefore, the receptor elements *emitting the absorbed wavelengths* lose heat. This specific pattern of heat loss generates neural impulses.

3. Substances producing odor emit particles in gaseous form. The particles become dissolved in the fluid of the nasal chamber. The fluid acts chemically on the sensitive hairs of the olfactory cells, setting up nerve impulses.

Receptors for smell are easily fatigued. After several minutes of continuous stimulation by a specific odor, the receptors lose the ability to recognize the odor. If another odor is immediately smelled, fatigue to the first in no way seems to impair the sensing of the second.

Many attempts have been made to classify odors, but none helps to explain the physiology of smell. Each substance causes its own particular sensation. A multitude of distinct odors can be recognized, and individual odors in a mixed smell can be distinguished.

GUSTATORY SENSE (SENSE OF TASTE)

Receptor Cells

Like the sense of smell, the sense of taste provides a chemical sensitivity for an organism, enabling it to decide if particles should be ingested or rejected. The specialized structures for the reception of taste are the taste buds. Approximately 9000 of these structures are found on the tongue. Taste buds are onion-shaped receptors containing a tiny pore opening onto the surface of the tongue. The buds are found in numerous small projections (*papillae*) on the tongue. The large taste buds forming a V-line on the posterior portion of the tongue are *vallate papillae*. The

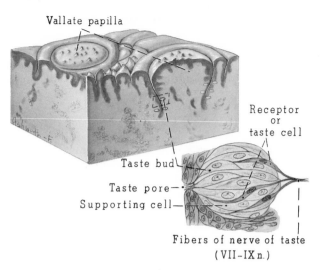

Vallate papilla

Receptor
or
taste cell

Taste bud

Taste pore—

Supporting cell—

Fibers of nerve of taste
(VII–IX n.)

Fig. 224. Taste bud and section from tongue showing where it is found.

fungiform papillae are numerous smaller taste buds covering the entire surface of the tongue (Fig. 224).

Physiology of Taste

Only when a substance is in solution can it move through the pore of the receptor to come in contact with the receptor cell located inside the taste bud. Differences in the surface of the receptor probably account for the selective absorption of chemicals by certain receptor cells. The receptor cells transmit stimuli to the dendrites of nerves when the cells are stimulated by chemicals. The dendrites respond by conducting nerve impulses to the nuclear taste center in the medulla. From the taste center connections are made with the thalamus and cerebral cortex. In the cortex, impulses produce the sensation of taste.

Most special senses are supplied by a single nerve extending from the receptor to the brain; however, taste is made possible by multiple nerves. It is served by the *chorda tympani* nerve (VII), for the front of the tongue; the *glossopharyngeal* nerve (IX), for the back of the tongue; and the *vagus* nerve (X), for the deeper recesses of the throat and pharynx.

According to the classic view, four basic taste receptors were present, each giving rise to the sensations of salt, sour, bitter, or sweet, when activated by an appropriate stimulus. More recent studies reveal combinations of sensitivity. The sense of taste has been found to be an important factor in nutrition. Animals deprived of the sense of taste suffer from malnutrition even when an adequate diet is available to them.

SUMMARY: SPECIAL SENSES

PROCESS OF SENSATION

1. For a sensation to occur, a stimulus, a receptor cell, a nerve impulse and an interpreting center must be present.

VISION

1. External structures of the eye: orbital cavity, containing the eyeball; extrinsic ocular muscles, providing support and rotary movement of the eyeball; eyelids, giving protection; conjunctiva, lining each eyelid; and lacrimal apparatus, lubricating the eye.

2. Internal structures of the eye:

   a. Layers of the eyeball: outer fibrous protective layer, consisting of sclera posteriorly, cornea anteriorly; middle vascular layer, consisting of choroid posteriorly, ciliary body and iris anteriorly; inner nervous layer, consisting of the retina.

b. Refracting media of the eye: the aqueous humor, filling the anterior cavity of the eyeball; the lens, which can change shape to focus the image properly; and the vitreous humor, filling the posterior cavity of the eye. These media bend light rays entering the eye and help focus them on the retina.

3. **Physiology of vision:**

a. Accommodation includes regulating the amount of light entering the eye, focusing the image, and aligning the visual axes.

b. The retina changes the image focused on it into nerve impulses. The retina contains rods sensitive to dim light and cones sensitive to bright light. The cones function in color vision. Rods and cones are receptor cells having photosensitive chemicals which decompose and initiate the nerve impulse. After initiation, nerve impulses are assembled in the outer nuclear and outer fiber layers, and are relayed in the inner nuclear and inner fiber layers of the retina. They are transmitted by ganglion cells, the axons of which form the optic nerve.

c. Binocular vision is possible because of muscular and nervous coordination of both eyes.

4. **Abnormalities of the eye:**

a. Problems of focus include nearsightedness (myopia), farsightedness (hyperopia), oldsightedness (presbyopia), and uneven focusing in different planes (astigmatism).

b. Other abnormalities include cataract, an aging process of the lens; corneal opacity; conjunctivitis, an inflammation of the conjunctiva; and stye, an infected follicle of the eyelash.

AUDITORY SENSE

1. **Sound vibrations in the air cause the eardrum to vibrate; the vibrations in turn are conveyed to the inner ear and transformed into nerve impulses.**

2. **Structures of the ear:**

a. External ear: the auricle collects sound waves and directs them through the external acoustic meatus to the tympanic membrane.

b. Middle ear includes the malleus, incus, and stapes. These three bones transmit sound vibrations from the tympanum to the inner ear and reduce the amplitude of large vibrations. Pressure on both sides of the tympanum is equalized by way of the auditory tube.

c. Inner ear: cochlear portion containing the organ of Corti, the end organ of hearing; semicircular canals and vestibule, forming a portion of the mechanism for balance of the body.

3. **Physiology of hearing:**

a. Creation of an impulse: sound waves stimulate the tympanum to vibrate; the tympanum causes bones of the middle ear to vibrate, conveying the sound to the inner ear; fibers of varying lengths within the organ of Corti of the inner ear are stimulated by specific frequencies of sound; movement of these fibers initiates nerve impulses.

b. Nerve pathway: nerves pass from the organ of Corti up the auditory nerve to the medulla; in the medulla, some of the fibers pass to the opposite side of the brain; thus, each ear sends fibers to both sides of the brain.

4. **Abnormalities of hearing:**
   a. Deafness: conductive or transmission deafness results from interference in the passage of sound vibrations through the external or middle ear; perceptive deafness results from disease of the organ of Corti or of the auditory nerve; central deafness results from damage to the auditory pathways of the brain.
   b. Other abnormalities: tinnitus, or ringing in the ear; perforations of the tympanic membrane.

OLFACTORY SENSE

1. **Receptor cells:** olfactory receptor cells are located in the olfactory epithelium in the nasal passage; the axons of olfactory cell bodies become the olfactory nerve.

2. **Physiology of smell:** three recent theories explaining the mechanism by which odors set up nerve impulses include:
   a. Substances dissolve in the membrane of the receptor cell to depolarize it.
   b. Substances absorb characteristic patterns of infrared wavelengths from the receptor cells.
   c. Substances act chemically on the receptor cells.

GUSTATORY SENSE

1. **Receptors:** approximately 9000 taste buds are found on the human tongue.

2. **Physiology of taste:** a substance must be in solution to be tasted; difference in configuration of the receptor surface probably results in selective absorption of specific chemicals by certain receptors; nerves of taste are facial, glossopharyngeal, and vagus; the classic view stated that four basic taste receptors existed (sweet, sour, bitter, and salt); recent studies reveal that combinations of sensitivity exist.

STUDY QUESTIONS: SPECIAL SENSES

1. Describe the function of the five external structures of the eye.
2. Explain the structure of the lacrimal apparatus.
3. Name the major components of the three layers of the eyeball.
4. Discuss the refracting media of the eye.
5. Explain the cause of glaucoma.
6. List three steps in visual accommodation.
7. Describe the rhodopsin cycle.
8. Summarize the nervous pathway from the rod and cone cells to the brain.
9. Explain the cause of binocular vision.
10. Differentiate myopia, hyperopia, presbyopia, and astigmatism.
11. List the components of the outer, middle, and inner ear.
12. Describe the functions of the middle ear.
13. Explain the mechanism of balance.
14. How does sound create nerve impulses?
15. Describe the types of deafness.
16. Explain the process of taste.

CHAPTER TEN

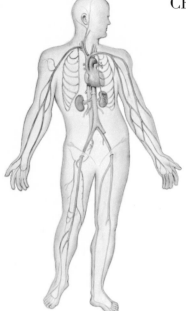

THE
CIRCULATORY
SYSTEM

In 1628, after 9 years of careful observation, William Harvey published the first scientific treatise demonstrating the continuous circulation of blood. Since that time, a great deal of physiologic and biochemical data on the circulatory system has accumulated. Recent advances, such as the replacement of diseased valves in the heart, have stirred the imagination. Dr. Albert Starr of the University of Oregon Medical School has actually replaced three heart valves with three artificial valves and the patient survived. Surgeons are working toward the day when the entire heart can be replaced by a transplant or a mechanical organ.

The circulatory system nourishes every part of the body. The fluid bathing the body tissues is blood; the pump circulating the blood is the heart; the tubes through which the blood flows are the blood vessels.

BLOOD (Fig. 225)

The Nature of Blood

Although blood appears homogeneous, if a thin layer is placed under a microscope, its heterogeneous character becomes obvious. If blood is centrifuged or allowed to stand, it separates into two distinct fractions. Less than

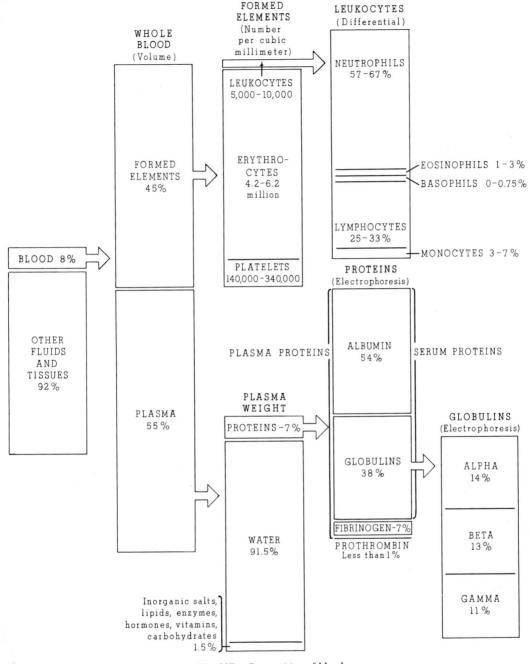

Fig. 225. Composition of blood.

Blood Cell Formation

one-half of the blood consists of "formed" elements—red blood cells, white blood cells, and platelets (Fig. 226). These normally constitute 38 to 52 per cent of the total blood volume. The remainder is the straw colored fluid, the *plasma*. The *hematocrit* is the percentage of "formed" elements by volume. Thus, if the percentage of "formed" elements is 45, the hematocrit is 45.

All blood cells originate from undifferentiated *mesenchymal* or *stem cells* called hemocytoblasts. Primitive cells of each family have similar morphologic characteristics and usually cannot be differentiated by appearance alone. As primitive cells change to the more mature cell forms,

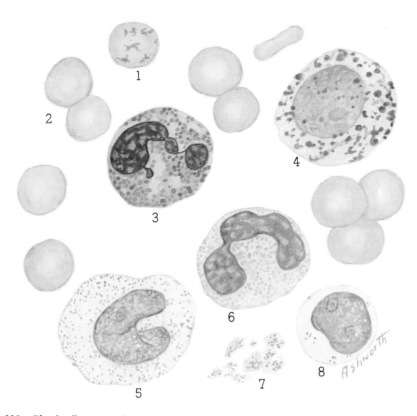

Fig. 226. Blood cells: 1. reticulocyte; 2. erythrocyte; 3. eosinophil (note the drumstick appendage); 4. basophil; 5. monocyte; 6. neutrophil; 7. platelets; and 8. lymphocyte.

they undergo alterations in nuclear and cytoplasmic characteristics; cells decrease in size; the relative and absolute size of the nucleus decreases (in the erythrocytic series, the nucleus actually disappears); and the intensity of the stain taken up by the cytoplasm diminishes (Fig. 227).

The first recognizable blood cells in the human embryo forming in islands within the *mesenchyme* of the yolk sac originate from hemocytoblasts. During the second month of intra-uterine life, the liver assumes a major role in the formation of blood cells. During the fifth month, the spleen is the dominant producer, but this activity rapidly subsides. At birth, some hematopoietic activity may remain in the liver but none is occurring in the spleen.

Development of blood cells within the bones commences during the fifth month of fetal life. Blood-forming elements appear initially in the centers of bone marrow cavities; the blood-forming centers later expand to occupy the entire marrow space. This widely dispersed blood cell formation continues until puberty, when the marrow in all the ends of the long bones becomes less cellular and more fatty. In the adult, only the skull, vertebrae, ribs, sterum, pelvis, humerus, and femur retain active red marrow formation. The total productive bone marrow in the adult is about 1400 gm. In elderly individuals, areas of bone marrow, once occupied by active cell production, become fat laden. This helps explain the difficulty elderly individuals experience in regenerating lost blood.

Types of Blood Cells

Erythrocytes. Just before a red cell reaches maturity, the nucleus is extruded, producing a biconcave disc. This disc is approximately 7 microns in diameter, with the size increasing as the pH of the blood diminishes. Thus, the erythrocyte is larger in venous than in arterial blood. The external limiting membrane of the red cell consists of protein and lipid. The membrane is readily permeable to such substances as water, urea, and salt. Erythrocytes provide a large ab-

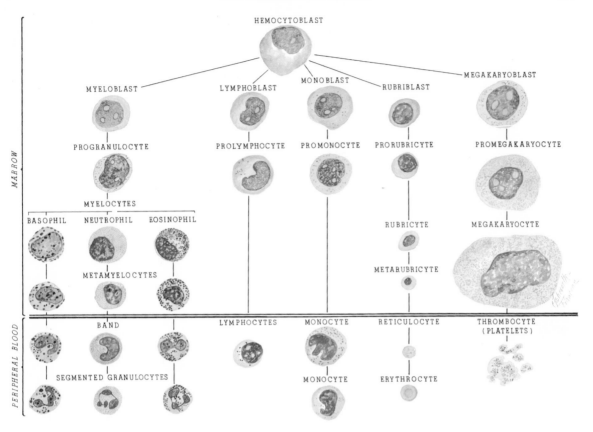

Fig. 227. Stages in the formation of the peripheral blood cells.

sorptive surface, the total surface area representing approximately 3200 square meters, or 1500 times the surface of the body itself.

The number of red cells per cubic millimeter of blood can be determined by counting a limited number of cells spread on a ruled microscopic slide, the hemocytometer. The red cell count is approximately 5,400,000 cells per cubic millimeter in males and 4,700,000 per cubic millimeter in females. Muscular exercise and emotional states are associated with a temporary increase in the number of red cells. The increase occurs from an outpouring of blood from sinusoids of the spleen, liver, and marrow.

Red blood cell production is stimulated by any factor lowering oxygen available to the bone marrow or body tissue. Thus, high altitude, hemorrhage, nutritional deficiencies, and endocrine disturbances may stimulate erythropoiesis (red blood cell formation). Red cell formation is under the control of the hormone *erythropoietin.* Erythropoietin production is influenced by the partial pressure of oxygen on certain cells of the body, including the kidney. It acts on the bone marrow to initiate the differentiation of stem cells into cells of the red cell series.

The life span of erythrocytes is approximately 120 days. When their usefulness is impaired by age, the red cells are destroyed by the spleen, liver, and bone marrow. Two to ten million red cells are destroyed each second, yet, due to replacement, the number of circulating cells remains remarkably constant.

Cells and cellular debris are engulfed by large cells called *macrophages.* When red cells are destroyed, hemoglobin is set free and broken down into globin and heme. The heme decomposes into bilirubin and iron. The iron is utilized to form new erythrocytes, or, if an excess of iron exists in the body, it is brought to the bone marrow, spleen, and liver for storage. Bilirubin is carried to the liver and excreted with the bile. It is the bilirubin that gives bile its golden-yellow color.

Hemoglobin. Hemoglobin, contained in the red cells, assumes an essential role in oxygen transport. It is formed during the manufacture of the red blood cells in the bone marrow. Hemo-

TABLE 30. White Blood Cells (Leukocytes).

TYPE	NUMBER/MM³	PER CENT	SOURCE	FUNCTION	INCREASED COUNT	DECREASED COUNT
Neutrophil	3000-6000	57-67	Red bone marrow	Phagocytosis	Pyogenic infections; leukemia	Toxic reactions such as occur with the administration of certain drugs
Eosinophil	150-300	1-3	Red bone marrow	Little known of exact physiology; non-phagocytic	Allergy, parasitic infections; leukemia	Administration of adrenocortical hormones
Basophil	0-100	1-3	Red bone marrow	Exact function unknown	Leukemia	Unknown
Lymphocyte	1500-3000	25-33	Lymph nodes, thymus, spleen, bone marrow	Production of antibodies; non-phagocytic	Infectious mononucleosis; chronic infections; viral infections; leukemia	Adrenocortical hormones
Monocyte	100-600	3-7	Bone marrow	As a macrophage	Tuberculosis; protozoal infection; leukemia	No known cause

globin is a conjugated protein (molecular weight, 68,000) consisting of an iron-containing pigment and a globin fraction. It carries over 98 per cent of the oxygen transported by the blood; less than 2 per cent is carried in simple solution in the plasma. Thus, hemoglobin increases the ability of blood to transport oxygen. The normal levels for hemoglobin are 15 gm./100 ml. in males and 13 to 14 gm./100 ml. in females.

A reduction in hemoglobin, or in the total number of red cells in the body, results in *anemia*. Anemia is characterized by a diminution in the capacity of the blood to transport oxygen to the tissues. It may arise from blood loss, increased red cell destruction, or decreased formation of red blood cells. Classifications of anemia are based on the size of the red cell and the amount of hemoglobin contained in each cell. Two common types are pernicious and iron deficiency anemias.

In pernicious anemia, there is a decrease in the total number of erythrocytes and a minor increase in the amount of hemoglobin found in each cell. Iron deficiency anemia usually follows chronic blood loss. When the supply of iron becomes depleted because of increased red blood cell formation to compensate for the blood loss, hemoglobin production is diminished and anemia results. This deficiency may also occur when the demand for iron is unusually great, as during infancy, adolescence, or pregnancy.

Hemolysis and crenation of red blood cells. *Hemolysis* occurs when hemoglobin becomes dissolved in the surrounding plasma because of injury of the cell membrane. It may result from osmotic or mechanical stress, and is characterized by a red tinge to the serum or plasma because of the escape of hemoglobin.

Crenation is a shriveling of the cell, noted when the cells are placed in a salt solution of high concentration. The fluid within the cell passes into the surrounding medium. Crenation does not alter the integrity of the cell wall and hemoglobin does not escape, thus differentiating it from hemolysis.

LEUKOCYTES (Table 30). White blood cells, or leukocytes, are classified on the basis of size, number, nuclear shape, and staining qualities of the cytoplasm. *Granulocytes* are the most numerous cell type and include: basophils, with cytoplasmic granules with an affinity for basic dye; eosinophils, with cytoplasmic granules with an affinity for an acid dye; and neutrophils, with granules that do not stain intensely with either dye.

The other major white cell types are lympho-

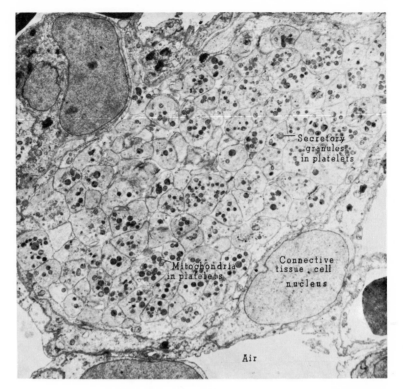

Fig. 228. A lung capillary containing numerous blood platelets. (Magnified 12,000×.)

cytes and monocytes. Lymphocytes possess a blue cytoplasm with a few, unevenly distributed granules. Monocytes possess a relatively large amount of cytoplasm with a round or kidney-shaped nucleus.

Diseases involving abnormalities of the white cell series. Many diseases are characterized by a change in the number of circulating leukocytes. An increase in the white cell count, generally indicating an acute infection, is called *leukocytosis. Leukopenia,* a reduction in the number of white cells, occurs occasionally in viral diseases.

The total white cell count ranges from 5000 to 10,000 per cubic millimeter; however, it may be as high as 500,000 per cubic millimeter in *leukemia.* Leukemia is characterized by a rapid and abnormal growth of leukocytes and by the presence of immature leukocytes in the peripheral blood. The type of leukocyte involved differentiates the varieties of leukemia— myelogenous (myeloid cell), lymphocytic (lymphocyte), and monocytic (monocyte).

Infectious mononucleosis is a disease associated with an increase in mononuclear leukocytes. It usually occurs in children and young adults, and is believed to be caused by a virus. The patient with infectious mononucleosis evidences a slightly elevated temperature, enlarged lymph nodes, fatigue, and a sore throat.

THROMBOCYTES. *Thrombocytes,* or *platelets,* are less than half the size of erythrocytes. They number from 140,000 to 340,000 per cubic millimeter of blood, are spherical or oval in shape, and are capable of ameboid movement. Thrombocytes function in blood clotting and are formed from fragments of the cytoplasm of megakaryocytes. Although the platelet is a fragment of cell, it contains many of the organelles normally present in cells (Fig. 228).

Blood Plasma

Blood plasma is a straw-colored liquid composed of a solution of water (91 per cent) and colloid (9 per cent). The total plasma volume and ratio of plasma to formed elements is held constant by the homeostatic mechanisms of the body. Serum differs from plasma in that the fibrinogen necessary for the clotting mechanism has been removed. Plasma can only be maintained if an anticoagulant is added to keep coagulation from occurring. After coagulation, the fibrinogen separates from plasma, leaving serum (see Table 31 for constituents of blood plasma).

TABLE 31.Blood Constituents in Normal and Abnormal States.

CONSTITUENT	NORMAL LEVEL	ALTERATIONS IN DISEASE STATES
Total bilirubin	Less than 1 mg./100 ml.	Increased in hemolytic anemia and in obstruction to biliary flow, such as a stone in the common bile duct
Calcium	4.5–5.5 mEq./l.	Increased in hyperparathyroidism; decreased in hypoparathyroidism
Total cholesterol	140–250 mg./100 ml.	Increased in hypothyroidism; decreased in hyperthyroidism and starvation
Fibrinogen	0.2–04 gm./100 ml.	Increased in severe infections; decreased in primary liver disease and malnutrition
Glucose	70–110 mg./100 ml.	Increased after meals and in diabetes mellitus; decreased in Addison's disease
Non-protein nitrogen (NPN)	20–35 mg./100 ml.	Includes urea, uric acid, creatinine, ammonia, and amino acids; increased in disease of the kidneys
Protein-bound iodine (PBI)	3–7 mg./100 ml.	Increased in hyperthyroidism; decreased in hypothyroidism
Phosphate	3–4.5 mg./100 ml.	Increased in renal disease and hypoparathyroidism, as well as in Addison's disease; decreased in vitamin D deficiency and hyperparathyroidism
Potassium	3.5 mEq./l.	Increased in Addison's disease and diseases of the kidney; decreased after diarrhea, and with administration of adrenocortical hormones

Total protein
  Albumin
  Globulin
	6–7.8 gm.%
	3.2–4.5 gm.%
	2.3–3.5 gm.%
		Decreased in diseases of the kidney and liver, and in malnutrition; globulin is elevated in chronic infection

Sodium	140–148 mEq./l.	Increased in diseases of the kidney; decreased in Addison's disease
Uric acid	2.6–7 mg.%	Increased in kidney disease and gout

The four major plasma proteins are albumin, globulin, fibrinogen, and prothrombin. Albumin is important in maintaining the osmotic equilibrium of the blood. Since albumin cannot pass through the capillary wall, it remains in the blood stream and exerts an osmotic pressure attracting water from the tissue spaces back into the blood stream. If plasma protein, particularly serum albumin, leaks from the capillaries as a result of injury, such as a severe burn, water cannot be retained and the blood volume drops. If the loss is severe, shock results. Treatment necessary to counteract this state includes the intravenous injection of serum albumin.

Globulin is important, since it contains antibodies involved in the body's immune mechanism. If globulin is examined by electrophoresis, it can be separated into three groups: alpha, beta, and gamma. The gamma globulin is the antibody fraction.

The electrophoretic method used in separating the plasma proteins involves placing the serum or plasma in an electric field, causing the negatively charged protein molecules existing as ions in plasma to migrate towards the positive electrode. The protein molecules move at different speeds depending on size, shape, and charge, and eventually become separated from each other.

Fibrinogen and prothrombin are important in the process of coagulation and will be discussed subsequently.

Blood Grouping (Fig. 229)

The safe administration of blood from donor to recipient requires typing and crossmatching. These procedures are necessary, since a patient receiving blood incompatible with his own can experience a serious or fatal reaction. The systems of classification are based on the presence of specific *antigens* (*agglutinogens*) in the red cell and the presence of specific *antibodies* (*agglutinins*) in the plasma or serum. The primary classification systems are the ABO and Rh (Table 32).

ABO GROUPING.Blood groups are named

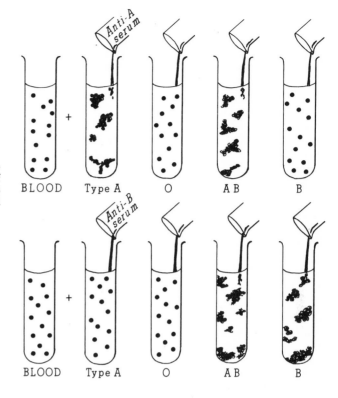

Fig. 229. If agglutination occurs when anti-A agglutinin is added to blood, this indicates the presence of antigen A; agglutination with the addition of anti-B indicates the presence of antigen B. In this way blood types can be determined.

for the antigenic substance contained in the red cell. The ABO group of an individual can be determined after the addition of a specifically prepared serum containing either anti-A or anti-B agglutinins. For example, if agglutination occurs when anti-A agglutinin is added to blood, it can be said that the blood contains antigen-A and is called type A blood. If agglutination occurs when two bloods are mixed, these are said to be incompatible bloods.

Rh factor. The Rh factor, so named because it was first found in the blood of the rhesus monkey, is a system consisting of 12 antigens. Of these, "D" is the most antigenic; the term Rh positive, as it is generally employed, refers to the presence of agglutinogen "D." The Rh negative individual does not possess "D" antigen, and consequently forms anti-D agglutinins when injected with "D" positive cells. Anti-D agglutinin does not occur naturally in the blood.

The initial transfusion of Rh positive blood into an Rh negative individual may merely sensitize the recipient and cause the development of agglutinins without the occurrence of severe symptoms; however, once sensitized, the recipient will probably experience a severe reaction

TABLE 32. Blood Grouping.

TYPE	PERCENTAGE OF POPULATION	RED CELL ANTIGENS OR AGGLUTINOGENS	PLASMA ANTIBODIES OR AGGLUTININS
ABO			
A	41%	A	Anti-B
B	10%	B	Anti-A
AB	4%	A, B	
O	45%	°	Anti-A, anti-B
Rh (D)			
Positive	85%	Rh	
Negative	15%		†

° Type O blood is sometimes called the "universal donor," since it does not contain agglutinogens A and B.

† Anti-Rh does not occur naturally in blood, but will result if an Rh negative individual is given Rh positive blood.

to subsequent infusions of Rh positive blood.

The same reactions often occur during pregnancy when the fetus of an Rh negative mother is Rh positive. Some positive red cells in the fetus leak across the placenta into the Rh negative blood of the mother, who produces agglutinins in response to this invasion. The maternal agglutinins then cross the placenta to the fetus and cause hemolysis (liberation of hemoglobin). If hemolysis in the fetus is severe, the infant will die before birth. Sometimes at birth the infant will show anemia or jaundice. When a woman is sensitized during pregnancy, the first child is often normal and only in subsequent pregnancies does hemolytic anemia develop. Sensitization does not occur if the father is Rh negative, because then the fetus will also be Rh negative.

Immune Mechanisms of the Body

DEFENSE AGAINST INFECTION. *Vaccination* is a method used to induce the formation of antibodies (agglutinins) in the blood. Protection is obtained when dead or altered agents (called antigens), which in the unaltered state produce disease, are introduced into the body. After an incubation period, the body builds up a store of antibodies, providing an immunity against these antigens, just as if the infectious organism had entered (active immunity). Specific antibodies are produced in the blood to protect against specific antigens. A means of obtaining temporary antibody protection is to inject gamma globulin containing many of the known antibodies. Injections of gamma globulin, often employed to induce protection against measles or poliomyelitis after exposure, provide the recipient with temporary antibody protection (passive immunity).

Although antibodies are essential for life, they can occasionally be harmful. Antibodies are responsible for various allergic states, such as asthma, hay fever, and eczema. Many individuals become sensitive or allergic to a variety of substances, including pollen, feathers, and dust. Antibody reactions also provide barriers to transplantation of tissues from one individual to another.

Auto-immune disease is an antibody reaction in which the body reacts against one of its own constituents as if it were foreign. Rheumatoid arthritis and certain types of inflammatory disease of the thyroid gland are considered by some to fall into the auto-immune category.

TRANSPLANTATION IMMUNOLOGY. Two new concepts have grown out of the study of transplantation immunology. The first is *tolerance*, the state of immunologic non-reactivity. This occurs when a young individual is exposed to an antigenic stimulus too early in life to form antibodies. The individual then develops a tolerance to the antigen and cannot produce antibodies against it later in life. The rare case of non-identical human twins exchanging blood-forming cells through a vascular anastomosis in utero (before birth) is an example of the development of tolerance. These individuals are known as *chimeras* (containing cells of two or more genetic origins). Chimeras will accept skin grafts from each other, just as if they were identical twins. Partial tolerance can now be produced in adults by giving chemicals or x-rays which suppress the immune response.

A second advance growing out of transplantation biology is the description of *runt disease* resulting from a reaction of graft against host instead of host against graft. It occurs after adult lymphocytes from a mouse or rat of one strain are injected into a newborn mouse or rat of a dif-

TABLE 33.   Characteristics of Blood.

CHARACTERISTIC	NORMAL VALUE
Specific gravity	Males, 1.057 Females, 1.053
Average blood volume	69 ml./kg. of body weight
Viscosity (relative to water)	Whole, 3.5–5.4 Plasma, 1.9–2.3
pH	Arterial, 7.39 Venous, 7.35
Arterial oxygen content	Total, 20.3 ml. oxygen/100 ml. of blood In plasma, 0.3 Combined with hemoglobin, 20.0

ferent strain. The host's defense systems are too immature to destroy the grafted cells, but the lymphocytes in the grafted cells often attack the host, and the growth of the lymphoid tissue of the host is retarded.

Characteristics of Blood

Sex differences. Sex differences can be detected from strained films of blood cells. The difference is present as a solitary nuclear appendage, shaped like a drumstick, in the neutrophils of the female (Fig. 226).

Osmotic pressure of the blood. The osmotic pressure of human blood is maintained by electrolytes, sugar, other crystalloids dissolved in plasma, and plasma protein. Variations in osmotic pressure resulting from changes in blood composition are corrected by the kidney.

Electrical conductivity of the blood. The conductivity of plasma is determined by its electrolyte content; consequently, the specific conductivity of plasma varies within narrow limits, since its ionic concentration is relatively constant. In contrast, the conductivity of blood varies within wide limits. This is because electrical conductivity of blood is inversely proportional to the fluctuating number of corpuscles. (See Table 33 for other characteristics of blood.)

Hemostasis

Three separate mechanisms are involved in hemostasis: platelet agglutination, contraction of blood vessels, and formation of a fibrin clot.

When a vessel larger than a capillary is cut or damaged, platelets rapidly accumulate at the site of injury and adhere to the vascular endothelium. The aggregate of platelets forms a temporary plug capable of arresting the bleeding in small arteries and veins. Simultaneous with platelet agglutination, vasoconstriction of muscle-containing vessels occurs. Shortly after the appearance of the initial aggregate, platelets fuse into a dense, structureless mass. The mass forms a temporary solid seal at the site of injury. When platelet agglutination occurs, a second type of vasoconstriction takes place affecting the injured vessel and many neighboring vessels. This is the result of the release of serotonin from platelets. Only after the sequence of platelet change does actual coagulation occur, completing the process of hemostasis with the formation of a fibrin clot.

The control of capillary bleeding is made possible by a different mechanism. Capillary constriction does not play a significant role, since capillaries do not contain contractile tissue. Also, platelet plugs have not been shown to develop in severed capillaries. It has been suggested that capillary bleeding may be arrested by adhesion of the endothelial walls of the capillary, aided by torn connective tissue fibers and pressure of tissue fluids.

MECHANISM OF COAGULATION. Coagulation of blood is the most effective and complex of the hemostatic mechanisms. Formation of a fibrin clot—the essence of the coagulation mechanism —involves the following steps: formation of thromboplastin activity; conversion of prothrombin to thrombin; and conversion of fibrinogen to fibrin.

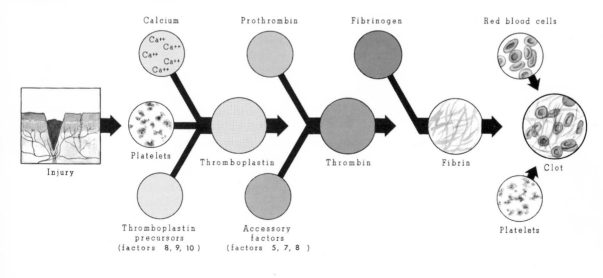

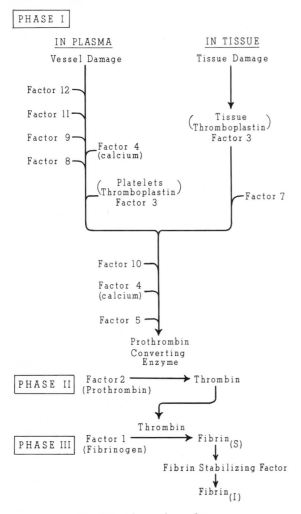

Fig. 231.   Phases of coagulation.

In the first phase, a platelet-plasma interaction yields thromboplastin. In the second phase, thromboplastin plus prothrombin, calcium, and an additional group of factors yield thrombin. In the third phase, thrombin plus fibrinogen produce the fibrin clot (Figs. 230 and 231).

At least 12 factors are involved in the clotting process. They are listed in Table 34 with their position in each of the three steps.

In stage one of the clotting process, the plasma factors involved are 4 (calcium), 8 (antihemophilic globulin), 9 (thromboplastin), and 10 (Stuart factor).

The second stage of coagulation involves the conversion of prothrombin to thrombin. In the actual coagulation of blood plasma, thromboplastin is capable of converting prothrombin to thrombin directly; however, it is believed that an accessory mechanism exists for the release of tissue thromboplastin. Conversion of prothrombin to thrombin under the influence of tissue thromboplastin requires the additional presence of factor 7.

In the third stage of coagulation, factor 1 (fibrinogen) is converted into fibrin by thrombin formed in the second stage. This conversion is believed to be accelerated by calcium. A fibrin-stabilizing factor maintains and strengthens the clot.

ANTI-CLOTTING FACTORS.   Antithrombins and heparin prevent spontaneous coagulation within the body. These are known as anticoagulants. It is ordinarily assumed that, unless there is access to injured surfaces, there is not enough thromboplastic substance liberated to begin the series of chemical reactions which results in clotting. *Heparin* occurs naturally in the body tissues, though it has rarely been demonstrated in blood. It reduces the ability of blood to clot by blocking the change of prothrombin to thrombin. Heparin is produced by *mast cells* found in most organs of the body, and is employed clinically to prevent the enlargement of clots in patients after clotting has already occurred (thrombosis).

The fibrinolytic system involves the digestion of fibrin clots into a number of soluble fragments. Fibrinolysis is mediated by an enzyme called *plasmin* or fibrinolysin, present in the body in the form of the active precursor, *plasminogen*. Plasminogen, a widely distributed globulin, is converted enzymatically to plasmin, a *proteolytic* enzyme capable of digesting the fibrin.

Dicumarol is a drug clinically employed as an anticoagulant. It inhibits the manufacture of clotting factors 2, 7, 9, and 10 by its inhibitory action on vitamin K, which is necessary for the synthesis of prothrombin.

ABNORMALITIES OF THE CLOTTING MECHANISM. Three of the more common abnormalities involving the clotting mechanism are internal clotting or thrombosis, hemophilia, and purpura.

Thrombosis is clotting in blood vessels. A clot, or thrombus, forming in the blood vessels of the leg or arm may be associated with local damage; if it should block the blood supply to the heart or brain, it can be fatal. An *embolus* is a clot that has become dislodged from its place of origin and has lodged elsewhere in the body.

Hemophilia is an hereditary bleeding disease characterized by delayed coagulation of the blood. It results from a diminished antihemophilic factor in the plasma. Treatment consists of transfusions with fresh blood or administration of the deficient factor.

Purpura is an hemorrhagic disease character-

TABLE 34. Mechanism of Coagulation.

INTERNATIONAL NOMENCLATURE	SYNONYMS	FUNCTION
Stage 1: Development of thromboplastic activity		
	Foreign surface	Stimulates platelets to release thromboplastin
	Platelets; thrombocytes	Release thromboplastin
12	Hageman factor (HF)	No bleeding disease in its absence in vitro, but much prolonged clotting time in vitro
8	Antihemophilic factor; antihemophilic globulin (AHG)	Prevents hemophilia; aids in the ability to make thromboplastin
9	Christmas factor; plasma thromboplastic component (PTC)	Influences the amount of thromboplastin formed; deficiency results in hemophilia
11	Plasma thromboplastin antecedent (PTA)	Necessary for early stages of intrinsic prothrombin activator formation
Stage 2: Conversion of prothrombin to thrombin		
2	Prothrombin	Converted to thrombin; synthesized in liver only in presence of vitamin K
3	Thromboplastin (tissue) or thromboplastic activity as generated in Stage 1	Promotes conversion of prothrombin to thrombin
4	Calcium	Catalyzes or takes part in several stages of coagulation
5	Proaccelerin, labile factor; accelerator globulin (ACG)	Accelerates conversion of prothrombin to thrombin
7	Proconvertin, stable factor; proconvertin, serum prothrombin conversion accelerator (SPCA)	Accelerates conversion of prothrombin to thrombin in presence of tissue thromboplastin, but not needed with intrinsic (plasma-derived) thromboplastin
10	Stuart factor	Necessary for both intrinsic and tissue thromboplastin; induced prothrombin activator formation
Stage 3: Conversion of fibrinogen to fibrin		
1	Fibrinogen	Converted to fibrin
	Thrombin	Catalyzes change of fibrinogen to fibrin
4	Calcium	Catalyst
	Fibrin-stabilizing factor	Stabilizes the fibrin clot

ized by loss of blood into the skin, subcutaneous tissues, and mucous membranes. The most characteristic lesions are the size of a small pinhead, but large extravasations can occur.

THE HEART (Fig. 232)

The heart is a four-chambered, hollow, muscular organ lying between the lungs in the middle mediastinum. Approximately two-thirds of its mass is to the left of the midline. It is about the size of a man's fist, and in the normal male weighs approximately 300 gm. The heart is shaped like an inverted cone, with its apex pointed downward (Figs. 233 and 234).

Structure

The structures of the heart include the *pericardium;* the wall enclosing the chambers, separated by valves; and the *arteries,* which supply blood to the heart muscle.

PERICARDIUM (Fig. 235). The pericardium is an invaginated sac consisting of two layers, an external fibrous and an internal layer (the serous membrane). The external fibrous layer, which has an inner surface of serous membrane,

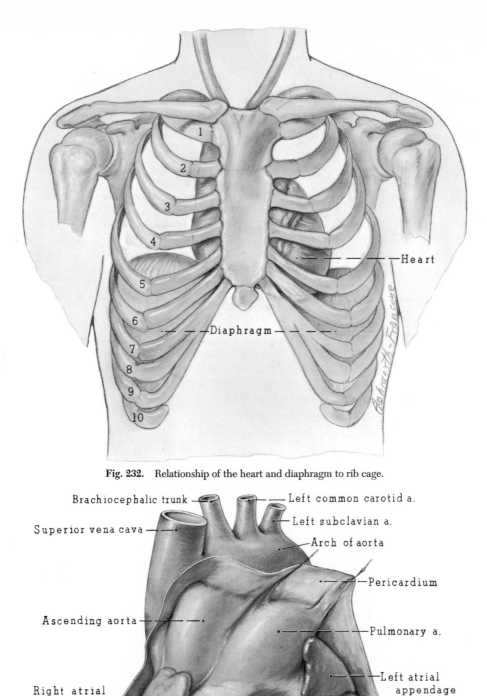

Fig. 232.   Relationship of the heart and diaphragm to rib cage.

Brachiocephalic trunk

Left common carotid a.

Superior vena cava

Left subclavian a.

Arch of aorta

Pericardium

Ascending aorta

Pulmonary a.

Left atrial appendage (auricle)

Right atrial appendage (auricle)

Left coronary a.

Right ventricle

Left ventricle

Right coronary a.

Right atrium

Pericardium

Heart

Diaphragm

1
2
3
4
5
6
7
8
9
10

Fig. 233.   Anterior view of the heart.

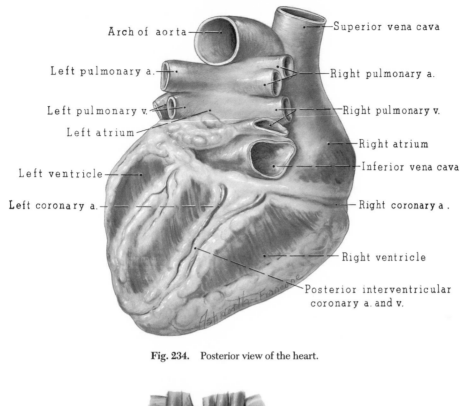

Arch of aorta ————— ● ·————— Superior vena cava

Left pulmonary a. ——● ● ————— Right pulmonary a.

Left pulmonary v. ——● ● ————— Right pulmonary v.

Left atrium —————

Left ventricle ————— ● ●————— Right atrium

Left coronary a. ————— ————— Inferior vena cava

————— Right coronary a.

————— Right ventricle

·————— Posterior interventricular
coronary a. and v.

Fig. 234. Posterior view of the heart.

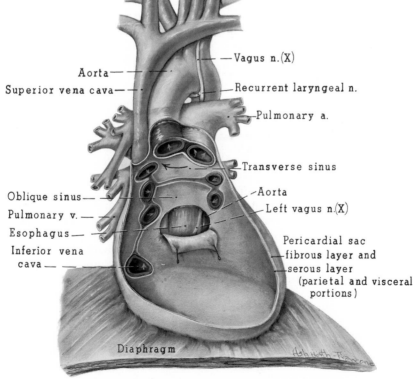

Aorta —————

Superior vena cava —————

————— Vagus n. (X)

————— Recurrent laryngeal n.

·————— Pulmonary a.

————— Transverse sinus

Oblique sinus ————— ————— Aorta

Pulmonary v. ————— ————— Left vagus n. (X)

Esophagus —————

Inferior vena
cava ————— Pericardial sac
—fibrous layer and
—serous layer
(parietal and visceral
portions)

Diaphragm

Fig. 235. The heart has been removed from the pericardial sac to show the relations of the blood vessels, esophagus, and vagus nerve.

is the parietal pericardium. The internal serous layer, which adheres to the heart and becomes the outermost layer of the heart, the epicardium, is the visceral pericardium.

Pericardial fluid is found between the parietal pericardium and the visceral pericardium. This serous fluid lubricates the two membranes with every beat of the heart as their surfaces glide over each other.

Pericarditis is an inflammation of the pericardium. It may be the result of a bacterial infection.

WALL OF THE HEART. The wall of the heart consists of three distinct layers—the *epicardium* (external layer), the *myocardium* (middle layer), and the *endocardium* (inner layer). The epicardium has mesothelial and subserous layers of connective tissue and is frequently infiltrated with fat. Coronary vessels supplying arterial blood to the heart traverse the epicardium before entering the myocardium. The myocardium consists of interlacing bundles of striated muscle fibers. This layer is responsible for the ability of the heart to contract. The endocardium lines the cavities of the heart, covers the valves, and is continuous with the lining membrane of the large blood vessels. Inflammation of the endocardium is called *endocarditis.*

CHAMBERS OF THE HEART. The heart is divided into right and left halves, with each half subdivided into two chambers. The upper chambers, the *atria,* are separated by the *interatrial septum;* the lower chambers, the *ventricles,* are separated by the *interventricular septum.*

The atria serve as receiving chambers for blood from the various parts of the body and pump blood into the ventricles. The ventricles, in turn, pump blood to the lungs and the remainder of the body.

The *right atrium* constitutes the right superior portion of the heart. It is a thin-walled chamber receiving blood from all tissues except the lungs. Three veins empty into the right atrium: the superior and inferior venae cavae, bringing blood from the upper and lower portions of the body; and the coronary sinus, draining blood from the heart itself. Blood flows from the atrium to the right ventricle.

The *right ventricle* constitutes the right inferior portion of the heart's apex. The pulmonary artery carrying blood to the lungs leaves from the superior surface of the right ventricle.

The *left atrium* constitutes the left superior portion of the heart. It is slightly smaller than the right atrium, with a thicker wall. The left atrium receives the four pulmonary veins draining oxygenated blood from the lungs. Blood flows from the left atrium into the left ventricle.

The *left ventricle* constitutes the left inferior portion of the apex of the heart. The walls of this chamber are three times as thick as those of the right ventricle. Blood is forced through the aorta to all parts of the body except the lungs.

VALVES OF THE HEART. There are two types of valves located in the heart: the *atrioventricular valves* (*tricuspid* and *mitral*) and the *semilunar valves* (*pulmonary* and *aortic*) (Figs. 236 to 239).

The atrioventricular valves are thin, leaf-like structures located between the atria and ventricles. The right atrioventricular opening is guarded by the tricuspid valve, so called because it consists of three irregularly shaped flaps (or cusps) formed mainly of fibrous tissue and covered by endocardium. These flaps are continuous with each other at their bases, creating a ring-shaped membrane surrounding the margin of the atrial opening. Their pointed ends project into the ventricle, and are attached by cords called the *chordae tendineae* to small muscular pillars, the *papillary muscles,* within the interior of the ventricles. The left atrioventricular opening is guarded by the mitral or bicuspid valve, so named because it consists of two flaps. The mitral valve is attached in the same manner as the tricuspid, but it is stronger and thicker since the left ventricle is a more powerful pump.

Blood is propelled through the tricuspid and mitral valves as the atria contract. When the ventricle contracts, blood is forced backward, passing between the flaps and walls of the ventricles. The flaps are thus pushed upward until they meet and unite, forming a complete partition between the atria and ventricles. The expanded flaps of the valves resist any pressure of the blood which might force them to open into the atria, since they are restrained by the chordae tendineae and papillary muscles.

The semilunar valves are pocket-like structures attached at the point at which the pulmonary artery and aorta leave the ventricles. The pulmonary valve guards the orifice between the right ventricle and the pulmonary artery. The aortic valve guards the orifice between the left ventricle and the aorta.

HEART SOUNDS. The characteristic heart sounds are caused by the sudden deceleration of a column of blood when the heart valves close. The first sound occurs at the onset of ventricular systole, and is caused when the mitral and tricuspid valves close. It has a characteristic dull quality of low pitch and has been described

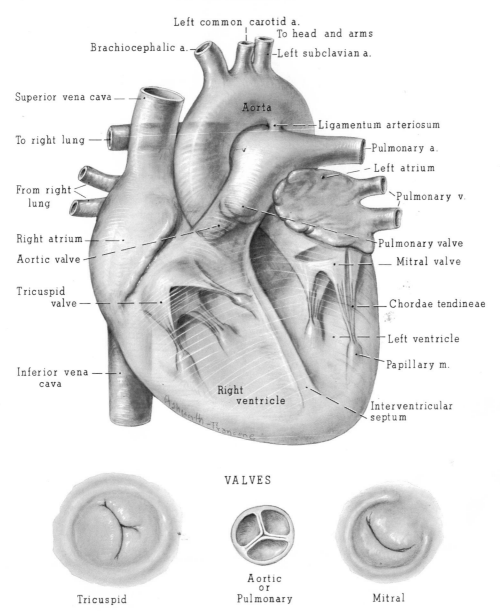

Fig. 236. Schematic "transparent" drawing of the heart showing the relations of the various heart valves.

classically by the syllable "lubb." The second heart sound is produced when the pulmonic and aortic semilunar valves close at the end of systole. It is described by the syllable "dupp" and is of a snapping quality. The first heart sound is followed after a short pause by the second. A pause about two times longer comes between the second sound and the beginning of the next cycle. The opening of the valves is silent.

BLOOD SUPPLY TO THE HEART. The heart is supplied by the *right* and *left coronary arteries* (Figs. 240 and 241). These vessels are the first

branches of the aorta. They encircle the heart and supply blood to all portions of the myocardium. The blood in the coronary arteries returns to the heart, either by way of the coronary veins or by special sinusoids in the myocardium.

The coronary arteries and their branches are as follows.

Left coronary artery. The anterior descending branch supplies blood to the left and right ventricles. The circumflex branch supplies blood to the left atrium and left ventricle.

Right coronary artery. The posterior de-

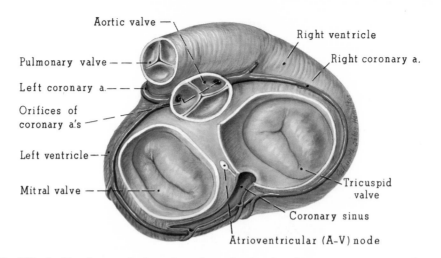

Fig. 237. Looking down on the heart from above, showing the valves, coronary arteries, and sinus.

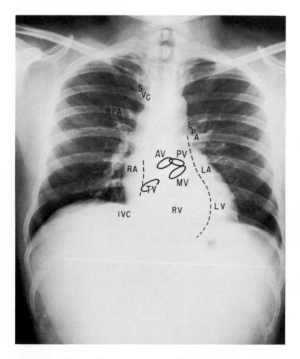

Fig. 238. X-ray of anterior aspect of thoracic region.

SVC—superior vena cava
RPA—right pulmonary artery
RA —right atrium
IVC—inferior vena cava
LPA—left pulmonary artery
LA —left atrium

LV —left ventricle
RV —right ventricle
AV —aortic valve
PV —pulmonary valve
MV—mitral valve
TV —tricuspid valve

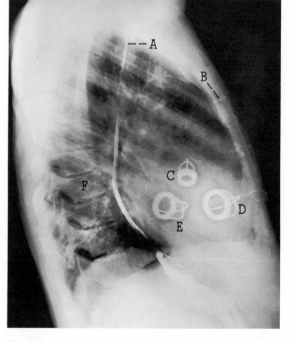

Fig. 239. Three artificial valves implanted in a patient's heart by Dr. A. Starr of the University of Oregon Medical School, showing: A. esophagus; B. wire sutures in sternum; C. aortic valve; D. tricuspid valve; E. mitral valve; and F. vertebral column.

296

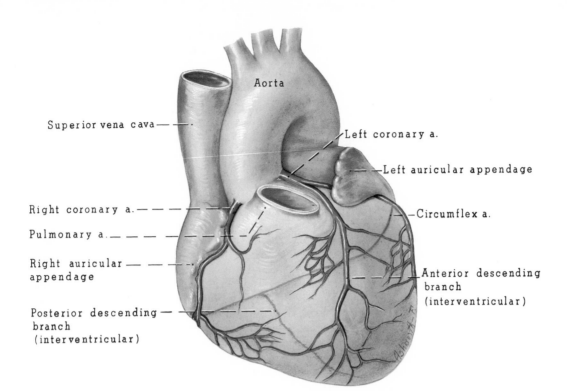

Superior vena cava

Aorta

Left coronary a.

Left auricular appendage

Right coronary a.

Circumflex a.

Pulmonary a.

Right auricular
appendage

Posterior descending
branch
(interventricular)

Anterior descending
branch
(interventricular)

Fig. 240.   Coronary arteries which supply the heart.

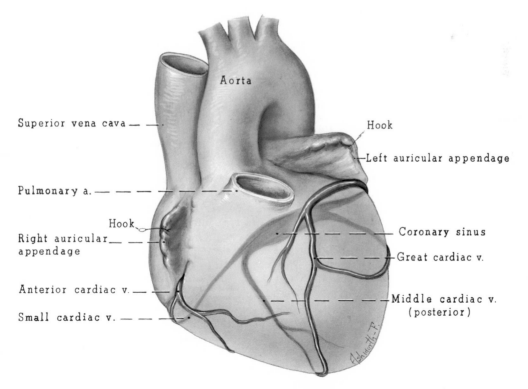

Superior vena cava

Aorta

Hook

Left auricular appendage

Pulmonary a.

Hook

Coronary sinus

Right auricular
appendage

Great cardiac v.

Anterior cardiac v.

Middle cardiac v.
(posterior)

Small cardiac v.

Fig. 241.   Venous drainage of the heart.

scending branch supplies blood to the left and right ventricles. The marginal branch supplies blood to the right atrium and right ventricle.

If the myocardium receives an inadequate oxygen supply, it cannot function properly. A primary sign of this inadequate supply is a peculiar, severe type of anterior chest pain called *angina pectoris*. Angina pectoris is relieved by rest or the administration of nitrites. Attacks of angina pectoris are usually precipitated by exertion or emotional tension. The pain, described as a feeling of tightness, typically radiates to the left shoulder and arm, left neck, and face, and is of short duration.

The pain of *myocardial infarction* causes more prolonged chest pain than angina pectoris. In this case, there is actual occlusion of some part of the arterial supply to the myocardium, resulting in injury or death of the heart muscle. When the myocardium is suddenly deprived of blood by an acute closure of the coronary artery, it can respond with a decrease in pumping efficiency, resulting in a drop in cardiac output. When a ventricle is injured, it requires a higher filling pressure to pump blood. Since the left ventricle is usually the site of injury, back pressure develops in the pulmonary vascular tree. Unless circulatory adjustments occur, death results from pulmonary edema (accumulation of fluid in the lungs).

Many operative procedures have been suggested to increase blood flow to the heart. These include grafting vascular tissue directly to the heart, irritating the epicardium by x-ray or chemicals, and implanting arteries into the myocardium. None of the above procedures has proved to be of value.

CARDIAC MUSCLE. Cardiac muscle differs from skeletal muscle in that it beats for a lifetime without long periods of rest. The sarcosome theory of muscle function is one explanation for this phenomenon. *Sarcosomes*, the mitochondria in muscles, bear important metabolic enzymes. The presence of sarcosomes within cardiac fibers safeguards the immediate enzymatic reversal or breakdown of metabolic wastes created during contraction of heart muscle. The wastes do not accumulate in heart muscle as they do in skeletal muscle, which has fewer sarcosomes. This is possibly the mechanism by which the heart can beat continuously without rest.

Cardiac Cycle

The heart exhibits a definite rhythmic cycle of contraction, with each portion contracting at a specific time. Figure 242 shows the cardiac cycle and the relationship among heart sounds, changes in ventricular volume, and pressure alterations in the left heart and aorta. The diagram suffices for study of both ventricles, since the events in each are the same.

The spread of electrical excitatory impulses through the ventricle is followed by contraction of the ventricle (ventricular systole). This results in a rise in the ventricular pressure. When ventricular pressure exceeds atrial pressure, the atrioventricular valves close, causing the first heart sound. When the ventricular pressure exceeds aortic pressure, the aortic valve opens and blood flows from the ventricle into the aorta. During this period, the ventricle and aorta become a common chamber with equal pressure.

The period of ventricular ejection is followed by relaxation of the ventricular muscle and an abrupt fall in ventricular blood pressure. When ventricular pressure falls below aortic pressure, the aortic valves close, creating the second heart sound. Further relaxation of the ventricle follows, resulting in a rapid drop of pressure to a level slightly below the atrial pressure. This fall in pressure promotes filling of the ventricles by the atria. The onset of ventricular filling is concurrent with the opening of the atrioventricular valve. During this period of ventricular filling (ventricular diastole), the atrium and ventricle are essentially a common chamber in which the pressure rises as blood enters from the great veins. Atrial contraction (atrial systole) produces a slight increase of pressure in two chambers; however, the majority of ventricular filling occurs early in diastole. Ventricular systole follows atrial systole and the cycle is repeated (Fig. 243).

Conducting System

Specialized sections of the myocardium, the sino-atrial node (SA node), the atrioventricular node (AV node), and the atrioventricular bundle of His (Purkinje system) initiate the sequence of events in the cardiac cycle and control the cycle's regularity (Fig. 244). The SA node is located in the wall of the right atrium. Its regular rate of electrical discharge sets the rhythm of contraction for the entire heart, and it is thus known as the pacemaker. The AV node, located in the right posterior portion of the interatrial septum, transmits the impulses set up by the SA node to the bundle of His. The bundle of His forwards the nerve impulses from the AV node to the ventricles and initiates depolarization—an electrochemical process which enables the heart muscle to contract.

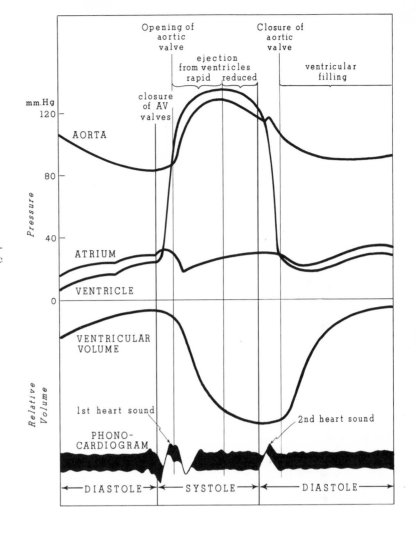

Fig. 242. Blood pressure, blood volume, and heart sounds during cardiac cycle.

CARDIAC RHYTHM AND RATE. The normal heart rate is 60 to 90 beats per minute. *Sinus tachycardia* is a condition characterized by a rhythmic beat at a rate of over 100 per minute. This occurs because the sino-atrial node is stimulated to set the pace at an increased rate. It can follow exercise or emotional disturbance, or result from disease. When the sino-atrial node has a rate of less than 60 beats per minute, *sinus bradycardia* is present. This rate may be normal in some individuals, particularly well-conditioned athletes.

The electrocardiograph (ECG). The electrocardiograph is an instrument used to measure cardiac rhythm and rate by recording the electrical impulses produced by the depolarization of the heart. Each portion of the cardiac cycle produces a different electrical impulse, causing the characteristic deflections of an ECG recording needle. The deflections, or waves, on the

recording apparatus are, named in order: P, Q, R, S, and T waves (Fig. 245). When the depolarization process occurs throughout the atria, the P wave is produced. When it occurs in the ventricles, the QRS complex is produced. The T wave is caused by repolarization of the ventricles. Electrocardiographic techniques and instrumentation offer a reliable method for detecting the presence of fetal life and multiple pregnancies. The electrocardiogram is important in the diagnosis of abnormal cardiac rhythms, including heart block, atrial flutter, atrial fibrillation, ventricular fibrillation, defective conduction through the bundle of His, and abnormalities of the ventricular wall (Fig. 246).

Atrioventricular block (heart block). Atrioventricular block is an impairment in the conduction of impulses from the atrium to the ventricle. The disturbance is located in the atrioventricular node and usually indicates myo-

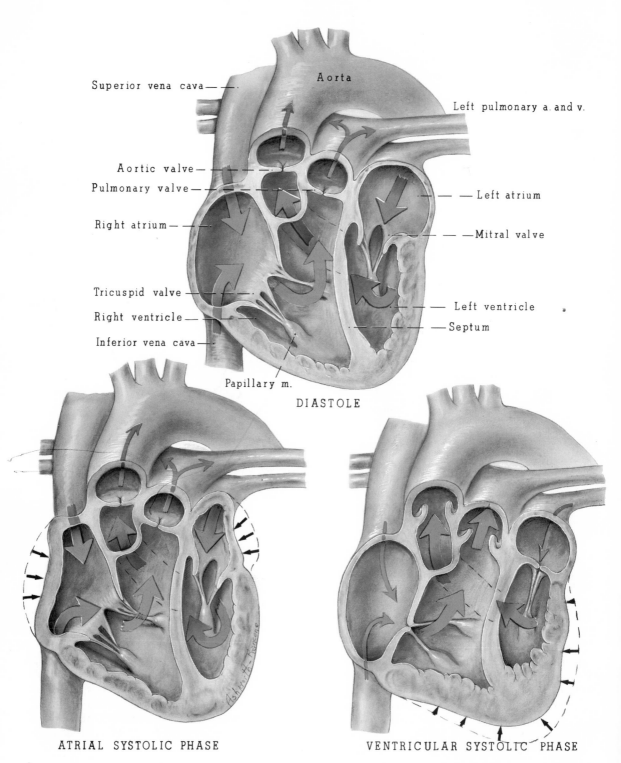

Superior vena cava

Aorta

Left pulmonary a. and v.

Aortic valve

Pulmonary valve

Right atrium

Tricuspid valve

Right ventricle

Inferior vena cava

Left atrium

Mitral valve

Left ventricle

Septum

Papillary m.

DIASTOLE

ATRIAL SYSTOLIC PHASE

VENTRICULAR SYSTOLIC PHASE

Fig. 243. Phases of the cardiac cycle. The size of the arrows indicates the volume of blood flow.

300

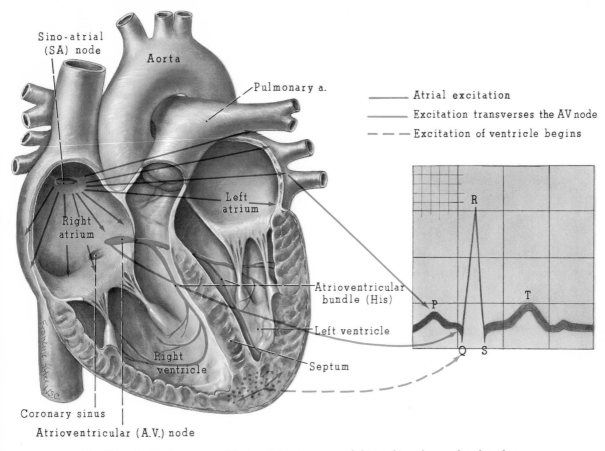

Fig. 244. Conducting system of the heart showing source of electrical impulses produced on electrocardiogram.

cardial disease. In the first degree block, a delay in atrioventricular conduction occurs. The delay cannot be clinically recognized, but is indicated by a prolonged PR interval in the electrocardiogram. Second degree atrioventricular block is recognized by the "dropped beat"; that is, ventricular contraction is completely missed at regular intervals. Thus, a ventricular rate one-half that of the atrial rate will be recorded on the ECG. Complete atrioventricular block (third degree block) represents a total dissociation of the atrial and ventricular rhythms. The ventricle sets its own rhythm in the atrioventricular node or in the bundle of His at a rate of 30 to 45 beats per minute. At times, the rate is higher.

Atrial flutter. In this cardiac disturbance, regular atrial rhythm is 240 to 360 beats per minute. Atrial flutter is actually an atrial tachycardia with a second degree atrioventricular block and is usually indicative of severe damage to the heart muscle. It is encountered occasion-

ally in normal hearts, but occurs mostly in patients with heart disease. Since the atrioventricular node cannot respond to each impulse, a 2:1, 3:1, or 4:1 block develops. This means that the atrioventricular node and ventricle respond to only one out of two, three, or four atrial impulses. Thus, the electrocardiogram can show an atrial rate of 240 and a ventricular rate of 120.

Atrial fibrillation. In atrial fibrillation, the excitation wave passes through the atrial musculature more rapidly and irregularly than in atrial flutter. The atrioventricular node is bombarded by numerous impulses. Atrial fibrillation is characterized by an irregularity of the rhythm and strength of the ventricular beat. Some beats are too weak to be felt as a pulsation in the peripheral arteries, because too little blood is ejected from the ventricles owing to inadequate ventricular filling from short diastole. Thus, the observer can count a rate of 140 beats per minute at the cardiac apex with a stethoscope and

ELECTROCARDIOGRAM

The wave of excitation spreading through the heart wall is accompanied by electrical changes.

The record of these changes is an ELECTROCARDIOGRAM (ECG)

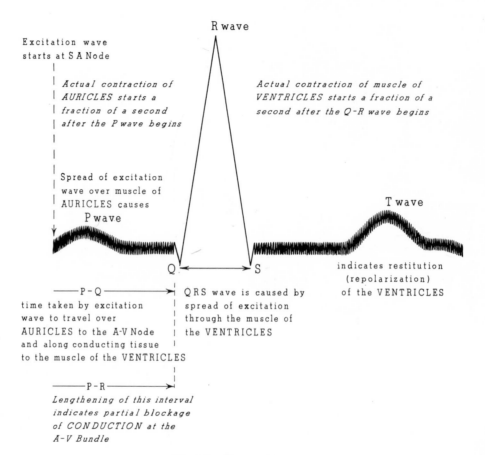

Excitation wave
starts at S A Node

Actual contraction of AURICLES starts a fraction of a second after the P wave begins

Actual contraction of muscle of VENTRICLES starts a fraction of a second after the Q-R wave begins

Spread of excitation wave over muscle of AURICLES causes
P wave

R wave

T wave

indicates restitution (repolarization) of the VENTRICLES

——— P-Q ———
time taken by excitation wave to travel over AURICLES to the A-V Node and along conducting tissue to the muscle of the VENTRICLES

QRS wave is caused by spread of excitation through the muscle of the VENTRICLES

——— P-R ———
Lengthening of this interval indicates partial blockage of CONDUCTION at the A-V Bundle

Fig. 245. Electrocardiogram.

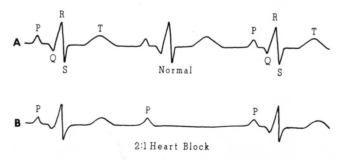

A   P R T   Normal
     Q S

B   P   2:1 Heart Block
         P   P

Fig. 246. An electrocardiogram. *A.* Normal. *B.* Heart block (there is only one ventricular contraction for every two atrial contractions).

palpate only 110 beats per minute at the wrist—a pulse deficit of 30. This pulse deficit represents the ventricular contractions which are too weak to transmit the pulse wave peripherally. Blood pressure determination in such cases is inaccurate, since it varies with the strength of the beat. Weak beats are not caused by myocardial weakness. They are caused by an inadequate diastolic filling period and, thus, by a reduced stroke volume.

Other abnormalities of cardiac rhythm. Paroxysmal atrial tachycardia is the commonest arrhythmia. It can occur at any age and often is not associated with severe heart disease. The heart rate is between 100 to 200 with a regular rhythm.

In ventricular fibrillation, a cessation of circulation is caused by ineffective ventricular contraction; death usually results.

Since the QRS wave represents the passage of a depolarization process through the ventricle, any pathology causing abnormal impulse transmission will alter the shape, voltage, or duration of the QRS complex.

Nervous Control of the Heart

The nervous control of the heart is maintained by the vagus nerve (parasympathetic) and the sympathetic nerves. The vagus nerve is the cardiac inhibitor, and the sympathetic nerves are the cardiac excitors.

Parasympathetic fibers supply the sino-atrial and atrioventricular nodes. A continuous restraining action on the rate of the heart is exerted by parasympathetic impulses. Stimulation of the vagus nerve depresses impulse formation and atrial contractility. It thereby reduces cardiac output and slows the heart rate. Parasympathetic stimulation can also produce varying degrees of heart block in diseased hearts.

The sympathetic nervous system influences the activity of the heart. Stimulation of the sympathetic nerves increases contractility of both atria and ventricles. The sympathetic nervous system is important in mediating the exercise response.

Cardiac Output

The volume of blood ejected per beat is known as the stroke volume. Stroke volume times the number of beats per minute is called the minute volume, or cardiac output. Under resting conditions, cardiac output approximates 2.7 liters per minute. The average volume of blood ejected by the heart per beat is 60 to 70 ml. The output of the heart depends on venous return, cardiac rate, and the force of cardiac contraction.

Venous return. Cardiac output increases with an increase in venous return. Venous return is influenced by the following factors: contraction of skeletal muscles squeezing the veins, forcing the blood to move; increased negative pressure in the pleural cavity with inspiration, pulling the blood toward the heart; and higher pressure in the capillaries than in the veins, forcing the blood toward the heart. Gravity aids the venous return from areas which are above the level of the heart. With a decreased blood volume, as in hemorrhage, venous return is lowered. Dilatation of the capillaries allows for pooling of blood and a consequent drop in venous return.

Heart rate. The frequency of the heart rate influences cardiac output by affecting the number of strokes per minute. In the resting individual with a constant venous return, the normal frequency of the heart provides sufficient diastolic time for both venous filling and recovery of the cardiac muscle. When the venous return is increased, a two or three-fold increase in stroke volume results.

Force of cardiac contraction. The force of the heart depends on the initial length of the fibers, the length of the diastolic pause, the oxygen supply, and the integrity and mass of the myocardium.

Starling's law of the heart states that "the energy of contraction is proportional to the initial length of the cardiac muscle fiber." The greater the initial length of the muscle fibers in the heart, the more forceful will be the contraction. Artificially increasing venous return distends the heart and intensifies the force of the beat. The greater inflow is handled by an increased output of the heart without a change in its rate. When the ventricle does not completely fill (for example, after hemorrhage), the force of the heartbeat is reduced. When the venous inflow during diastole is increased, as in muscular exercise, the beats become more forceful. If, as a result of excessive filling, the fibers are overstretched, a weak contraction results with diminished cardiac output; consequently, the heart does not adequately empty. The force of the heart is diminished if the diastolic phase is too short and there is not adequate filling.

Closed Cardiac Massage

When the heart stops, the procedure of choice for maintaining circulation is closed cardiac mas-

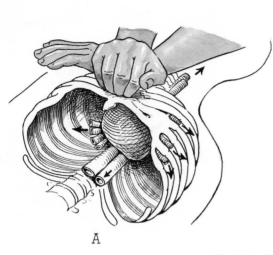

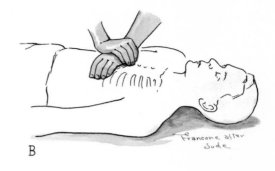

Fig. 247.   Closed cardiac massage.

sage. Closed cardiac massage must be started as soon as possible after the heart stops. If as long as 4 minutes is allowed to elapse, there can be irreversible damage to the brain.

In performing closed cardiac massage, the patient should be placed on a firm surface. Cardiac massage should not be undertaken with the patient lying on a soft bed. The individual performing the massage stands at right angles to the trunk of the patient, with one hand on top of the other, and places the heel of the hand over the patient's sternum, applying pressure vertically about once every second. The sternum should move approximately 2 inches toward the vertebral column. At the completion of each

maneuver, the hands are completely relaxed to permit full chest expansion. Throughout external cardiac massage, an assistant should maintain mouth-to-mouth or mouth-to-nose ventilation (Fig. 247).

BLOOD VESSELS

Structure

Blood vessels are divided into several types on the basis of size, function, and histologic characteristics. Classes include large, or elastic,

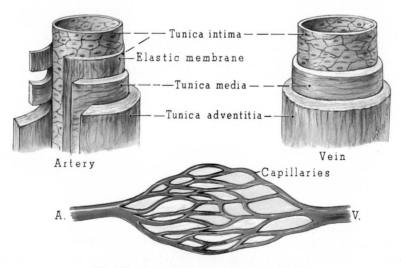

Fig. 248.   Component parts of arteries and veins.

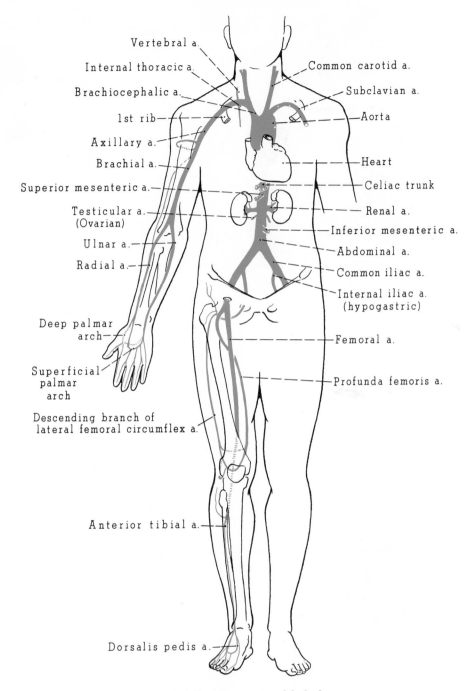

Fig. 249. Major arteries of the body.

arteries; medium sized, or muscular, arteries; small arteries, or arterioles; capillaries; and veins. Blood vessels are composed of three layers: a *tunica adventitia,* a *tunica media,* and a *tunica intima* (Table 35 and Fig. 248).

THE CIRCULATORY SYSTEM

The circulatory system can be studied in terms of several smaller units—the systemic system, the pulmonary system, and the portal system

VESSEL	OUTER LAYER: TUNICA ADVENTITIA	MIDDLE LAYER: TUNICA MEDIA	INNER LAYER: TUNICA INTIMA
Large arteries (elastic)	Thick layer, consisting of connective tissue	Layer consists largely of elastic fibers with some muscle	Thin endothelial cells resting on connective tissue
Muscular arteries (medium)	Thick layer, consisting of connective tissue	Fewer elastic fibers, more smooth muscle	Thin endothelial cells resting on connective tissue
Small arteries (arterioles)	Thin	Consists of muscular tissue	Layer composed almost entirely of endothelium
Capillaries	Absent	Absent	Endothelial layer one cell thick
Veins	Thin layer	Thinner; little muscle or elastic tissue	Endothelial lining with scant connective tissue

TABLE 35.   Structure of Blood Vessels.

(Figs. 249 to 269). The circulatory system of the fetus differs from that of the adult; it too will be studied as a separate unit.

Systemic Circulation

The systemic circulation carries oxygen, nutrients, and wastes for the entire body. All systemic arteries spring from the aorta. The aorta emerges from the superior surface of the left ventricle, passes upward underneath the pulmonary artery as the *ascending aorta,* and then turns to the left as the *aortic arch,* passing downward as the *desending aorta.* The descending aorta, lying close to the vertebral bodies, passes through the diaphragm to the level of the fourth lumbar vertebra. It terminates by dividing into the two common iliac arteries. The descending aorta is divided into the thoracic seg-

Text continued on page 325.

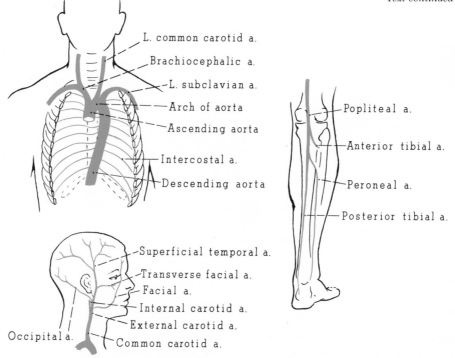

Fig. 250.   Major arterial supply to the chest, face, and lower leg.

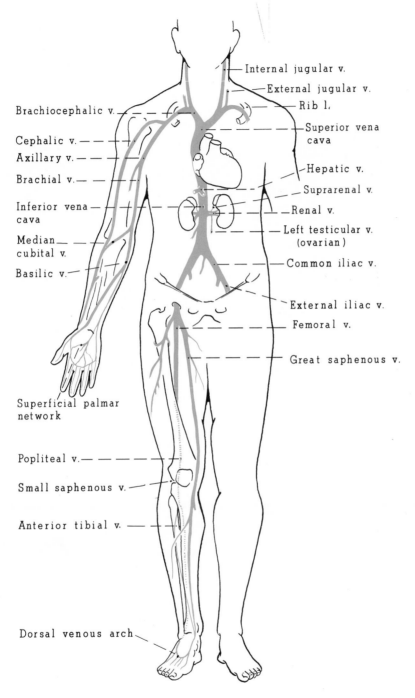

Internal jugular v.

External jugular v.

Rib 1.

Brachiocephalic v.

Superior vena cava

Cephalic v.

Axillary v.

Brachial v.

Hepatic v.

Suprarenal v.

Inferior vena cava

Renal v.

Left testicular v. (ovarian)

Median cubital v.

Basilic v.

Common iliac v.

External iliac v.

Femoral v.

Great saphenous v.

Superficial palmar network

Popliteal v.

Small saphenous v.

Anterior tibial v.

Dorsal venous arch

Fig. 251. Major veins of the body.

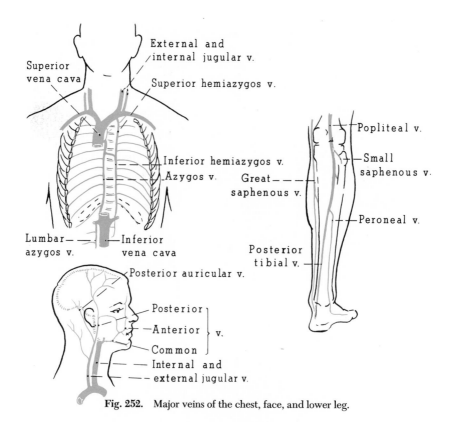

Fig. 252. Major veins of the chest, face, and lower leg.

The labels in the figure are:

Superior vena cava

External and internal jugular v.

Superior hemiazygos v.

Inferior hemiazygos v.

Azygos v.

Popliteal v.

Small saphenous v.

Great saphenous v.

Peroneal v.

Lumbar azygos v.

Inferior vena cava

Posterior tibial v.

Posterior auricular v.

Posterior

Anterior

Common

v.

Internal and external jugular v.

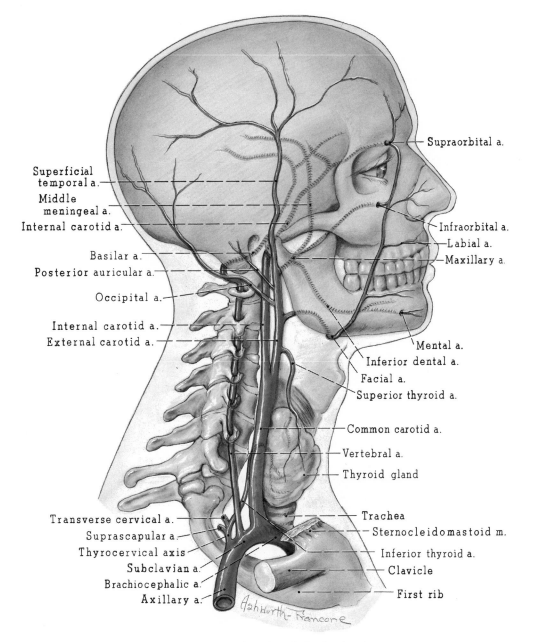

Superficial temporal a.

Middle meningeal a.

Internal carotid a.

Basilar a.

Posterior auricular a.

Occipital a.

Internal carotid a.

External carotid a.

Transverse cervical a.

Suprascapular a.

Thyrocervical axis

Subclavian a.

Brachiocephalic a.

Axillary a.

Supraorbital a.

Infraorbital a.

Labial a.

Maxillary a.

Mental a.

Inferior dental a.

Facial a.

Superior thyroid a.

Common carotid a.

Vertebral a.

Thyroid gland

Trachea

Sternocleidomastoid m.

Inferior thyroid a.

Clavicle

First rib

Ashworth-Francone

Fig. 253. Arterial supply to the head and neck.

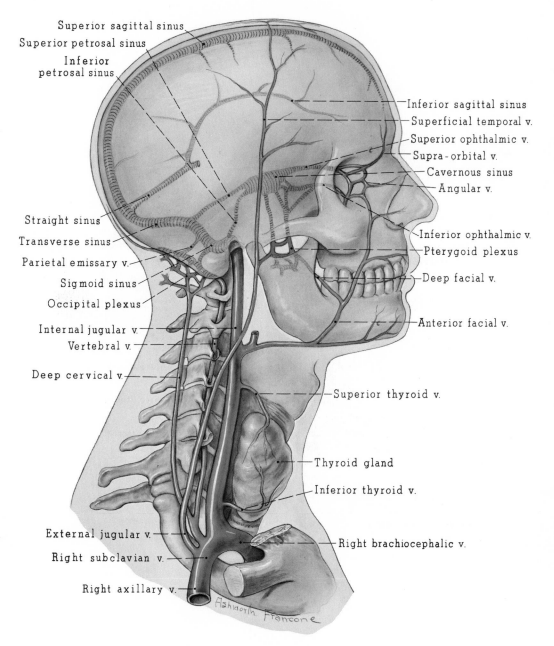

Superior sagittal sinus

Superior petrosal sinus

Inferior petrosal sinus

Inferior sagittal sinus

Superficial temporal v.

Superior ophthalmic v.

Supra-orbital v.

Cavernous sinus

Angular v.

Straight sinus

Transverse sinus

Parietal emissary v.

Sigmoid sinus

Occipital plexus

Inferior ophthalmic v.

Pterygoid plexus

Deep facial v.

Anterior facial v.

Internal jugular v.

Vertebral v.

Deep cervical v.

Superior thyroid v.

Thyroid gland

Inferior thyroid v.

External jugular v.

Right subclavian v.

Right axillary v.

Right brachiocephalic v.

Fig. 254.   Venous drainage of the head and neck.

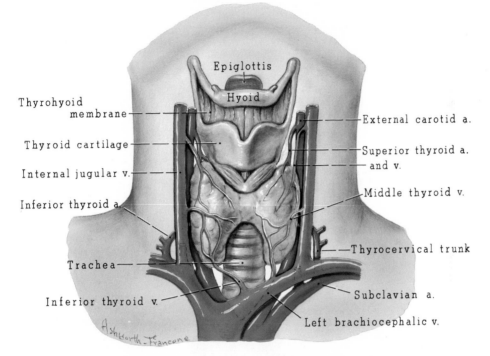

Thyrohyoid membrane

Thyroid cartilage

Internal jugular v.

Inferior thyroid a.

Trachea

Inferior thyroid v.

Epiglottis

Hyoid

External carotid a.

Superior thyroid a. and v.

Middle thyroid v.

Thyrocervical trunk

Subclavian a.

Left brachiocephalic v.

Fig. 255. Arterial supply and venous drainage of the neck.

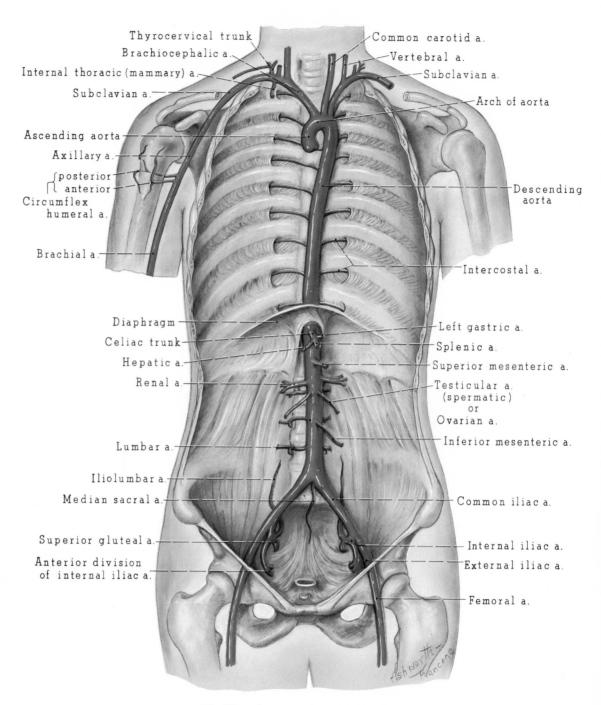

Thyrocervical trunk

Brachiocephalic a.

Internal thoracic (mammary) a.

Subclavian a.

Common carotid a.

Vertebral a.

Subclavian a.

Arch of aorta

Ascending aorta

Axillary a.

{ posterior
  anterior
Circumflex
humeral a.

Descending
aorta

Brachial a.

Intercostal a.

Diaphragm

Celiac trunk

Hepatic a.

Renal a.

Left gastric a.

Splenic a.

Superior mesenteric a.

Testicular a.
(spermatic)
or
Ovarian a.

Lumbar a.

Inferior mesenteric a.

Iliolumbar a.

Median sacral a.

Common iliac a.

Superior gluteal a.

Anterior division
of internal iliac a.

Internal iliac a.

External iliac a.

Femoral a.

Fig. 256.   The aorta and its major branches.

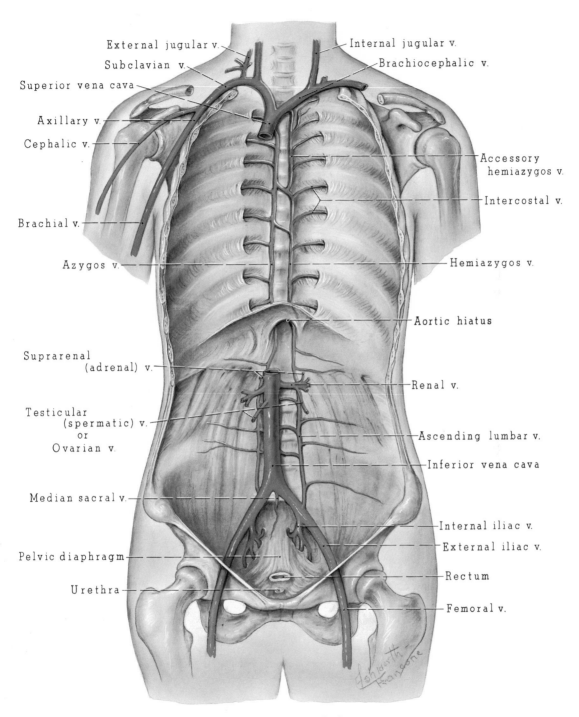

External jugular v. — Internal jugular v.
Subclavian v. — Brachiocephalic v.
Superior vena cava —
Axillary v. —
Cephalic v. — Accessory hemiazygos v.
Intercostal v.
Brachial v. —
Azygos v. — Hemiazygos v.
Aortic hiatus
Suprarenal (adrenal) v. —
Renal v.
Testicular (spermatic) v. or Ovarian v. —
Ascending lumbar v.
Inferior vena cava
Median sacral v. —
Internal iliac v.
External iliac v.
Pelvic diaphragm —
Rectum
Urethra —
Femoral v.

Fig. 257. Vena cava and tributaries.

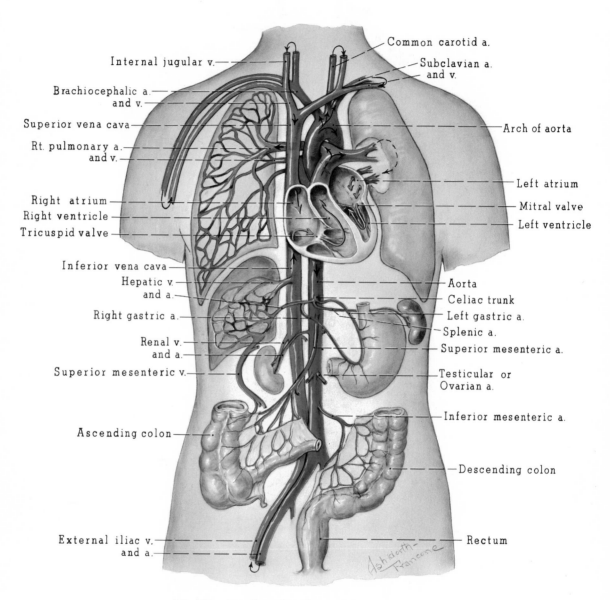

Internal jugular v.

Brachiocephalic a.
and v.

Superior vena cava

Rt. pulmonary a.
and v.

Right atrium
Right ventricle
Tricuspid valve

Inferior vena cava
Hepatic v.
and a.

Right gastric a.

Renal v.
and a.

Superior mesenteric v.

Ascending colon

External iliac v.
and a.

Common carotid a.

Subclavian a.
and v.

Arch of aorta

Left atrium
Mitral valve
Left ventricle

Aorta
Celiac trunk
Left gastric a.
Splenic a.
Superior mesenteric a.

Testicular or
Ovarian a.

Inferior mesenteric a.

Descending colon

Rectum

Fig. 258.   Arterial supply and venous drainage of organs.

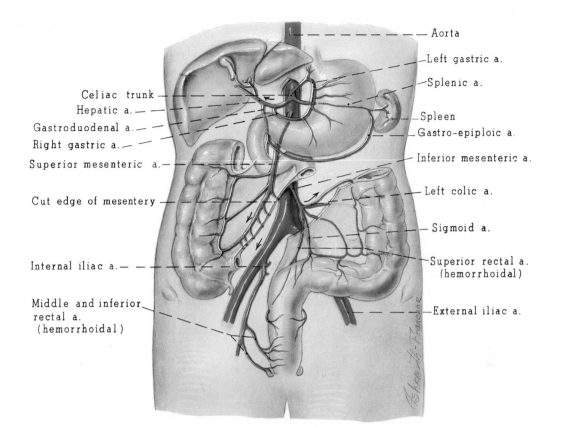

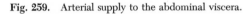

Fig. 259. Arterial supply to the abdominal viscera.

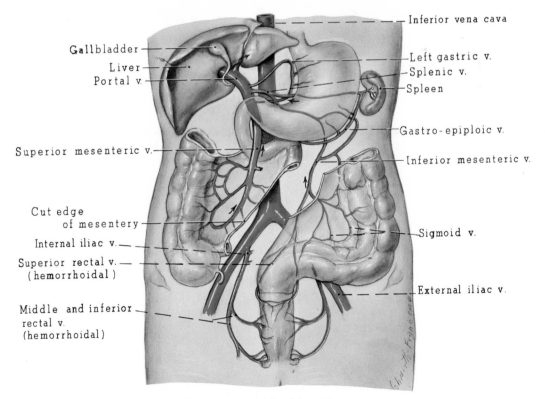

Fig. 260. Veins of the abdominal viscera.

315

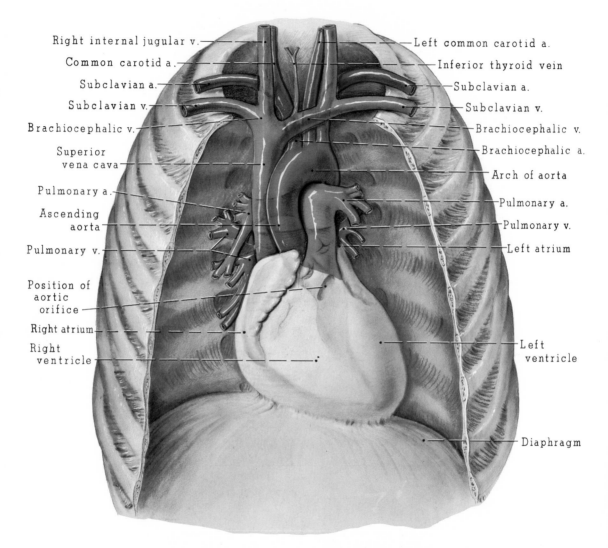

Right internal jugular v.

Common carotid a.

Subclavian a.

Subclavian v.

Brachiocephalic v.

Superior
vena cava

Pulmonary a.

Ascending
aorta

Pulmonary v.

Position of
aortic
orifice

Right atrium

Right
ventricle

Left common carotid a.

Inferior thyroid vein

Subclavian a.

Subclavian v.

Brachiocephalic v.

Brachiocephalic a.

Arch of aorta

Pulmonary a.

Pulmonary v.

Left atrium

Left
ventricle

Diaphragm

Fig. 261. The heart in situ, showing its relation to the chest cavity and diaphragm with the major
arteries and veins of the chest.

316

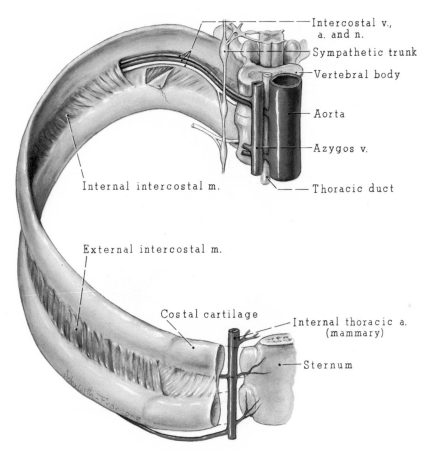

Intercostal v.,
a. and n.

Sympathetic trunk

Vertebral body

Aorta

Azygos v.

Thoracic duct

Internal intercostal m.

External intercostal m.

Costal cartilage

Internal thoracic a.
(mammary)

Sternum

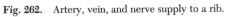

Fig. 262. Artery, vein, and nerve supply to a rib.

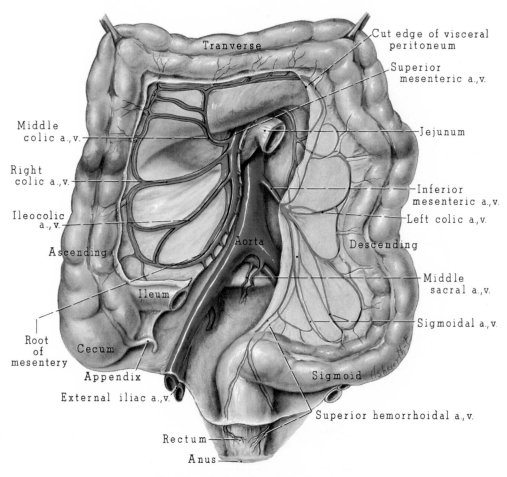

Tranverse

Cut edge of visceral
peritoneum

Superior
mesenteric a.,v.

Middle
colic a.,v.

Jejunum

Right
colic a.,v.

Inferior
mesenteric a.,v.

Ileocolic
a.,v.

Left colic a.,v.

Ascending

Descending

Aorta

Ileum

Middle
sacral a.,v.

Sigmoidal a.,v.

Root
of
mesentery

Cecum

Appendix

Sigmoid

External iliac a.,v.

Superior hemorrhoidal a.,v.

Rectum

Anus

Fig. 263.   Blood supply to the large intestine.

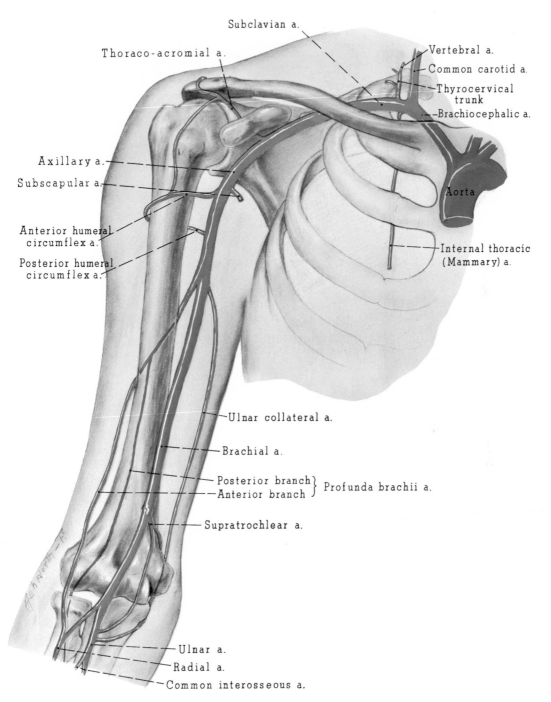

Subclavian a.

Thoraco-acromial a.

Vertebral a.

Common carotid a.

Thyrocervical
trunk

Brachiocephalic a.

Axillary a.

Subscapular a.

Anterior humeral
circumflex a.

Posterior humeral
circumflex a.

Aorta

Internal thoracic
(Mammary) a.

Ulnar collateral a.

Brachial a.

Posterior branch
Anterior branch } Profunda brachii a.

Supratrochlear a.

Ulnar a.

Radial a.

Common interosseous a.

Fig. 264. Arteries of the right shoulder and upper arm.

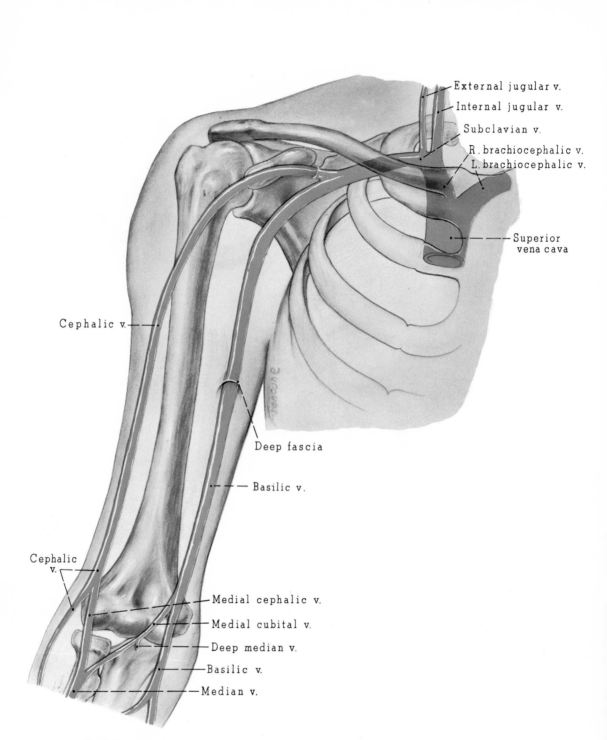

External jugular v.

Internal jugular v.

Subclavian v.

R. brachiocephalic v.
L. brachiocephalic v.

Superior vena cava

Cephalic v.

Deep fascia

Basilic v.

Cephalic v.

Medial cephalic v.

Medial cubital v.

Deep median v.

Basilic v.

Median v.

Fig. 265. Veins of the right shoulder and upper arm. The basilic vein pierces the deep fascia in the region of the middle of the arm.

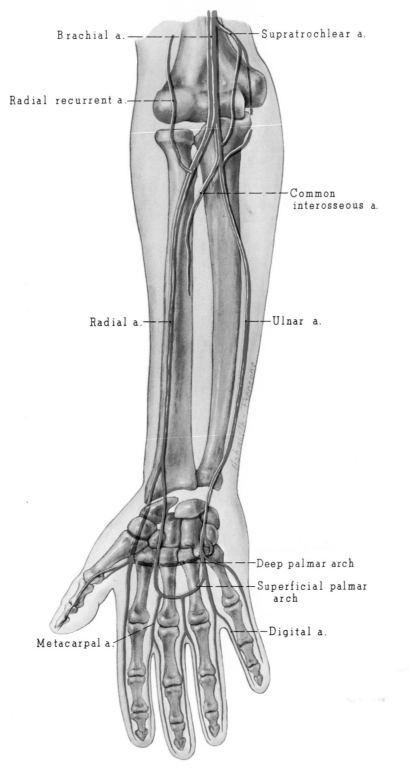

Brachial a.

Supratrochlear a.

Radial recurrent a.

Common interosseous a.

Radial a.

Ulnar a.

Deep palmar arch

Superficial palmar arch

Digital a.

Metacarpal a.

Fig. 266. Arteries of the right lower arm.

321

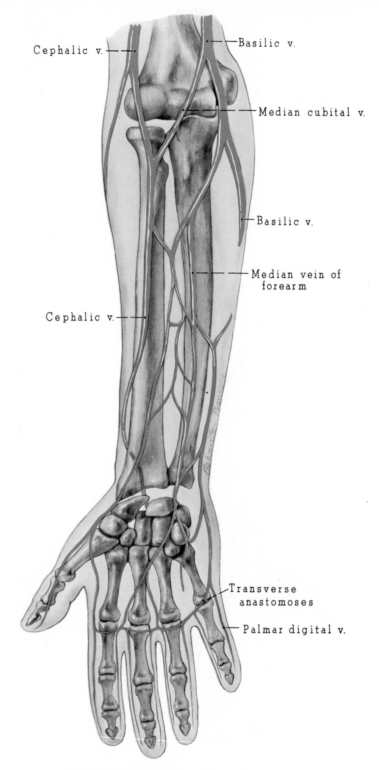

Cephalic v.

Basilic v.

Median cubital v.

Basilic v.

Median vein of forearm

Cephalic v.

Transverse anastomoses

Palmar digital v.

Fig. 267. Venous drainage of the right forearm and hand.

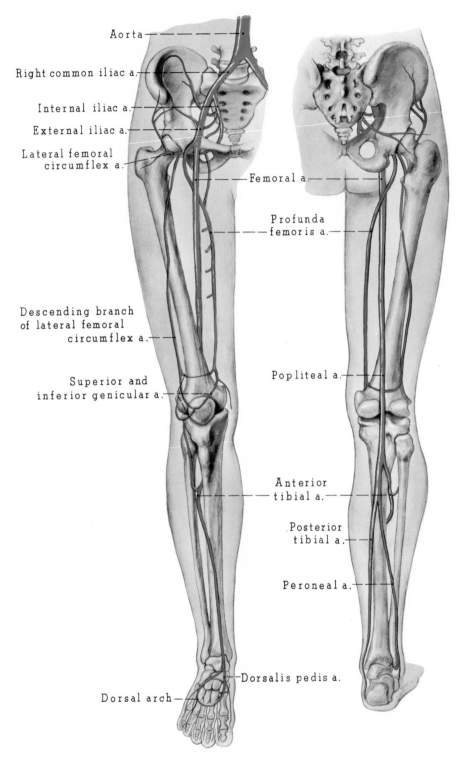

Aorta

Right common iliac a.

Internal iliac a.

External iliac a.

Lateral femoral
circumflex a.

Femoral a.

Profunda
femoris a.

Descending branch
of lateral femoral
circumflex a.

Popliteal a.

Superior and
inferior genicular a.

Anterior
tibial a.

Posterior
tibial a.

Peroneal a.

Dorsalis pedis a.

Dorsal arch

Fig. 268. Arteries of the right pelvis and leg.

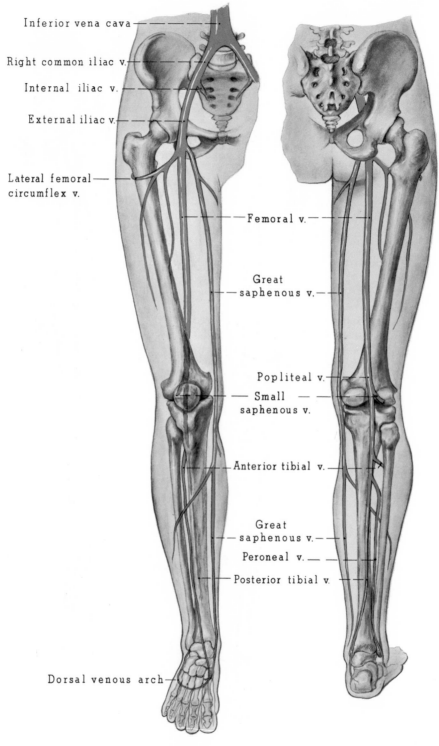

Inferior vena cava

Right common iliac v.

Internal iliac v.

External iliac v.

Lateral femoral
circumflex v.

Femoral v.

Great
saphenous v.

Popliteal v.

Small
saphenous v.

Anterior tibial v.

Great
saphenous v.

Peroneal v.

Posterior tibial v.

Dorsal venous arch

Fig. 269.   Veins of the right pelvis and leg.

Continued from page 306.

ment (above the diaphragm) and the abdominal segment (below the diaphragm). Major arteries of the body spring from the aorta. They are described in Figs. 270 to 273.

The veins emerge from the capillaries. All veins of the systemic circulation flow into either the inferior or superior vena cava, which in turn empties into the right atrium. The major veins of the body are described in Figs. 270 to 273.

Veins are equipped with valves to facilitate venous return (Fig. 274). The valves are delicate, bicuspid pockets opening in the direction of blood flow. Valves permit blood flow in a central direction, but prevent the regurgitation of flow when the pockets become filled and distended.

Varicose veins. Varicose veins are a dilatation of the superficial veins, usually occurring in the lower extremities. The dilatation results from increased pressure within the veins, as often occurs if the individual stands for long periods of time. It is thought that there is a genetic predisposition to the development of varicose veins. Pregnancy and obesity hasten the development of dilated veins in the lower extremities. Treatment of varicose veins is surgical removal. The veins involved (the long and short saphenous veins) carry little circulation and consequently there is almost no deficit following their removal.

Atherosclerosis. Atherosclerosis, a condition characterized by a deposition of lipid-containing material beneath the intima of the blood vessels, occurs only in arteries, especially at junctions. The disease frequently results in thrombosis or occlusion of coronary or cerebral blood vessels. Excessive fats in the diet can be an important factor in the cause of atherosclerosis, but here also there is a genetic predisposition. This disease is the number one medical problem in the United States today.

Pulmonary Circulation

The pulmonary system carries blood from the right ventricle to the lungs and back to the left atrium. The pulmonary trunk, originating from

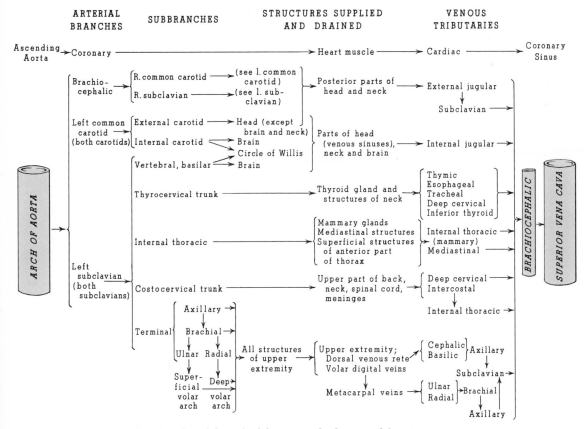

Fig. 270.   Branches of the arch of the aorta and tributaries of the superior vena cava.

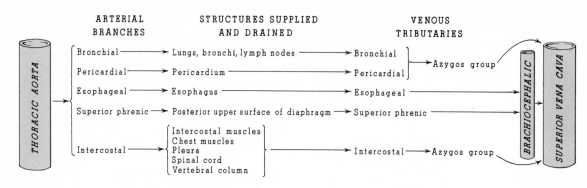

Fig. 271. Branches of the thoracic aorta and tributaries of the superior vena cava.

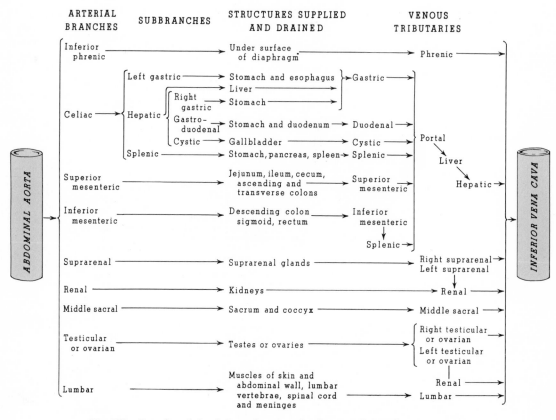

Fig. 272. Branches of the abdominal aorta and tributaries of the inferior vena cava.

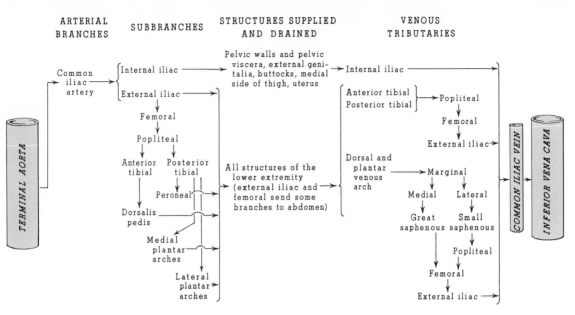

Fig. 273. Branches of the terminal aorta and tributaries of the inferior vena cava.

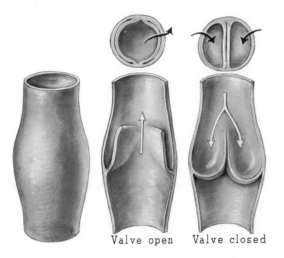

Valve open   Valve closed

Fig. 274. Veins contain bicuspid valves which open in the direction of blood flow, but prevent regurgitation of flow when pockets become filled and distended.

laries. Capillaries surround air sacs (alveoli) and pick up oxygen and release carbon dioxide. Gradually, the capillaries unite, assuming the characteristics of veins. Veins join to form pulmonary veins which carry oxygenated blood from the lungs to the left atrium.

A pulmonary embolus is a clot lodged in the pulmonary artery (Fig. 275). It can result from blood, air, fat, a tumor, or clumps of bacteria. An embolus can obstruct the main pulmonary artery or one of its large branches. This condition often results in death. Frequently, the patient will recover if the main pulmonary artery is not involved. If the major pulmonary artery is obstructed, cardiac output falls suddenly, the skin becomes pale because of intense vasoconstriction, the blood pressure drops, and the patient manifests evidences of shock. There is usually an increased heart rate.

Portal System

Blood flowing to the liver comes from the hepatic artery (20 per cent) and the portal vein (80 per cent); blood leaving the liver flows through the hepatic vein which empties into the inferior vena cava. The hepatic arterial blood supplies oxygen requirements for the liver. Blood from the abdominal viscera, particularly

the superior surface of the right ventricle, passes diagonally upward to the left across the route of the aorta. Between the fifth and sixth thoracic vertebrae, the trunk divides into two branches—the right and left pulmonary arteries—which enter the lungs. After entering the lungs, the branches subdivide, finally emerging as capil-

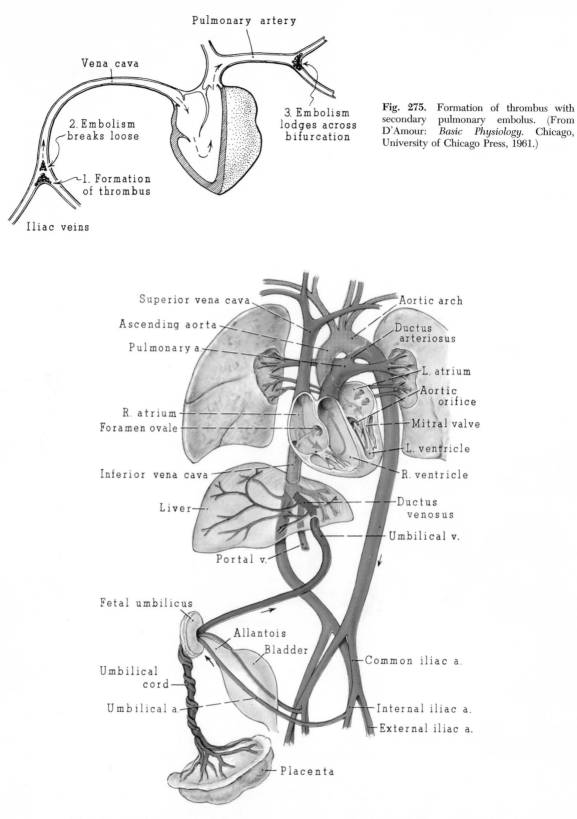

Vena cava

Pulmonary artery

2. Embolism breaks loose

3. Embolism lodges across bifurcation

1. Formation of thrombus

Iliac veins

Fig. 275. Formation of thrombus with secondary pulmonary embolus. (From D'Amour: *Basic Physiology.* Chicago, University of Chicago Press, 1961.)

Superior vena cava

Ascending aorta

Pulmonary a.

Aortic arch

Ductus arteriosus

L. atrium

Aortic orifice

R. atrium

Foramen ovale

Mitral valve

L. ventricle

Inferior vena cava

Liver

R. ventricle

Ductus venosus

Umbilical v.

Portal v.

Fetal umbilicus

Allantois

Bladder

Umbilical cord

Common iliac a.

Umbilical a.

Internal iliac a.

External iliac a.

Placenta

Fig. 276. Circulatory system of the fetus. (For comparison with adult circulation, see Fig. 277.)

the intestinal tract, passes into the portal vein and then into the liver. Substances in the portal blood are processed by the liver; agents such as fibrinogen and prothrombin are added to the blood in the liver.

Fetal Circulation

The circulatory system of the fetus differs from that of the adult, since the lungs and alimentary canal of the fetus are non-functional. These differences disappear at birth or shortly thereafter. The primary features distinguishing fetal from adult circulation can be seen in Table 36 and Figs. 276 and 277.

Oxygenated blood is carried from the placenta to the fetus by the umbilical vein. It then passes by way of the inferior vena cava via the liver through the ductus venosus. From the inferior vena cava, the blood enters the right atrium, passing through the foramen ovale into the left atrium, into the left ventricle, and out the aorta, distributing arterial blood to the head and upper extremities.

Blood from the upper extremities returns via the superior vena cava into the right atrium, where it is largely deflected into the right ventricle (in contrast to blood from the inferior vena cava, which is deflected through the foramen ovale into the opposite atrium).

From the right ventricle, a portion of the blood flows into the pulmonary artery supplying the lungs. The largest fraction flows through the ductus arteriosus to the aorta. It enters the aorta distal to the point at which the blood of the

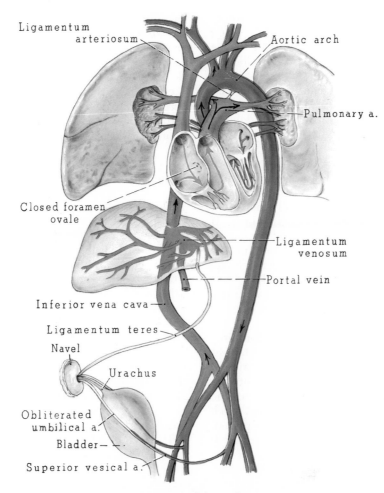

Fig. 277. Adult circulation.

TABLE 36.   Differences in Adult and Fetal Circulation.

STRUCTURE	FUNCTION IN FETUS	FUNCTION IN ADULT
Umbilical artery	Joins fetus to placenta	Atrophies to become the lateral umbilical ligament
Umbilical vein	Joins fetus to placenta	Becomes the round ligament of the liver (ligamentum teres)
Ductus venosus	Vessel connecting the umbilical vein to the inferior vena cava	Becomes a fibrous cord (ligamentum venosum) embedded in the wall of the liver
Foramen ovale	An opening between the two atria	Closes shortly after birth
Ductus arteriosus	Blood vessel connecting the pulmonary artery with the aorta	Closes and atrophies after birth, becoming the ligamentum arteriosum

head leaves. Some of the blood supplies the lower portion of the body. The remainder returns to the placenta via the umbilical arteries.

At birth, changes are the result of inflation of the lungs, permitting routing of the blood through the pulmonary system instead of the umbilical vessels. The changes are described in Table 36.

CONGENITAL DEFECTS. The most common congenital defects are patent ductus arteriosus, ventricular septal defects, atrial septal defects, the so-called tetralogy of Fallot, and coarctation of the aorta (Fig. 278).

A *patent ductus arteriosus* is a condition characterized by persistence of the channel joining the left pulmonary artery to the aorta. This occurs normally in the fetus, and usually the patent ductus closes within a few weeks after birth. If it does not close, it must be closed surgically.

Septal defects are small holes within the septum between the atria or ventricles. Small openings usually cause little difficulty; large openings frequently result in death shortly after birth. Septal defects are closed directly, employing the heart-lung machine.

The *tetralogy of Fallot* is a bizarre combination of defects including pulmonary stenosis (narrowing of pulmonary artery), ventricular septal defect, enlargement of the right ventricle, and apparent dextroposition of the aorta. The result of this combination of defects is that much of the blood does not flow through the pulmonary system. The most characteristic feature is severe cyanosis. A common procedure for correcting this defect is to shunt the blood from the systemic circulation to the pulmonary circulation; this is accomplished by joining the sub-clavian artery surgically to the pulmonary artery. Currently, the tetralogy of Fallot is frequently treated by a direct attack, using the heart-lung machine and correcting the abnormalities.

Coarctation of the aorta is a congenital defect, involving a drastic narrowing of the aorta. It causes an increased work load on the left ventricle. If severe, collateral circulation develops. It is corrected either by removing the constricted portion and joining the two open ends of the aorta or by substituting a plastic portion for the removed part of the aorta.

Blood Pressure

Blood pressure is pressure exerted by the blood against the walls of the vessels. The term applies to arterial, capillary, and venous pressure (Fig. 279). Usually it indicates pressure existing in the large arteries—commonly, the brachial artery just above the elbow. The blood pressure is highest in the brachial artery at the time of contraction of the ventricles (ventricular systole). This level is known as the *systolic pressure*. Pressure during ventricular diastole (relaxation of the ventricles) is called *diastolic pressure* and is principally the result of force exerted by the elastic rebound of the arterial wall. Blood pressure is usually expressed as a fraction—for example, as 120/80, in which 120 represents systolic pressure and 80, diastolic pressure.

The magnitude of systolic pressure depends upon the amount of blood ejected from the ventricle, the level of pre-existing diastolic pressure, and the elasticity of the aorta. The diastolic pressure depends upon the duration of diastole and

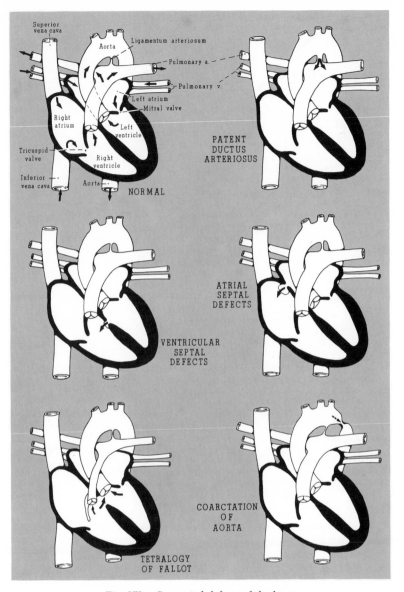

Superior
vena cava
Aorta
Ligamentum arteriosum
Pulmonary a.
Pulmonary v.
Left atrium
Mitral valve
Right
atrium
Left
ventricle
Tricuspid
valve
Right
ventricle
Inferior
vena cava
Aorta
NORMAL

PATENT
DUCTUS
ARTERIOSUS

VENTRICULAR
SEPTAL
DEFECTS

ATRIAL
SEPTAL
DEFECTS

TETRALOGY
OF FALLOT

COARCTATION
OF
AORTA

Fig. 278.   Congenital defects of the heart.

the peripheral resistance. The longer the duration of diastole, the lower the diastolic pressure. Both systolic and diastolic pressures are influenced by cardiac rate, stroke volume, size, and elasticity of all components of the arterial bed.

Blood pressure is subject to fluctuations. In general, the healthy individual has a systolic pressure of 100 to 120 mm. of mercury and a diastolic pressure of 60 to 80 mm. of mercury. Asthenic individuals often have a constantly low blood pressure (hypotension), with a systolic pressure of 90 to 100, and a diastolic pressure of 50 to 60.

Variations in systolic blood pressure are expected in normal persons. Exercise may cause a rise in systolic pressure.

A blood pressure difference of 10 to 15 mm. of mercury often exists between the two arms of an individual. The higher pressure is usually found in the right arm. A pressure difference greater than 10 to 15 mm. of mercury should arouse suspicion, since it might be the result of coarctation of the aorta between the origins of the right and left subclavian arteries.

The upper limits of normal blood pressure are

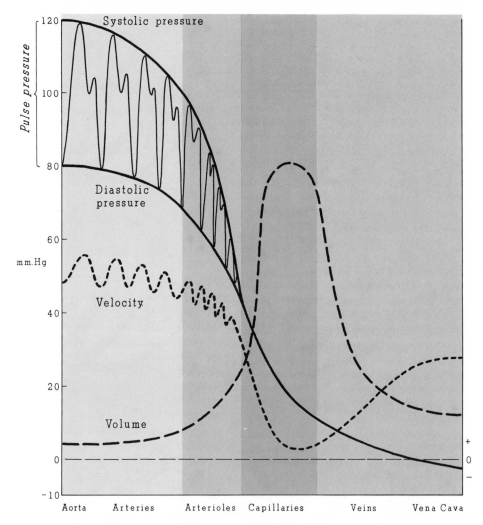

Fig. 279.   Blood pressure, blood velocity, and volume of the vascular tree in various segments of the circulatory system. (From Zoethout and Tuttle: *Textbook of Physiology*, twelfth edition. St. Louis, The C. V. Mosby Co., 1955.)

usually defined as 140 mm. of mercury systolic and 90 mm. diastolic. Pressures above this level (hypertension) shorten life expectancy.

BLOOD PRESSURE MEASUREMENT.   Blood pressure is measured with a *sphygmomanometer.* The pressure of blood within the artery is balanced by an external pressure exerted by air contained in a cuff applied externally around the arm. Actually, what is measured is the pressure within the cuff. The steps employed in determining blood pressure with a sphygmomanometer are the following:

1. The cuff is wrapped securely around the arm above the elbow.

2. Air is pumped into the cuff with a rubber bulb until pressure in it is sufficient to stop the

flow of blood in the radial artery. At this point, the radial pulse disappears. Pressure within the cuff is shown on the scale of the sphygmomanometer.

3. The observer places a stethoscope over the brachial artery just below the elbow and gradually releases the air from within the cuff. The decreased air pressure permits the blood to flow, filling the artery below the cuff. Faint tapping sounds corresponding to the heartbeat are heard. When the sound is first noted, the air pressure from within the cuff is recorded on the scale. This pressure is equal to the systolic blood pressure.

4. As the air in the cuff is further released, the sounds become progressively louder. Then

the sounds change in quality from loud to soft and finally disappear. At the point where the sounds change from loud to soft, the manometer reading corresponds to the diastolic pressure.

The American Heart Association recommends that when a wide difference exists between the point and level at which the sound becomes dull or muffled and the point at which the sound completely disappears, the level at which the sound completely disappears should also be recorded as diastolic blood pressure. If the two levels are identical, only one level would be recorded.

REGULATION OF BLOOD PRESSURE. Five factors function in the maintenance of arterial blood pressure.

1. *Cardiac factor.* The volume of blood expelled per stroke is a determinant of the systolic pressure.

2. *Peripheral resistance.* Peripheral resistance is provided chiefly by the arterioles, which vary their diameter and hence size of the vascular bed over a wide range. The blood pressure falls approximately 20 mm. of mercury from the aorta to the smaller arteries, and an additional 50 to 60 mm. of mercury after passage through the arterioles. This pressure drop is chiefly caused by energy loss from friction.

3. *Blood volume.* Since the arterial system is elastic, it has an adequate blood volume. If volume is low, there will be reduced blood pressure (hypotension). This can occur in a patient who is hemorrhaging.

4. *Viscosity.* Blood has a viscosity five times that of water. Increased viscosity causes a greater resistance to flow, and therefore higher arterial blood pressure.

5. *Elasticity of the arterial walls.* Arterial elasticity influences systolic and diastolic pressures. It plays a significant role only if the blood pressure is above 30 to 40 mm. of mercury. When the elasticity of the larger arteries is diminished, as in atherosclerosis, the diastolic pressure may fall and the systolic pressure rises, because less energy is absorbed in the arterial walls to be used in diastole. The arteries then behave like rigid pipes.

CAPILLARY BLOOD PRESSURE. The capillary blood vessels lie between the arterioles and small veins. The capillary blood pressure falls progressively from the arteriolar end to the venous end of the capillary bed.

Pressure in the arteriolar end of the vascular bed averages 32 mm. of mercury. In the midportion of the capillary bed, it averages 20 mm. of mercury. At the venous end, it averages 12 mm. of mercury. Increased constriction of the arterioles tends to lower capillary blood pressure. A decrease in arteriolar tone permits more blood to flow into the capillaries, causing the capillary blood pressure to rise. Obstruction of the venous outflow increases capillary pressure.

VENOUS BLOOD PRESSURE. In a recumbent individual, the venous pressure in the median basilic vein varies from 4 to 8 mm. of mercury. The pressure progressively drops from the periphery to the heart. In the right atrium, the pressure is usually around 0. (See page 303 for discussion).

NERVOUS AND CHEMICAL CONTROL OF BLOOD PRESSURE. The nervous system causes rapid changes in blood pressure and blood flow by regulating the size of blood vessels. The diameter of vessels is controlled by vasoconstrictor and vasodilator nerves influenced by medullary centers.

The vasomotor center in the medulla is affected by multiple factors. Chemoreceptors, located in the aorta and carotid arteries, are responsive to concentrations of oxygen, carbon dioxide, and blood pH. These chemoreceptors relay messages to the vasomotor center. Pressoreceptors in the arteries notify the vasomotor center of changes in blood pressure. Pressoreceptors are more important than chemoreceptors in homeostasis of blood pressure.

Blood pressure can be influenced by tumors in the suprarenal medulla (pheochromocytomas). The tumors secrete large amounts of epinephrine and norepinephine (sympathetic system hormones). These cause vasoconstriction and create an elevation in blood pressure.

Pulse

An impulse can be felt over an artery lying near the surface of the skin. The impulse is secondary to alternate expansion and contraction of the arterial wall resulting from the beating heart. When the heart ejects blood into the aorta, its impact on the elastic walls creates a pressure wave continuing along the arteries. This impact is the pulse. All arteries have a pulse, but it is most easily felt where the vessel approaches the surface of the body. The pulse is readily distinguished at the following locations (Fig. 280).

1. Radial artery: on radial side of wrist.

2. External maxillary (facial) artery: at the point of crossing the mandible.

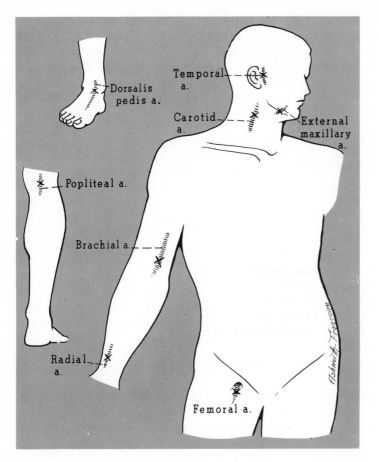

Fig. 280. The pulse is readily distinguished at any of the above pressure points.

3. Temporal artery: at the temple above and to the outer side of the eye.

4. Carotid artery: on the side of the neck.

5. Brachial artery: on the inner side of the biceps.

6. Femoral artery: in the groin.

7. Popliteal artery: behind the knee.

8. Dorsalis pedis artery: anterosuperior aspect of the foot.

The radial artery is most commonly used to check the pulse. Several fingers should be placed on the artery just proximal to the wrist joint. More than one fingertip is preferable because of the large, sensitive surface available to palpate the pulse wave. During palpation of the pulse, certain data should be recorded, including the number of beats per minute, the force and strength of the beat, and the tension offered by the artery to the finger. Normally, the interval between beats is of equal length. Irregularity occurs when there is abnormal cardiac rhythm, such as in atrial fibrillation. In this condition, as previously noted, there is a pulse deficit, with the rate counted at the apex being greater than that counted at the radial artery of the wrist.

Blood Volume

The normal adult has a blood volume of approximately 5 liters. Normal blood volume may be reduced by a loss of whole blood in hemorrhage, a deficiency of red cells (anemia), or a loss of plasma. Dilation of the arterioles, venules, and capillaries traps blood in the periphery of the vascular system, thus causing a diminished available blood volume without actual blood loss. An increase in blood volume occurs in certain diseases, but is usually less marked than blood loss.

The integrity of the endothelial membrane of the capillaries is a vital factor in maintaining normal blood volume. Many factors alter the permeability of the capillaries. When the endothelium is injured, its permeability to plasma proteins is increased, leading to a loss of fluid into the interstitial spaces. Damage to the endothelium can occur from many factors, including toxins and hypoxia.

SHOCK. A reduction in blood volume frequently produces shock. Shock is an impairment of the circulation resulting from stress or injury; the damage reduces the output of blood from the

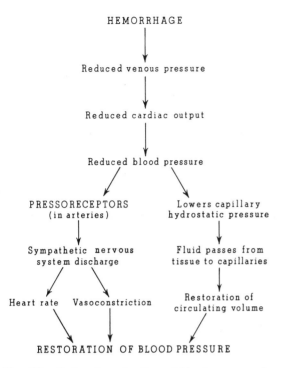

HEMORRHAGE

↓

Reduced venous pressure

↓

Reduced cardiac output

↓

Reduced blood pressure

↙   ↘

PRESSORECEPTORS   Lowers capillary
(in arteries)   hydrostatic pressure

↓   ↓

Sympathetic nervous   Fluid passes from
system discharge   tissue to capillaries

↙   ↘   ↓

Heart rate   Vasoconstriction   Restoration of
circulating volume

↘   ↓   ↙

RESTORATION OF BLOOD PRESSURE

Fig. 281. Factors in restoration of blood pressure after hemorrhage has occurred.

heart to a level below that needed for normal cellular function.

Shock is characterized by apprehension, cold skin, cyanosis of the fingertips, reduced blood pressure, shallow respiratory activity, sweating, and rapid pulse. A loss of over 40 per cent of the blood volume causes vascular collapse (collapse of the arteries). This condition frequently does not respond to blood transfusions and is known as "irreversible shock." Sudden losses of small quantities of blood can produce consequences more serious than slow losses of large volumes.

Massive injury to the heart leading to an inadequate cardiac output is an important cause of shock. Usually, however, in the absence of hemorrhage or actual damage to the heart, the reason for loss of effective circulating blood volume is not clearly understood. Three widely held views which attempt to explain this blood loss are increased permeability of the capillary walls, actual plasma loss, and generalized dilation, with a pooling of the blood in the peripheral capillary bed.

Physiologic responses to shock following hemorrhage. In shock following hemorrhage, the reduced blood volume diminishes venous

pressure. This lowers the cardiac output, and blood pressure drops. With the drop in blood pressure, pressoreceptors are stimulated and fluid passes from the tissues to the capillaries. Stimulation of pressoreceptors is followed by a sympathetic nervous system discharge, raising the heart rate and producing vasoconstriction. The end result of raising the cardiac rate, vasoconstriction, and restoration of circulating volume is a restoration of blood pressure (Fig. 281).

Techniques Employed to Evaluate the Heart and Vascular System

Right heart catheterization. Right heart catheterization is performed by inserting a catheter (a long tube) into the antecubital vein (at the elbow), the saphenous vein, or the femoral vein. The catheter, which is opaque to x-ray, is advanced into the right atrium, right ventricle, and pulmonary artery under fluoroscopy. This procedure, by measuring pressure and oxygen saturation in the right heart chamber, is used to diagnose valvular abnormalities of the right side of the heart (Fig. 282).

Circulation time. The circulation time between two points in the cardiovascular system is measured by injecting an indicator substance into one area of the circulation and recording its arrival time at another. Arm to lung circulation time is measured by timing the appearance of ether in the lung after its injection into a peripheral vein. Arm to tongue circulation is measured by injecting a substance such as calcium gluconate or decholin into the antecubital vein and recording the time until the patient tastes this material. Circulation time depends on the velocity of blood flow and the dimensions of the circulatory pathway involved. A high cardiac output is generally associated with a reduced circulation time. A low cardiac output accompanying venous congestion usually has a prolonged circulation time.

Angiocardiography. X-ray outlines of the cardiac chambers and great vessels are provided by rapidly injecting x-ray opaque material through an arm vein or through a catheter threaded into the right or left side of the heart. This procedure is followed by a series of rapid exposures to x-ray or to x-ray movies called cine-angiography. Angiocardiography permits direct visualization of abnormal circulatory pathways and provides one of the best methods of detecting the site and extent of congenital abnormalities of the heart. It can also be used to study arteries and veins.

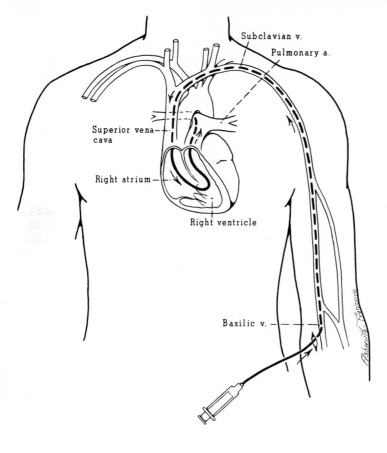

Subclavian v.

Pulmonary a.

Superior vena-
cava

Right atrium—

Right ventricle

Basilic v.

Fig. 282.   Right heart catheterization.

SUMMARY: THE CIRCULATORY SYSTEM

BLOOD

1. **Blood is composed of blood cells and blood plasma.**

2. **Blood cell formation:**

   a. Cells originate from undifferentiated mesenchymal cells within the body.

   b. Embryology: cells form in liver, spleen, and bones during fetal life. Widely dispersed blood cell formation occurs in bones until puberty, after which only flat bones produce cells.

3. **Types of blood cells:**

   a. Red blood cell: size varies slightly with the acidity of the blood; number of cells increases under conditions lowering amount of oxygen available to body.

      (1) Red cell formation is under control of the hormone erythropoietin.

      (2) Aging red cells are destroyed by macrophages.

      (3) Cells contain hemoglobin carrying oxygen for tissues; reduction in hemoglobin or number of red cells results in anemia.

      (4) Hemolysis is the rupture of a red cell; crenation implies shrinking.

   b. White blood cells: granulocytes, monocytes, and lymphocytes (see Table 30).

      (1) Many diseases involve a change in the number of circulating leukocytes.

   c. Platelets: formed from megakaryocytes; essential in coagulation.

4. **Blood plasma:**

    a. Composition: water and colloid (see Table 31).

    b. Plasma protein: serum albumin, serum globulin, prothrombin, and fibrinogen.

5. **Blood grouping:**

    a. Based on the antigens and the antibodies found in the blood (see Table 32).

    b. The most important classifications are ABO and Rh.

        (1) Several Rh factors exist; the most important is "D."

        (2) Rh incompatibility between mother and fetus can cause hemolytic anemia in the child.

    c. Immune mechanisms of the body:

        (1) Defense against infection.

            (a) Antibodies found in blood attack foreign substances entering body.

            (b) Vaccination is an artificial method of inducing antibody formation.

            (c) Antibodies are necessary for life, yet show harmful effects such as allergic reactions or auto-immune disease.

        (2) Transplantation immunology:

            (a) Tolerance is characterized by immunologic non-reactivity. This results from exposure to certain antibodies early in life before immune mechanism is established.

            (b) Runt disease is a situation in which antibodies of the graft attack the host. (It occurs especially if the host is too young to have developed its own antibodies.)

6. **Characteristics of blood** (see Table 33):

    a. Sex can be differentiated by female sex chromatin on neutrophils.

    b. Kidney controls osmotic pressure of blood.

    c. Electrical conductivity is determined by the electrolyte content of plasma and the number of corpuscles in blood.

7. **Functions of blood: temperature regulation and mechanism of transport.**

8. **Hemostasis:**

    a. Major mechanisms are platelet agglutination, contraction of blood vessels, and formation of a fibrin clot.

    b. Coagulation: involves 12 clotting factors (see Table 34); stages of coagulation are:

        (1) Formation of thromboplastin activity.

        (2) Conversion of prothrombin to thrombin.

        (3) Conversion of fibrinogen to fibrin.

    c. Anticoagulants exist naturally or can be injected.

        (1) Heparin: blocks conversion of prothrombin to thrombin.

        (2) Fibrinolysis: dissolves blood clot.

        (3) Dicumarol: inhibits vitamin K, factors 7 and 10.

    d. Abnormalities of the clotting mechanism: thrombosis, internal clotting without known injury; hemophilia, slow clotting; purpura, loss of blood into the skin.

HEART

1. **Structure:**

    a. Approximately the size of a man's fist; lies in the middle mediastinum between the lungs.

    b. Pericardium: fibroserous sac surrounding the heart; a serous fluid is found between the visceral and parietal layers of the serous portion of the pericardium. This fluid lubricates the membranes.

    c. Wall of the heart consists of three layers: epicardium (external); myocardium (middle); and endocardium (inner).

    d. Chambers: divided by septa into right atrium and ventricle and left atrium and ventricle.

    e. Valves of heart: atrioventricular valves, tricuspid and bicuspid, separate the atria from the ventricles. The semilunar valves, the pulmonary and the aortic, separate the ventricles from the pulmonary artery and the aorta. The characteristic heart sounds are caused by closing of the valves.

    f. Blood supply to the heart: supplied by right and left coronary arteries; inadequate supply causes angina pectoris (sharp pains in the chest radiating down the arm); occlusion of a coronary artery can result in myocardial infarction.

    g. Cardiac muscle: contains sarcosomes, efficient type of mitochondria possibly permitting the heart to beat without rest.

2. Cardiac cycle:

    a. Contraction is systole; relaxation is diastole.

    b. Blood flows through the heart from right atrium, through right ventricle, pulmonary system, left atrium, left ventricle, and into aorta.

3. Conducting system of heart:

    a. Components: sino-atrial node, atrioventricular node, and atrioventricular bundle of His.

    b. Cardiac rhythm and rate: controlled by the conducting system; rapid rate is sinus tachycardia; slow rate is sinus bradycardia.

    c. Electrocardiograph: measures cardiac rhythm and rate.

    d. Atrioventricular block: results from impairment of conduction of impulses from atrium to ventricle.

    e. Atrial flutter: atrial tachycardia and atrioventricular block; regular rhythm exists.

    f. Atrial fibrillation: atrial contraction is rapid and irregular; ventricular contraction is also irregular.

    g. Other abnormalities: ventricular fibrillation, atrial tachycardia.

4. Nervous control of the heart:

    a. Vagus (parasympathetic) nerve is cardiac inhibitor; sympathetic nerves are cardiac excitors.

5. Cardiac output:

    a. Increases when venous return increases.

    b. If venous return increases, fibers stretch to take in increased flow.

    c. Force of cardiac contraction: depends on the initial length of cardiac muscle fibers, length of the diastolic pause, oxygen supply, and integrity and mass of the myocardium.

       (1) Starling's law: "The energy of contraction is proportional to the initial length of the muscle fibers of the heart."

6. Closed cardiac massage:

    a. Employed to provide circulation after heart has stopped beating.

BLOOD VESSELS

1. Structure (see Table 35):

    a. Veins have valves to aid blood flow.

CIRCULATORY SYSTEMS

1. **Systemic circulation:** includes blood flow to all parts of the body except lungs.

2. **Pulmonary circulation:** includes flow of blood through the right ventricle, pulmonary arterial system, lungs, pulmonary venous system, and left atrium. A pulmonary embolus is an embolus that lodges in a pulmonary artery, often resulting in death.

3. **Portal circulation:** blood from the abdominal viscera passes through the liver via the portal vein; substances in the blood are processed in the liver.

4. **Fetal circulation:** differs from adult circulation (see Table 36).

   a. Congenital defects: patent ductus arteriosus, ventricular and atrial septal defects, tetralogy of Fallot, and coarctation of the aorta.

5. **Blood pressure:**

   a. Systolic and diastolic: systolic pressure results from contraction of the ventricles; diastole from relaxation of the ventricles. Blood pressure is subject to wide variations, depending on the type of individual.
   b. Blood pressure is measured with a sphygmomanometer.
   c. Regulation of blood pressure: arterial pressure is maintained by the heart, peripheral resistance, blood volume, blood viscosity, and elasticity of the arterial wall.
   d. Capillary blood pressure falls progressively from the arteriolar to the venous end of the capillary.
   e. Nervous and chemical control: vasoconstriction and vasodilatation exert an influence on blood pressure. Sensory receptors, including the chemoreceptors and the pressoreceptors found in the arteries, notify the brain of existing conditions and lead eventually to vasoconstriction or vasodilatation; chemical secretions can also cause vasoconstriction or vasodilatation.

6. **Pulse:**

   a. The pulse results from alternate expansion and contraction of the arterial wall and from the beating of the heart. The pulse is most easily felt in an artery near the surface of the body, though it is present in all arteries.

7. **Blood volume:**

   a. Influenced by vasoconstriction and dilation; most important factor is the permeability of the capillary walls.
   b. Reduction in blood volume results in shock; reaction of the body to shock includes vasoconstriction and hemodilution. This response increases the circulating blood volume.

8. **Techniques employed to evaluate the heart and vascular system:**

   a. Right and left heart catheterization, used in the study of valvular defects.
   b. Circulation time: used as a measure of cardiac output.
   c. Angiocardiography: an x-ray outline of the heart and great vessels.

STUDY QUESTIONS: THE CIRCULATORY SYSTEM

1. Describe the major components of blood.
2. Explain the factors causing an increase in red blood cell production.
3. Briefly explain the function of hemoglobin.
4. Describe several types of anemia.
5. Differentiate hemolysis and crenation.

6. List the classes of white blood cells.
7. Differentiate plasma and serum.
8. Briefly describe the four proteins.
9. Explain the reason an Rh positive baby born to an Rh negative mother may suffer from hemolytic anemia.
10. Outline the manner in which vaccination protects the body against diseases.
11. Explain the phenomena of tolerance and "runt disease."
12. List the major functions of blood.
13. Name the three separate processes involved in hemostasis.
14. Briefly summarize the clotting mechanism.
15. Explain the two anti-clotting factors found naturally in the body.
16. List three abnormalities of the clotting mechanism.
17. Briefly summarize the structure of the wall of the heart.
18. Explain the functions of the heart valves.
19. Differentiate angina pectoris and myocardial infarction.
20. List the steps of the cardiac cycle.
21. Follow the course of a nerve impulse through the conducting system of the heart.
22. Differentiate sinus tachycardia and sinus bradycardia.
23. Describe the theory of the ECG used to diagnose various heart ailments.
24. Differentiate atrial flutter and atrial fibrillation.
25. Discuss the nervous control of the heart.
26. State several factors causing increases in venous return.
27. Discuss Starling's law of the heart.
28. Differentiate the structures of the various types of blood vessels.
29. Summarize the procedure for cardiac massage.
30. Describe the systemic, pulmonary, and portal circulatory systems.
31. Show the difference between fetal and adult circulation.
32. Discuss two types of congenital defects.
33. Differentiate systolic and diastolic blood pressure.
34. Explain the way a sphygmomanometer is used.
35. List the five major factors involved in the maintenance of arterial blood pressure.
36. Explain the nervous and chemical control mechanisms over vasoconstriction and dilatation.
37. Summarize the events occurring during the body's response to shock.
38. Describe three methods used in the study of the heart and vascular system.

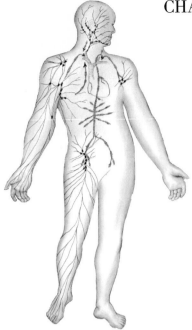

THE LYMPHATIC SYSTEM

DESCRIPTION OF LYMPH

Tissue fluid in the lymphatic vessels is called *lymph*. Its composition is similar to that of plasma, except for the absence of proteins of higher molecular weight. Lymph contains large numbers of white cells, particularly lymphocytes, a few platelets, and a few erythrocytes. It is generally a clear liquid, but lymph from the intestines becomes milky after a meal. The milky appearance results from the presence of minute fat globules collected from the alimentary tract. Such fat-laden lymph is called *chyle*.

Fig. 283. Diagrammatic representation of lymphatic system, showing its relationship to the circulatory system.

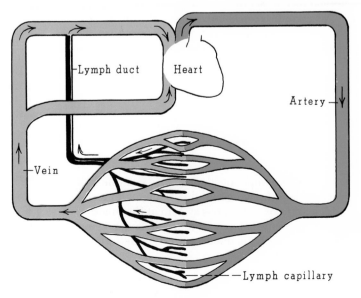

341

ANATOMY

The lymphatic system consists of lymph capillaries, lymphatic vessels, lymphatic ducts, and lymph nodes (Figs. 283 and 284).

Lymph Capillaries

Lymph capillaries, originating from microscopic blind ends, are the smallest conducting vessels of the lymphatic system. They are thin-walled tubes composed of a single layer of endothelial cells. The capillaries carry lymph from tissue spaces to the lymphatic vessels. Lymph capillaries of the intestine, the *lacteals*, are of importance, since most digested fat is absorbed through them. Each villus, a minute projection from the mucous membrane of the intestine, contains a lacteal which absorbs digested fat.

Lymph Vessels

Lymph vessels into which the lymph capillaries drain have three-layered walls similar to the walls of veins. The larger lymph vessels, unlike lymph capillaries, have valves permitting lymph to flow in only one direction. These valves give lymph vessels a characteristic beaded appearance.

All lymph vessels are directed toward the thoracic cavity. They converge into either the *right lymphatic duct* or the *thoracic (left lymphatic) duct*. Both ducts empty into the venous system.

Right Lymphatic Duct

The right lymphatic duct is a vessel one-half inch in length, lying on the scalenus anterior muscle. It joins the venous system at the junction of the right internal jugular and subclavian veins. The right lymphatic duct returns lymph from the upper surface of the right lobe of the liver, the right lung and pleura, the right side of the heart, the right arm, and the right side of the head and neck. The thoracic duct originates in the abdomen at the upper end of the *cisterna chyli*, an elongated sac located under the right crus of the diaphragm. The cisterna is a receiving area for lymph from the three major lymph vessels—the right lumbar, left lumbar, and intestinal trunks. The right and left lumbar trunks convey lymph from the lower extremities, the pelvis, the kidneys, the suprarenal glands, and the deep lymphatics of the abdominal walls. The intestinal trunk carries lymph from the stomach, the spleen, a major portion of the liver, and the small intestine.

Thoracic Duct

The thoracic duct ascends to the right side of the lower thoracic vertebral bodies. It is located between the thoracic aorta and the azygos vein. At the level of the aortic arch, the thoracic duct crosses obliquely to the left and continues superiorly, lying to the left side of the esophagus. The thoracic duct arches laterally behind the left carotid sheath at the root of the neck, and enters the circulatory system at the junction of the left internal jugular and subclavian veins. This duct returns lymph from the lower extremities, the abdomen (except for the upper surface of the right lobe of the liver), the left side of the thorax, the left side of the head and neck, and the left upper limb.

If the thoracic duct is severed, 1 or more liters of lymph can be lost during a 24-hour period. The consequent loss of protein, fat, and sugar normally present in lymph will result in weight loss. If a major lymphatic vessel is cut, lymph eventually clots—but more slowly than plasma, since lymph contains less fibrinogen, less prothrombin, and an excess of antithrombin.

Lymph Nodes

Lymph nodes are small oval bodies found at intervals in the course of the lymphatic vessels. Each node consists of lymphatic tissue enclosed

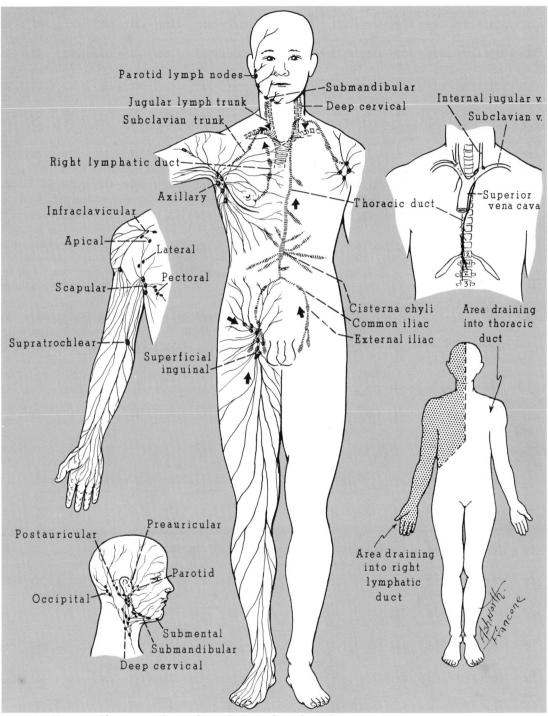

Parotid lymph nodes
Jugular lymph trunk
Subclavian trunk

Submandibular
Deep cervical

Internal jugular v.
Subclavian v.

Right lymphatic duct

Superior
vena cava

Axillary

Infraclavicular

Apical

Lateral

Scapular

Pectoral

Thoracic duct

Supratrochlear

Superficial
inguinal

Cisterna chyli
Common iliac
External iliac

Area draining
into thoracic
duct

Preauricular

Postauricular

Parotid

Area draining
into right
lymphatic
duct

Occipital

Submental
Submandibular
Deep cervical

Deep collecting channels and their lymph nodes
Superficial collecting channels and their lymph nodes

Fig. 284. Plate of the lymphatic system and drainage.

343

in a fibrous connective tissue capsule (Fig. 285).

Lymph passes through several groups of nodes before entering the blood. Within the nodes it is filtered and receives lymphocytes, globulin, and antibodies. Lymph nodes serve as efficient filters for red blood cells and bacteria, but are ineffective barriers against viruses. Lymph enters the nodes through several afferent channels and leaves through one or two efferent channels.

Lymph nodes usually appear in groups, among which are the following: superficial nodes, including the cervical (neck), axillary (axilla), and inguinal (groin) nodes; and deep nodes, including the iliac (in the iliac fossa), lumbar (adjacent to the lumbar vertebrae), thoracic (root of the lungs), mesenteric (attachment of the mesentery of the small intestine), and portal (portal fissure of the liver) nodes.

CLINICAL CONSIDERATIONS

Lymph nodes filter products resulting from bacterial and non-bacterial inflammation and prevent the products from entering the general circulation. This process often produces tender-ness and swelling in nodes of an infected area. If bacteria in an area drained by a node become too numerous, they may attack the node itself, resulting in an abscess (a localized collection of pus in a cavity formed when tissue disintegrates).

Lymphangitis is an inflammation of a lymphatic vessel in which narrow red streaks may be seen in the skin extending from the infected area to the draining group of lymph nodes. These streaks represent inflamed subcutaneous lymph vessels.

Lymph node enlargement may be local or widespread and may be accompanied by signs of acute inflammation, including heat and tenderness. As a result of inflammation, nodes may fuse with one another instead of remaining discrete. Causes of lymph node enlargement include infection, allergy, primary disease of the node (such as Hodgkin's disease), leukemia, and spread of malignant disease from elsewhere in the body.

One feature of the lymphatic system is its significance in the spread of tumors. Carcinoma, a type of cancer, occasionally produces a secondary growth in regional lymph nodes. Many of these secondary growths (metastases) result from tumor emboli detaching from the point of origin

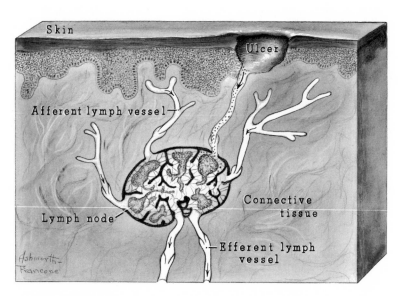

Fig. 285. Diagrammatic drawing of a lymph node in the area of an infected ulcer.

and lodging in nodes of the lymphatic vessels. In general if the tumor has reached the lymph nodes at the time of surgery, the outlook for survival of the patient is less favorable.

LYMPH FLOW

Control

Since the lymphatic system does not contain a contractile apparatus, it must depend on outside factors for propulsion of lymph. These factors include continuous formation of new lymph pushing old lymph forward; pulsations of arteries producing a massaging effect on lymph vessels; peristaltic contractions of the intestine propelling chyle along the lymph vessels; rhythmic peristaltic contractions of smooth muscle fibers in segments of lymph vessels between valves; the massaging action of the skeletal muscles on the lymph vessels; and pressure changes in the thoracic duct secondary to respiration.

Rate

The normal rate of lymph flow is increased by many factors, including the following:

1. Increased capillary permeability may result from fever, toxins, or anoxia.

2. Increased capillary pressure may follow venous obstruction. When venous pressure exceeds 12 to 15 cm. of water, a definite increase occurs in fluid filtering out of the blood capillaries into the tissue spaces.

3. Increased functional activity of the local region produces an increased flow of fluid from the capillaries resulting from vasodilatation. Muscular activity stimulates the flow along the lymph vessels through a massaging action.

PHYSIOLOGY

Lymph vessels have three major functions. Most important, they return to the blood vessels vital substances—chiefly proteins—which have leaked out in the capillary beds. Lymph vessels also provide drainage channels into lymph nodes for toxic or malignant products. The intestinal lymphatic vessels assume an important role in absorption of digested fats.

Lymph nodes have several functions. They filter and to some extent quarantine noxious products of inflammatory or malignant lesions; they produce lymphocytes and release them into the blood; and they function in producing immunity to diseases and transplanted tissue (homologous).

One of the most challenging problems for the physiologist is to explain why lymph vessel walls seem to be permeable in one direction only. Experimentally bacteria, red blood cells, and graphite particles have been shown to penetrate the lymphatic system without difficulty. Yet once these substances have penetrated, they seem to be retained and to find their way into the blood stream via larger ducts without leakage.

RELATED ORGANS

Three organs closely related to the lymphatic system are the spleen, tonsils, and thymus.

Spleen

LOCATION AND STRUCTURE. The spleen is a soft, vascular, oval body, 5 inches long and 3 inches wide, weighing approximately 7 ounces. It lies in the left upper abdomen beneath the diaphragm and behind the lower ribs and costal cartilages (Fig. 286).

The splenic hilum is the site of entrance and exit of the vessels of the spleen. The body of the spleen has a covering of elastic tissue and smooth muscle. From this investment partitions pass into the substance, reaching the hilum and dividing the organ into compartments. In these compartments one can see a sponge-like network of cells separated by many blood channels called sinusoids. The elastic nature of the framework allows the spleen to vary its size considerably.

FUNCTION. The spleen has five major functions.

1. *Blood destruction.* Old red blood cells, having reached their normal life span of approximately 120 days, are destroyed in the spleen by a large mass of reticulo-endothelial tissue.

2. *Blood production.* The spleen exerts an effect on production and release of blood cells from bone marrow.

3. *Immunologic function.* The spleen is a source of production of antibodies and contains a large mass of lymphatic tissue.

4. *Blood storage.* The spleen serves as a reservoir for blood. It undergoes rhythmic variations in size in response to physiologic demands

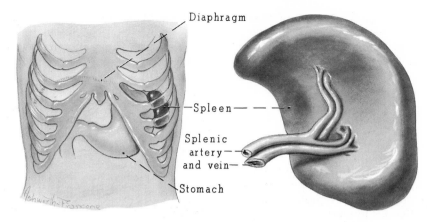

Fig. 286. The spleen and its relation to the stomach and rib cage.

such as exercise and hemorrhage, and thus influences the volume of circulating blood.

5. *Blood filtration.* The spleen serves as a part of the body's defense mechanism by filtering microorganisms from the blood.

A man can survive with no apparent disability if his spleen has been removed; however, diseases affecting the spleen may profoundly affect several important body functions.

Tonsils

Several groups of tonsils, forming a ring of lymphatic tissue, guard the entrance of the alimentary and respiratory tracts from bacterial invasion. The components of this ring are the palatine tonsils, nasopharyngeal tonsils (adenoids), and lingual tonsils (Figs. 287 and 288).

The *palatine tonsils,* known more commonly as the "tonsils," are two oval masses of lymphoid tissue attached to the side wall of the back of the mouth between the anterior and posterior pillars. The tonsils are larger in children than in adults.

The *nasopharyngeal tonsil,* or *adenoid,* is a mass of lymphatic tissue located in the nasal pharynx extending from the roof of the nasal pharynx to the free edge of the soft palate (Fig. 288). The adenoids are present in infants and children.

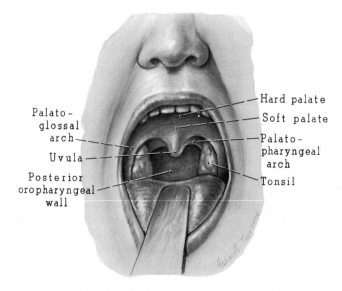

Fig. 287. Relationship of tongue, uvula, and tonsils.

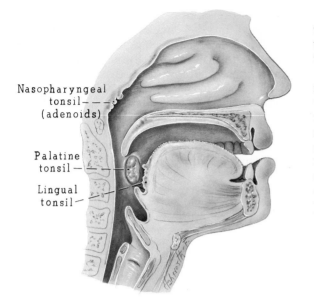

Lingual tonsils are two masses of lymphoid tissue found on the dorsum of the tongue, extending from the vallate papillae of the tongue to the epiglottis (Fig. 288).

Chronic infection of the tonsils is not so common as was once suspected. The term "chronic tonsillitis" is frequently misused to indicate any type of sore throat occurring when the tonsils are still present. With tonsillitis, enlargement and tenderness of the anterior cervical lymph nodes are common. The tonsils may be enlarged and red or covered with pus. If both tonsils and adenoids are infected, the lymph nodes of the posterior triangle of the neck enlarge.

Fewer tonsillectomies and adenoidectomies are being performed today than were done 30 years ago. This is because recent knowledge indicates that removal of tonsils and adenoids may not significantly lower the incidence of upper respiratory infection unless the tonsils themselves have been infected. Tonsils form a protective barrier for the mouth, throat, larynx, trachea, and lungs. They may also be important in the development of immune bodies; however, true recurrent infection of the tonsils is still an indication for their removal by operation.

Fig. 288. The nasopharyngeal tonsils extend from the roof of the nasal pharynx to the free edge of the soft palate; the palatine tonsils are attached to the side walls of the back of the mouth between the anterior and posterior pillars; and the lingual tonsils are located on the dorsum of the tongue from the vallate papillae of the tongue to the epiglottis.

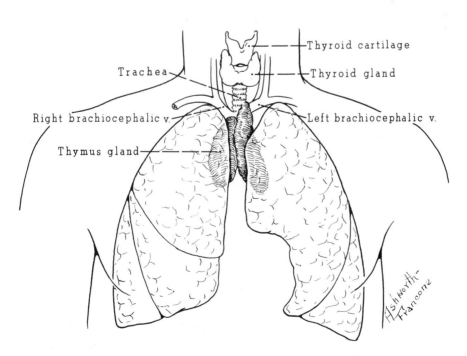

Fig. 289. Location of thymus gland and relationship to lungs.

Thymus

The thymus is a flat, pinkish-gray, two-lobed organ lying high in the chest anterior to the aorta and posterior to the sternum (Fig. 289). In fetal life and early childhood, it is large in relation to the rest of the body. After birth its growth slows, and by the age of puberty it begins to atrophy. This suggests that the thymus is the primary source of lymphocytes in utero and shortly after birth. When lymphocytes are liberated into the circulation from the thymus, they settle in organs such as the spleen or lymph nodes. Thus, cells from the thymus are believed to eventually give rise to cells responsible for many immunologic functions of the body. Recent experiments in newborn mice have shown that removal of the thymus at birth permits homologous skin grafts to persist for long periods of time, indicating that absence of the thymus may have interfered with antibody production.

SUMMARY: THE LYMPHATIC SYSTEM

DESCRIPTION OF LYMPH

1. Similar in composition to tissue fluid and plasma.
2. Fat-laden lymph is called chyle.

ANATOMY

1. Lymph capillaries pick up tissue fluid; capillaries of the intestine are lacteals.
2. Capillaries merge to form vessels; larger vessels have valves to control flow.
3. Vessels converge into the right lymphatic duct and thoracic duct, emptying directly into the circulatory system.

    a. One or more liters of lymph can be lost from a severed major duct in 24 hours.
    b. Lymph will clot, but less quickly than blood.

4. The lymph nodes are found at intervals along lymph vessels.

    a. The nodes serve as filters for lymph.
    b. The nodes appear in groups in the body.

CLINICAL CONSIDERATIONS

1. Nodes may form an abscess or become otherwise infected if attacked by bacteria.
2. Nodes may enlarge or fuse in various disease states.
3. Secondary tumors may collect and grow in lymph nodes.

CONTROL AND RATE OF LYMPH FLOW

1. No pumping apparatus exists in the lymphatic system. Outside forces, therefore, must be depended on to propel the lymph.

PHYSIOLOGY

1. Lymphatics drain tissue spaces, provide drainage channels into lymph nodes, and absorb digested fats.
2. Lymph nodes filter blood, provide lymphocytes, and play a role in immunity.
3. Physiologists are trying to learn why substances can enter lymph capillaries, yet not leave them.

RELATED ORGANS

1. **Spleen:**

    a. Located in the left upper abdomen.
    b. Contains numerous tissue spaces for blood storage.
    c. Functions: destruction, production, storage, and filtration of blood; immunologic function.

2. **Tonsils:**

    a. Lymphatic tissue forms a protective ring (the tonsils) around the entrance to the alimentary and respiratory tracts.
    b. The ring consists of the palatine, nasopharyngeal (adenoids), and lingual tonsils.
    c. Tonsils can become infected. Their protective importance is now recognized.

3. **Thymus:**

    a. Located superiorly in the chest between the aorta and sternum.
    b. Large in fetal and early life, becomes smaller after puberty.
    c. Produces lymphocytes and antibodies.

STUDY QUESTIONS: THE LYMPHATIC SYSTEM

1. Explain the two major functions of the lymphatic system.
2. Describe the composition of lymph.
3. Name the two major lymph ducts and list the areas drained.
4. Describe the cisterna chyli.
5. Explain why blood clots faster than lymph.
6. Explain the purpose of valves in the lymphatic vessels.
7. Outline the structure and function of lymph nodes.
8. Describe the causes and characteristics of lymphangitis.
9. List three possible causes of lymph node enlargement.
10. Name three factors responsible for normal lymph flow.
11. List three factors that may increase lymph flow.
12. Describe the location and structure of the spleen.
13. List the major functions of the spleen.
14. Explain the function of the tonsils.
15. When should tonsils be removed?
16. Describe the growth of the thymus during the first two decades of life.

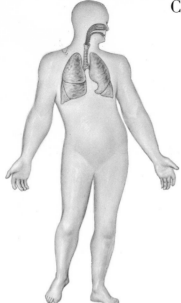

THE RESPIRATORY SYSTEM

HISTORY

The rising and falling of the chest proved mysterious to the Greeks and Romans as they observed the changes in rate and rhythm during excitement and fear. To them, air was an intangible, divine spirit known as "pneuma," presumably entering the body at birth and leaving it at death. Aristotle actually believed that respiratory activity cooled the blood. Five hundred years later, in 170 A.D., Galen showed that the arteries were filled with blood and that the lungs added and removed something from the blood. In addition, Galen recognized several of the respiratory muscles and nerves. Circulation of the blood was traced through the lungs in the 17th century by William Harvey. Scheele, a Swedish chemist, demonstrated in 1770 that air contained an invisible material essential to life and to the burning of a flame. In 1785, Priestley and Lavoisier showed that this substance was oxygen.

GENERAL FUNCTION

The respiratory system functions in the interchange of gases between the organism and its environment. It includes those organs concerned with this exchange of gases—specifically the intake of oxygen and the release of carbon dioxide. The exchange of gases between the blood and the air taken into the lungs is called *external respiration*. The exchange of gases between the circulatory fluids, such as blood, lymph, tissue fluid, and cells, is called *internal respiration*.

All life processes depend primarily on the release of energy (food). The basic reaction for this is: $C_6H_{12}O_6 + 6O_2 \rightarrow 6H_2O + 6CO_2 + energy$. This is physiologic oxidation or destructive metabolism (catabolism). Maintenance of life depends on a continuous supply of oxygen and a continuous removal of carbon dioxide.

ANATOMY

The lung is the essential organ of respiration. The nose, paranasal sinuses, pharynx, larynx, trachea, and bronchi are parts of an open passage leading from the lungs to the exterior comprising the upper respiratory tract.

The Nose

The external nose consists of a framework of bone, hyaline cartilage, and fibro-areolar tissue. There are three cartilages: septal, lateral, and alar. The septal cartilage divides the nasal cavity into two lateral halves. The lateral cartilages are wing-like expansions of the septal cartilages. The alar cartilages are U-shaped and are located on the sides of the nose below the lateral cartilages.

The bony roof of the nose consists of an anterior portion, the nasal and frontal bones; a middle portion, the cribriform plate of the ethmoid; and a posterior portion, parts of the sphenoid, vomer, and palatine bones. The floor of the nose is formed by the maxillary and palatine bones.

The nasal fossa or internal nose is composed of two wedge-shaped cavities separated by a septum (Fig. 290). The crests of the nasal bones form the superior aspect; the middle area of the septum is the perpendicular plate of the ethmoid; and the posterior aspect of the septum is bordered by the vomer and sphenoid bones. Inferiorly, the crests of the maxilla and palatine bones complete the septum.

The lateral wall of the nose has superior, middle, and inferior conchae or turbinates; bony projections form the sides covering the superior, middle, and inferior meatuses (air passages) respectively. Each concha is covered by a thick mucous membrane, functioning to warm and moisten air (Fig. 291).

The nasal cavity or vestibule is lined with thick, stratified squamous epithelium containing sebaceous glands. The spongy conchae increase the amount of tissue surface within the nose, and the respiratory epithelium of the conchae secretes mucus. Mucous membranes also filter out bacteria and dust particles. Air must be warmed; otherwise the tissue lining the respiratory tract functions poorly. Absence of moisture for even a few minutes destroys the cilia of the respiratory epithelium.

The nose filters substances in two ways.

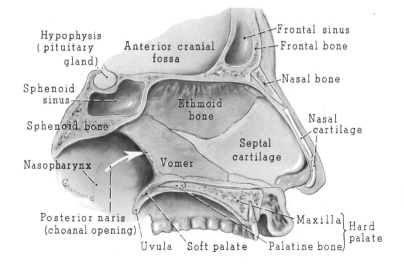

Fig. 290. Sagittal section through nose showing components of nasal septum.

Hypophysis (pituitary gland)

Anterior cranial fossa

Frontal sinus

Frontal bone

Nasal bone

Sphenoid sinus

Sphenoid bone

Ethmoid bone

Nasopharynx

Vomer

Septal cartilage

Nasal cartilage

Posterior naris (choanal opening)

Uvula   Soft palate

Maxilla

Palatine bone

Hard palate

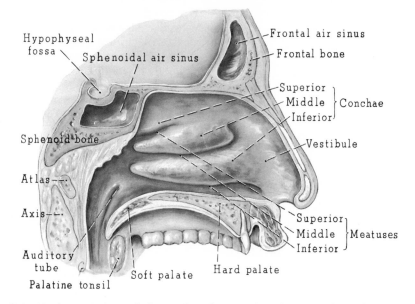

Fig. 291. Nasal septum removed, showing lateral aspect of nasal cavity with conchae (turbinates).

(1) Vibrissae (the hairs that can be seen in the nose) around the anterior nares filter out the coarsest bodies such as insects. (2) Air currents passing over the moist mucosa in curved pathways deposit fine particles such as dust, powder, and smoke against the wall. These fine particles are subsequently conveyed to the pharynx and swallowed.

The mucous membrane of the nose continues anteriorly with the skin lining the vestibule and posteriorly with the mucous membrane of the nasopharynx. The nasal mucous membrane is coated with cilia that wave back and forth about 12 times per second. These help the mucus to clean the air. The superior portion of the nose is lined with neuro-epithelial tissue containing olfactory cells functioning in the sensation of smell.

The Paranasal Sinuses (Figs. 292 and 293)

Paranasal sinuses are continuous with the nasal cavity and are covered with mucous membrane. Although they are paired, they are commonly asymmetrical. The paired sinuses include the *maxillary, frontal, ethmoid,* and *sphenoid* sinuses. The primary function of paranasal sinuses is to lighten the bones of the skull. Secondarily, they function to provide mucus for the nasal cavity and act as resonant chambers for the production of sound.

The maxillary sinuses are the largest of the paranasal sinuses. Each is located in the maxilla and opens into the middle meatus. The frontal sinuses, located in the frontal bone superior and medial to the orbit, empty into the middle meatus. The ethmoid air cells are numerous irregularly-shaped air spaces arranged in three groups—anterior, middle, and posterior on either side; they are separated from the orbital cavity by a thin, paper-like lamina of bone and open into the middle and superior meatuses. The mastoid air cells open into the middle ear.

The sphenoid sinus is in the sphenoid bone. It is located posterior to the eye, behind the upper portion of the nasal cavity. An infection of the sphenoid sinus can damage vision due to its proximity to the optic nerve. Drainage from the sphenoid sinus is into the superior meatus.

The nasolacrimal duct extends from the eye to the inferior meatus and drains the lacrimal secretions constantly bathing the surface of the eye (see Chapter Nine).

The Pharynx

The pharynx is a musculomembranous tube 5 inches in length, extending from the base of the skull to the esophagus. The posterior aspect abuts against the cervical vertebrae. The pharynx is divided into three parts—nasal, oral, and laryngeal.

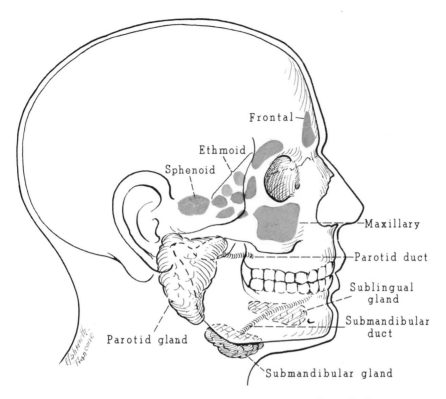

Fig. 292. Lateral view of head showing sinuses and salivary glands.

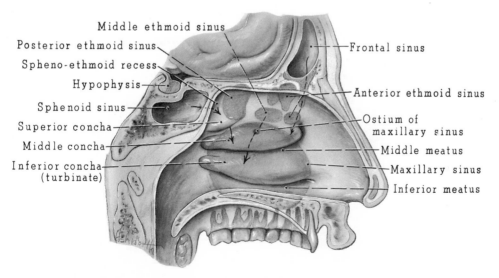

Fig. 293. Sagittal section of the nasal cavity showing anatomy of the sinuses and direction of normal drainage. Note that drainage from frontal, maxillary, and anterior sinuses is into the middle meatus, while the posterior ethmoid and sphenoid sinuses drain into the superior meatus.

The nasopharynx lies behind the *choanae*, or posterior nares. The oral pharynx opens into the mouth through the fauces and extends from the soft palate above to the hyoid bone below. The naso- and oropharynx are separated by the soft palate, a membranous sheet of muscle covered by mucous membrane. The laryngopharynx lies below the hyoid bone and behind the larynx.

There are four openings into the nasopharynx —two from the auditory (eustachian) tubes and two from the nose, the posterior nares. The oropharynx has a single opening called the *fauces* which communicates with the mouth. The laryngopharynx opens into the larynx and esophagus.

The *adenoids* or pharyngeal tonsils lie in the nasopharynx near the posterior nares. If they become enlarged, they can obstruct the posterior nares. When an individual has enlarged ade-

noids, mouth breathing and a nasal or plugged quality to the voice develop. The palatine tonsils at the lateral margins of the throat and the lingual tonsils at the base of the tongue are located in the oropharynx. The palatine tonsils are commonly referred to as "the tonsils" and are removed when a patient has a tonsillectomy (see Chapter Eleven). The pharynx serves as a passage for two systems—the respiratory and the digestive. It also assumes an important function in the formation of sound, particularly in the creation of vowel sounds.

The Larynx (Figs. 294 and 295)

The larynx or "voice box" connects the pharynx with the trachea. Its opening is at the base of the tongue. The larynx is broad superiorly

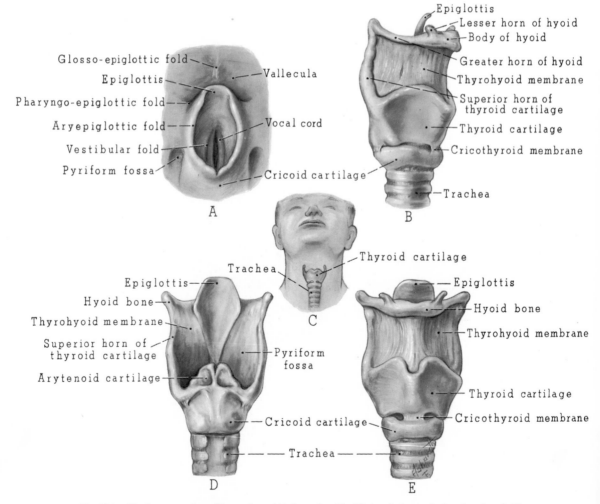

Fig. 294. The larynx as viewed from above (*A*), from the side (*B*), in relation to the head and neck (*C*), from behind (*D*), and from the front (*E*).

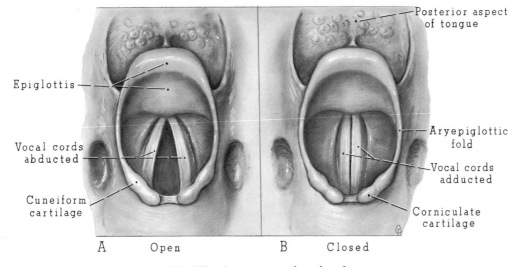

Epiglottis

Vocal cords abducted

Cuneiform cartilage

Posterior aspect of tongue

Aryepiglottic fold

Vocal cords adducted

Corniculate cartilage

A   Open   B   Closed

Fig. 295. Superior view of vocal cords.

and shaped like a triangular box. It joins the trachea inferiorly, where it is narrower and round. It consists of nine cartilages united by extrinsic and intrinsic muscles as well as by ligaments.

There are three paired and three unpaired cartilages of the larynx.

Unpaired	Paired
Thyroid	Arytenoid
Cricoid	Cuneiform
Epiglottic	Corniculate

The *thyroid* cartilage is the largest cartilage in the larynx. It gives the anterior aspect of the larynx its characteristic triangular shape and is sometimes called the "Adam's apple." In the male the thyroid cartilage increases in size at puberty.

The leaf-shaped *epiglottis* is attached to the superior border of the thyroid cartilage. It has a hinged, door-like action at the entrance to the larynx. During swallowing, it acts as a lid to prevent aspiration of food into the trachea. The *cricoid* cartilage is the most inferior of the nine laryngeal cartilages; it is shaped like a signet ring with the signet facing posteriorly. The *arytenoid cartilages* are small and are attached to the superior portion of each cricoid lamina. The arytenoid cartilage is pyramidal in shape. The *corniculate cartilages* extend from the arytenoid cartilages medially and backward. Each corniculate cartilage is a small cone of elastic tissue articulating with an arytenoid cartilage. The *cuneiform cartilage* is a small elastic cartilage at the base of the epiglottis.

MUSCULATURE OF THE LARYNX. Two sets of muscles are found in the larynx, extrinsic and intrinsic. The vagus nerve, by way of its superior and recurrent laryngeal branches, supplies these muscles. The extrinsic muscles take origin in structures surrounding the larynx and function to move the larynx. The intrinsic muscles are located within the larynx proper. These muscles open and close the glottis during inspiration and expiration. They close the laryngeal aperture and glottis during swallowing and regulate the tension of the vocal folds in the production of sound. Both the intrinsic and extrinsic muscles are composed of striated muscle fibers.

The cricothyroid joint is located on the medial and posterior surface of each plate of the thyroid cartilage. This joint permits the thyroid cartilage to swing up and down. When the thyroid cartilage swings superiorly, a higher note is produced; when it swings inferiorly, lower notes are produced.

The cricoarytenoid joint is important in movements of the vocal cords. The *rima glottidis* is a space between the cords. Pitch depends on the length and space between the cords. In the female, the cords are shorter, more taut, and closer together, producing the characteristic high voice. In the male, the cords are longer, less taut, and farther apart, producing the characteristic low voice.

The larynx is supplied by branches of the vagus nerve, including the *recurrent laryngeal* and *superior laryngeal branches*. The recurrent laryngeal nerve enters the larynx from below and behind the cricothyroid joint. The superior nerve passes into the larynx by piercing the thyrohyoid membrane. The recurrent laryngeal nerve is mainly motor, supplying the muscles to the larynx, while the superior laryngeal nerve is chiefly sensory. If the recurrent laryngeal nerve is injured during surgery of the thyroid, hoarseness or an inability to speak may result.

FUNCTION OF THE LARYNX. The chief function of the larynx is *phonation*. The pitch of sound is determined by the shape and tension of the vocal cords. Long, lax cords produce low-pitched tones and short, tense cords give higher tones. The voice is refined by the nose, mouth, and pharynx, as well as by the sinuses which act as sounding boards and resonating chambers. The organs of phonation in man are similar to those of many animals much lower in the animal hierarchy; however, man has a greater variety and control of his sounds because of greater development of the related association areas of the brain.

The Trachea

The trachea or "windpipe" is a cylindrical tube about 4 to 5 inches in length, consisting of from 15 to 20 horseshoe-shaped hyaline cartilages separated by fibrous and muscular tissue. The trachea is flattened posteriorly where it comes into contact with the esophagus. It extends from the level of the sixth cervical vertebra to the fifth thoracic vertebra and divides into two primary bronchi. The inferior portion of the trachea is crossed by the arch of the aorta. The thyroid gland lies anterior to the second, third, and fourth tracheal rings.

The trachea consists of four layers: mucosa, submucosa, cartilage, and adventitia. The inner layer (mucosa) has ciliated, pseudostratified columnar epithelium with goblet cells. These cilia sweep inhaled particles to the pharynx to be swallowed. The submucosa is loose connective tissue containing glands and fat cells. The adventitia is dense connective tissue with elastic and reticular fibers continuous with the surrounding connective tissue.

FUNCTION OF THE TRACHEA. The trachea functions as a simple passageway for air to reach the lungs; occasionally it becomes occluded, either from swelling of air passages, accumulated secretions, or aspirations of material into it. Occlusion of the trachea necessitates either a tracheotomy or a tracheostomy (Fig. 296). The term *tracheotomy* means merely an opening into the trachea. *Tracheostomy* is a procedure in

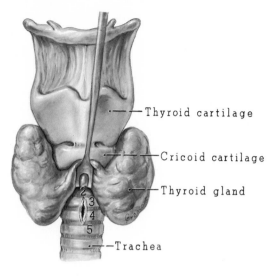

Fig. 296.   Incision for a tracheotomy.

Thyroid cartilage
Cricoid cartilage
Thyroid gland
Trachea

which the trachea is brought to the skin or a tube is placed into it to maintain patency for a period of time. A tracheotomy or tracheostomy is performed for emergency release of obstructions at or above the level of the larynx. Symptoms of laryngeal obstruction are frightening and include difficult respiration (dyspnea) and inspiratory stridor (a harsh, high-pitched sound often heard in laryngeal obstructions).

The Bronchi

The two bronchi split from the trachea at the level of the superior border of the fifth thoracic vertebra. The right bronchus differs from the left in that it is shorter and wider and takes a more vertical course. Foreign bodies from the trachea usually enter the right bronchus because of these characteristics. The bronchi lie posterior to the pulmonary vessels with the left behind the aorta. Inferiorly, as the bronchi become narrower, the cartilaginous rings assume a plate-like shape and finally disappear at the bronchiole (see Fig. 301). With the decrease in cartilage, there is a concomitant increase in smooth muscle. The epithelial lining of the trachea loses its cilia and decreases in size. It changes from pseudostratified columnar to cuboidal and finally to squamous as it becomes a bronchiole. The lining of the walls of the alveoli consists of simple squamous epithelium allowing gases to pass readily to and from the pulmonary capillaries.

The nerves supplying the trachea and bronchi are derived from the vagus by way of the recurrent laryngeal branch, and from the sympathetic division of the autonomic nervous system. The arterial supply to the trachea is from the inferior thyroid arteries; the arterial supply to the bronchioles comes from the bronchial arteries which take origin from the aorta.

The Thoracic Cavity

The thoracic cavity is separated from the abdomen by the diaphragm, a large sheet of muscle. The center of the cavity contains other structures between the lungs which are enclosed in an oblong, wide area called the *mediastinum*. The mediastinum, the middle compartment of the chest, is located between the two pleural cavities. It is bounded anteriorly by the sternum, posteriorly by the bodies of the 12 thoracic vertebrae, superiorly by the thoracic inlet, and inferiorly by the diaphragm. The sides of the mediastinum are formed by the mediastinal pleura.

The mediastinum is divided into superior and inferior components by an imaginary line extending from the sternal angle to the disc between the fourth and fifth thoracic vertebrae (Fig. 297). The inferior mediastinum is subdivided into three divisions by the heart, which acts as the key structure in this subdivision. That portion of the inferior mediastinum containing the heart is known as the *middle mediastinum*. The *anterior mediastinum* is the portion anterior to the heart, and the *posterior mediastinum* is that part situated behind the heart.

CONTENTS OF THE MEDIASTINAL SPACES. The superior mediastinum contains the arch of the aorta and its three branches: the brachiocephalic, the left common carotid, and the left subclavian. The brachiocephalic veins, the left upper half of the superior vena cava, the vagus nerve, the phrenic nerve, the left recurrent laryngeal nerve, the esophagus, the trachea, the thoracic duct, the thymus, and some lymph nodes are also in the superior mediastinum. The anterior mediastinum contains a few lymph nodes and areolar tissue.

In the middle mediastinum can be found the heart, the ascending aorta, the lower half of the superior vena cava, the azygous vein, the bifurcation of the trachea, the pulmonary artery, the pulmonary veins, the phrenic nerves, and the bronchial lymph glands. The posterior mediastinum contains the esophagus, the descending thoracic aorta, the vagi, the thoracic duct, the azygous and hemiazygous veins, and the accessory hemiazygous vein.

There are two pleural cavities lined with pleura on either side of the mediastinum in the thorax. Each lung is enclosed in *visceral pleura*. Another layer of serous membrane, the *parietal*

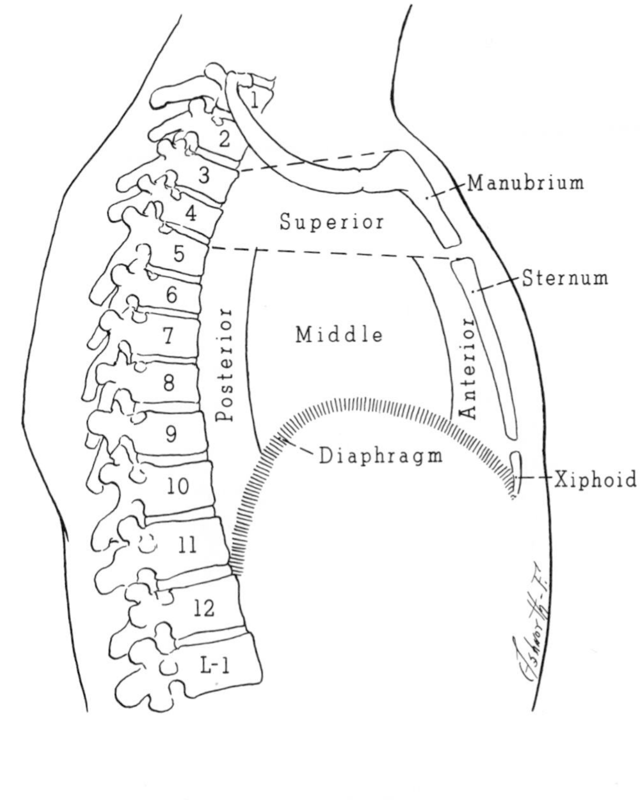

Fig. 297. Subdivisions of the mediastinum.

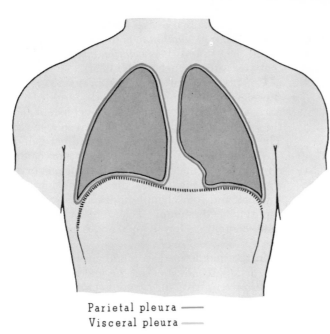

Fig. 298. Lungs and associated visceral and parietal pleura.

Parietal pleura ——
Visceral pleura ——

pleura, is in close contact with the diaphragm and interior border of the chest. Between the visceral and parietal pleurae is a potential space containing a small amount of pleural fluid for lubrication. The normal pleural arrangement allows for respiration with minimal friction, but when the pleura is inflamed (pleurisy), breathing becomes painful.

The Lungs (Figs. 298 and 299)

The lungs are cone-shaped organs completely filling the pleural spaces, extending from the diaphragm to about 1½ inches above the clavicle (Fig. 300). The part of the lung above the clavicle is called the *cupula.* The medial surface of each lung is concave around the mediastinum. The

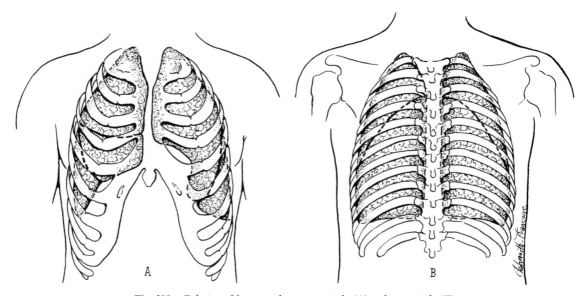

Fig. 299. Relation of lungs to thorax anteriorly (A) and posteriorly (B).

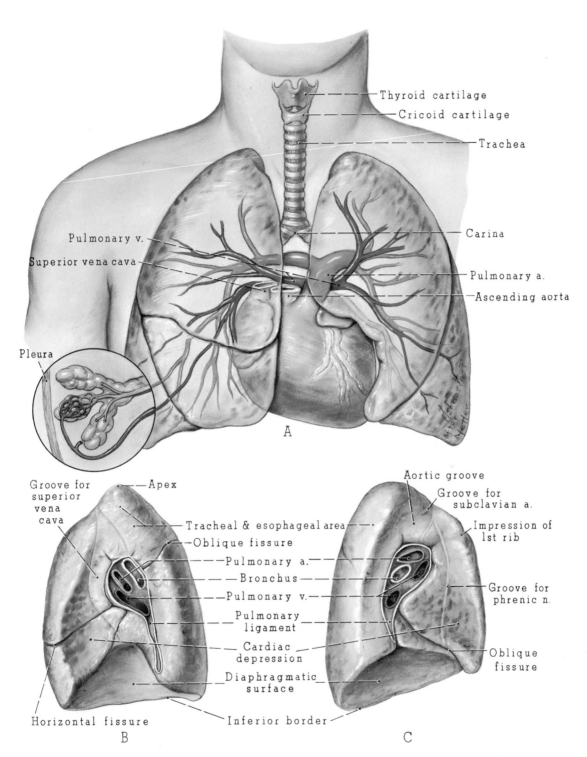

Thyroid cartilage
Cricoid cartilage
Trachea

Pulmonary v.
Superior vena cava

Carina
Pulmonary a.
Ascending aorta

Pleura

A

Groove for superior vena cava
Apex
Tracheal & esophageal area
Oblique fissure
Pulmonary a.
Bronchus
Pulmonary v.
Pulmonary ligament
Cardiac depression
Diaphragmatic surface
Horizontal fissure
Inferior border

Aortic groove
Groove for subclavian a.
Impression of 1st rib
Groove for phrenic n.
Oblique fissure

B

C

Fig. 300. *A.* Relationships of lungs to heart and pulmonary vessels. *B.* Medial aspect of right lung. *C.* Medial aspect of left lung.

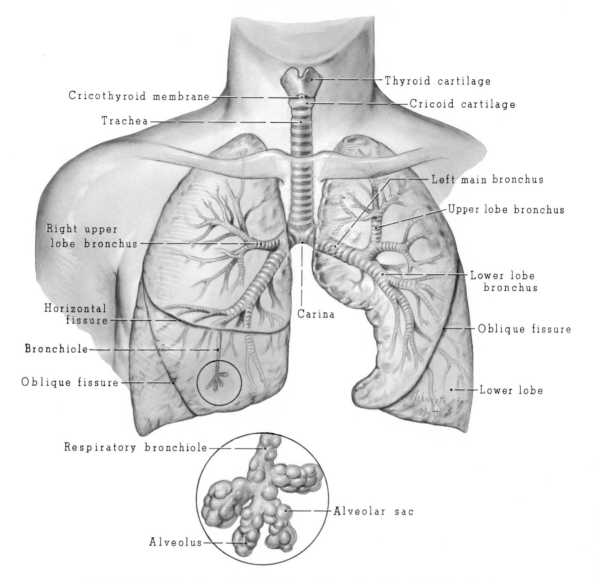

Fig. 301. Distribution of bronchi within the lungs. Enlarged inset shows detail of an alveolus.

primary bronchi and pulmonary arteries enter a slit in each lung called the *hilum* via the root of the lungs—the only real connection of the lungs with the body itself.

The lungs are divided by fissures (Fig. 301). The *oblique* and *horizontal fissures* divide the right lung into superior, middle, and inferior lobes. On the left side, there is only an oblique fissure, dividing the left lung into superior and inferior lobes. Additional units of the lung are recognized, each supplied by a single segmental bronchus. There are ten bronchial segments in the right lung and eight in the left (Fig. 302). The *alveoli* are the functional units of the lungs. Gaseous exchange between blood and air occurs only in the alveoli (Figs. 303 and 304).

The adult lung is a spongy mass frequently blue-gray in color because of inhaled dust and soot in the respiratory lymphatics. In contrast, the lung of a baby is pink, since no foreign material has yet entered. Prior to the age of 3 weeks, some of the pulmonary tissue can be incompletely filled with air. At birth, the lungs are filled with fluid; when the first breath is taken, the

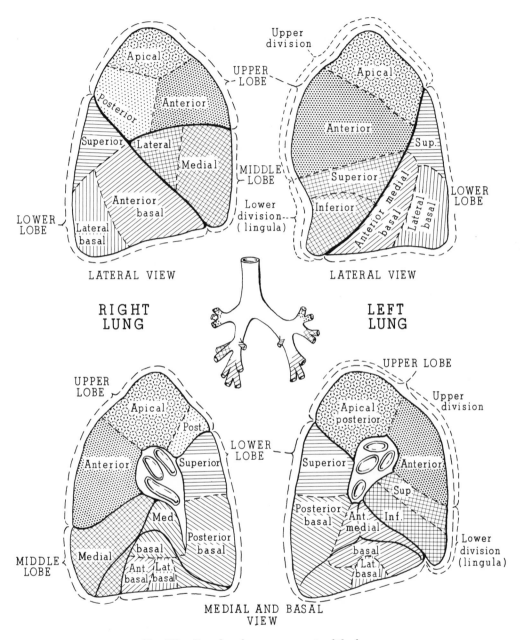

Fig. 302. Bronchopulmonary segments of the lungs.

361

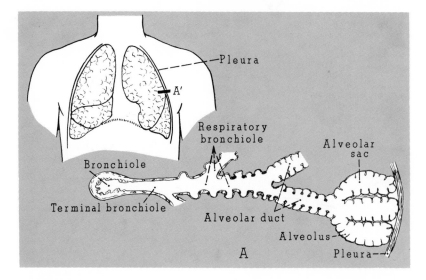

Fig. 303. Branching of the bronchiole into the functional unit, the alveolus.

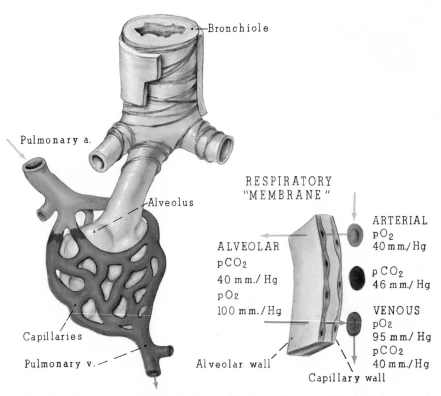

Fig. 304. Basic microscopic functional unit of the lung. (Courtesy of Roche Laboratories.)

lungs begin to become spongy, eventually filling with air to a degree similar to that found in the adult.

Recent investigations have shown that the air spaces in the lung are coated with a complex lipoprotein fraction which lowers the surface tension. This lipoprotein equalizes the tension in the air spaces as they expand and contract and helps to bring an even distribution of pressure between large and small alveoli. By decreasing the overall pressure, it reduces the muscular effort required for respiration. The lipoprotein has the additional functions of assisting the osmotic forces as they act across the lung surface and of keeping the film of moisture on the surface from drawing fluid into the air spaces.

The interior of the lung is by far the most extensive body surface in contact with the environment. In the normal adult, this area is approximately the size of a tennis court. Normal life processes require about 1 square meter of lung surface for each kilogram of body weight.

RESPIRATION

Internal and External Respiration

Respiration is divided into two components— *internal respiration,* a process in which cells trade carbon dioxide for fresh oxygen (cellular breathing); and *external respiration,* a process in which oxygen from the lungs enters the blood and carbon dioxide and water vapor are exhaled. External respiration is further divided into inspiration and expiration. Inspiration is accomplished by coordinated muscular contractions that increase chest volume, while expiration is ordinarily entirely passive.

Inspiration is initiated by contraction of the diaphragm and external intercostal muscles, causing elongation and increase of the diameter of the chest (Fig. 305). This increase in volume brings about a decrease in intrathoracic pressure —the pressure between the lungs and chest wall —from about −2 to −6 mm. of mercury in quiet respiration. The combination of decreased intrathoracic pressure and cohesion of the visceral and parietal pleurae causes the lungs to expand. Expansion lowers the intrapulmonic pressure (pressure inside the lungs) to −2 mm. of mercury; consequently there is a pressure gradient established from the atmosphere to the alveoli, resulting in inspiration. Actually, the inspiratory muscles cannot overcome a pressure greater than that produced by 4 feet of water; therefore, breathing air at atmospheric pressure is impossible in deeper water.

The reverse process occurs during expiration. Relaxation of the inspiratory muscles decreases the size of the thorax. This increases intra-

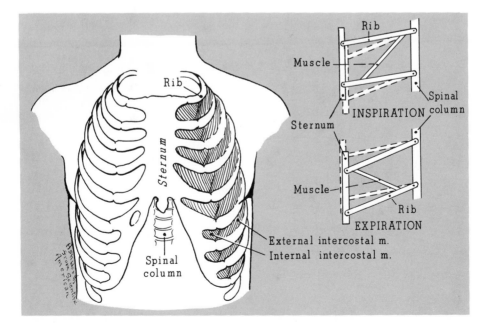

Fig. 305. Thorax with associated actions during normal respiration.

thoracic pressure from −6 to −2 mm. of mercury, which, together with the elastic recoil of the lungs, decreases the size of the lungs. Decreased lung size increases intrapulmonic pressure from −2 to 4 mm. of mercury. This pressure gradient from alveoli to atmosphere forces air out (Fig. 306).

Compliance is the expansibility of the lungs and thorax. This term refers to the volume increase in the lungs for each unit increase in intra-alveolar pressure. Compliance of normal lungs and thorax is 0.13 liter per ml. of water pressure; in other words, each time the alveolar pressure is increased by 1 ml. of water pressure, 130 ml. of lung expansion occurs. Conditions such as pulmonary fibrosis, emphysema, and pulmonary edema affect lung compliance.

At all times, the intrathoracic pressure is negative. This negative pressure is caused partly by the elasticity of the lungs attempting to force the lung to contract, and partly by the elasticity of the chest wall in an outward direction. When an opening is made in the chest wall, as frequently occurs in car accidents or in thoracic surgery, air enters the thorax because of the relation of the atmosphere to the intrathoracic pressure gradient. This allows the lungs to collapse and the chest to expand, a condition known as *pneumothorax*. Since the two pleural cavities are not connected, the pneumothorax is usually unilateral; however, the increased pressure on the opened side pushes the mobile mediastinum toward the uninvolved side, exerting pressure on the normal lung and decreasing its efficiency.

Types of Respiratory Activity

The two types of respiratory activity are *costal* and *diaphragmatic* (abdominal). Costal breathing is shallow and is characterized by upward and outward movement of the chest. It is seen in runners at the conclusion of a race. Costal breathing involves the use of the external intercostal and accessory muscles of respiration, such as the sternocleidomastoid. Diaphragmatic breathing, on the other hand, involves the use of the diaphragm rather than the intercostal muscles. Diaphragmatic breathing is deep; it is characterized by movement of the abdominal wall caused by contraction and descent of the diaphragm. This type of respiration is usually seen during sleep.

Since the object of breathing is to allow a given volume of fresh air to enter the blood every minute, the question of which is more efficient—rapid, shallow breathing or slow, deep breathing—is often asked. To answer this question, it should be remembered that the exchange of oxygen and carbon dioxide occurs only in the tiny, thin-walled alveoli. It does not take place in the trachea, bronchi, and bronchioles. Therefore, during each respiration, approximately 150 ml. of air ventilates the dead space, accomplishing little in so far as the exchange of gas is concerned. The greater the number of respirations per minute, the greater the amount of this useless ventilation. From this point of view, it is more economical to take a few large breaths rather than many smaller ones. On the other hand, pressure-volume studies reveal that the work accomplished by each respiration tends to increase as the square of the volume. From this second point of view, it is more economical to take many small breaths per minute. It is apparent that the greatest efficiency lies somewhere between the two extremes. Careful calculations indicate that approximately 15 respirations per minute, each of about 500 ml. in volume, provide the necessary ventilation of the alveoli with the least possible expenditure of energy.

Normal, quiet breathing, whether it be of the costal or diaphragmatic type, is known as *eupnea*. *Apnea* is a temporary cessation of breathing. *Dyspnea* is difficult breathing. *Orthopnea* is the inability to breathe in a horizontal position. *Hyperpnea* is an increased depth of breathing. *Tachypnea* is excessively rapid and shallow breathing.

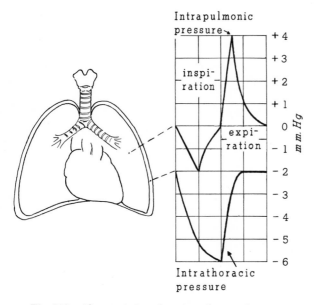

Fig. 306. Changes in intrathoracic and intrapulmonic pressures during respiration.

GAS TRANSPORT

Dalton's Law

In considering gas transport, Dalton's law of partial pressures must be understood. This law states that the partial pressure of a gas in a mixture of gases is related directly to the concentration of that gas and the total pressure of the mixture. For example, partial pressure of oxygen (pO_2) in the air is equal to the concentration of oxygen in the air—usually about 21 per cent times the total barometric pressure of the air at sea level (760 mm. of mercury). Stated simply, $pO_2 = 21$ per cent $\times$ 760 mm. of mercury = 159.6 mm. of mercury.

The partial pressure of a gas in a liquid is proportional to the amount of gas dissolved in the liquid. The amount dissolved is directly related to the partial pressure of the gas in the environment. A gas will diffuse into a liquid from a gaseous mixture over the liquid. For this reason, the blood flowing through the lungs tends to equilibrate its gaseous partial pressure with that of the alveolar air; that is, the pO_2 and pCO_2 of the blood leaving the lungs are nearly equal to the pO_2 and pCO_2 of the alveolar air.

Oxygen Transport

The partial pressure principle would explain the transport of 0.5 ml. of oxygen per 100 ml. of blood. This, however, is well below the level necessary to sustain life. There must be another method of oxygen transport in the blood. This other mechanism is the transport of oxygen as *oxyhemoglobin*. About 19 ml. of oxygen per 100 ml. of blood can chemically combine with hemoglobin to form oxyhemoglobin. This is by far the most important means of oxygen transport. Total oxygen transport is then about 20 ml. per 100 ml. of blood—19 ml. by oxyhemoglobin, and 0.5 ml. by physical solution in the plasma. The most common expression of this is to say that the blood has 20 volumes per cent oxygen (20 ml. oxygen per 100 ml. blood).

Since most oxygen is transported with hemoglobin, the amount of hemoglobin present influences the amount of oxygen that can be carried; therefore, anemia is frequently accompanied by a low oxygen transport (see Chapter Ten).

At lower and higher pCO_2 tensions, oxygenation of the hemoglobin is relatively increased and decreased, respectively. This is because hemoglobin has a greater affinity for oxygen at a higher pH than at a lower pH; this phenomenon is known as the *Bohr effect*. The pH of the blood is usually directly related to the pCO_2; that is, a high pCO_2 is associated with a low pH, and a low pCO_2 with a high pH.

Carbon Dioxide Transport

Carbon dioxide is transported in the blood in several ways.

1. About 60 per cent of the CO_2 is carried in the plasma in the form of bicarbonate (HCO_3^-). CO_2 is released from the tissues, forcing to the right the reaction shown at the bottom of this page.

2. About 25 per cent of the CO_2 is carried in unstable combinations with the amine groups as carbaminohemoglobin (carboxyhemoglobin). This is formed and carried in the red cells of the blood. The carbon dioxide association with hemoglobin is greater at a high pCO_2 than at a low pCO_2.

3. A smaller amount is carried as physically dissolved CO_2 in both plasma and cells.

The volume of gaseous exchange in the lungs is a function of several factors: partial pressure differences in the alveolar and venous blood; total available alveolar surface; respiratory minute volume (total air inspired in 1 minute, or respiratory rate times the volume per respiration); total amount of blood available in the lungs; and rate of blood flow through the lungs.

CONTROL OF RESPIRATION

Respiratory Centers in the Brain

Neurogenic mechanisms controlling respiration are located in the reticular substance of the medulla oblongata and pons. This poorly defined area is known as the *respiratory center*. In the ventral part of the lower end of the fourth ventricle are located *inspiratory centers*, which, when stimulated, cause the inspiratory muscles to contract. *Expiratory centers* lie lateral and

$$\text{lungs} + H_2O \rightleftharpoons H_2CO_3 + \text{buffers} \rightleftharpoons HCO_3^- + H^+ \text{ protein}$$
$$\uparrow \qquad\qquad\qquad\qquad \downarrow \qquad\qquad\qquad\qquad (\text{and } H_2PO_4^-)$$
$$CO_2 \qquad\qquad\qquad \text{proteinate}$$
$$\uparrow \qquad\qquad\qquad (\text{and } HPO_4^-)$$
$$\text{Tissues}$$

dorsal to the inspiratory ones. When these are stimulated, the inspiratory muscles relax and expiration occurs.

Two additional bilateral centers located superiorly in the brainstem are the *apneustic* and *pneumotaxic centers*. Stimulation of the apneustic center brings on forceful inspiration with a duration of 20 to 30 seconds and weak expirations lasting only 2 to 3 seconds. Stimulation of the pneumotaxic center inhibits the apneustic type of breathing. Although the apneustic and pneumotaxic centers do not have a basic rhythmicity of their own, they do modify and control the medullary centers to provide a better respiratory rhythm.

The *Hering-Breuer reflex* helps control depth and rhythmicity of respiration. Stretch receptors in the visceral pleura are activated when the lungs are stretched or expanded. These receptors transmit impulses through the vagus to the medulla, where they inhibit the inspiratory center and stimulate the expiratory center. One of the major effects of the Hering-Breuer reflex is to prevent overinflation of the lungs. This reflex helps to maintain the basic rhythmicity of the lungs.

The cerebral cortex plays a part in respiratory control. The motor area (precentral gyrus) of the cerebrum sends impulses to the respiratory center. This is the mode of voluntary respiratory control by which one holds his breath; however, this control can only dominate respiration up to a certain level of arterial blood pH, at which time the individual breathes even against his will. A person, therefore, cannot kill himself by holding his breath.

There appears to be a respiratory drive originating in the forebrain. This drive arises under a variety of conditions, such as temperature of the blood circulating through the hypothalamus. Neurons lying in the reticular formation and extending as far rostrally as the mammillary level of the hypothalamus are very sensitive to CO_2. Other forebrain systems influencing respiration seem to involve consciousness, since the mere anticipation of physical exercise increases ventilation long before the chemical drive arises. The forebrain respiratory drive is associated with emotional behavior. It is currently believed that the hypothalamus is connected with the neurons in the medullary reticular formation facilitating inspiration.

Factors Affecting Respiration

Factors mediating changes in respiration include pCO_2, pO_2, and pH of arterial blood. Nor-

mal arterial blood pCO_2 is 38 to 40 mm. of mercury. When it increases, the inspiratory centers in the medulla are stimulated; conversely, decreased pCO_2 slows breathing.

The pCO_2 acts both directly on the respiratory center and on the carotid and aortic receptors. Although there is a difference of opinion as to which of the respiratory regulators is more important, most investigators favor the concept that the direct influence on the respiratory center predominates.

A low pH increases both rate and depth of respiration by stimulating carotid and aortic chemoreceptors, as well as respiratory centers. The hydrogen ion concentration, or pH, acts much like the pCO_2 on the respiratory centers. The effect of pCO_2 and pH are additive; that is, their effects may summate to give a greater respiratory influence than either alone, or their effects may cancel one another.

The control of receptors by pO_2 is not nearly so important as control by pCO_2. The oxygen-sensitive chemoreceptors are not stimulated until sufficiently low pO_2 is established so that tissue anoxia develops. When these chemoreceptors are stimulated, impulses travel to the respiratory center to increase breathing. Under very low pO_2, however, respiration is inhibited. The reason oxygen pressure normally assumes a minor role in the control of breathing is that the respiratory rate can drop to one-half or rise to over 100 times of normal without appreciably influencing the amount of blood oxygenated (Fig. 307).

Breathing oxygen in a chamber pressurized to 2 atmospheres greater than atmospheric pressure allows higher tissue oxygen tensions. This permits circulatory arrest for 30 minutes in hypothermic dogs (dogs with body temperature reduced), improves safety in operations on children with heart disease, and aids in treatment in patients with tetanus (anaerobic infection). Hyperbaric chambers are now being employed in medical centers throughout the United States for medical administration of pressurized oxygen.

Blood pressure also influences the rate of breathing. A sudden drop of arterial pressure brings about an increase in the respiratory rate, and a sudden rise in pressure brings about a decrease in respiratory rate. This pressure effect is minor in respiration but major in circulation.

Different sensory stimuli can also elicit reflex respiratory effects. For example, severe pain usually causes increased ventilation, and a sudden cold stimulus brings about temporary apnea. Another stimulus, that of stretching the anal

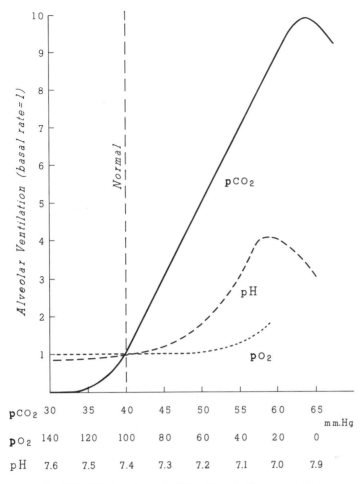

Fig. 307. Relative effects of pCO₂, pH, and pO₂ on respiration.

sphincter, increases the respiratory rate. Stretching the anal sphincter is sometimes employed to stimulate respiration during emergencies.

Still another influence on respiratory rate comes from a reflex originating in the joints of the body. Movement of a limb produces afferent impulses which then reflexly increase the rate and occasionally the depth of respiration. For example, if one runs very fast for a short distance, respiration is increased beyond the expected increase caused by a higher pCO_2 alone.

Age is another factor influencing respiratory rate. At birth the rate is rapid—from 40 to 70 times per minute. This decreases with age, so that at about 1 year, 35 to 40 times per minute is normal; at 5 years, about 25 times per minute is normal; at 10 years, 20; at 25 years, 16 to 18. With old age, however, the rate can increase again to more than 20 times per minute.

Respiration plays an important role in the control of body heat in lower animals, since the skin of these animals is generally covered with hair, which interferes with heat loss. In addition, lower animals do not possess sweat glands; therefore, the mechanism of panting is employed for dissipation of heat. Humans do not pant, but increased body heat does increase ventilation. Therefore, due to the heat produced by metabolism, the ventilatory rate is increased to a much greater extent during increased metabolism than would result from the mere influence of carbon dioxide produced from metabolism.

RESPIRATORY PHENOMENA

Cough

A *cough* is a mechanism for clearing obstructions of the airway. During coughing, forcible expiratory effort against the closed glottis first raises the air pressure in the chest. The glottis then suddenly opens, reducing pressure in the trachea and large bronchioles to atmospheric level. The high pressure still remaining in the major air spaces of the lung around the trachea collapses the membranous posterior wall of the trachea inward. As a result, air passes out through a much narrower trachea with a great force and velocity, blowing out foreign material and mucus with it.

Sneeze

A *sneeze* might be described as an upper respiratory cough. In the preparatory stages more and more air is inspired, and at the climax air is expelled with explosive force. During a sneeze the glottis is wide open and air meets its chief resistance in the mouth or nasal passages, so that the expiratory blast serves to clear the passages of the nose or mouth just as the cough clears the bronchi and trachea.

Yawn

Yawning aids respiration by more completely ventilating the lung. In ordinary breathing apparently not all of the alveoli of the lungs are equally ventilated; some actually periodically close. The blood passing through collapsed alveoli enters the arterial system without being oxygenated and dilutes the average oxygen content. In other words, arterial blood becomes slightly more venous. Collapsed alveoli are opened by the long, deep inspiration of the yawn. Most muscles of the body participate in this maneuver. The yawn may also serve the purpose of sneezing and help remove stagnant blood which has accumulated in blood vessels.

Hiccup

A *hiccup* is an abnormal response serving no known useful purpose. It is a spasmodic contraction of the diaphragm, resulting from stimulation either in the diaphragm itself or in the respiratory center of the brain, and caused by substances in the blood or by local circulatory abnormalities. The vocal cords usually open during inspiration (vocalization is produced normally only during expiration) and are apparently closed during the hiccup; the vibrations produce the characteristic sound. Persistent hiccups can generally be halted by inhalation of air containing 5 to 7 per cent carbon dioxide.

Cheyne-Stokes Breathing

Cheyne-Stokes breathing is a period of gradually increasing hyperpnea, followed by a period of progressive slowing of respiration eventuating in apnea, followed by another period of hyperpnea, and so forth. Cheyne-Stokes breathing occurs because of the following sequence. A factor causes an individual to overbreathe for a brief period of time with removal of carbon dioxide from the blood. After a delay, the blood with low carbon dioxide tension reaches the brain, causing activity of the respiratory center to diminish, along with a resulting slowing or cessation of respiration. When respiration ceases, carbon dioxide in the blood rises and another delay ensues. On reaching the respiratory center of the brain, blood with an increased CO_2 tension causes increased respiratory activity, resulting again in the rapid removal of carbon dioxide from the blood. This cycle is begun again, and the pattern of Cheyne-Stokes breathing recurs.

In the normal individual, "damping" systems block repetitive Cheyne-Stokes cycling of respiration. But from the basic principles of respiratory control it can be predicted that many abnormalities in the control system could provide a Cheyne-Stokes cycling of respiratory activity. These include increased time required for transmission of blood from the lungs to the brain, decreased functional residual capacity of the lungs, increased sensitivity of the brain to changes in concentration of gases in the blood, or decreased oxygenation of blood, increasing responsiveness of the chemoreceptor mechanisms to changes in blood-gas concentration.

MECHANICS OF BREATHING

The normal resting chest volume in a man of average size is about 3 liters. Normal inspiration increases this volume by approximately 500 ml. Forced maximum inspiration raises this to 6 liters. Forced maximum expiration lowers the chest volume to approximately 1 liter. The lung volumes are divided as follows (Fig. 308).

Vital capacity: the volume of air that can be expired after a maximal inspiration or the volume that can be inspired after maximal expiration.

Total lung capacity: the total volume of air in the lungs upon maximal inhalation, including residual volume.

Tidal volume: the amount of air that moves into the lungs with each inspiration. The average figure for an adult male is 500 cc.

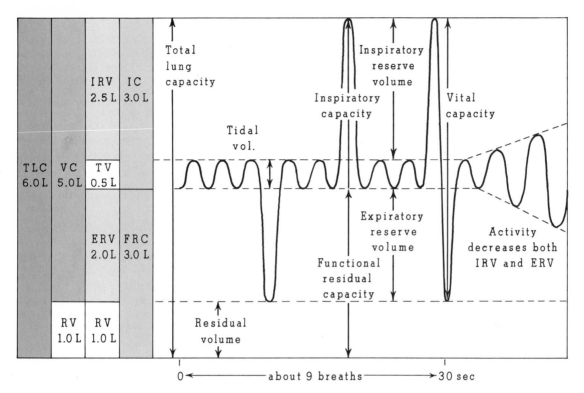

Fig. 308. Spirometric graph showing respiratory capacities and volumes.

Residual volume: the air remaining in the lungs even after maximal forced expiration.

Inspiratory capacity: the volume capable of being inspired at the end of a quiet respiration plus the tidal volume.

Inspiratory reserve volume: the volume capable of being inspired after quiet inspiration (IC minus IRV equals tidal volume).

Expiratory reserve volume: the volume capable of being expired at the end of a quiet expiration.

Functional residual capacity: expiratory reserve volume plus residual volume.

It will be noted that "capacities" consist always of two or more "volumes." The volumes and capacities are primarily dependent on the size and build of the individual. They change with body position, for the most part decreasing when the individual assumes a recumbent position and increasing when he stands. This is caused by abdominal pressure on the diaphragm during recumbency, along with an increase in pulmonary volume in this position, thus decreasing the space available for air.

Clinically, respiratory volumes and capacities are measured by using a spirometer. Spirometric study provides a graphic record of the volume that can be expelled from the lung after a maximum inspiration (vital capacity) and the rate at which the air can be expired. It can also be used to record the rate and depth of ventilation. The record is obtained by having the patient breathe in and out of the spirometer; movements are translated by means of a pen to the moving drum of a kymograph. Spirometry is an initial step in the physiologic evaluation of a patient with labored respiration. The test may be indicated in the diagnosis of bronchial asthma and emphysema.

COMMON RESPIRATORY DISORDERS

The most important respiratory disorders are those in which the blood fails to become oxygenated. Nearly all respiratory problems tend toward anoxia. Anoxia is sometimes manifested in *cyanosis.* This term refers to the fact that the skin, mucous membranes, and nail beds turn blue because of an increased presence of deoxygenated hemoglobin in the capillaries.

Atelectasis. Atelectasis of the lungs is a condition in which there is an incomplete expansion of the alveoli, along with production of areas of relatively airless pulmonary parenchyma. This may be manifested in partial or total collapse of the lung. The same elastic properties that collapse the aveoli also cause a partial collapse of the blood supply to that portion of the lung; therefore, the major portion of the blood still goes to the aerated portion of the lung. Atelectasis of even 50 per cent of the lung, or for that matter of an entire lung, often does not greatly diminish the aeration of blood. The most common causes of atelectasis are a chest wound which permits air to leak into the pleural cavity, and blockage of a primary bronchus or one of the smaller bronchial tubes following general anesthesia given for major surgery.

Emphysema. Emphysema is a condition in which the alveoli of the lungs are dilated and the walls of the alveoli are atrophied and thin. It may result from any factor producing marked chronic distension of the lungs, particularly during expiration, such as asthma or chronic bronchitis. A patient with emphysema has a barrel-shaped chest, and in severe cases the patient exhibits clubbing of the fingers (pulmonary osteoarthropathy). Emphysema is rapidly becoming one of the most common respiratory diseases, since it is frequent in older people and the average age of the population increases each year.

Bronchiectasis. Bronchiectasis is characterized by dilatation of the bronchi. It results from three factors: (1) flaccidity of the bronchial walls following chronic inflammation of the bronchial tree; (2) increase in the distending forces, as from long, continued cough; and (3) traction on the wall, as from fibrous tissue formation in the lung secondary to an inflammatory disease such as pneumonia. The symptoms of bronchiectasis are cough, voluminous sputum, and labored respiration on exertion.

Asthma. Asthma is a condition of recurrent labored respiration caused by intermittent obstruction of the bronchi; it is characterized by wheezing and prolonged expiration. Outflow of air through the bronchioles is obstructed more than inflow, permitting the asthmatic to inspire more easily than to expire. The lungs become increasingly distended; with long-standing asthma, the chest adopts a barrel-shaped appearance. In children asthma is commonly caused by sensitivities to food; in adults it is frequently caused by sensitivities to pollen. Allergic reactions cause localized edema in the walls of the terminal bronchioles and spasm of the smooth muscle walls. An asthmatic attack can be precipitated by an emotional crisis as well as by an allergen.

Pneumonia. Pneumonia is an inflammation of the lungs in which the alveoli are partially filled by fluid and white blood cells. The alveolar walls become inflamed, and there is generalized edema of the lung tissue. As in many other pulmonary diseases, carbon dioxide is adequately excreted, but oxygenation of the blood is diminished. This is caused by the fact that carbon dioxide passes through the alveolar walls about 20 times as readily as does oxygen. Pneumonia occurs most frequently in young children and in the aged. In 95 per cent of the instances, the disease is due to an organism, the pneumococcus; the remainder of cases are caused by streptococci and the *Hemophilus influenzae* bacillus (Fig. 309).

Tuberculosis. In tuberculosis, the tubercle bacilli invade the lungs, producing a local tissue reaction. Initially, the area is invaded by macrophages and then becomes walled off by fibrous connective tissue. Thus, a characteristic "tubercle" is produced. In the late stages, secondary infection by other bacilli is present and more fibrosis results. The fibrosis reduces the lung compliance and lowers the vital capacity. Fibrosis also lowers the total pulmonary membrane area and increases the thickness of the membrane, thus decreasing the capacity for pulmonary diffusion.

Pulmonary edema. Pulmonary edema influences respiration in much the same way as pneumonia. It is caused by an insufficiency of the left heart in pumping blood from the lungs to the rest of the body. This is generally the result of

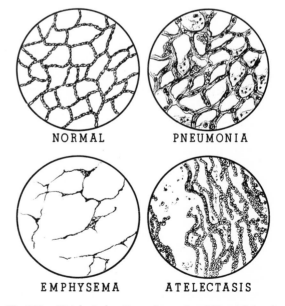

NORMAL   PNEUMONIA

EMPHYSEMA   ATELECTASIS

Fig. 309. Histological sections of normal and diseased alveoli.

cardiac insufficiency caused by poor blood supply to the muscles of the heart, but can also be caused by mitral or aortic valvular disease.

Infarction of the lungs. The commonest source of pulmonary infarction is an embolus from the right atrium or from the lower extremities and pelvis which eventually obstructs a branch of the pulmonary artery. The symptoms of pulmonary infarction are a sudden onset of labored respiration, often with collapse of the lung and a bloody sputum. The acute onset is characteristic and can be followed rapidly by death.

Air embolism. Air embolism is an unusual complication which occasionally follows the opening of a large vein in the neck during a surgical operation or the accidental injection of large volumes of air with blood transfusions. In the dog it is necessary to introduce 90 ml. of air to produce death; however, the administration of even a small amount of air into the pulmonary vein—for example, as little as 1 ml.—can cause death, since it frequently lodges in the brain.

Sinusitis. Sinusitis in the acute stage is manifested by pain referred to the maxillary and frontal sinuses. The nose is plugged, and nasal and postnasal mucus discharges occur. In the chronic form of sinusitis, the postnasal discharge becomes persistent.

Signs and symptoms associated with respiratory disturbances include the following. A productive cough—or for that matter, a non-productive cough—is a symptom common to disease of the trachea, bronchi, bronchioles, or pulmonary parenchyma, whether infectious or due to tumor. *Hemoptysis*, or blood-streaked sputum, accompanies disease of the lung. Involvement of the pleura by infection or by tumor is associated with pain intensified by respiration and coughing.

Spontaneous pneumothorax is characterized by pain and breathlessness. Breathlessness is a common symptom in pulmonary disease whenever there is decreased vital capacity below the normal minimum for the particular patient. This might be caused by pulmonary consolidation, emphysema, or disease of the heart.

ARTIFICIAL RESPIRATION

Mouth-to-Mouth Resuscitation

In 1958, the American Medical Association published a symposium concluding that mouth-to-mouth resuscitation was superior to all other means of artificial respiration. It is currently believed that mouth-to-mouth resuscitation is the only technique assuring adequate ventilation in all cases. The subject is placed in a supine position; the rescuer, behind the subject, grasps the subject's lower jaw and lifts it vertically upward. The rescuer then places his mouth over the subject's mouth and exhales. It is important that the subject's nostrils are either pinched shut or covered by the rescuer's mouth during resuscitation (Fig. 310).

There are many types of respirators for artificial respiration.

Iron Lung

The *tank respirator* (iron lung) is the apparatus which first made prolonged artificial respiration a practical matter. The patient is placed into a rigid tank from which only his head protrudes, and an airtight seal is made around his neck. To provide inspiration the bellows is expanded, so that the pressure in the tank becomes subatmospheric. Pressure in the patient's upper airway is atmospheric, so that the air flows along the trachea into the lungs. This flow of air continues until the lungs are sufficiently inflated for the elastic resistance of the lungs and the paralyzed chest wall to equalize the differences between atmospheric pressure and the pressure within the tank. The intrathoracic pressure lies between the pressure in the trachea and that within the tank, with its precise level depending on the elastic resistance of the lungs and chest wall. The principal use of the tank respirator is in patients with weakness of the respiratory muscles such as sometimes occurs in poliomyelitis. The disadvantage of a tank respirator is that it is cumbersome and the patient is rather inaccessible to other forms of treatment and diagnosis.

Intermittent Positive Pressure Respiration (Fig. 311)

Most medical centers in the United States currently use different pieces of equipment for *intermittent positive pressure respiration*. This is administered through an endotracheal tube passed into the nose or mouth. The larynx will not tolerate the presence of a tube for extended periods of time, and 24 hours is probably as long as it should be left in place. For long term intermittent positive pressure respiration, it is necessary to introduce gas into the lungs through a

ARTIFICIAL RESPIRATION
MOUTH-TO-MOUTH (MOUTH-TO-NOSE) METHOD

(1) If there is foreign matter visible in the mouth, wipe it out quickly with your fingers or a cloth wrapped around your fingers.

Tilt the head back so the chin is pointing upward.

(2) ⬆ Pull or push ⬇ the jaw into a jutting-out position.

(3)

(4) Open your mouth wide and place it tightly over victim's mouth. At same time pinch victim's nostrils shut.

(5) Or close the nostrils with your cheek.

(6) Or close the victim's mouth and place your mouth over the nose.

Blow into the victim's mouth or nose. If you are not getting air exchange, recheck the head and jaw position (see drawings above at left).

(7) If you still do not get air exchange, quickly turn the victim on his side and administer several sharp blows between the shoulder blades in the hope of dislodging foreign matter.

Resume breathing procedure.

THE AMERICAN NATIONAL RED CROSS

Fig. 310.   Mouth-to-mouth respiration. (Courtesy of The American National Red Cross.)

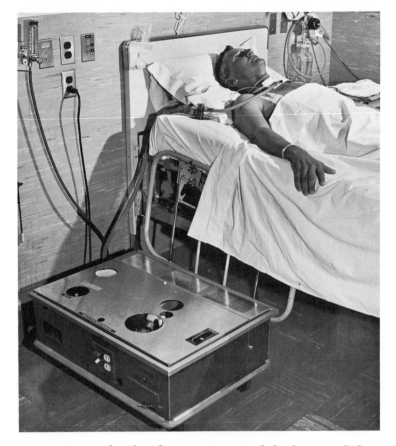

Fig. 311. Intermittent positive pressure respiration, used on a patient who requires artificial respiration and a tracheostomy. This treatment, sometimes required for several days, has saved lives. (Tracheotomy is merely an incision in the trachea, whereas a tracheostomy is the establishment of an air passage through an opening in the trachea to the outside, usually through a tracheostomy tube.)

tracheotomy. When the patient is ill, a tracheotomy tube with an inflated cuff is usually employed to make an airtight seal with the walls of the trachea. This serves two purposes—prevention of saliva, vomit, or other foreign material from passing into the chest, and prevention of air which is blown into the chest from leaking through the nose and mouth. The tracheostomy tube is connected to the tubing from a respirator which, during inspiration, provides pressure above atmospheric pressure. Air passes into the chest until the pressure in the airway is balanced by the elastic resistance of the lungs and chest wall. The intrathoracic pressure is raised but remains less than the pressure in the airway. The intrathoracic pressure is, therefore, higher than atmospheric pressure applied to the trunk, limbs, and veins, so that intermittent positive pressure respiration impedes the venous return during inspiration in precisely the same way as the tank respirator. The principal use of intermittent positive pressure respiration is for the patient who not only requires artificial respiration but also needs a tracheostomy.

SUMMARY: THE RESPIRATORY SYSTEM

HISTORY

1. Contributions by Aristotle, Galen, Scheele, Priestley, and Lavoisier.

ANATOMY

1. Nose:

    a. Cartilages form external nose: septal, lateral, and alar.
    b. Bony walls:
        (1) Roof: nasal, frontal, ethmoid, sphenoid, vomer, and palatine bones.

      (2) Floor: maxillary and palatine bones which also form the hard palate of the mouth.

  c. Internal nose:

      (1) Right and left divisions separated by the septum.

      (2) Superior, middle, and inferior meatuses separated by superior, middle, and inferior conchae (turbinates).

      (3) Openings: anterior nares to outside; posterior nares to pharynx.

      (4) Lining epithelium: thick, stratified squamous containing sebaceous glands.

  d. Functions: serves as air passage, warms air, filters air, moistens air, serves as organ of smell, and aids in phonation.

2. Paranasal sinuses (all paired):

  a. Lining of mucous membrane continuous with the nasal cavity.

  b. Maxillary: largest, opens into middle meatus.

  c. Frontal: nearest eye; opens into middle meatus.

  d. Ethmoid: numerous and irregular; anterior middle and posterior groups open into middle and superior meatuses.

  e. Mastoid: near auditory tube; opens into nasopharynx.

  f. Sphenoid: near optic nerve; empties into superior meatus.

  g. Nasolacrimal duct: opens into inferior meatus; drains tears from eyes.

3. Pharynx:

  a. Musculomembranous tube lined with mucous membrane.

  b. Nasopharynx, behind nose; oropharynx, behind mouth; and laryngopharynx, behind larynx.

  c. Nasopharynx—four openings: two auditory tubes and two posterior nares.

  d. Oropharynx—one opening: the fauces.

  e. Laryngopharynx—two openings: into larynx and into esophagus.

  f. Contains pharyngeal tonsils (adenoids) in nasopharynx; palatine and pharyngeal tonsils in oropharynx.

  g. Functions: serves as a passageway for food and air and aids in phonation.

4. Larynx:

  a. At the upper end of trachea; broad at top and narrower at bottom.

  b. Nine cartilages:

      (1) Unpaired: thyroid (Adam's apple), cricoid (signet ring), and epiglottis (lid to larynx).

      (2) Paired: arytenoid, cuneiform, and corniculate.

  c. Vocal cords are fibro-elastic bands stretched across interior of larynx; false vocal cords are folds of mucous membrane; rima glottidis is opening between true vocal cords.

  d. Lining is ciliated respiratory epithelium.

  e. Musculature: extrinsic and intrinsic.

  f. Nerve supply: vagus via superior and recurrent laryngeal nerves.

  g. Function: phonation.

      (1) Long, lax cords give low-pitched voice.

      (2) Short, tense cords give high-pitched voice.

5. Trachea:

  a. Smooth muscular tube containing 15 to 20 C-shaped cartilages with the opening of the "C" facing posteriorly.

  b. Four to 5 inches long from larynx to bronchi.

  c. Functions: serves as passageway to and from lungs.

  d. Tracheotomy: opening into trachea; tracheostomy; tube into trachea.

6. **Bronchi:**

    a. Formed by branching of trachea; the right primary bronchus is shorter, wider, and more vertical. Bronchi continue to branch down to terminal alveoli having walls a single cell thick.

    b. Functions: passageways for air to and from lungs; alveoli provide large surface for exchange of gases between blood and air.

7. **Thorax:**

    a. Four subdivisions:

        (1) Two pleural portions: each containing a lung surrounded by visceral and parietal pleura.

        (2) Pericardial portion: containing heart and pericardial sac.

        (3) Mediastinum.

            (a) Superior mediastinum contains arch of aorta and its three branches, brachiocephalic veins, inferior vena cava, vagus and phrenic nerves, left recurrent laryngeal nerve, esophagus, trachea, thoracic duct, thymus, and lymph nodes.

            (b) Inferior mediastinum: anterior portion contains lymph nodes and fat; middle portion contains heart, pericardium, ascending aorta, superior vena cava, trachea, pulmonary artery, pulmonary veins, phrenic nerves, and bronchial lymph glands; posterior portion contains esophagus, aorta, vagus nerves, thoracic duct, and azygous veins.

    b. Function: to house heart, lungs, etc., and aid in respiration.

8. **Lungs:**

    a. Structure:

        (1) Cone-shaped organs filling essentially the entire thorax with the heart; extends from just above the clavicle to the diaphragm.

        (2) Divisions: right lung has three lobes with ten bronchopulmonary segments; left lung has two lobes with eight bronchopulmonary segments.

        (3) Covering: visceral pleura.

    b. Function: lungs enable blood and air to come close enough together to allow gas exchange.

RESPIRATION

1. **Internal respiration (cell breathing).**

2. **External respiration (lung breathing).**

    a. Inspiration: accomplished actively by contractions of diaphragm and external intercostal muscles.

    b. Expiration: accomplished passively by elastic recoil of chest and lungs upon relaxation of inspiratory muscles.

3. **Compliance: term applied to expansibility of the lungs and thorax.**

4. **Pneumothorax: expansion of the chest and collapse of the lungs upon opening of the pleural space.**

5. **Types of respiration:**

    a. Diaphragmatic (abdominal): characterized by abdominal movement caused by descent and ascent of the diaphragm, as seen in a sleeping person.

    b. Costal: characterized by upward and outward movements of the chest, as seen in a runner after a sprint.

GAS TRANSPORT

1. Dalton's law: partial pressure of a gas in a gaseous mixture is related to concentration of the gas and to total pressure of the mixture.

2. Partial pressure of a gas in liquid is proportional to the amount of gas dissolved in the liquid; the amount dissolved is directly related to partial pressure of the gas in the environment.

3. Oxygen transport in blood:

    a. About 98 per cent by chemical combination with hemoglobin to form oxyhemoglobin.
    b. About 2 per cent by physical solution in plasma.

4. Carbon dioxide transport in blood:

    a. About 60 per cent is carried in plasma as bicarbonate (HCO_3^-).
    b. About 25 per cent is carried in unstable hemoglobin combinations, mainly carbaminohemoglobin.
    c. Some is carried as physically dissolved CO_2 in plasma and cells.

CONTROL OF RESPIRATION

1. Inspiratory and expiratory centers in medulla and pons.

2. Apneustic and pneumotaxic centers in the brainstem modify and control the medullary centers.

3. Hering-Breuer reflexes inhibit respiration and enhance expiration upon increased alveolar pressure; decreased alveolar pressure stimulates inspiration and inhibits expiration.

4. Cerebral cortex gives the means by which we voluntarily hold our breath.

5. A forebrain respiration center.

6. Factors affecting respiration:

    a. Arterial blood pCO_2; increased pCO_2 increases respiration up to a point and above this depresses it.
    b. Arterial pO_2; decreased pO_2 increases respiration to a certain level and below this depresses respiration.
    c. A low arterial pH increases respiration.
    d. Sensory stimuli such as pain, sudden cold, and stretching the anal sphincter can elicit respiratory changes.
    e. Reflexes from joints in the body can increase breathing.
    f. Age affects respiratory rate, which generally decreases until old age.
    g. Body heat increases respiration.

RESPIRATORY PHENOMENA

1. Cough: forcible expiratory effort against the closed glottis raises the air pressure in the chest; the glottis suddenly opens, blasting air and obstructions from the airway.

2. Sneeze: same as cough, except that air is forced against the mouth and nasal passages instead of the glottis; it clears the upper respiratory tract.

3. Yawning: more completely ventilates lung; elicited by a critical amount of stale air in the lungs.

4. Hiccup: an abnormal response serving no purpose; often halted by breathing air containing 5 to 7 per cent CO_2.

5. Cheyne-Stokes breathing: increasing hyperpnea, followed by apnea, followed by hyperpnea, and so on.

MECHANICS OF BREATHING

1. Amount of air exchanged is directly related to gas pressure difference between atmosphere and lung alveoli and inversely to lung and chest resistance to air flow.

   a. Measured by a spirometer.
   b. Tidal volume: volume breathed during normal, quiet respiration.
   c. Vital capacity: total lung capacity minus air that cannot be forced out.
   d. Residual volume: air left in lungs after maximum expiration.

COMMON RESPIRATORY DISORDERS

1. Most disorders are manifested in cyanosis.

2. Atelectasis: collapse of part or all of a lung or both lungs.

3. Emphysema: alveoli are dilated and the walls are atrophied.

4. Bronchiectasis: dilation of the bronchi manifested in symptoms of cough, voluminous sputum, and labored respiration upon exertion.

5. Asthma: periodic labored respiration usually caused by allergy or emotion; prolonged asthma causes a barrel-shaped chest.

6. Pneumonia: inflammation of the lungs in which the alveoli are partially filled with fluid and white blood cells.

7. Tuberculosis: a bacillus invades the lungs, causing local tissue reaction and fibrosis.

ARTIFICIAL RESPIRATION

1. Mouth-to-mouth resuscitation is superior to all other means of artificial respiration.

2. Iron lung allows prolonged artificial respiration.

3. Intermittent positive pressure respiration is used for a patient who needs both a tracheostomy and artificial respiration.

STUDY QUESTIONS: THE RESPIRATORY SYSTEM

1. List the functions of the nose.
2. Name the structures separated by the turbinates.
3. Describe the largest paranasal sinus. At what point does it communicate with the nasal vestibule?
4. List the four openings into the nasopharynx.
5. Name the three paired and the three unpaired laryngeal cartilages. Describe the largest laryngeal cartilage.
6. Discuss the nerve supply to the larynx.
7. Describe the true vocal cords. What is the name of the space between the cords?
8. Why do most foreign bodies lodge in the right main stem bronchus?
9. What is the mediastinum? How is it subdivided?
10. How many lobes are in the right lung? How many are in the left lung?
11. What are the serous membranes around the lungs called?

12. Review what is meant by lung compliance.
13. Describe what occurs when the pleural cavity is exposed to the atmosphere.
14. Is inspiration usually active or passive? Is expiration usually active or passive?
15. Is rapid, shallow breathing or slow, deep breathing more efficient? Why?
16. How is most oxygen carried in the blood to the tissues? What is another means of oxygen transport in the blood?
17. How is most carbon dioxide carried in the blood from the tissues? What are the other means of carbon dioxide transport?
18. What is the major "humoral" influence on respiration?
19. Name six factors influencing the respiratory rate of the individual.
20. Discuss the difference between a cough and a sneeze.
21. Describe what is meant by vital capacity.
22. Define atelectasis, emphysema, and pneumonia.
23. What is cyanosis?

CHAPTER THIRTEEN

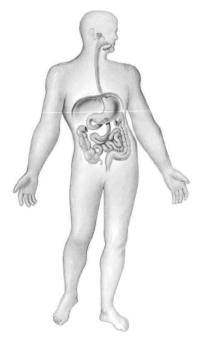

THE
DIGESTIVE
SYSTEM

HISTORY

The history of medicine gives an interesting account of the ideas and events leading to our present state of knowledge of the digestive system. In the early 19th century many physical and chemical theories of digestion were entertained, but these were only meagerly substantiated or correlated. The detailed workings of the gastrointestinal system as a whole were largely a matter of dispute—even in the reliable textbooks of the period, one of which contained William Hunter's amusing remark that "Some physiologists will have it that the stomach is a mill, that it is a fermenting vat, and others, again, that it is a stew-pan; but, in my view of the matter, it is neither a mill, a fermenting vat, nor a stew-pan; but a stomach, gentlemen, a stomach."

There was little factual knowledge concerning the relation between structure and function in the digestive system until 1833, when a significant advance was made with the publication of William Beaumont's "Experiments and Observations on the Gastric Juice and the Physiology of Digestion." The subject of this study was Alexis St. Martin, a Canadian voyageur who had been accidentally wounded by the discharge of a musket. The shot "entered posteriorly, and in an oblique direction, forward and inward, literally blowing off integuments and muscles the size of a man's hand, fracturing and carrying away the anterior half of the sixth rib, fracturing the fifth, lacerating the lower portion of the left lobe of the lungs, the diaphragm, and perforating the stomach."

After surgical repair and healing, there remained an aperture 2½ inches in circumference in both the wall of the stomach and the side of the patient. Beaumont attempted to close this wound but failed; subsequently, the natural protrusion of the layers of the stomach in a sort of fistula (an abnormal passage leading from the abdominal wall to one of the hollow abdominal organs) produced a permanent valve, which prevented the escape of gastric contents even when the stomach was full, but which could easily be depressed to permit the entrance of a tube or other instrument and the introduction of food substances. The interior of the stomach could be seen with the naked eye.

Realizing the unique opportunity presented, Beaumont conducted a series of experiments between 1825 and 1833, during which time St. Martin enjoyed normal, robust health. The most important of Beaumont's pioneering results contain concepts accepted as fundamental today.

EMBRYOLOGY OF THE GASTRO-INTESTINAL TRACT (Fig. 312)

The primitive digestive tube is formed by the yolk sac entoderm and is divided into the *foregut, midgut,* and *hindgut.* At the cephalic and caudal extremes of this tube the entoderm of the gut comes into contact with depressions on the surface ectoderm called the stomodeum and proctodeum respectively. The membranes thus formed rupture to produce oral and anal openings. Occasionally, the formation of the anal opening is incomplete, resulting in an imperforate anus. In this condition, the lower intestine does not have an external opening. Surgical correction must be completed within 48 hours after birth or death results.

The peritoneum of the abdominal cavity is formed from the mesoderm surrounding the entodermal digestive tube. This mesoderm splits making two layers. One lines the digestive tube

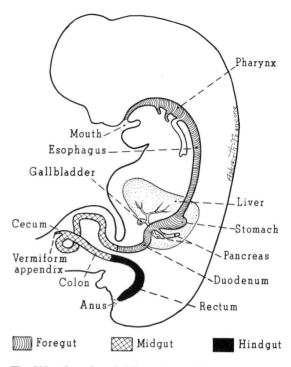

Fig. 312. Growth and differentiation of the primitive gut. For further explanation see text.

and eventually becomes the visceral peritoneum; the other layer lines the inner surface of the body wall and becomes the parietal peritoneum.

As growth and differentiation continue, the primitive gut undergoes many alterations. The cranial portion of the foregut gives rise to the mouth, pharynx, and associated structures. The caudal portion of the foregut forms the esophagus, stomach, duodenum, liver, gallbladder, and pancreas.

The primitive midgut becomes the portion of the intestine extending from the caudal end of the duodenum through the proximal two-thirds of the transverse colon. The midgut elongates in the fifth week of embryonic life to form the primary intestinal loop. The remainder of the large colon is derived from the primitive hindgut.

During elongation and rotation of the primitive intestine, there is a period during which it cannot be contained within the more slowly expanding abdomen. It therefore extrudes into the umbilical cord. A form of abnormal development occurs in which the intestine fails to return to the abdominal cavity, producing an *omphalocele,* a sac of the umbilical cord containing nearly all the small intestine and the proximal portion of the large intestine. When a child is born with this condition, an immediate operation is required. The contents, at surgery, are replaced into the abdomen and the defect corrected.

An *umbilical hernia* can result secondarily if the loops protrude through an inadequately closed umbilical ring after having once returned normally. Most umbilical hernias in children will close spontaneously and are, therefore, treated only by adhesive strapping.

The development of the digestive system is complete after 4 months of intra-uterine life. Component structures of the digestive system resemble those of the adult in every respect, except that at birth the liver is proportionately larger, since it is functionally more active in the fetus.

ANATOMY (Figs. 313 to 315)

The digestive system consists of (1) a long, muscular tube beginning at the lips and ending at the anus, including the mouth, pharynx, esophagus, stomach, and small and large intestine; and (2) certain large glands located outside the digestive tube, including the salivary glands, liver, gallbladder, and pancreas—all of which empty their secretions into the tube. The major functions of the digestive system are the digestion and absorption of ingested food and the elimination of solid wastes.

Mucous Membrane

Any discussion of the component parts of the gastrointestinal tract should be preceded by a consideration of the term *mucous membrane*. The mucous membrane functions in protection as well as absorption. The problem of protection is made difficult by the fact that the epithelial membrane must also be thin enough to be absorptive. Since one of the major protective devices is the secretion of mucus, the term *mucous membrane* is utilized for the wet epithelial membrane. Mucous membrane usually refers to the epithelial lining with its underlying connective tissue (lamina propria or tunica propria). It can contain smooth muscle deep to the lamina propria known as the muscularis mucosae.

Lips

The lips have an outer surface covered by skin. The red, free margins represent a zone of

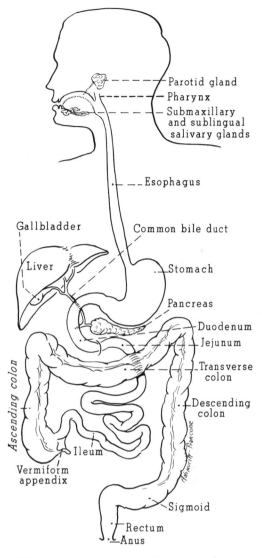

Fig. 313. The digestive system and its associated structures.

transition from skin to mucous membrane. The epithelium of the inner surface of the lip is stratified squamous and is similar to the epithelium found on the inner surface of the cheek, pharynx, and esophagus. The substance of the lip consists of striated muscle fibers with fibroelastic connective tissue.

Cheeks

The cheeks or side walls of the mouth, lined by stratified squamous epithelium, contain several accessory muscles of mastication, notably the

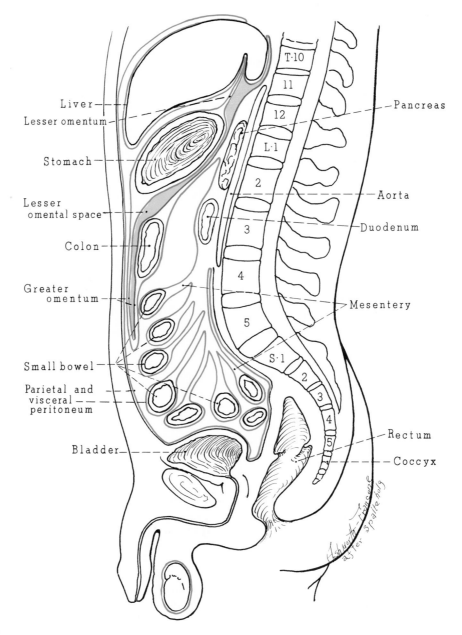

Fig. 314. Mid-sagittal section through trunk, showing parietal and visceral peritoneum. (Note relationship between abdominal viscera and mesenteries.)

382

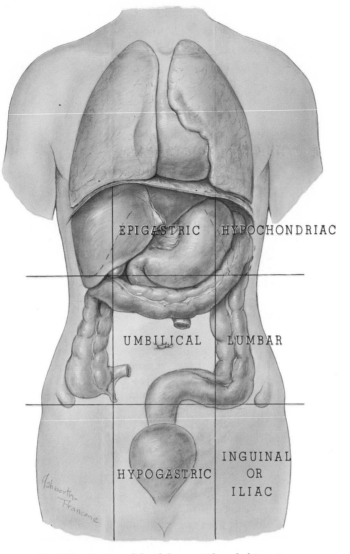

EPIGASTRIC   HYPOCHONDRIAC

UMBILICAL   LUMBAR

HYPOGASTRIC

INGUINAL
OR
ILIAC

Fig. 315.   Regions of the abdomen with underlying viscera.

buccinators, which prevent food from escaping the chewing actions of the teeth.

Teeth (Fig. 316)

Teeth develop in the seventh fetal week from ectodermal tissue and are all constructed on the following basic plan.

1. The exposed portion of the crown has an external covering of hard *enamel* and an internal ivory substance, the *dentine*.

2. The portion embedded in the alveolus of the jaw is covered by cementum and is called the *root*.

3. The central *pulp cavity* contains blood vessels and nerves.

4. Periosteal tissue lines the tooth socket, supplying nourishment.

Each type of tooth is adapted to its function—incisors for cutting, canines for grasping, and molars for grinding.

Solid food must be reduced to small particles before it can undergo chemical changes in the digestive tract. The teeth accomplish this function. Faulty teeth cause indigestion or malnutrition.

Dental caries, primarily a childhood disease which destroys the enamel, is at least partially preventable by ingesting fluoride. When optimal

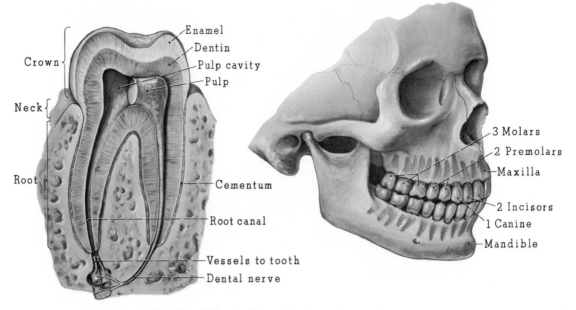

Fig. 316. Mid-sagittal view of molar tooth, vertical position.

amounts of fluoride are ingested during dental development, a reduction in caries of about 60 per cent can be expected. Fluoridation of water is a widely accepted method of supplying dental fluoride. An alternative method, the oral fluoride supplement, is required for children in communities without natural or artificial fluoridation of water. It is most important for pregnant women to have an adequate intake of fluoride during the first trimester of gestation.

Pyorrhea is an inflammatory process of the gums in which the teeth become loose and fall out. Bacteria from dental infection can spread through the blood to the heart, causing inflammation of the lining membrane of the heart (bacterial endocarditis).

Tongue

The floor of the mouth contains the tongue, which is composed of muscle fibers winding in three different directions, thus making it a movable structure. The tongue functions to mix saliva with food and to keep the mass pressed between the teeth for chewing before it pushes the food backward for swallowing. Numerous taste buds are scattered over the surface of the tongue (Fig. 317).

Palate

The palate or roof of the mouth consists of two parts: an anterior portion, the hard palate,

formed by the maxillary and palatine bones; and a posterior portion, the soft palate, composed of muscles ending in a free projection called the *uvula*. The opening of the pharynx lies behind the uvula (Fig. 318).

Pharynx

The pharynx is the portion of the digestive tract serving as a passageway for both the respiratory and digestive systems. It permits an individual to breathe through his mouth even if the nasal passages are obstructed. The pharynx has longitudinal and circular muscle layers of the striated type. The circular muscles are called constrictors.

Layers of the Wall of the Digestive Tract

A basic histologic plan is seen throughout the remainder of the digestive tract, although there are individual features peculiar to each region. In general the wall of the digestive tract is composed of the following layers.

Mucous membrane or tunica mucosa. This is the innermost layer of the digestive tract; it is composed of a superficial epithelium and an underlying support of connective tissue, the *lamina propria*, with a thin arrangement of smooth muscle fibers, the muscularis mucosae. Glandular cells of the mucosa secrete digestive

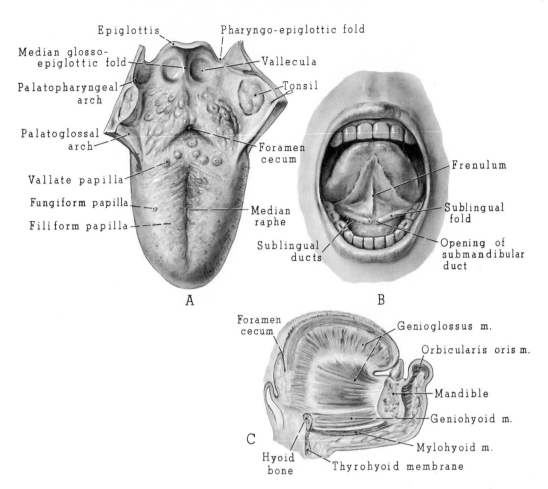

Epiglottis

Pharyngo-epiglottic fold

Median glosso-epiglottic fold

Vallecula

Palatopharyngeal arch

Tonsil

Palatoglossal arch

Foramen cecum

Vallate papilla

Fungiform papilla

Median raphe

Filiform papilla

A

Frenulum

Sublingual fold

Sublingual ducts

Opening of submandibular duct

B

Foramen cecum

Genioglossus m.

Orbicularis oris m.

Mandible

Geniohyoid m.

C

Mylohyoid m.

Hyoid bone

Thyrohyoid membrane

Fig. 317. *A*. Dorsal view of the tongue. *B*. Anterior view of the oral cavity with tongue raised. *C*. Mid-sagittal section through the tongue.

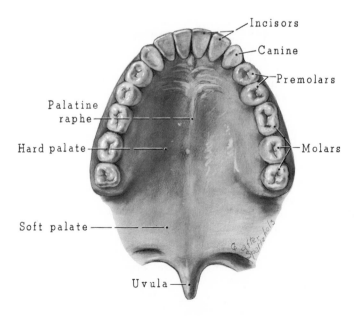

Incisors

Canine

Premolars

Palatine raphe

Hard palate

Molars

Soft palate

Uvula

Fig. 318. Roof of mouth with adult teeth.

juices and mucus. Only mucus is secreted in the esophagus and colon. Accumulations of lymphoid tissue are often found in supporting connective tissue.

Submucous layer or tela submucosa. This layer is composed of areolar connective tissue with numerous lymphatics, blood vessels, and nerves. It is found between the mucous and muscular layers and acts to compensate for changes in size of the digestive tube during the passage of food.

Muscular layer or muscularis externa. This consists of smooth muscle fibers in two distinct sections. The inner circular layer, when contracted, narrows the lumen of the tube. The longitudinally arranged fibers of the outer layer serve to shorten the tube by their contraction. Autonomic nerve endings are located in the muscular layer.

Serous layer or adventitia. The outermost covering is called the visceral peritoneum or serosa, with the *parietal peritoneum* located between the *visceral peritoneum* and the abdominal wall. The peritoneal cavity exists in many areas of the abdomen between the visceral peritoneum and parietal peritoneum.

Esophagus

The esophagus is a long, straight tube communicating in a direct path with the stomach. Passage of food is facilitated by ordinary gravitational forces, as well as by the type and arrangement of muscles in the tube itself. The esophagus extends from the pharynx to the stomach for a distance of 10 inches. It is posterior to the trachea and anterior to the vertebral column; it passes through the diaphragm in front of the aorta to enter the stomach.

Although the esophagus is similar to the remaining portions of the digestive tract, there are a few differences. For instance, the epithelium of the esophagus is stratified squamous, whereas the epithelium of the stomach and intestine is columnar. The muscularis layer of the upper one-third of the esophagus is striated, and that of the lower one-third is smooth. A transitional zone exists in the middle and contains both striated and smooth muscle. The outer covering of the esophagus is not serous but is thickened and fibrous in nature.

Stomach

The stomach, the most dilated portion of the digestive tract, lies under the diaphragm just below the costal margin in the upper abdomen. It serves mainly as a storage center for food prior to passage into the duodenum, but it permits some digestion.

The stomach consists of three parts: the *fundus,* an upper portion ballooning toward the left; a *body,* the central portion; and the *pylorus,* a relatively constricted portion at the terminal end just before the entrance into the duodenum (Fig. 319).

The wall of the stomach is composed of the same three layers found in other regions of the digestive tract, with certain modifications. The stomach, in addition to having an external longitudinal and an inner circular layer of smooth muscle, has an oblique layer located inside the circular one extending from the fundus to the pyloric antrum. The circular muscle layer is thickened in the pyloric region to form the pyloric sphincter, allowing chyme (the semifluid mass of partially digested food) to pass in only one direction. At birth, and occasionally in adult life, the pyloric sphincter is weak and regurgitation results.

Small Intestine

The small intestine extends from the distal end of the pyloric sphincter to the cecum. It is approximately 18 feet in length and is divided into three portions: the duodenum, jejunum, and ileum. The duodenum, named because it is about equal in length to the breadth of 12 fingers, is the shortest, widest, and most fixed portion of the small intestine. It receives secretions of the liver and pancreas. The junction between the duodenum and jejunum is demarcated by a ligamentous band known as the suspensory ligament to the duodenum (Treitz's) (Fig. 320). The junction between the jejunum and ileum is arbitrary. These three segments can be differentiated grossly by the number of branches of the arterial arcades in their fan-shaped suspending mesenteries. The duodenum is supplied by branches of the celiac artery and the remainder of the small intestine by branches of the superior mesenteric artery.

Histologically the wall of the small intestine is typical of the digestive tract as a whole, but it is distinguished by a large number of villi projecting into its lumen. Tubular glands, known as the crypts of Lieberkühn, are found between the bases of the villi. Brunner's glands are found in the small intestine, located in the submucosa of the duodenum. Simple cuboidal or columnar epithelium lines the small intestine (Fig. 321).

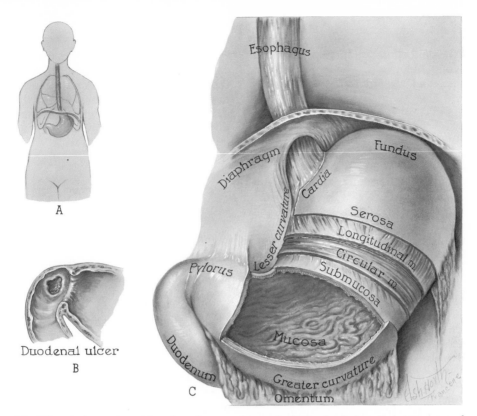

Fig. 319. *A.* Anatomic position of esophagus and stomach. *B.* Duodenal ulcer. *C.* Anterior view of the stomach with portion of the anterior wall removed. (Note the various layers which make up the stomach wall.)

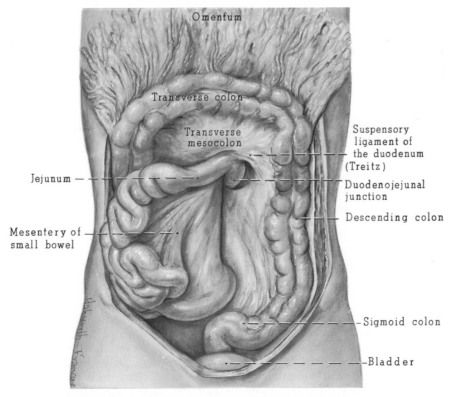

Fig. 320. Anterior view of the intestine with greater omentum raised. The small bowel has been retracted to show the junction of the duodenum and jejunum.

The cells of the epithelium are interspersed with mucus-secreting goblet cells. The occurrence of these cells increases toward the caudal end of the digestive tube.

Large Intestine

The large intestine differs from the small in several ways, including its greater width and the following characteristics (Fig. 322):

1. There are no villi on the surface of the tunica mucosa.

2. The longitudinal muscle layer is limited to three bands visible on the surface called *taeniae coli.*

3. Many appendices epiploicae, or extensions of fat-filled peritoneum, are apparent along the free border.

4. The outer walls of the transverse colon possess sacculations called *haustra.*

The *cecum,* or first portion of the large intestine, is an elongate pouch situated in the right lower portion of the abdomen. Attached to its base is a slender tube, the vermiform (worm-like) process, or appendix, which has a cavity communicating with the cecum. Infection frequently develops in the appendix. When infection occurs, it is usually secondary to some obstruction of the appendix by feces, producing damage and inflammation. Appendicitis is treated by removing the appendix to prevent rupture and peritonitis (inflammation of the peritoneum).

The *ascending colon* extends upward from the cecum on the right posterior abdominal wall to the under surface of the liver just anterior to the right kidney. The *transverse colon* overlies the coils of the small intestine and crosses the abdominal cavity from right to left below the stomach.

The *descending colon* begins near the spleen, passing downward on the left side of the abdomen to the iliac crest, and becoming the pelvic colon. The descending colon is 6 inches in length and does not possess a mesentery. The pelvic or sigmoid colon is so called because of its S-shaped course within the pelvic cavity.

Rectum

The rectum lies on the anterior surface of the sacrum and coccyx and terminates in the narrow anal canal (Fig. 323). Vertical folds called rectal columns can be seen, each containing an artery and vein, the latter being subject to enlargements known as hemorrhoids (Fig. 324).

Hemorrhoids are either internal or external and can cause bleeding and pain. An external hemorrhoid is covered by skin and an internal one by mucosa. Factors predisposing to hemorrhoids include constipation, increased intra-abdominal pressure (as in pregnancy) and a general hereditary weakness of the vein wall.

SECRETION, MOTILITY, AND DIGESTION (Tables 37 and 38)

Functions of the Mouth

The structures contained within the mouth prepare the food for digestion. Chewing motion has the effect of thoroughly mixing the food with salivary secretions to facilitate swallowing. Ptyalin, the only digestive enzyme contained in saliva, is thus brought into intimate contact with the starch of food breaking it into less complex forms. Ptyalin can also function to remove food debris lodged between the teeth.

SALIVARY GLANDS. There are three pairs of salivary glands: *parotid, submaxillary,* and *sublingual.* The parotid glands are located in the subcutaneous regions of the cheek, anterior and inferior to the ears. The parotid duct opens just opposite the second upper molar. Each submaxillary gland is located in the floor of the mouth close to the angle of the jaw. The submaxillary duct opens lateral to the point at which the frenulum attaches to the tongue. The sublingual gland is located under the mucous membrane of the floor of the mouth, just lateral to the tongue. Several sublingual ducts open either near the tongue or into the submaxillary duct (Fig. 292).

Mechanism of salivary secretion. Two types of cells are found within the salivary glands: *serous cells,* producing a clear, watery secretion; and *mucous cells,* producing a thick, mucous secretion. The parotid gland consists almost entirely of serous cells. The submandibular gland contains both serous and mucous cells in approximately equal proportions. The sublingual gland consists of mucous cells. The salivary glands are innervated by both sympathetic and parasympathetic nerve fibers. Stimulation of parasympathetic fibers produces a copious, watery secretion; stimulation of sympathetic fibers results in a viscous secretion of smaller volume.

The salivary glands empty their secretions into the mouth. These secretions moisten and lubricate the food and aid in chewing, swallowing, and tasting. *Ptyalin* is the principal enzyme

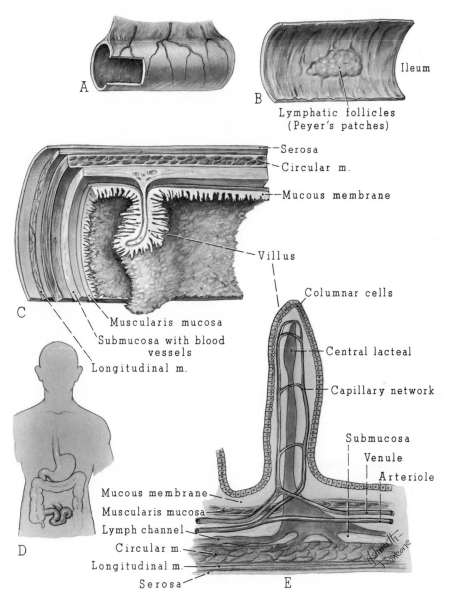

A

B

Ileum

Lymphatic follicles
(Peyer's patches)

Serosa

Circular m.

Mucous membrane

Villus

Columnar cells

Central lacteal

Capillary network

Submucosa

Venule

Arteriole

C

Muscularis mucosa

Submucosa with blood
vessels

Longitudinal m.

D

Mucous membrane

Muscularis mucosa

Lymph channel

Circular m.

Longitudinal m.

Serosa

E

Fig. 321. *A.* Segment of small intestine. *B.* Interior view of intestine with Peyer's patch. *C.* Layers composing intestinal wall. *D.* Anatomic position showing stomach and large and small intestines. *E.* Mid-sagittal section through villus.

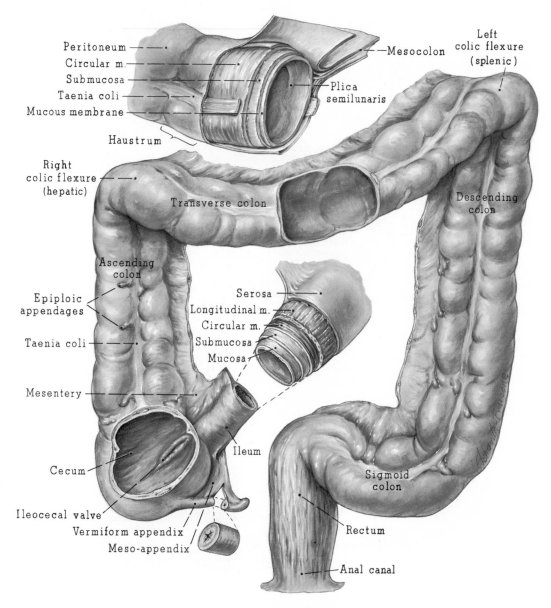

Peritoneum
Circular m.
Submucosa
Taenia coli
Mucous membrane
Haustrum

Mesocolon
Left colic flexure (splenic)
Plica semilunaris

Right colic flexure (hepatic)
Transverse colon
Descending colon

Ascending colon

Epiploic appendages

Taenia coli

Mesentery

Serosa
Longitudinal m.
Circular m.
Submucosa
Mucosa

Ileum

Cecum

Ileocecal valve

Vermiform appendix

Meso-appendix

Sigmoid colon

Rectum

Anal canal

Fig. 322. Position and structure of the large intestine. The walls of both large and small intestines have been enlarged and dissected to show their various layers.

TABLE 37. Principal Digestive Enzymes.

ENZYME	SOURCE	SUBSTRATE	PRODUCTS	OPTIMAL pH
Ptyalin	Salivary glands	Starch	Smaller carbohydrate polymers (minor physiologic role)	6.7
Pepsin	Parietal cells of stomach	Protein	Polypeptides	1.6-2.4
Gastric lipase	Stomach	Fat	Glycerides, fatty acids (minor physiologic role)	—
Enterokinase	Duodenal mucosa	Trypsinogen	Trypsin	—
Trypsin	Exocrine pancreas	Denatured proteins and polypeptides	Small polypeptides (also activates chymotrypsinogen to chymotrypsin)	8.0
Chymotrypsin		Proteins and polypeptides	Small polypeptides	8.0
Nucleases		Nucleic acids	Nucleotides	—
Carboxypeptidases		Polypeptides	Smaller polypeptides*	—
Pancreatic lipase		Fat	Glycerides, fatty acids, glycerol	8.0
Pancreatic amylase		Starch	Maltose units	6.7-7.0
Aminopeptidases	Intestinal glands	Polypeptides	Smaller polypeptides**	8.0
Dipeptidase		Dipeptide	Amino acids	—
Maltase Lactase Sucrase		Maltose Lactose Sucrose	Hexoses (glucose, galactose and fructose)	5.0-7.0 5.8-6.2 5.0-7.0
Nucleotidase		Nucleotides	Nucleosides, phosphoric acid	—
Nucleosidase		Nucleosides	Purine or pyrimidine base, pentose	—
Intestinal lipase		Fat	Glycerides, fatty acids and glycerol	8.0

*Removal of C-terminal amino acid   **Removal of N-terminal amino acid

TABLE 38. Gastrointestinal Hormones.

HORMONE	SOURCE	AGENTS STIMULATING PRODUCTION	ACTION
Gastrin	Gastric mucosa of the pyloric antrum	Distention and protein derivatives in the region of the pyloric antrum	Stimulates the secretion of HCl by the parietal cells of the gastric glands
Enterogastrone	Mucosa of the small intestine	Fats, sugar, and acid in the intestine	Inhibits gastric secretion and motility
Secretin	Duodenal mucosa	Polypeptides and acid in the duodenum	Stimulates secretion of watery, enzyme-poor pancreatic juice
Pancreozymin		Products of protein digestion in the duodenum (proteoses and peptones)	Stimulates the production of an enzyme-rich pancreatic juice
Cholecystokinin		Fat in the duodenum	Contraction of the gallbladder
Villikinin	Mucosa of the small intestine	Chyme in the intestine	Stimulates movements of the intestinal villi

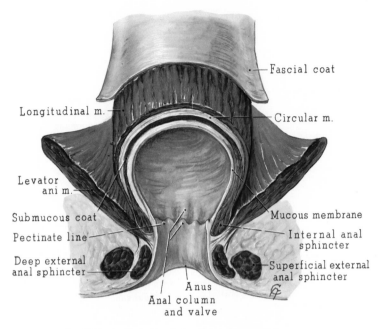

Fig. 323.   Anal canal and the various layers of the rectum.

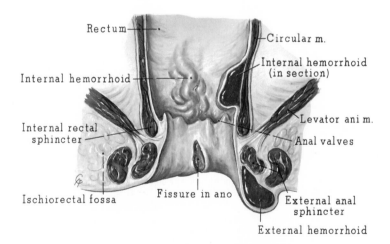

Fig. 324.   Common disorders of the anal canal.

secreted by the salivary glands. It initiates digestion by hydrolyzing starch and glycogen to maltose. However, the total effect of ptyalin in the mouth, esophagus, and later on in the stomach, is minimal. It is inactivated by the acid medium of the stomach. Saliva does not have a digestive effect on either fat or protein. Approximately 1200 ml. of saliva, 97 per cent of which is water, is normally secreted each day.

The characteristics and the actual volume of saliva are related to the type of food ingested. For example, acid substances and dry foods produce a large volume of thin, watery saliva; milk or cold water produce a smaller volume of viscous saliva. The enzymatic content of saliva varies with the stimulus. Meat and weak acids stimulate the production of similar volumes of saliva, but the enzyme content is greater with meat than with weak acids. It is not known how these alterations in volume and content occur, except that they are simple nerve reflexes which can be conditioned. The smell, sight, and thought of food stimulate salivary secretion.

During periods of dehydration when the body has lost large quantities of fluid, salivary secretion is reduced or suppressed completely. This may also occur at times of emotional stress. Irritation of the esophageal, gastric, and duodenal mucous membranes reflexly stimulates salivary secretion. Thus, excessive salivation may be an early warning sign of disease of the upper digestive tract.

SWALLOWING (Fig. 325). The process of swallowing (deglutition) is divided into three stages: buccal, pharyngeal, and esophageal. Only the buccal phase is under voluntary control. In this stage, the tongue squeezes the bolus of food backward from the oral cavity and presses it against the soft palate. At the same time, the levator veli palatini muscles raise the soft palate and push it against the posterior wall of the pharynx, closing the nasopharynx and preventing regurgitation of fluid or food through the nose. As the bolus of food passes over the posterior portion of the tongue, the larynx rises. From this point on, the process of swallowing becomes involuntary.

In the pharyngeal phase, the tongue forces the bolus of food backward against the epiglottis, which then folds to become a hood over the laryngeal orifice. The entrance of the larynx is also protected by the sphincteric action of the surrounding muscles. Food streams past the lateral edges of the epiglottis to the portion of the pharynx immediately posterior to the larynx and then to the esophagus. At this point, the third or esophageal stage commences as the cri-

copharyngeus muscle relaxes, allowing the food to enter the esophagus.

Functions of the Esophagus

The entrance of a solid bolus of food into the esophagus initiates a primary peristaltic wave. If a portion of the esophagus remains distended, afferent nerve impulses along parasympathetic fibers (vagus) will stimulate secondary propulsive waves and increase salivation. When the vagus nerve is severed, contractions are abolished. When pressure in the esophagus is greater than that in the stomach, the cardiac sphincter relaxes, permitting the entrance of food into the stomach. This relaxation occurs before the esophageal peristaltic wave reaches the cardiac sphincter. The cardiac sphincter has not been defined anatomically but is present physiologically. It is probably a segment of the lower esophagus in which alterations in muscle tone produce the effect of sphincteric action.

Functions of the Stomach

Three major functions have been ascribed to the stomach: storage of food; mixing the food

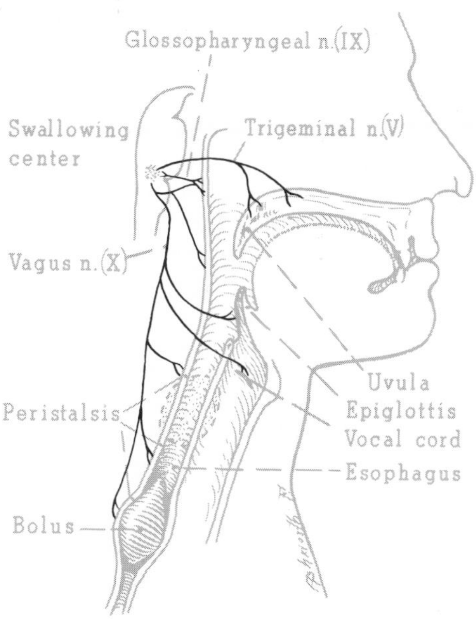

Fig. 325. Movement of bolus down esophagus. The trigeminal nerve controls the muscles of mastication; the glossopharyngeal nerve, the stylopharyngeus muscle; and the vagus nerve, esophageal peristalsis.

with gastric secretion until chyme is formed; and permitting the food to slowly empty into the duodenum at a rate suitable for proper digestion and absorption by the small intestine.

SECRETION.   The mucosa of the stomach contains gastric glands lying perpendicular to the surface. These glands consist of the *chief* (zymogen) cells producing pepsinogen; *parietal* cells producing hydrochloric acid; and *mucous* neck cells producing mucin. Pepsinogen is the precursor of pepsin, an enzyme which breaks proteins into proteoses and peptones (shorter protein chains), but not into the individual amino acids. To be active, pepsin must be in a medium with a pH below 4. The mucin of the gastric juice functions to protect the lining epithelium of the stomach by neutralizing the strongly acid contents. Mechanically, mucin serves as a protective layer; insufficient production of mucin may be a factor in the development of gastric ulcer.

Regulation of gastric secretion.

Gastric secretion is conventionally divided into phases designated according to the region where the stimuli are active: cephalic, gastric, and intestinal. The phases not only overlap in time, but also interact to such an extent that no truly useful estimate can be made of the relative contribution of each. For example, interruption of the cephalic phase greatly reduces the response to the gastric phase.

Cephalic phase.   The cephalic phase of gastric secretion is mediated through the vagus (parasympathetic) nerves in response to the sight, smell, or taste of food, or from the act of eating. It is abolished by sectioning the vagus nerves. Stimulation of the parasympathetic nuclei in the medulla or hypothalamus, which occurs when the blood sugar drops below 50 mg. per cent, will also elicit the cephalic response. Lowering blood sugar by injecting insulin intravenously is the basis for a test used to check the integrity of the vagus nerves following surgery.

The efferent vagal impulses associated with the cephalic phase act in two ways to stimulate acid secretion: cholinergic stimulation of the parietal cells directly (see Chapter Eight), and cholinergic stimulation of the gastrin-producing cells of the pyloric antrum. The hormone gastrin then stimulates the parietal cells (Table 38).

Gastric phase.   The gastric phase of secretion is usually considered as being mediated solely by the hormone *gastrin*, which stimulates secretion of acid by the parietal cells. Gastrin is released by cells of the pyloric antrum through chemical stimuli or by mechanical stimuli such as distension. The release of gastrin caused by these stimuli may involve extragastric nerve pathways or a pathway comprising nerve plexuses within the wall of the stomach.

Intestinal phase.   As foodstuffs and their digestive breakdown products pass along the small bowel, nervous and hormonal reflex mechanisms are stimulated which increase or decrease stomach secretion and motility. The responses are of a lesser magnitude than in the gastric phase and their importance is difficult to assess.

Inhibition of gastric secretion.

The interplay between stimulation and inhibition of gastric secretion determines the activity of the gastric glands at any one time. Two inhibitory mechanisms have been well characterized; one operates through the stomach, the other through the duodenum.

The presence of a strong acid in the pyloric antrum results in a decrease in gastric secretion. It is believed that a pH of less than 2.5 inhibits the release of gastrin from the pyloric antrum and thereby decreases the secretion of acid from the parietal cells. The duodenal inhibitory mechanism is of a different nature. Acid, hypertonic solutions, or fat in the lumen of the duodenum stimulate the release of the hormone enterogastrone, which inhibits both acid secretion by the parietal cells and gastric motility.

Despite all the mechanisms for inhibiting oversecretion of acid and damage to the mucosal wall of the stomach and duodenum from this acid, *peptic ulceration* frequently occurs. A peptic ulcer is an ulcer in either the stomach or the duodenum. The major goal of both medical and surgical treatment of peptic ulcer is to reduce the production of hydrochloric acid by the parietal cells of the stomach. Medical reduction of parietal cell secretion involves neutralizing the acid after secretion by ingestion of antacids or by the use of anticholinergic drugs to block the stimuli for the secretion of acids.

Until a few years ago, the principal surgical means of reducing acidity was to remove the major portion of the stomach secreting hydrochloric acid. Now, the principal aim of surgical treatment is to reduce the stimuli for acid secretion. Surgically this is accomplished by cutting the vagus nerves and by removing the gastrin-producing pyloric gland area (antrum). Sectioning the vagus nerves is associated with an impairment of gastric emptying; when this operation is employed, the surgeon must perform a concomitant drainage procedure allowing the pylorus to drain freely into the duodenum, or must actually join the stomach to the jejunum to aid gastric emptying after surgery.

MOTILITY. The stomach receives large volumes of food without a subsequent increase in pressure because of what is sometimes called "receptive relaxation." This phenomenon is not completely understood, but is believed to be influenced by extrinsic nerves, since a decrease in tone occurs even before food enters the stomach. After food enters, it gradually moves toward the pylorus and is moved along by peristaltic contractions occurring three times per minute. These begin in the lower portion of the fundus and progress toward the pylorus, terminating with contractions of the pyloric sphincter.

Contraction of the pyloric sphincter causes the food which has been propelled by the peristaltic wave to be pushed against the wall of the pyloric region, with the major fraction of it being forced back into the body of the stomach. This narrowing of the pyloric canal reduces regurgitation of duodenal contents. Thus, it can be seen that the pyloric region of the stomach has the most pronounced influence on mechanical digestion, and on the preparation of food for small intestinal digestion and absorption.

The rate of gastric emptying is determined by a variety of factors, including total volume and consistency of gastric content and chemical composition of the food. The rate is decreased by both mechanical and chemical stimulation of the duodenum. Mechanical stimulation of the duodenum involves the enterogastric reflex along the vagus nerves. This inhibits antral peristalsis. Chemical stimulation causes release of the hormone *enterogastrone*, which decreases gastric motility and secretion.

DIGESTION. While food remains in the stomach, the action of salivary ptyalin continues until the pH is lowered by permeation of the gastric hydrochloric acid. Proteins are broken down to proteoses and peptones by the action of pepsin. Fats are not hydrolyzed in the stomach to an appreciable extent but are merely mixed with the mass of food to form a coarse emulsion.

Functions of the Small Intestine

SECRETION. The crypts of Lieberkühn are lined by intestinal glands and represent the major source of enzymes produced by the mucosa of the small intestine. These enzymes are not true secretory products but are actually intracellular substances which have been liberated from sloughed mucosal cells. Among the enzymes are enterokinase, aminopeptidase, nuclease, lipase, amylase, invertase (sucrase),

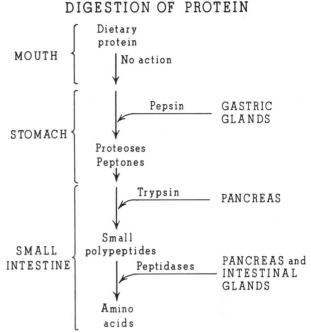

Fig. 326. Digestion of protein. Note that protein is broken down to proteoses and peptones in the stomach and to small polypeptides and amino acids in the small intestine.

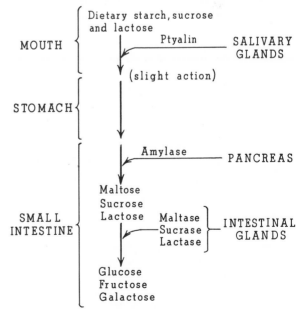

Fig. 327. Digestion of carbohydrate. Note that the major digestion of carbohydrate occurs in the small intestine with the end products being glucose, fructose, and galactose.

lactase, and maltase. It is believed that of these only enterokinase and amylase are secreted, the others being cellular substances.

Direct chemical or mechanical stimulation of the mucosa itself is the most important stimulus for small intestinal secretion. Secretion is also stimulated by the parasympathetic division of the autonomic nervous system and is inhibited by the sympathetic division.

MOTILITY. Segmentation and peristalsis are the two major types of movement of the small intestinal wall. The segmenting contraction is rhythmic in nature and divides the intestine into short segments. Segmenting contractions are believed to originate in the muscle tissue itself rather than in the nerves and are, therefore, referred to as myogenic. *Peristalsis* is a term used to describe a wave of contraction superimposed upon rhythmic segmental contraction with the effect of moving intestinal contents toward the rectum. Ordinarily, these waves occur at irregular intervals and travel for varying distances.

Movements of the villi of the small intestine are caused by contraction of the fibers of the muscularis mucosae which pass into the villus and are attached to the lacteal and basement membrane. Contraction of the fibers is caused by stimulation by a hormone, *villikinin*, liberated by the duodenal mucosa when the acid chyme from the stomach strikes the mucosa.

DIGESTION. The chyme entering the small intestine consists of partially emulsified fat, carbohydrate, and protein. Although digestion normally begins in the mouth and stomach, the enzymes secreted into the duodenum by the pancreas and intestinal wall, along with the bile from the liver, are capable of initiating and completing the digestive process.

Proteins are acted upon first by trypsin and chymotrypsin which break the protein molecule into polypeptides. These, in turn, are broken down by aminopeptidases and carboxypeptidases into the constituent amino acids (Fig. 326).

Carbohydrates enter the duodenum in the form of starch, small polysaccharides, disaccharides, and monosaccharides. The starch and small polysaccharides are hydrolyzed under the influence of pancreatic amylase to maltose. The principal disaccharides (maltose, lactose, and sucrose) are hydrolyzed to monosaccharides by the appropriate enzymes—maltase, lactase, and sucrase. The final products are, therefore, glucose, galactose, and fructose. Cellulose is not digested in the human alimentary tract, since

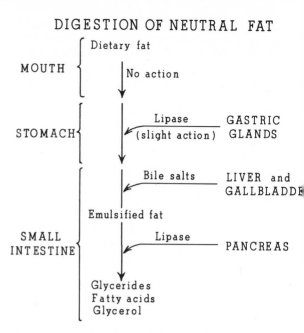

DIGESTION OF NEUTRAL FAT

Fig. 328.   Digestion of neutral fat, the end products being glycerides, fatty acids, and glycerol.

there are no appropriate enzymes to break it down (Fig. 327).

Fats are hydrolyzed by the lipases present in the small intestine. The end products are free fatty acids, monoglycerides, diglycerides, triglycerides, and glycerol (Fig. 328).

Nucleic acids (RNA and DNA) are first split into nucleotides by the pancreatic nucleases. The nucleotides are then split into purine and pyrimidine nucleosides and phosphoric acid by the small intestinal nucleotidases. Finally, the purine and pyrimidine nucleosides are separated into their constituent pentose sugars and purine and pyrimidine bases by intestinal nucleosidases. Refer to Table 37 for the principal digestive enzymes and their actions.

Functions of the Large Intestine

Colonic function begins with the entrance of intestinal contents into the cecum through the ileocecal valve. This valve functions to permit the gradual passage of small amounts of bowel contents into the colon, while at the same time preventing a return into the small intestine.

The ileum ends in the cecum in an oblique angle forming an invagination in the cecal wall. At this point two transverse lips form the ileo-

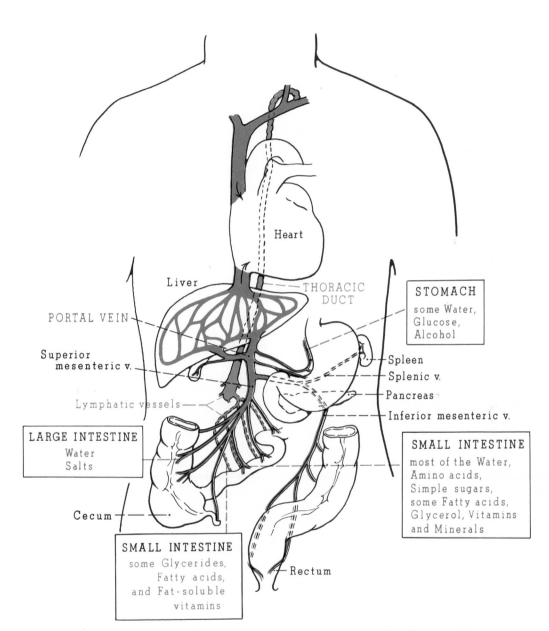

Fig. 329.   Products of digestion are absorbed in the stomach and small and large intestines.

cecal valve. During the process of digestion, the valve opens rhythmically at frequent intervals, permitting the ejection of about 15 cc. of fluid to enter the cecum. Emotional excitement or ingestion of food is known to increase the frequency of these ejections.

The fluid contents accumulate on the cecal side of the valve, and although the cecum may be filled by a considerable column of fluid, the ileum is still able to eject its contents into the cecum against the weight of this column.

The colonic contents are propelled by what is known as *mass peristalsis*. This type of propulsion consists of infrequent contractions en masse for considerable distances. The mass movements occur normally as infrequently as two or three times in 24 hours and can be associated with ingestion of food, initiated by the gastrocolic reflex.

The pelvic colon serves as a storehouse for feces, which are transferred into the rectum by peristaltic movements. Such a transfer initiates the defecation reflex which in turn is stimulated by distention of the rectum and mediated through centers in the medulla and sacral spinal cord. If an individual repeatedly ignores the defecation reflex, reconditioning of the reflex occurs with the end result that rectal distention is no longer followed by an urge to defecate; consequently, feces are retained in the rectum and colonic stasis ensues.

A considerable amount of fluid is added to the intestinal contents as they pass through the stomach and small bowel. Digestive juices are approximately 95 per cent water. Much of the water is reabsorbed, the remaining waste, known as feces, becomes characteristically firm as it is moved along by peristaltic waves of contraction and relaxation.

Bacteria are present in the feces. The excrement discharged from the small intestine may remain in the colon to incubate and synthesize nutritional factors such as vitamins, particularly vitamin K. The colon does not have a secretory function, but mucus does serve as a lubricant.

ABSORPTION

Stomach

Absorption through the gastric mucosa is limited, but small amounts of water, simple salts, glucose, and alcohol can be absorbed (Fig. 329).

Small Intestine

The small intestine, with its large number of villi, is the site of most absorption in the gastrointestinal tract. Each villus is covered by columnar epithelium and consists of a central core of vessels, an artery, a vein, and a lymphatic vessel (lacteal). A rich vascular plexus lies beneath the basement membrane of the villus. The major absorption of carbohydrate, protein, and fat occurs in the small intestine.

CARBOHYDRATE. The process of digestion breaks ingested carbohydrate down to monosaccharides. These are absorbed into the portal blood and transported to the liver.

Due to their physical properties, it would be logical to assume that monosaccharides move across the intestinal epithelium by a process of simple diffusion; however, it is known that glucose and galactose are absorbed at a much higher rate than mannose and xylose, whereas the rate of fructose absorption occupies an intermediate position. In other words, hexoses are absorbed more readily than the smaller pentoses. This is the reverse of what would be expected if the mechanism of absorption were that of simple diffusion. Investigations have demonstrated that while absorption of glucose and galactose is an *active* process dependent on certain energy-yielding reactions, other sugars are absorbed by simple diffusion. The intermediate position held by fructose is caused by an enzyme contained in the intestinal mucosa which slowly converts fructose to glucose; consequently, fructose is absorbed in part as fructose and in part after conversion to glucose.

It is believed that the active process of absorption involves a carrier molecule which combines with the sugar temporarily and then releases it after it has been transported across the intestinal epithelium.

PROTEIN. Proteins are absorbed only after being broken down to their constituent amino acids. Less is known about the absorption of amino acids than of sugar and fats; however, recent evidence indicates that the naturally occurring amino acids are actively transported and that a carrier mechanism is involved.

FATS. Absorption of fat presents a different problem from that of other foods, since fats occurring in the diet are water insoluble. Considerable experimentation has led to the conclusion that complete hydrolysis of some dietary fat does occur, but that mainly non-hydrolyzed monoglycerides and diglycerides are present and readily absorbed. It seems likely that some triglycerides are also absorbed. Resynthesis to triglycerides takes place in the intestinal mucosa. The triglycerides then appear in the intestinal lymph as an emulsion of chylomicrons.

It has been found that bile salts are necessary for the proper emulsification of digested fat. The manner in which emulsified particles pass through the intestinal membrane is not known. Most of the ingested fats are absorbed in the ileum.

Water and Electrolytes

Water and electrolytes are absorbed in both the small and large intestines. Electrolytes (salts) are absorbed most rapidly in the proximal portions of the small intestine because of the larger surface area and greater membrane permeability. It is also known that monovalent ions, such as sodium, potassium, chloride, and bicarbonate, are absorbed more readily than the polyvalent ions, such as calcium, magnesium, and sulfate. The mechanism by which electrolytes cross a membrane is diffusion caused by a concentration and electrical gradient; however, sodium can be actively transported by a mechanism referred to as the "sodium pump" (see Chapter Two).

Iron is most readily absorbed if it is present in the intestine in its insoluble, inorganic ferrous form. Most dietary iron is organic and ferric in form, but is usually changed in the stomach to the ferrous component. It is now apparent that the acceptor mechanism for ferrous iron exists in the mucosa and is in equilibrium with plasma iron. The acceptor is a protein called *apoferritin*. Iron crosses the intestinal epithelium in the ferrous state, is oxidized to the ferric form, and then combines with apoferritin to yield ferritin. Prior to entering the blood, it is reduced and picked up by a globulin and transported in the ferric state.

In view of the slow equilibrium between mucosal and plasma iron, rapid relief of anemia is best achieved by the intramuscular administration of iron. Iron is most readily absorbed from the proximal portion of the small intestine. Absorption is favored when the mucosal iron content is low, since the mucosal iron content reflects the iron concentration in the plasma.

Calcium absorption occurs in the stomach and duodenum. It is dependent on the existence of an acid pH. If the pH is high, insoluble calcium salts are formed. Although the mechanism of calcium absorption is unknown, it is believed to be an active process, since calcium can be absorbed against a concentration gradient and its absorption decreased by metabolic inhibitors.

It has been found that dietary protein and vitamin D facilitate calcium absorption.

The absorption of water occurs by the simple physical process of osmosis.

Malabsorption Syndromes

General consequences of malabsorption syndromes include weight loss, disturbances of acid-base balance, impaired calcium absorption, and vitamin deficiencies. Patients with a malabsorption syndrome show diarrhea, weight loss, and weakness. Among the underlying mechanisms producing abnormal absorption can be included insufficient intestinal surface area, alteration in bowel motility, alteration in intraluminal pressure, alterations in the autonomic nervous system, deficiencies in digestive enzymes, and diseases of the bowel lining.

ACCESSORY STRUCTURES

The pancreas, liver, and gallbladder are derivatives of that portion of the digestive tube which forms the small intestine and are intimately associated with the physiology of digestion.

Pancreas

The pancreas is a large, lobulated gland resembling the salivary glands in structure (Fig. 330). It has both exocrine and endocrine functions, its digestive enzymes being secreted by small glands called acini. The secretions are eventually collected by the major pancreatic duct and emptied into the duodenum. The constituents of the pancreatic fluid are sodium, bicarbonate, and digestive enzymes including trypsin, chymotrypsin, carboxypeptidase, amylase, and lipase. Some of these are excreted as inactive precursors (zymogens) such as trypsinogen or chymotrypsinogen, but are activated on contact with the intestinal mucosa.

The endocrine part of the pancreas consists of millions of tiny scattered epithelial masses embedded within the pancreatic acinar tissue. These scattered epithelial masses are called the pancreatic islets, or islets of Langerhans, and produce the two hormones, insulin and glucagon (see Chapter Fifteen).

Pancreatic secretion is under the control of the

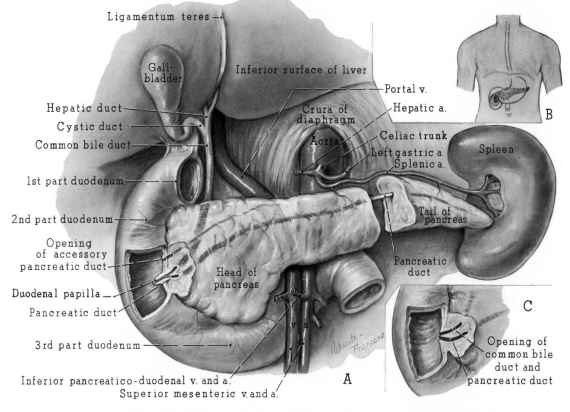

Fig. 330. *A.* Relationship of the pancreas to the duodenum, showing the pancreatic and bile ducts joining at the duodenal papilla. A section has been removed from the pancreas to expose the pancreatic duct. *B.* Anatomic position of the pancreas. *C.* Common variation.

hormones *secretin* and *pancreozymin,* which are released from the duodenal mucosa and carried to the pancreas by the blood. Secretin, causing the release of a thin, watery fluid, and pancreozymin are secreted by the duodenal mucosa as a result of stimulation by the acid gastric contents in the duodenum.

Liver

The liver is the largest organ in the body and is located in the upper part of the abdominal cavity under the dome of the diaphragm (Fig. 331). It is demarcated into four lobes. The two main lobes are the right and left, separated by the falciform ligament. The main right lobe is subdivided into a right lobe proper, the quadrate lobe, and the caudate lobe.

The superior surface of the liver, in contact with the diaphragm, is smooth and convex. The inferior surface of the liver is concave and exhibits impressions marking the point at which the liver is in contact with the abdominal viscera. Blood is transported to the liver from the digestive tract and spleen via the portal vein and from the aorta via the hepatic artery. The portal vein and hepatic artery enter the liver through a region called the porta hepatis; both the artery and vein are accompanied by bile ducts and lymphatic vessels. The portal vein and hepatic arteries repeatedly branch, making the liver a highly vascularized organ.

The liver lobule is the functional unit of the liver. It is composed of branching cords of epithelial cells radiating from the center to its periphery. Branches of the portal vein and hepatic arteries, accompanied by a bile duct, are situated adjacent to the liver lobule in the interlobular connective tissue. Liver sinusoids occur between these cords. These sinusoids receive blood from the hepatic artery and portal vein.

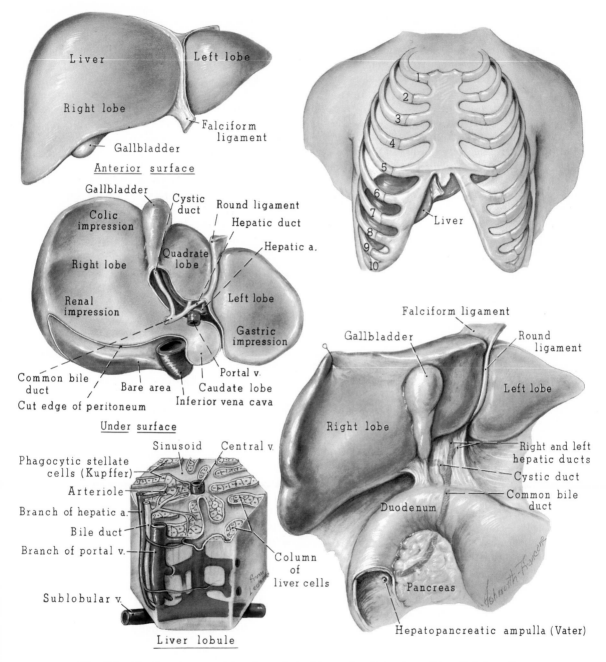

Liver

Left lobe

Right lobe

Falciform
ligament

Gallbladder

Anterior surface

1
2
3
4
5
6
7
8
9
10

Liver

Gallbladder

Cystic
duct

Round ligament

Hepatic duct

Colic
impression

Quadrate
lobe

Hepatic a.

Right lobe

Left lobe

Renal
impression

Gastric
impression

Common bile
duct

Bare area

Portal v.

Caudate lobe

Inferior vena cava

Cut edge of peritoneum

Under surface

Falciform ligament

Gallbladder

Round
ligament

Left lobe

Right lobe

Right and left
hepatic ducts

Cystic duct

Common bile
duct

Duodenum

Sinusoid

Central v.

Phagocytic stellate
cells (Kupffer)

Arteriole

Branch of hepatic a.

Bile duct

Branch of portal v.

Column
of
liver cells

Sublobular v.

Pancreas

Liver lobule

Hepatopancreatic ampulla (Vater)

Fig. 331. The liver, its normal location, relationships, and unit structure. (*Liver Lobule* section courtesy of Lederle Laboratories.)

Phagocytic cells line the sinusoids. These engulf bacteria and other foreign particles in the blood. Blood flows from the sinusoids of the liver to the central vein of the lobule and continues to the hepatic veins via the intercalated (sublobular) and collecting veins.

The bile ducts, which drain the major right and left lobes of the liver, are formed by union of the bile capillaries, taking origin between the cords of liver cells. The bile ducts from the major lobes unite to form the hepatic duct which is joined by the cystic duct from the gallbladder to form the common bile duct. (See Fig. 330 for the relationship of the common bile duct, pancreatic duct, and duodenum.)

The liver, although considered a structural and functional part of the digestive system, functions in many activities not directly concerned with the process of digestion. Among these are hematopoiesis and coagulation, phagocytosis, and detoxification. The liver produces erythrocytes in the embryo—and in some abnormal states in the adult. It also synthesizes prothrombin and fibrinogen, both of which are necessary for coagulation of blood. The liver destroys old and worn-out erythrocytes and removes bacteria and foreign bodies from the blood via its Kupffer cells, which are a part of the reticulo-endothelial system (system of macrophages) (see Chapter Ten). It functions in detoxification by changing nitrogenous wastes, such as ammonia, into the less toxic urea. The mechanisms by which the liver detoxifies include conjugation, methylation, oxidation, and reduction.

DIGESTIVE FUNCTION OF THE LIVER. In relation to digestion and absorption, the major function of the liver is the production of bile. Bile contains bile salts and bile pigments, and consists for the most part of water. It is formed in a volume of 500 to 1000 ml. daily, and is concentrated by the gallbladder.

Production of bile is a continuous process which increases when food is present in the digestive tract. The nervous system is not important in biliary secretion. Fat and protein are effective, whereas carbohydrates are relatively ineffective in stimulating biliary secretion. The mechanism by which foodstuffs stimulate secretion of bile is unknown. Breakdown products of digestion possibly directly stimulate the liver cells to produce bile. The fact that the presence of bile in the intestine increases biliary secretion more than the increase produced by food alone has led to a group of studies concluding that bile salts represent the most important stimulus for secretion of bile by the liver.

The influences of the liver on nutrition include production of bile; storage of glycogen, releasing it as glucose when needed; storage of vitamins A, D, E, and K, as well as B_{12} and certain other water-soluble vitamins; and metabolism of carbohydrates, fats, and proteins.

Cirrhosis is a disease of the liver representing a progressive degeneration of liver cells; it is characterized by an increase in connective tissue throughout the liver lobules. In its most common form, alcoholic cirrhosis, the disease is preceded by a dietary deficiency. The alcoholic person tends to have a reduced intake of fat, protein, and carbohydrate, as well as vitamins, especially B_{12}. Whether the deficiency in itself leads to cirrhosis, or whether the deficiency merely renders the organ more susceptible to alcohol, thus permitting a direct action of some other dietary factor, is unsettled. Additional processes occurring in the liver will be discussed in the section dealing with metabolism of foodstuffs.

Gallbladder

The gallbladder is a sac-like structure attached to the inferior surface of the liver serving as a reservoir for bile. The cystic duct of the gallbladder joins the ductal system from the liver to form the common bile duct (Fig. 332).

Bile consists chiefly of water, cholesterol, pigments, inorganic salts, and salts of bile acids. Water, chloride, and bicarbonates are absorbed in the gallbladder, increasing the relative concentration of bile salts. The concentrated bile is then stored in the gallbladder until expelled. *Cholelithiasis*, stones in the gallbladder, is associated with a chronic inflammation of the bladder wall, giving rise to a loss of normal capacity to absorb and concentrate.

Jaundice is a yellowish discoloration of the skin, mucous membrane, and body fluids because of an excess of biliary pigment. The most common type is *obstructive jaundice*, which is caused by internal occlusion of the bile duct by gallstones or by a growth such as a tumor. *Hemolytic jaundice* is a form of jaundice which results from an abnormally rapid formation of bile pigments following hemolysis (destruction of red blood cells). *Hepatic jaundice* is impaired excretion of bile due to damage to the hepatic cells.

Cholecystitis is an inflammation of the gallbladder. A patient with cholecystitis will experience intermittent attacks of severe pain, most often after heavy meals. Belching is a common finding with cholecystitis, as is intolerance to fats and leafy vegetables.

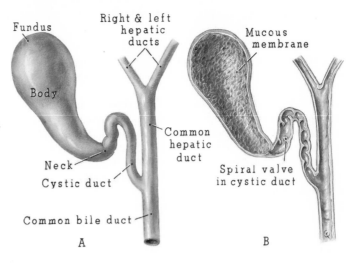

Fig. 332. *A.* External view of the gallbladder. *B.* Sagittal section through the gallbladder.

Contraction of the gallbladder with expulsion of bile into the duodenum is stimulated by a hormonal mechanism. The presence of certain foodstuffs—particularly fat in the duodenum—causes release of a hormone, *cholecystokinin*, which then reaches the gallbladder via the blood and brings on contraction. It may be identical with pancreozymin. Gallbladder contraction occurs within 30 minutes following a meal.

NUTRITION AND METABOLISM

Foodstuffs

Three major types of foodstuffs are digested and absorbed in the gastrointestinal tract: carbohydrate, lipid, and protein (Fig. 333).

CARBOHYDRATE. Carbohydrates are organic compounds composed of carbon, hydrogen, and oxygen. The ratio of hydrogen to oxygen is $2:1$, as it is for water. The basic structure of a carbohydrate is a monosaccharide. The most common monosaccharides are glucose, fructose, and galactose.

A monosaccharide molecule contains alcohol groups and either an aldehyde or a ketone group. The monosaccharides are classified as aldoses or ketoses respectively on the basis of this characteristic. They are usually joined together into larger chemical compounds known as polysaccharides, or—more specifically—starches, glycogens, pectins, and dextrins. In addition to being found in polysaccharide form, monosaccharides combined in pairs are called disaccharides. The

Carbohydrates
- Oxidized to liberate energy (heat)
- Stored as glycogen
- Converted into fat

Fat
- Oxidized to liberate energy (heat)
- Stored as fat
- Converted into sugar (glucose)

Protein
- Oxidized to liberate energy (heat)
- Utilized in production of protoplasm
- Converted into fat
- Converted into glucose

Fig. 333. Metabolism of carbohydrate, fat, and protein.

most common disaccharides found in the diet are sucrose, maltose, and lactose. Carbohydrates are regarded as essential in the diet, although experimental evidence indicates that the human body is capable of synthesizing carbohydrates from protein and fat.

LIPID.   The term *lipid* is used to refer to a large group of compounds including fats, waxes, phospholipids, glycolipids, and sterols. Our major concern will be with a description of neutral fats. Neutral fats, or triglycerides, are composed of a glycerol molecule and three fatty acids. Fatty acids found in lipids generally contain 10 to 20 carbon atoms, with 14, 16, and 18 being the most common. Naturally occurring fatty acids contain an even number of carbon atoms.

The terms *saturated* and *unsaturated* refer to the number of hydrogen atoms present. A double bond can exist between one or more pairs of carbon atoms, rather than the full complement of hydrogen atoms. This results in an unsaturated fatty acid. The importance of unsaturated fats in the diet has probably been overemphasized, but it is known that a small quantity is essential. If double bonds do not exist between carbon atoms, the fatty acid is saturated.

PROTEIN.   Protein is the basic constituent of protoplasm and, thus, forms a portion of all living tissue. It is the predominant constituent in certain tissues such as muscle; it differs from carbohydrate and other foodstuffs in that it contains nitrogen, sulfur, and phosphorus, in addition to carbon, hydrogen, and oxygen. The protein molecule is composed of a number of units linked together. These units or building blocks are called amino acids. Twenty-three amino acids have been identified as constituents of the protein molecule in human tissues. Some proteins contain nearly all of these in varying proportions, while others contain only three or four.

In the synthesis of the protein molecule, chains of amino acids (polypeptides) are formed by the linkage of the basic amino (NH_2) group of one amino acid with the acid (COOH) group of another and the liberation of a molecule of water. The junction CO-NH is called the *peptide linkage*. The reverse process is the degradation to amino acids by breaking the peptide linkage and is known as *hydrolysis*.

Essential and non-essential amino acids. Dietary amino acids are of two types: essential and non-essential. An essential amino acid is one which the body itself cannot synthesize, at least rapidly enough to satisfy needs. The adult human probably requires eight essential amino acids.

These are tryptophan, lysine, methionine, threonine, phenylalanine, leucine, isoleucine, and valine.

Histidine and arginine, called "essential" amino acids by some authors, are actually synthesized in the body, but only in amounts sufficient to meet the demands of maintenance, not of growth and repair. Other amino acids are known as non-essential amino acids. In fact, non-essential ones are just as important as the essential ones, since both types are required for protein synthesis.

VITAMINS.   Vitamins, by definition, are essential nutrients required in small amounts to maintain good health. Their usual source is food, but some can be synthesized in the body. Vitamins are not chemically similar to each other and have widely divergent properties and functions; however, they are all organic in nature and can be separated into two groups by virtue of their solubility characteristics. The fat-soluble vitamins are A, D, E, and K; the water-soluble vitamins include the B-complex, C, and compounds with related activity (see Table 39).

Metabolism of Foodstuffs (Fig. 334).

The term metabolism includes *anabolism* and *catabolism*. Anabolism is the process of building complex molecules from simpler ones. Catabolism is the reverse process. The steps involved in both anabolism and catabolism are referred to as intermediary metabolism or just metabolism.

CARBOHYDRATE (Fig. 335).   Glucose is the major product of carbohydrate digestion. Therefore, this section will be concerned mainly with the fate of *glucose*. Small amounts of fructose and galactose are converted to glucose or glycogen in the liver.

The amount of glucose in the blood varies considerably because of several factors increasing and decreasing glucose in the blood. In brief, the glucose absorbed from the gut is carried by the portal blood to the liver, where it is converted to glycogen. The remainder passes into the systemic blood and may either be oxidized in the tissues (glycolysis) for energy production (see Chapter Two), converted to fat for storage, synthesized to lactose in the mammary glands, or utilized in the synthesis of tissue glycolipids and mucopolysaccharides.

Glycogenesis.   Glycogenesis is the process of glycogen formation. In this process, the glucose enters the cell and is phosphorylated to glucose-6-phosphate by the enzyme glucokinase in the presence of phosphate donor ATP. Glucose-6-

TABLE 39.   Vitamins.

VITAMIN	SOURCE	FUNCTION	DEFICIENCY
Fat Soluble			
A	Yellow vegetables, fish liver oils, milk, butter, eggs	Essential for maintenance of normal epithelium; synthesis of visual purple for night vision	Faulty keratinization of epithelium; susceptibility to night blindness
D	Egg yolk, fish liver oils, whole milk, butter	Facilitates absorption of calcium and phosphorus from the intestine; utilization of calcium and phosphorus in bone development	Rickets in children; osteomalacia in adults
E	Lettuce, whole wheat, spinach	Essential for reproduction in rats; no definite function has been determined in humans	Sterility in rats; no known effects on humans
K	Liver, cabbage, spinach, tomatoes	Synthesis by the liver of prothrombin; necessary for coagulation	Impaired mechanism of blood coagulation
Water Soluble			
B-Complex:			
B_1 (thiamine)	Whole grain cereals, eggs, bananas, apples, pork	Coenzyme in metabolism of carbohydrate as thiamine pyrophosphate (cocarboxylase); maintains normal appetite and normal absorption	Beriberi, polyneuritis
B_2 (riboflavin)	Liver, meat, milk, eggs, fruit	Coenzyme in metabolism (as flavoprotein)	Glossitis, dermatitis
B_6 (pyridoxine)	Whole grain cereal, yeast, milk, eggs, fish, liver	Coenzyme (as pyridoxal phosphate) in amino acid metabolism	Dermatitis
Niacin	Liver, milk, tomatoes, leafy vegetables, peanut butter	Niacinamide in metabolic processes, especially energy release	Pellagra
B_{12}	Liver, kidney, milk, egg, cheese	Maturation of erythrocytes	Pernicious anemia
Pantothenic acid	Egg yolk, lean meat, skim milk	Necessary for synthesis of acetyl coenzyme A, metabolism of fats, synthesis of cholesterol, and antibody formation	Neurologic defects
Folic acid	Fresh, leafy green vegetables, liver	Production of mature erythrocytes	Macrocytic anemia
Biotin	Liver, egg, milk; synthesized by bacteria in the intestinal tract	Coenzyme in amino acid and lipid metabolism	Not defined in man, since a large excess is produced by intestinal flora
C (ascorbic acid)	Citrus fruits, tomatoes, green vegetables, potatoes	Production of collagen and formation of cartilage	Scurvy; susceptibility to infection; retardation of growth, tender, swollen gums, pyorrhea, poor wound healing

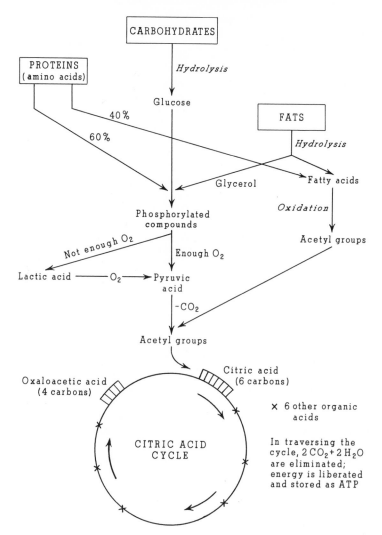

Fig. 334. Metabolism of carbohydrates, fats, and proteins. See Chapter Two for additional information on intermediary metabolism.

phosphate is then converted to glucose-1-phosphate by the enzyme phosphoglucomutase. Glucose-1-phosphate is in turn converted to uridine diphosphoglucose (UDPG) which then forms glycogen.

Glycogenolysis. Glycogenolysis is the breakdown of glycogen to re-form glucose in the cell. Glycogenolysis occurs by splitting each glucose molecule from the glycogen polymer by a process called phosphorylation. Phosphorylation is catalyzed by the enzyme phosphorylase. In the resting condition, this enzyme is in an inactive state and must be activated. The product of the phosphorylation process is glucose-1-phosphate. This in turn can be converted to glucose-6-phosphate. Glucose-6-phosphate is broken down

to glucose and phosphoric acid by the enzyme glucose-6-phosphatase, which is found *only in the liver.* The glucose next re-enters the blood.

Glyconeogenesis. The process by which liver glycogen can be built up from non-carbohydrate precursors which are converted first into glucose and then to glycogen is known as glyconeogenesis. For example, certain amino acids are known to be glucogenic, meaning that after deamination they yield keto acids which can be converted to glucose and glycogen. This is, in fact, an important source of liver glycogen. During starvation tissue protein is actually broken down, and its glucogenic amino acids are utilized for glycogen formation in the liver to maintain the blood glucose level. Glyconeogenesis is

CARBOHYDRATE METABOLISM

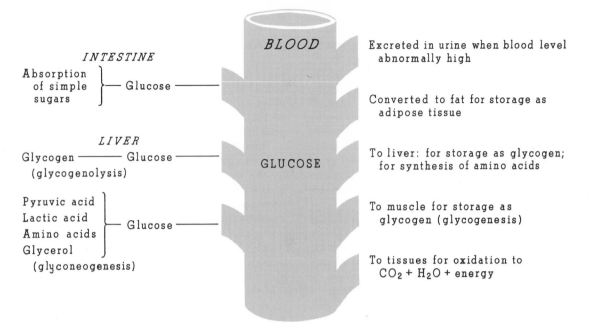

Fig. 335.   Metabolism of carbohydrate.

initiated largely by the release of gluco-corticoids from the cortex of the suprarenal gland.

Maintenance of normal blood sugar levels. The maintenance of a relatively high concentration of glucose in the blood is important for the normal function of the brain and heart. The liver helps to maintain the blood sugar level by storing glucose as glycogen when the concentration of glucose in the blood is excessive, or by releasing glucose into the blood when the level in the blood drops.

Hormonal control of the blood sugar level is important in the maintenance of normal values. Hyperglycemia (high blood glucose concentration) is generally prevented by the regulatory effect of insulin produced by islet tissue of the pancreas. In the face of a high blood glucose level, the beta cells of the islets release insulin. Insulin promotes glucose transport into the tissue cells and lowers the blood glucose level. As the blood glucose level decreases, the output of insulin also diminishes.

When the blood glucose concentration falls below normal (hypoglycemia), sympathetic centers in the brain are stimulated, particularly those in the hypothalamus. In turn, a large quantity of adrenalin is released from the medulla of the suprarenal gland, causing an increase in phosphorylase activity in the liver and enhancing the breakdown of glycogen (glycogenolysis) with subsequent release of glucose into the blood. Another mechanism for *increase* of the blood sugar level is the action of the hormones of the suprarenal cortex (gluco-corticoids). Adrenocorticotropic hormone (ACTH) is believed to be released from the adenohypophysis when a normal quantity of carbohydrate is not available to cells. Gluco-corticoids increase liver glycogen and blood sugar by increasing gluconeogenesis and lowering glucose utilization. Thyroxin also increases the rate of gluconeogenesis, possibly by increasing the mobilization of fat and lipid from cells.

The cause of diabetes mellitus is still not clearly defined (see Chapter Fifteen). Disturbances of carbohydrate metabolism are the result of alterations in balance between several forces. The pancreatic islet tissue, suprarenal cortex, adenohypophysis, and thyroid all exert specific effects on the blood sugar level. In the final analysis, however, it is the liver that is the site of ultimate control.

PROTEIN. The bulk of protein ingested as food is hydrolyzed into amino acids. Amino acids in turn are absorbed from the intestine into the portal circulation and carried to the liver. In the liver, amino acids can enter into the metabolic economy in two ways—by incorporation into the various proteins of the body; or by conversion to nitrogen-free intermediates, which may be catabolized by the same mechanisms making available the energy of fat and carbohydrate.

The liver is responsible for synthesis of protein and regulation of interchange between stored and circulating protein. Amino acids do not remain fixed within the configuration of a given protein molecular complex, but are in a constant state of dynamic flux between tissue and blood.

Contrary to popular opinion, the purpose of protein in the diet is not only to influence tissue growth or repair. Probably the major portion of ingested protein is deaminated and utilized for purposes other than that of tissue synthesis (Fig. 336).

Deamination. The process by which the liver influences alterations in amino acids is complex. In addition to protein synthesis, involving the linkage of amino acids to build complex protein aggregates, other important changes in amino acids are brought about by the liver.

The liver is the site of deamination, a process by which amino acids not necessary for protein synthesis, are stripped of their nitrogen-containing amino groups. The residue of the deaminated amino acid molecules can then be used as a direct source of energy. Deaminated amino acids not needed for immediate energy can be converted to glucose or fat for storage. The amino group which is a by-product of the deamination process, is converted to urea by the liver and excreted in the urine as a waste product. Synthesis of urea further emphasizes the protective action of the liver and its importance in some major problems of excretion.

Transamination. In addition to deamination, the process of transamination is carried out by the liver. During transamination, the amino acid, instead of being converted to urea, is transferred to certain keto acid molecules. This intermolecular shift of the amino acid groups from one molecule to another serves to explain the mode of synthesis of some of the non-essential amino acids by the liver. The process of transamination is equally important in terms of the non-nitrogenous residues formed by products of such reactions; certain non-nitrogenous by-product molecules resulting from processes of transamination are believed to play vital roles

PROTEIN METABOLISM

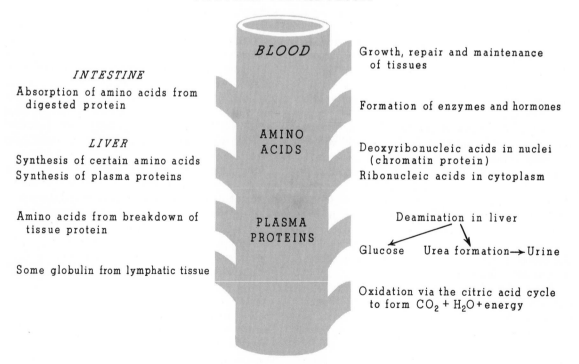

Fig. 336.   Metabolism of protein.

in oxidation-reduction systems concerned with intermediary metabolism of carbohydrate and protein.

Protein storage. The possibility of storage of amino acids is largely an unsettled problem, although it is evident that storage of protein occurs to a limited degree following ingestion of quantities greater than those needed for immediate nitrogen demands. It must be emphasized, however, that the storage mechanism for protein is of a limited and temporary nature. Protein deficiency will occur after a short period of protein lack.

Experimental evidence indicates that the liver is the first to store protein. Conversely, the liver is the first to give up protein during states of depletion, thus explaining to some degree its curious susceptibility to damage in malnutrition.

LIPID. Lipids are absorbed in several forms. Short chain fatty acids and glycerol are absorbed directly into the portal blood. Chylomicrons consisting of triglycerides, phospholipids, and cholesterol esters of fatty acids travel in the intestinal lymphatics to the thoracic duct, and from there empty into the left brachiocephalic vein at the base of the neck. Chylomicrons also contain protein in combination with fat, and therefore the term liproprotein is employed. Following absorption, fat is either oxidized or stored in the body. Fat is stored in characteristic locations, known as fat depots, but is present in most tissues. Contrary to popular opinion, fat depots and cellular fats do not remain static until starvation or acute energy demands their mobilization. Fat throughout the body is in a continual state of exchange. Fatty acids are being constantly transported and interchanged in position. It has been shown that as much as one-half of the total body fat reserve changes position daily. It is thus apparent that the need for maintaining the fat in a transportable form is constant (Fig. 337).

Beta oxidation. The liver is the organ most intimately concerned with lipid metabolism. It lengthens and shortens carbon chains, desaturating and saturating them. The liver oxidizes fatty acids to CO_2 and water. The process of oxidizing fatty acids to acetyl coenzyme A (part of which forms citric acid in the citric acid cycle

LIPID METABOLISM

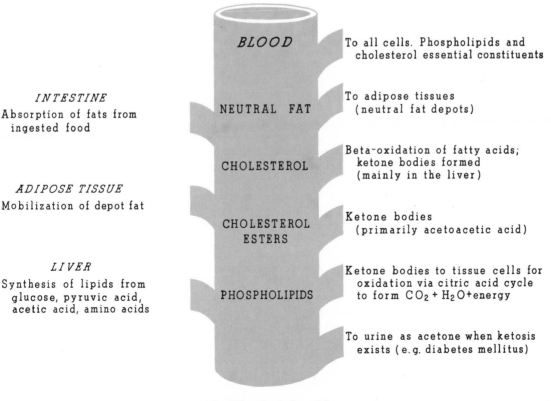

Fig. 337. Metabolism of fats.

and is completely oxidized to CO_2 and water) is called *beta oxidation*.

Cholesterol metabolism. The role of cholesterol in human metabolism is incompletely understood. It is known that cholesterol of animal origin is absorbed from the intestine in conjunction with neutral fats and that bile salts play an essential role in the uptake of these lipids; however, the cholesterol of exogenous sources is not necessary to the body economy. Cholesterol is synthesized in patients on cholesterol-free diets from acetyl coenzyme A. It is known that the synthesis of cholesterol is carried out largely by the liver, and that free cholesterol is excreted in the bile. The importance of bile salts in preventing the precipitation of cholesterol is well known. The volume of cholesterol in the bile appears to be independent of the dietary intake and the level of cholesterol in the blood. Most cholesterol in the bile is reabsorbed and carried back to the liver, where it is re-excreted in the cyclic manner. Cholesterol is the precursor of several hormones, such as cortisol and progesterone.

Energy Metabolism

Four forms of energy are present in the living organism: chemical, electrical, mechanical, and thermal. Of these, only chemical energy is able to supply energy needed by the cells of the body. Chemical energy can be transformed into three other forms, but these are irreversible transformations; therefore, a constant source of chemical energy is necessary for use by the cells. This source is the metabolic pool, which exists in the fluids of the body. The metabolic pool is in turn supplied from stored chemical energy of ingested food. Figure 334 illustrates the production of energy from proteins, carbohydrates, and fats.

Chemical energy is used to perform work. The categories of work energy are mechanical, electrical, and chemical. Chemical energy is transformed to work in the form of mechanical energy when a muscle shortens and performs, such as in the lifting of a load. It is transformed in the form of electrical energy when a nerve impulse is transmitted, and provides chemical energy during synthetic reactions. During the buildup of complex molecules, chemical energy is stored at the expense of energy supplied by the breakdown of other molecules. The body is only 20 per cent efficient in converting chemical energy to work energy. The remainder appears as thermal energy or heat. Some work energy is ultimately converted to heat. Thus, some mechanical work of the heart is converted to heat in overcoming friction as blood passes through the circulatory system.

Thus, it is apparent that the chemical energy of the body is ultimately converted to heat, either directly from chemical reactions or indirectly from work energy. This heat, derived from metabolic processes, can be used to maintain body temperature at an optimal level for certain chemical reactions; however, the heat generated is quite often more than necessary for this purpose, and the body has the problem of ridding itself of excess heat.

BASAL METABOLIC RATE. Basal metabolism or basal metabolic rate (BMR) is the term applied to the exchange of energy occurring in a fasting and resting individual. It is determined clinically 12 to 24 hours after the last meal, usually in the morning following a normal period of sleep. During the test period, no voluntary muscle movement should occur. The room temperature is comfortable and the patient is physically and mentally at rest. The energy exchange so determined is that required to maintain the vital activities of the body. The units of BMR are usually given in calories per hour. The most important factors to consider when comparing values of various individuals are body size, sex, and age. Determinations of BMR are based on oxygen consumption.

Factors influencing BMR. When a resting individual ingests food, heat production is increased above the basal level. This increased heat production produced simply from eating is known as the specific dynamic action of foods and varies with the type of food ingested. Protein has a greater specific dynamic action than either fat or carbohydrate. Increased heat production is caused primarily by the intermediary metabolism of absorbed foods.

Other factors influencing the total exchange of energy in the living organism include temperature and muscular exercise. Thyroid hormone exerts a considerable influence on the rate at which cellular oxidation occurs, and excesses and deficits of circulating thyroid hormone modify the metabolic rate. Certain other substances, such as male sex hormones, growth hormone, epinephrine, and norepinephrine increase the metabolic rate because of their stimulating effect on cellular activity.

TEMPERATURE REGULATIONS. Mammals and birds are *homeothermic* animals, which means that they are capable of maintaining a nearly constant internal body temperature. If the body temperature varies with environmental changes, the term *poikilothermic* is employed.

Regulation of body temperature includes both heat production and heat dissipation. Metabolism constantly supplies heat and is considered a major heat source. Metabolic activity can be increased to provide more heat, but it cannot be effectively lowered in the temperature-regulating process.

Evaporation of water is a mechanism for heat loss. Evaporation does not necessarily necessitate sweating, since there is a continuous diffusion of water molecules through the skin. Water evaporation also occurs through the lungs. Approximately 20 to 25 per cent of the basal heat production is lost by evaporation. This can be markedly increased in man during sweating and in animals by panting and salivation. Radiation, convection, and conduction are terms used to describe other mechanisms by which heat exchange can take place between the body and environment.

Temperature is a valuable barometer of disease. The figure 98.6° F. is usually quoted as the normal mouth temperature; however, in the normal individual there is some fluctuation. Upon awakening in the morning, the basal temperature can be as low as 97° F. This temperature usually rises during the day to reach 99° F. in the latter part of the afternoon. The temperature of the environment, unless extreme, does not greatly influence body temperature, since regulating mechanisms for heat maintain a homeothermic state. Heat is conserved by capillary constriction and lost with capillary dilatation. The body temperature is lowest in the female at the time of menstruation. In the aged, the temperature is usually lower than during the younger years.

Temperature can be determined most accurately rectally. The rectal temperature is approximately 0.9° F. higher than oral temperature. With a fever the difference is reduced between rectal and oral temperatures. Use of the axillary thermometer is reliable only if the axilla is sufficiently moist to exclude air and permit the skin to closely surround the bulb of the thermometer. The temperature in the axilla is usually 1 or 2 degrees lower than in the mouth. In taking an oral or rectal temperature, the thermometer should be allowed to remain in place for at least 5 minutes. The drinking of hot or cold fluids prior to taking the temperature will cause erroneous results. When taking an axillary temperature, the thermometer must be held with the upper arm closely pressed against the chest wall for at least 5 minutes.

Physiologic responses to cold. Increased heat production as an early response to cold injury is one of the major factors in the maintenance of the homeothermic state. Among the conditions increasing heat production are shivering, hormones, and specific dynamic action of food.

Cold acts primarily on the peripheral nervous system, but also to some extent upon the hypothalamus, particularly after prolonged exposure. In all species a decrease of average body temperature occurs after prolonged exposure to cold.

Muscles are stimulated to activity by increasing muscle tension and are stimulated to increase heat production by shivering. Both suprarenal and thyroid glands potentiate this affect. The adenohypophysis is also stimulated to increase the secretion of thyrotrophic and adrenocorticotrophic hormones which, in turn, stimulate secretion of thyroxin and cortisone. These hormones elevate the metabolic rate in the muscle without shivering, particularly in smaller animals.

Physiologic responses to heat. The transportation of heat by convective transfer from the interior of the body to the body surface is one of the important homeostatic functions of the circulatory system. During exercise or exposure to ambient temperatures above normal, there is an increased transfer of heat via the circulatory system over and above that which is conducted normally through the superficial tissues.

The vasomotor response is effective in altering the thermal conductance of peripheral tissues, thus modifying the flow of heat to the cool surface of the skin, tongue, and upper respiratory passages. The control of vasomotor exchange is one of the three effective components in the thermoregulatory mechanism. The other two are the metabolic response to cold, and sweating or panting in response to heat. With higher ambient temperatures, there can be an increase in peripheral conduction up to sixfold or even as high as twentyfold during exercise, brought about by a reduction in vasomotor tone and active vasodilating influences.

Heat exhaustion. Heat exhaustion or heat collapse is characterized by sweating, weakness, reduced blood pressure, rapid pulse, normal or slightly elevated temperature, and the general findings of circulatory collapse. Heat exhaustion is associated with prolonged periods of hot weather and is precipitated by excessive exposure to sun or physical exertion. The onset of heat exhaustion and heat cramps is often preceded by a prolonged period of physical exertion in a hot and humid environment. Large, unreplaced losses of salt and water are the most important factors in the development of heat exhaustion. Treatment should be directed toward restoring the body fluid and temperature to normal and to re-establishing vasomotor tone. It is important to remove the patient to a cool environment. Administration of salt water solutions is beneficial.

Heatstroke. Heatstroke, or sunstroke, is characterized by high fever and profound coma and occurs primarily in individuals over the age of 60. As in heat cramp and heat exhaustion, when environmental temperature exceeds body temperature, heat must be lost by evaporation of sweat. A high relative humidity impedes the evaporation of sweat, and body temperature rises with an increase in the rate of sweating. Somewhere in this vicious cycle, sweat glands cease to function and body temperature rises to alarming levels because of absorption of heat from the environment. The patient lapses into coma. The reason for this sudden failure of thermal regulation is unknown. Heatstroke is a medical emergency, since the disease results from a breakdown of the thermoregulatory mechanisms. Treatment directed primarily toward reducing body temperature is best accomplished by placing the patient in a tub of ice water.

Differential characteristics of heat cramp, heat exhaustion, and heatstroke. Heat cramp is the mildest of the syndromes associated with excessive exposure to hot and humid environments. Cardiovascular and thermoregulatory mechanisms are intact. The patient has an essentially normal blood pressure but sweats profusely; his skin is moist and warm. The body temperature is normal or only slightly elevated. In *heat exhaustion* a loss of vasomotor control of the blood vessels occurs, along with circulatory shock. The skin is pale and cold. Since the patient sweats, the skin is moist, cold, and clammy. The pulse is rapid and the blood pressure low. In *heatstroke* a loss of thermoregulatory control occurs and sweating stops. The skin is flushed, hot, and dry, the pulse bounding and full, and the blood pressure elevated. Fever, delirium, and coma are present.

SUMMARY: THE DIGESTIVE SYSTEM

HISTORY

1. **William Beaumont presented the first significant advance in relating structure and function of the digestive system in 1833.**

EMBRYOLOGY

1. **Primitive digestive tube:**

   a. The foregut gives rise to the mouth, pharynx, esophagus, stomach, liver, gallbladder, and pancreas.
   b. The midgut becomes the portion of intestine extending from the caudal end of the duodenum through the proximal two-thirds of the transverse colon.
   c. The hindgut is the remainder of large bowel.

ANATOMY

1. **The digestive system consists of a long, muscular tube and certain large glands located outside the tube.**

   a. Mucous membrane functions in protection and absorption.
   b. Lips are striated muscle fibers covered with stratified squamous epithelium.
   c. Cheeks contain several accessory muscles of mastication.
   d. Teeth function to mechanically separate food.
      (1) Teeth consist of enamel, dentine, root, pulp cavity, and periosteal tissue.
      (2) Types include incisors, canines, and molars.
      (3) Dental caries: a disease which destroys enamel; it may be partially preventable by ingestion of fluoride.
      (4) Pyorrhea: an inflammatory process of gums.

   e. Tongue: a movable structure composed of muscle fibers and covered with numerous taste buds.
   f. Palate:
      (1) Hard: an anterior portion composed of maxillary and palatine bones.
      (2) Soft: a posterior portion ending in a free projection called the uvula.
   g. Pharynx: a passageway for both respiratory and digestive systems.
   h. Wall of the digestive tract:
      (1) Composed of mucosa, submucosa, muscularis mucosa, and adventitia.
   i. Esophagus extends from pharynx to stomach.
   j. Stomach:
      (1) The most dilated portion of the digestive tract.
      (2) A storage center for food.
      (3) Consists of fundus, body, and pylorus.
   k. Small intestine:
      (1) Extends from the distal end of the pyloric sphincter to the cecum; it is approximately 18 feet in length and is divided into duodenum, jejunum, and ileum.
      (2) Numerous villi on wall serve an absorptive function; crypts of Lieberkühn found at bases of villi.
   l. Large intestine:
      (1) Differs from the small intestine in that no villi are present, whereas there are taenia coli, appendices epiploicae, and haustra.
      (2) Consists of the cecum, an elongated pouch in the right lower abdomen with attached appendix; the ascending colon, extending upward from the cecum on the right posterior abdominal wall to the undersurface of the liver; the transverse colon, crossing the abdominal cavity from right to left below the stomach; and the descending colon, passing down the left side of the abdomen to the iliac crest, becoming the pelvic colon.
   m. Rectum extends from the pelvic colon to the narrow anal canal; hemorrhoids are a painful condition caused by diseased veins in the anus.

SECRETION, MOTILITY, AND DIGESTION

1. **Functions of the mouth:**

   a. Three pairs of salivary glands: parotid, submaxillary, and sublingual.
      (1) Two types of cells within the salivary glands: serous and mucous.
      (2) Innervated by both sympathetic and parasympathetic systems.
      (3) Ptyalin is the principal enzyme secreted.
   b. Three stages in swallowing include the buccal, pharyngeal, and esophageal.

2. **Function of the esophagus: peristaltic waves of the muscular wall propel food to the stomach.**

3. **Functions of the stomach:**

   a. Storage of food, mixing of food with gastric secretion, and permitting gradual emptying of stomach contents into the duodenum.
      (1) Secretion: chief cells produce pepsinogen and parietal cells produce HCl; mucous neck cells protect stomach lining.
         (a) Regulation of secretion: cephalic, gastric, or intestinal.
         (b) Motility: food enters the cardiac portion, is stored in the fundus, and moves slowly toward the pylorus; it is then propelled through the sphincter to the duodenum.
         (c) Digestion: proteins are broken down to proteoses and peptones by pepsin.

4. **Functions of the small intestine include secretion, motility and digestion.**

   a. The crypts of Lieberkühn are major sources of enzymes of the small intestine.
   b. Segmentation and peristalsis are two major types of movement within the small intestine.
   c. Protein digestion to amino acids is completed by trypsin, chymotrypsin, aminopeptidases, and carboxypeptidases.
   d. Carbohydrate digestion is completed by the action of pancreatic amylase, maltase, lactase, and sucrase.
   e. Fats are hydrolyzed by lipases.
   f. Nucleic acids are broken down by pancreatic nucleases, nucleotidases, and nucleosidases.

5. **Functions of the large intestine:**

   a. A storehouse for feces transferred into the rectum by peristalic movements.
   b. Water reabsorbed.
   c. Contains bacteria which synthesize nutritional factors.

ABSORPTION

1. **The stomach is a site of little absorption.**

2. **The small intestine is the main site of absorption of carbohydrates, proteins, and fats.**

   a. Carbohydrates are absorbed into capillaries as monosaccharides by simple diffusion.
   b. Protein is absorbed into the capillaries as amino acids, primarily through a process of active transport.
   c. Fats are absorbed into lacteals of the lymphatic system.

3. **Water and electrolytes are absorbed by both small and large intestines by a process of diffusion utilizing the concentration and electrical gradient.**

4. **Malabsorption syndromes might be caused by insufficient intestinal area, alteration in bowel motility, alteration in intraluminal pressure, deficiencies in digestive enzymes, and diseases of the bowel lining.**

ACCESSORY STRUCTURES

1. **The pancreas has both exocrine and endocrine functions, secreting pancreatic juice and insulin.**

   a. Digestive secretion is under the control of secretin and pancreozymin.

2. **The liver is the largest organ in the body.**

   a. Its two lobes are separated by the falciform ligament; the right lobe is subdivided into the right lobe proper, the quadrate lobe, and the caudate lobe.
   b. Supplied by the portal vein and hepatic artery.
   c. Liver lobule: the functional unit of the liver.
   d. Functions: hematopoiesis and coagulation, phagocytosis, detoxification, digestion, and metabolism.
      (1) Production of bile—essential in emulsification of fat.
      (2) Storehouse for glycogen.
      (3) Storehouse for vitamins A, D, E, K, B_{12}, and others.
      (4) Metabolism of carbohydrates, fats, and proteins.
   e. Cirrhosis: the progressive degeneration of liver cells with an increase in connective tissue throughout the lobules.

3. **Gallbladder:**

   a. Attached to inferior surface of the liver.
   b. Serves as a reservoir for bile.
   c. The cystic duct joins the ductal system of the liver to form a common bile duct.
   d. Jaundice: a yellow discoloration of skin, mucous membrane, and body fluids; types include obstructive, hemolytic, and hepatic jaundice.
   e. Cholecystitis: inflammation of the gallbladder.

NUTRITION AND METABOLISM

1. **The three foodstuffs digested and absorbed in the gastrointestinal tract are carbohydrates, lipids, and proteins.**

   a. Carbohydrates are organic compounds consisting of carbon, hydrogen, and oxygen.
      (1) Basic structure is the monosaccharide which contains aldoses or ketoses.
   b. Lipids are primarily neutral fats or triglycerides composed of glycerol molecule and three fatty acids.
      (1) The terms *saturated* and *unsaturated* refer to the number of hydrogen atoms present.
   c. Protein:
      (1) The basic constituent of protoplasm.
      (2) Contains nitrogen, sulfur, and phosphorus, in addition to carbon, hydrogen, and oxygen.
      (3) Building blocks are amino acids.
         (a) Chains of amino acids form polypeptides.
         (b) Each amino acid is characterized by an amino group, NH_2, and a carboxyl group, COOH, linked together to form peptide linkages.
         (c) Essential and non-essential amino acids are utilized by the body.
   d. Vitamins:
      (1) Essential nutrients required to maintain health; they may be fat-soluble (A, D, E, K) or water-soluble (B-complex, C, etc.).

2. **Metabolism involves anabolism and catabolism.**

   a. Carbohydrate metabolism:
      (1) Glycogenesis, the process of glycogen formation.
      (2) Glycogenolysis, or the breakdown of glycogen to re-form glucose in cell.
      (3) Glyconeogenesis is the formation of glucose from non-carbohydrates.
      (4) Normal blood sugar level is maintained by the liver, which stores glucose as glycogen and releases glucose into the blood, and by hormonal control such as insulin and glucocorticoids.
   b. Protein metabolism:
      (1) Protein synthesis occurs in the liver.
      (2) Deamination strips nitrogen-containing amino group from amino acid (the residue is then a direct source of energy).
      (3) Transamination: amino acid is transferred to certain keto acid molecules.
      (4) Storage: a mechanism of limited and temporary nature; the liver is the primary site.
   c. Lipid metabolism:
      (1) Fat depots in continual state of flux.
      (2) Beta oxidation oxidizes fatty acids to acetyl coenzyme A.
      (3) Cholesterol is synthesized in body from acetyl coenzyme A.
   d. Energy metabolism:
      (1) Chemical energy is transformed into work in form of mechanical, electrical, and chemical energy.
         (a) Chemical energy is ultimately converted to heat.

(2) Basal metabolic rate: the exchange of energy occurring in a fasting and resting individual.
   (a) Factors influencing BMR are food ingestion, temperature, and muscular exercise.
(3) Regulation of temperature involves heat production and dissipation.
   (a) Evaporation of water, radiation, convection, and conduction.
   (b) Temperature as barometer for disease: normal: 98.6° F. oral; rectal temperature is usually 0.9° F. higher than oral.
   (c) Conditions increasing heat production include shivering, hormones, and specific dynamic action of food.
   (d) Increased temperature increases transfer of heat via circulatory system.
   (e) Excessive heat causes heat cramp (mildest of syndromes associated with excessive exposure to hot and humid environment), heat exhaustion (loss of vasomotor control of blood vessels and circulatory shock), and heatstroke (loss of thermoregulatory control; sweating stops).

STUDY QUESTIONS: THE DIGESTIVE SYSTEM

1. Describe the wall of the small intestine.
2. Discuss the anatomic differences between the small and large intestine.
3. Review the regulation of salivary secretion.
4. Discuss gastric secretion with respect to the type of cell and the substance secreted.
5. Review the stages of gastric secretion.
6. Discuss the regulation of gastric emptying.
7. Review the digestion of protein, carbohydrate, and neutral fat.
8. Discuss absorption of the products of digestion, paying particular attention to the substances absorbed and the site of absorption.
9. Describe the exocrine function of the pancreas and the regulation of pancreatic secretion.
10. Name the lobes of the liver and review the blood supply of the liver.
11. Discuss the function of bile in digestion and absorption.
12. Review the functions of the liver.
13. Differentiate anabolism and catabolism.
14. Review the regulation of blood sugar level.
15. Review the interrelationships involved in metabolism of the various foodstuffs.
16. Discuss the production and use of energy in the body.
17. Discuss the meaning of basal metabolic rate (BMR).
18. Review the factors that influence BMR.
19. Differentiate homeothermic and poikilothermic.
20. Discuss heat production and heat dissipation.
21. Review the physiologic responses to cold and heat.

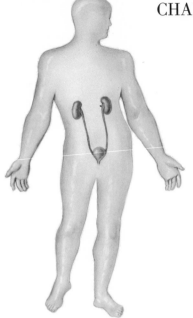

THE
URINARY
SYSTEM

During the Egyptian era, 5000 years ago, the diagnosis of diabetes was actually made when the physician tasted the urine for sweetness. Later, during the Middle Ages, disease in general was evaluated by visually examining the urine. Medical reports during this time frequently stated that "the pulse was normal, the urine normal, yet the patient died." Urine became an accurate clue to body function only after the perfection of the microscope.

The urinary system is one of the four excretory systems of the body; the others are the large bowel, the skin, and the lungs. It consists of the kidneys, which produce urine; the ureters, which convey urine to the bladder; and the urethra, which discharges urine from the bladder.

KIDNEYS

Embryology of the Urinary System (Fig. 338)

The urinary system passes through three successive stages of embryonic development. The earliest and simplest is the stage of the *pronephros*, a vestigial structure consisting of several rudimentary tubules and a collecting duct (the longitudinal pronephric duct). The first formed tubules regress before the last ones develop; by

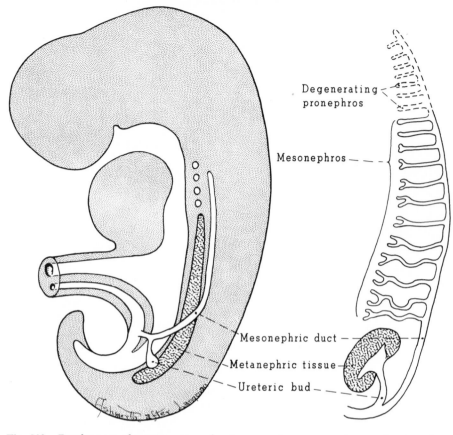

Fig. 338. Development of urinary system showing pronephros, mesonephros, and metanephros.

the end of the fourth week of embryonic life, the entire pronephros has disappeared, with the exception of the persisting caudal portion of the longitudinal pronephric duct.

The pronephros is replaced by the more advanced system, the *mesonephros*. During regeneration of the pronephric system, the first tubules of the mesonephros appear. These tubules grow rapidly. On their medial side they develop an internal glomerulus emptying into the existing longitudinal pronephric duct, now known as the mesonephric duct. By the end of the second month, only a few of the excretory tubules and glomeruli persist. The remains of these are later found near the testis and the ovary. The fate of the longitudinal mesonephric duct differs with the sex of the embryo. In the male it persists as the ductus deferens, but in the female it disappears almost entirely (Chapter Seventeen).

During regression of the mesonephric system, a third urinary organ known as the *metanephros* or permanent kidney develops. The collecting ducts of this system are formed from an outbudding of the mesonephric duct called the ureteric bud. This bud grows in a dorsocranial direction and penetrates the metanephric tissue. As the collecting system penetrates the metanephros, the distal end of each newly formed tubule is covered by a tissue cap. The cap separates from the main tissue mass and forms cell clusters on each side of the tubule, each cluster developing into a small vesicle and giving rise to an excretory unit, the nephron.

The ascent of the kidney follows the rapid spinal growth of the embryo and the continuous cranial growth of the ureteric bud. By the end of the fifth month, the metanephros has shifted from the pelvic to the lumbar region. During its "ascent," rotation occurs through a 90° angle, resulting in the adult mediolateral position of the kidney. The metanephros becomes functional even before birth, excreting urine by the third or fourth month of gestation, at which time the bladder empties periodically into the amniotic cavity.

Congenital Malformations

Polycystic kidneys. Polycystic kidneys are caused by a failure of the tubules of the collecting system to fuse with the mesodermal-derived tubules of the functioning nephron, resulting in many cyst-like structures. This is an hereditary abnormality which in its more severe form is not compatible with life. A patient with this abnormality usually dies before the age of 1. In milder cases sufficient kidney tissue is present to maintain life up to the fiftieth year.

Horseshoe kidney. From the initial position in the pelvis, the kidney normally ascends to the lumbar region. On occasion the kidneys join each other at their lower poles during the ascent. This fused kidney is known as a "horseshoe kidney" and occurs about once every 1000 births. In most instances, the kidney is fused at its lower pole. These fused kidneys are capable of normal function, but stones are slightly more common because of the angulation of the ureter which results in stasis of the urinary flow.

Gross Anatomy (Figs. 339 and 340)

In the newborn the kidney is about three times as large in proportion to body weight as in the adult. The weight of the kidney ranges from 125 to 170 grams in the adult male, and from 115 to 155 grams in the adult female.

The kidneys are bean-shaped organs lying on the muscles of the posterior abdominal wall —the psoas major, the quadratus lumborum, and the diaphragm. Each is posterior to the peritoneum and is, therefore, *retroperitoneal* in position. Since the kidneys are in contact with the diaphragm, they move slightly with this structure during respiration.

The upper poles of the kidneys are on a level with the upper border of the twelfth thoracic vertebra; their lower poles extend to the level of the third lumbar vertebra. The right kidney is usually slightly lower than the left, possibly because of its close relationship to the liver. Anteriorly, the right kidney is covered by the suprarenal gland, the hepatic flexure of the colon, the descending portion of the duodenum, and the liver. The suprarenal gland, splenic flexure of the colon, stomach, pancreas, jejunum, and spleen are related to the anterior surface of the left kidney.

There are three renal capsules: the true capsule, the surrounding perirenal fat, and the renal fascia. The *true capsule* of the kidney, the capsule proper, is a smooth, transparent fibrous membrane closely applied to the surface. Normally it can be readily stripped from the organ. Adipose tissue, *perirenal fat*, surrounds the capsule proper and is in turn enclosed by the renal fascia, a thin fibrous layer which anchors the kidney to the surrounding structures and helps maintain the normal position of the organ.

When the kidney is inflamed, the renal tissue becomes adherent to the true capsule and cannot be removed without tearing the organ. If the adipose capsule or the renal fascia is deficient, ptosis (dropping) of one or both kidneys can occur.

EXTERNAL STRUCTURE. Each kidney presents an anterior and posterior surface and a convex lateral border. Medially the renal artery, vein, and nerves, as well as lymphatic vessels, enter and leave the concave surface through a notch called the *hilum*. The cavity, located at the hilum, is a sac-like collecting portion called the *pelvis*, representing the upper expanded portion of the ureter.

INTERNAL STRUCTURE (Fig. 341). The kidney, in cross section, exhibits an inner darkened area, the *medulla*, and an outer pale area, the *cortex*. The medulla consists of from eight to 12 *renal pyramids*, with apices converging into projections known as papillae, which in turn are received by cavities (calyces) of the pelvis. The cortex consists of the peripheral layer extending from the capsule to the bases of the pyramids, and the *renal columns* traversing the area between the pyramids. It is divided into lobules composed of convoluted and radiant portions.

Vascular supply. Arteries from the aorta enter the hilum, or notch, on the medial surface of each kidney. After entering the hilum, the arteries divide into several branches called *interlobar arteries*. These extend to the boundary of the cortex and medulla of the kidney, where they branch as the *arcuate* arteries which form arches across the bases of the pyramids. *Interlobular* arteries extend from the arcuate arteries into the convoluted portion of the cortex, the fine branches entering the glomerular tufts. Efferent vessels leaving the glomerulus are distributed through the cortex and medulla along the tubule and unite to form interlobular and medullary veins which, in turn, empty their contents into the arcuate veins between the cortex and the medulla. The arcuate veins converge to form interlobar veins joining to empty into the renal vein. The *renal vein* leaves the kidney at the hilum draining into the inferior vena cava.

Innervation of the kidneys. The kidneys receive a rich supply of sympathetic, vasoconstrictor fibers extending from the fourth thoracic to the fourth lumbar segment of the spinal cord. Afferent fibers from the renal pelvis and ureters assume an important role in pain of renal origin and in the causation of anuria (absence of urine) caused by reflex vasoconstriction.

Lymphatic network of the kidneys. The lymphatic channels in the perirenal fat and those deep to the capsule proper form a superficial system. A deep group surrounds the tubules and blood vessels and both groups freely anastomose.

Microscopic Anatomy (Figs. 342 and 343)

The functioning renal unit is called the *nephron.* Each kidney contains about one million nephrons, each consisting of a renal corpuscle and tubular system. The blood supply initially comes into close relationship with the nephron by a tuft of capillaries called the *glomerulus* resting in a cup-like depression of the tubular system called the *glomerular capsule,* or Bowman's capsule. Together these structures comprise the renal corpuscle, or malpighian body. A long tubule consisting of a proximal convoluted portion, a loop of Henle, and a distal convoluted portion extends from the glomerular capsule. The tubule unwinds from the cortical area and ends by joining other nephrons in a larger collecting tube. The tubules give a striated appearance to the medulla, and the renal corpuscles give a fine granular appearance to the cortex. Urine is discharged at the apex of the medullary pyramid into the calyces of the pelvis and then flows down the ureter.

The point at which a portion of the distal convoluted tubule comes in contact with the afferent arteriole is called the *juxtaglomerular apparatus,* secreting renin, which is thought to be of importance in the regulation of blood pressure.

Kidney Regeneration

Renal reserve is dependent on the regenerative capacity of the kidney. When one kidney is removed, the opposite organ undergoes an enlargement because of an increase in size of the contained nephrons rather than an increase in total number of nephrons. Only 25 per cent of the total renal mass is necessary for survival of the individual. The epithelium of the renal tubules can regenerate after injury—for example, in poisoning due to mercury; however, the entire nephron does not regenerate.

Kidney Transplantation (Fig. 344)

During the last 5 years almost 300 homologous kidney transplants have been done on patients dying of renal failure. Despite massive therapy with chemical immuno-suppressive agents (diminishing antibody formation), homologous transplants generally do not function for long periods of time; the best result in homologous transplants occurs when the transplant is made between a mother and child. Kidney transplants between *identical twins* will function for years.

It should be noted that even in transplants between identical twins, the cause of damage to the original kidney subsequently effects the transplanted kidney; despite acceptance of the transplant, the patient dies.

Another problem in transplantation of the kidney is one of logistics, particularly of preservation of the kidney prior to transplantation. In general, sub-zero preservation is probably superior to preservation above zero, but no organ can be successfully frozen and remain alive. Currently, in the Department of Surgical Research at the University of Oregon Medical School, the freezing point of an entire kidney has been depressed to 6 degrees below zero without the kidney actually freezing (soft state), and the kidney has been retransplanted as an autologous kidney (from the same animal to the same animal). When the opposite kidney is removed, the stored kidney sustains life as the only remaining kidney.

Physiology of Urine Formation

URINE COMPOSITION (Table 40). Urine is 90 per cent water, in which salts, toxins, pigments, hormones, and wastes from protein metabolism are dissolved. It is a complex aqueous solution of inorganic and organic substances. The urinary output is approximately 1500 cc. daily, containing 60 gm. of solutes.

MECHANISM OF URINE FORMATION AND EXCRETION (Table 41). Three processes are involved in the formation of urine: glomerular filtration, tubular reabsorption, and tubular secretion.

Glomerular filtration (Fig. 345).

The glomerulus acts as a semipermeable membrane permitting a protein-free ultrafiltrate of plasma to pass through. The glomerular filtrate has a pH of approximately 7.4 with a specific gravity of 1.010. Normal levels of various substances exist in the following concentrations:

glucose	80 mg./100 ml.
urea nitrogen	15 mg./100 ml.
sodium	140 mEq./l.
chloride	100 mEq./l.
bicarbonate	27 mEq./l.
potassium	4.5 mEq./l.

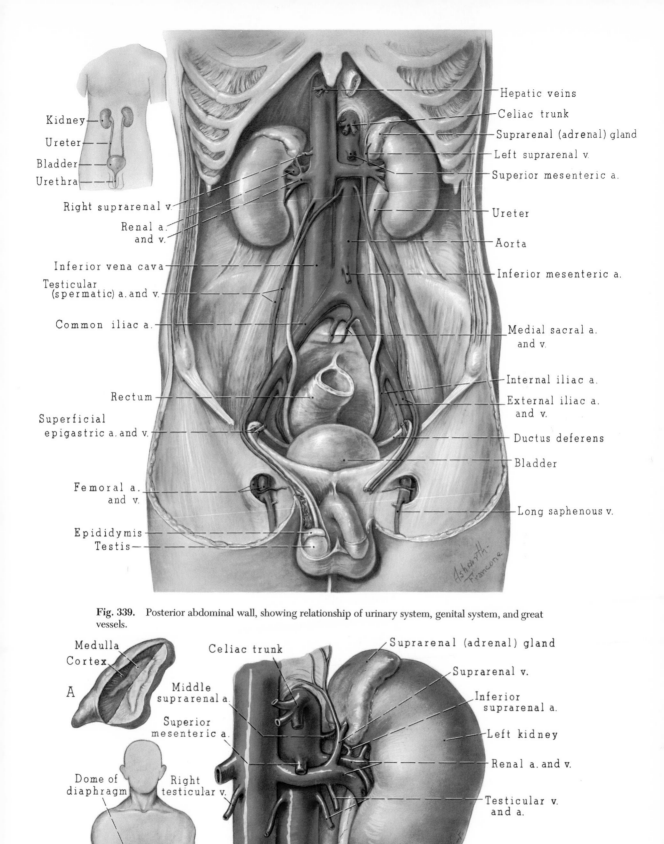

Kidney
Ureter
Bladder
Urethra

Right suprarenal v.
Renal a. and v.
Inferior vena cava
Testicular (spermatic) a. and v.
Common iliac a.
Rectum
Superficial epigastric a. and v.
Femoral a. and v.
Epididymis
Testis

Hepatic veins
Celiac trunk
Suprarenal (adrenal) gland
Left suprarenal v.
Superior mesenteric a.
Ureter
Aorta
Inferior mesenteric a.
Medial sacral a. and v.
Internal iliac a.
External iliac a. and v.
Ductus deferens
Bladder
Long saphenous v.

Fig. 339. Posterior abdominal wall, showing relationship of urinary system, genital system, and great vessels.

Medulla
Cortex
A

Celiac trunk
Middle suprarenal a.
Superior mesenteric a.

Dome of diaphragm
B
Kidney
Ureter

Right testicular v.
Aorta
Inferior vena cava
Ureter

Suprarenal (adrenal) gland
Suprarenal v.
Inferior suprarenal a.
Left kidney
Renal a. and v.
Testicular v. and a.
C

Suprarenal (adrenal) gland

Fig. 340. *A.* Suprarenal gland sectioned to show the medulla. *B.* Anatomic position of kidney and suprarenal glands. *C.* Anterior aspect of left kidney, showing adrenal gland and vascular supply.

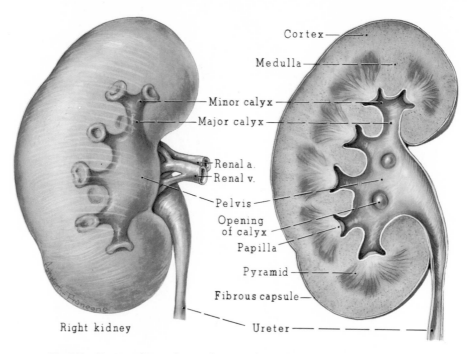

Fig. 341. Entire and sagittal views showing relation of calyces to kidney as a whole.

TABLE 40.   Composition of Urine.

Solutes 60 gm. daily	Organic wastes 35 gm.	Urea	30 gm.
		Creatinine	1–2 gm.
		Ammonia	1–2 gm.
		Uric acid	1 gm.
		Others	1 gm.
	Inorganic salts° 25 gm.	Chloride	Sodium
		Sulfate	Potassium
		Phosphorus	Magnesium

° Sodium chloride is the chief inorganic salt in urine.

TABLE 41.   Functions of Different Parts of Nephron.

PART OF NEPHRON	FUNCTION
Glomerulus	Produces filtrate of protein-free plasma
Proximal convoluted tubule and loop of Henle	Absorption of Na^+, K^+, and glucose by active transport; Absorption of Cl^- by diffusion; Obligatory water absorption by osmosis
Distal convoluted tubule	Absorption of Na by active transport; ADH-controlled absorption of water; Secretion of H^+, K^+, and certain drugs such as penicillin and Diodrast by active transport
Collecting tubule	Water absorption by osmosis

As can be seen, the filtrate produced is similar to plasma without plasma proteins. The process of glomerular filtration is essentially a passive one, similar to the diffusion of substances from the vascular capillary to the interstitial spaces.

The hydrostatic pressure in the glomerulus is normally about 70 mm. of mercury; the colloid osmotic pressure of the plasma proteins averages about 32 mm. of mercury. This is slightly higher than colloid osmotic pressure of other capillaries in the body because large volumes of fluid are lost in the glomerular capillaries, thereby increasing the protein concentration. The pressure in the glomerular capsule surrounding the capillaries is 20 mm. of mercury. Glomerular pressure tends to force fluid out of the capillaries, while the colloid osmotic pressure and the pressure within the glomerular capsule tend to keep fluid from leaving the glomerulus. Therefore, the net force or *filtration pressure* represents the glomerular pressure minus plasma colloid osmotic pressure, and glomerular capsular pressure. The normal filtration pressure is about 18 mm. of mercury. Glomerular hydrostatic pressure (70 mm. Hg) minus glomerular colloid osmotic pressure (32 mm. Hg) minus capsular pressure (20 mm. Hg) equals filtration pressure, 18 mm. Hg.

Approximately 1200 ml. of blood or 24 per cent of the total cardiac output passes through the kidney per minute. Of this, the fluid outflow from all glomeruli of both kidneys is about 125 ml. per minute. The rate of *glomerular filtration* varies directly with the filtration pressure.

Tubular reabsorption.

Of the 125 ml. of glomerular filtrate formed each minute, approximately 124 ml. is reabsorbed by the renal tubules. Only 1 ml. passes into the urine. During its passage through the tubule, the glomerular filtrate is changed by a process of selective reabsorption of water and chemical substances from the filtrate back into the blood.

Reabsorption involves either a process of active or passive transport. In *active transport* a substance is transported across the membrane against a concentration or electrical gradient and requires the expenditure of energy by the body —for example, glucose reabsorption. *Passive transport* takes place when the substance is reabsorbed by simple diffusion and energy is not required, such as in water reabsorption by the tubules.

The mechanism of active transport is adapted to the continuous transfer of substances from one side of the cellular membrane to another. Renal tubules are devoted largely to carrying on a series of transport processes. Chief among these is the active transport of sodium from the glomerular filtrate into the blood. This process requires the major part of oxygen consumption in the kidney and not only restores to the body most of the sodium temporarily lost in the glomerular filtrate, but by its electrical effect leads to the absorption of chloride accompanying the sodium.

The clearance concept. Approximately one-fifth of the plasma water entering the kidney is filtered into Bowman's capsule, most of which is subsequently reabsorbed in various portions of the tubule. During passage through this extravascular system, a fraction of the glomerular filtrate is entirely reabsorbed, while other fractions are reabsorbed poorly, if at all. In this way the plasma is "cleared" of varying amounts of certain substances. For instance, of 125 ml. of filtrate produced per minute, none of the creatinine is reabsorbed, and thus all of it is cleared from the plasma. Therefore, the plasma clearance of creatinine is said to be 125 ml. per minute. Thus, the kidney acts as an organ for clearing plasma, removing substances not needed by the body, while conserving substances required.

Glucose and *amino acids,* for instance, are normally almost completely reabsorbed. Both are nutrients and must be conserved. Certain other substances—including sodium, potassium, bicarbonate, calcium, magnesium, phosphate, and chloride ions—are variably reabsorbed, depending on the daily needs of the body.

Glucose reabsorption. Glucose is removed from the glomerular filtrate in the proximal convoluted tubule by a process involving an enzymatic carrier system. The cells of the tubule reabsorb glucose and water with it. If there is a defect in the tubular carrier mechanism, glycosuria (sugar in the urine) and polyuria (increased volume of urinary output) result. In diabetes mellitus, glycosuria is a result of an excessive concentration of sugar in the glomerular filtrate. Glucose is one example of a molecule that is selectively reabsorbed by the tubules.

Sodium transport. It is well known that active transport of sodium occurs in both the proximal and distal tubules. Renal tubules regulate the sodium concentration of the extracellular fluid by reabsorbing large quantities of sodium from the tubular fluid when the extracellular concentration of sodium drops, and by failing to reabsorb sodium when the concentration is high. The mechanism is as follows:

A low sodium ion concentration stimulates the adrenal cortex to increase secretion of aldoste-

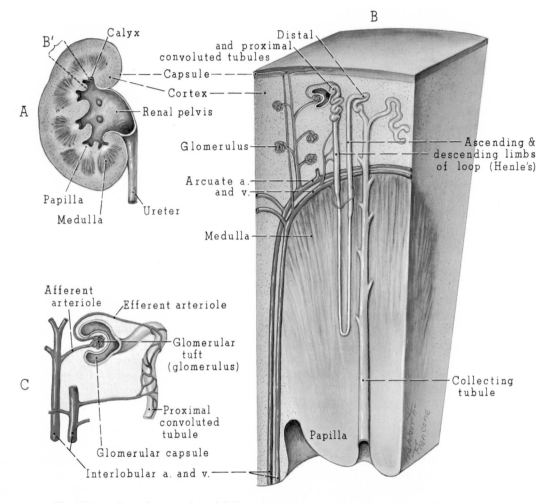

Fig. 342. *A.* Sagittal section through kidney showing gross structure (note pelvis, calyces, medulla, cortex). *B.* Nephron and its relationship to medulla and cortex. The dotted lines in *A* show the area of the kidney from which this section was taken. *C.* Magnified view of nephron.

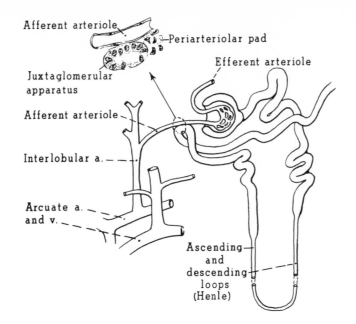

Fig. 343.   Detail of glomerulus showing vascular supply, juxtaglomerular apparatus, and tubule.

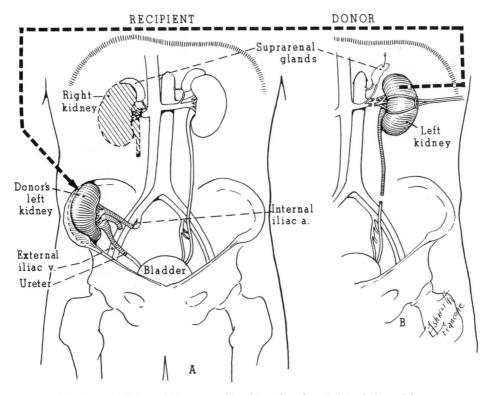

Fig. 344.   *A* illustrates kidney transplanted to right pelvis. *B* shows kidney of donor.

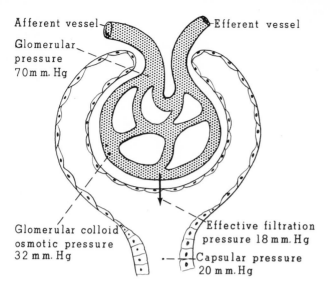

Afferent vessel

Glomerular
pressure
70 m m. Hg

Efferent vessel

Glomerular colloid
osmotic pressure
32 m m. Hg

Effective filtration
pressure 18 m m. Hg

Capsular pressure
20 m m. Hg

Fig. 345. The normal filtration pressure is about 18 mm. of mercury. Glomerular hydrostatic pressure (70 mm. Hg) minus glomerular colloid osmotic pressure (32 mm. Hg) minus capsular pressure (20 mm. Hg) equals filtration pressure, 18 mm. Hg.

rone. This substance in turn is carried by the blood to the tubules and excites the tubular epithelial cells to transport increased quantities of sodium from the tubules into the peritubular capillaries. An excess of sodium in the extracellular fluid inhibits aldosterone secretion. As a result, large quantities of sodium fail to be reabsorbed and are, therefore, lost into the urine.

The action of most useful diuretics can be attributed to the property of inhibiting the mechanism for the active transport of sodium. When active transport is reduced, an increased loss of sodium results in a roughly equivalent increased loss of water into the urine. Stimulation of active sodium transport by adrenocortical hormones is an essential feature of salt retention leading to edema (accumulation of fluid in the interstitial spaces) and cardiac failure when steroids are given.

Potassium. In the normal individual, the *clearance* of potassium is less than 12.5 ml. per minute. It was originally believed that active reabsorption was the only process involved in potassium clearance; however, recent evidence indicates that all filtered potassium is reabsorbed by the proximal tubules and that the potassium found in the urine is actively secreted by the distal tubule.

Regulation of other ions. Though the precise mechanism for regulating other ions in the body fluids is not nearly so well understood as the regulation of sodium, it has been shown that the renal tubules regulate the concentration of chloride, bicarbonate, calcium, magnesium, and phosphate.

Water reabsorption. The reabsorption of plasma water filtered through the glomerulus occurs in the collecting duct as well as other portions of the tubule. Approximately 110 of 125 ml. of glomerular filtrate per minute is passively absorbed in the proximal tubule. Water reabsorption is passive in the proximal tubule, the distal convoluted tubule, and collecting duct; however, its reabsorption in the distal portion of the nephron and the collecting duct is also dependent on the osmolarity of the extracellular fluid surrounding the distal nephron.

Osmoreceptors located in the anterior hypothalamus can be stimulated by increased osmolar concentration following loss of water, or by increases in plasma electrolytes. When stimulated, these osmoreceptors presumably activate the hypothalamic neurohypophyseal mechanism to increase the production of ADH (antidiuretic hormone), which, in turn, acts on the cells of the distal tubule, increasing the permeability of these cells to water. Water then flows from the nephron back into the plasma.

When the body takes in enough water to reestablish iso-osmolarity, secretion of ADH decreases and the cells of the distal convoluted tubule and collecting duct become less permeable to water. Simultaneously, the urinary output increases and the specific gravity or osmolarity drops. *Diabetes insipidus* is a disease characterized by a large 24-hour output of urine with a low specific gravity. It is caused by a deficiency of ADH secretion by the neurohypophysis.

Tubular secretion.

In addition to active reabsorption, the renal tubules are capable of active transport from the vascular to the tubular side of the epithelial cells;

this is known as tubular secretion. Reabsorption, as previously described, implies active transport from the tubular to the vascular side.

Large volumes of acids are formed in the body at the end of metabolic processes. Unless these are removed by the kidneys, a disturbance in the acid-base balance toward the acid side results. The distal tubules secrete large quantities of hydrogen ions and help maintain proper acid-base balance. The proximal tubule also secretes certain drugs such as penicillin and Diodrast (used for x-ray of the kidneys).

Diseases Associated With the Kidney

Essential hypertension is influenced by hereditary and endocrine factors, but the primary cause is unknown. The classic experiments of Goldblatt demonstrated that renal ischemia (diminished blood supply and oxygenation) leads to the release from the kidney of the enzyme *renin* by the juxtaglomerular region of the kidney. When renin is released into the blood, it acts on a circulating alpha-2 globulin to form angiotensin-1 (formerly termed angiotonin). This is further split by a circulating enzyme into angiotensin-2. Angiotensin-2 is responsible for constricting the arterioles producing an elevated blood pressure. It is not known whether angiotensin-2 acts directly or indirectly on blood vessels.

Nephritis. Acute glomerulonephritis (inflammation of the kidney) generally develops during the first two decades of life, 10 to 20 days after an acute infection. Most patients recover spontaneously; only in 2 per cent does the disease become chronic. Chronic nephritis (Bright's disease) can result in hypertension and eventually uremia. *Pyelonephritis* on the other hand is caused by actual invasion of renal tissue by bacteria.

Uremia. Uremia, literally meaning "urea in the blood," is a symptom complex which follows renal insufficiency and involves other systems. One of the characteristic signs of uremia is a "uremic" odor to the breath caused by NH_3 produced by bacterial decomposition of large amounts of urea in the saliva. Most patients with uremia have an elevated blood pressure caused by retention of the water and solute normally excreted by the kidney.

Dialysis (Fig. 346)

Hemodialysis exploits the simple principle of diffusion. A semipermeable membrane is inter-posed between the blood of the patient and a wash solution. The changes that follow depend on the characteristics of the membrane and the molecular composition of the solution as compared to that of the blood. If there is a relatively high level of any substance in the blood of a patient and none in the wash solution, that substance will diffuse from the patient into the solution. Urea, potassium, phosphate, and other molecules present in toxic quantities in the uremic patient can be removed by hemodialysis.

A model of an artificial kidney shown in Fig. 346 includes a steel tub 2 feet deep and 2 feet in diameter. In the center is a spiral of cellophane tubing connected to plastic tubes, carrying the blood from the patient to be purified in the wash solution and then back again to the patient. Microscopic pores are present in the cellophane tubing through which elements with a molecular weight of less than 5000 can pass.

At the beginning of treatment, the artificial kidney is primed with blood matching that of the recipient, insuring a continuous flow of blood. The tub is filled with 25 gallons of ordinary tap water, heated to body temperature by coils at the base of the machine. Chemicals including salt, sugar, sodium bicarbonate, and other components of the blood in normal concentrations are dissolved in the water. This solution bathes the outside of the cellophane spiral, which is about 20 yards long when extended. Excess substances pass from the blood through the porous walls of the tubing into the bath solution, where they are retained.

It is now possible by hemodialysis to keep patients alive without any functioning kidney tissue for as long as 5 years.

URETERS

The ureters are two tubes lying retroperitoneally and functioning to convey urine from the kidneys to the bladder. Each begins as a number of *calyces*, joining to form two or three short tubes uniting into a funnel-shaped dilatation known as the renal pelvis. The ureter proper passes from the pelvis to the posterior aspect of the urinary bladder. Each is 25 to 30 cm. in length, 4 to 5 mm. in diameter, and consists of outer fibrous, middle muscular, and inner mucous layers. Contraction of the muscular layer produces characteristic peristaltic waves beginning at the renal pelvis and ending at the bladder.

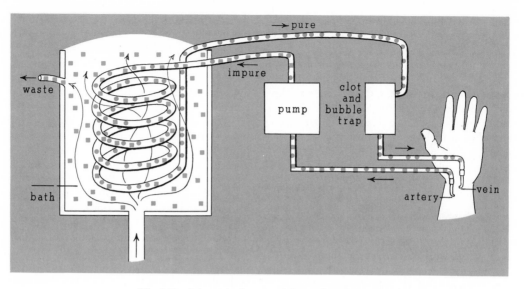

Fig. 346. Schematic diagram of the artificial kidney.

As the ureter leaves the hilum of the kidney, it traverses the perirenal fat surrounding the kidney. It crosses the psoas muscle and, just before reaching the pelvic brim, passes over the bifurcation of the common iliac vessels. The right ureter lies adjacent to the inferior vena cava with the ileocolic vessels located between it and the peritoneum, while the left ureter is crossed by the left colic vessels. The lower one-third of each ureter lies against the pelvic wall and follows the curvature of the pelvis descending toward the midline to pierce the wall of the bladder.

Narrowed areas along the course of the ureter are of practical importance, since stones are likely to lodge at these narrowed points. The first narrowed area or constriction is at the junction of the ureter and renal pelvis; the next is at the point at which the ureter crosses the iliac artery; the third is at the position of entrance of the ureter into the bladder wall. At all three of these regions the lumen is sufficiently narrowed so that stones frequently become lodged.

The location of the ureter in the female is of particular interest, since its proximity to the uterus and cervix predisposes it to injury during surgery of the uterus. The female ureter lies close to the unattached border of the ovary on the lateral wall of the pelvis and enters the base of the broad ligament crossed by the uterine artery. As it approaches the bladder it lies adjacent to the cervix, where it can be injured in removal of the uterus (hysterectomy).

A double ureter is not an uncommon abnormality; it can be either partial or complete. If two completely separate ureters exist on one side, the two ureteral orifices are usually present on the same ureteric ridge. Occasionally the ureter is ectopic—that is, opening into an abnormal location such as the urethra itself or the vagina. An ectopic ureter can cause incontinence (continuous dripping), especially when its opening into the urogenital tract occurs below the sphincter of the bladder. Ectopic ureter should be considered in the young female child with enuresis.

URINARY BLADDER (Figs. 347 and 348)

The urinary bladder lies posterior to the symphysis pubis; it is separated from the rectum by the seminal vesicles in the male and by the vagina and uterus in the female. The superior surface of the bladder is covered by peritoneum. Laterally the bladder is supported by the levator ani musculature, and posteriorly it rests on the obturator internus muscle.

Basically, the bladder consists of two parts—a small triangular area near the mouth of the bladder called the trigone, on which both the ureters and urethra open; and the detrusor muscle (smooth muscle of bladder wall), forming the principal portion of the body.

The trigonal muscle extends inferiorly on the floor of the proximal urethra and anchors the ureters as the bladder fills. The detrusor muscle encircles the vesical neck and also extends inferiorly adjacent to the proximal urethra.

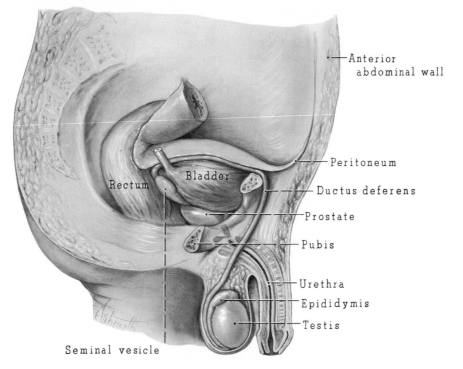

Fig. 347. Sagittal section through the male pelvis.

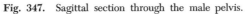

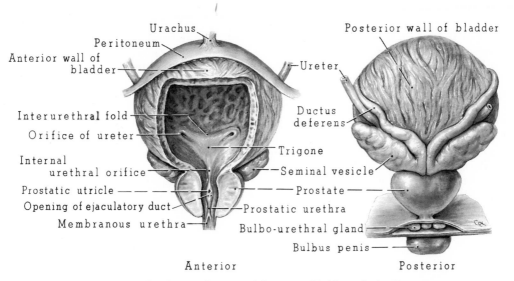

Fig. 348. Internal and external aspects of the urinary bladder and related structures.

The wall of the bladder is composed of four layers (from within outward): *mucosal, submucosal, muscular,* and *serosal.* Transitional epithelium lines the mucosal layer.

BLOOD, NERVE, AND LYMPH SUPPLY TO THE BLADDER. The arteries supplying the bladder originate from branches of the internal iliac, middle hemorrhoidal, internal pudendal, and obturator vessels. Veins do not accompany the arteries but arise from a freely anastomosing plexus of venous channels emptying into the internal iliac veins.

Urinary bladder activity is controlled by the parasympathetic nervous system with centers in the spinal cord. There is no evidence that sympathetic fibers are concerned with micturition other than that they constrict the blood vessels of the bladder.

Micturition

The bladder serves as a reservoir for urine, gradually filling and becoming distended. In the distended state, the muscular wall contracts and the pressure within the bladder increases. The normal capacity of the bladder is from 300 to 350 ml. As the volume increases, the tension rises. When the pressure within the bladder reaches 18 cm. of H_2O, stretch and tension receptors are stimulated producing the desire to urinate. Voluntary control can be exerted until the bladder pressure increases to 100 cm. of H_2O, at which point involuntary micturition begins.

Normally micturition is under voluntary control of the brain. It is currently believed that the entire urethra in the female and the prostate and the membranous urethra in the male function as the internal sphincter of the bladder. Impulses from the brain to the lumbosacral region of the cord stimulate the bladder. Pressure sufficient to accomplish voiding is created by contraction of the detrusor muscles, the abdominal wall, fixation of the chest wall and diaphragm, and relaxation of the perineal and the urethral musculature.

Enuresis. Enuresis (involuntary bed-wetting during sleep by a child over 3 years of age) can be caused by many factors, including local irritation of the bladder and urethra and emotional in-

stability. When the child possesses a normal mental capacity and does not have actual disease, the outlook is favorable. The habit of voiding voluntarily should be established in children by the third year.

URETHRA

The male urethra is a narrow musculomembranous tube extending from the bladder to the external urethral meatus. It follows a tortuous course for a distance of approximately 8 inches and is divided into three portions: prostatic, membranous, and cavernous.

The first part, the *prostatic urethra,* commences at the bladder neck (outlet of the bladder) and traverses the prostate to the two-layered triangular ligament. The *membranous urethra* lies between the two layers of the triangular ligament, connecting the penile and prostatic urethrae. The *cavernous urethra* (penile portion) extends from the triangular ligament to the urethral orifice.

The urethra serves as the distal portion of the urinary tract for eliminating urine from the body; additionally, the male urethra is the terminal portion of the reproductive tract serving as a passageway for semen.

The female urethra is 1½ inches in length and is supported by the anterior wall of the vagina. The urethral wall consists of three layers: mucosal, submucosal, and muscular. Skene's glands open into the urethra just within the external urinary meatus. The female urethra is generally recognized as being surrounded by a complex network of glands and ducts forming ideal foci for chronic infection. These are lined by stratified squamous epithelial cells with large nuclei. The lining of the ducts is similar to that of the urethra. The epithelial lining of the female urethra is subject to hormonal influence and takes part in the general atrophy of the adjacent vaginal mucosa in the postmenopausal period. The urethral meatus is bathed by vaginal, uterine, and rectal discharges throughout life, exposing the delicate urethral structures to irritation and bacterial invasion.

SUMMARY: THE URINARY SYSTEM

KIDNEYS

1. **Embryology:**

   a. The kidneys pass through three stages of development: the pronephros, mesonephros, and metanephros. In the adult male the mesonephric duct persists as the ductus deferens, the passageway for reproductive fluid from the testis to the urethra. In the female it disappears.

2. **Congenital malformations:**

   a. Polycystic kidney: cyst-like structures result when the functioning nephron tubules fail to fuse with the collecting ducts during development. This condition is usually not compatible with life.

   b. Horseshoe kidney: the lower poles of the kidneys fuse, preventing normal ascent to the adult lumbar position.

3. **Gross anatomy:**

   a. The kidneys are two bean-shaped organs, retroperitoneal in position, situated on the musculature of the posterior abdominal wall at the level of the twelfth thoracic and first three lumbar vertebrae. The right kidney is slightly lower than the left.

   b. Three renal capsules surround the kidney: the capsule proper, perirenal fat, and the renal fascia.

   c. External structure: the hilum is a notch on the concave surface of the kidney where the renal vessels and nerves enter and leave the kidney substance.

   d. Internal structure: the inner layer is called the medulla; the outer layer is the cortex. The renal pyramids are triangular-shaped wedges of medulla with apices projecting as papillae and ending in the calyces of the ureters. Renal columns are inward extensions of cortex between the pyramids.

   e. Vascular supply: renal vessels enter the hilum and divide into interlobar vessels that travel to the cortex and break up into arcuate vessels. Interlobular vessels extend from the arcuate vessels into the cortex.

4. **Microscopic anatomy:**

   a. Capillaries enter the glomerular capsule to form a capillary tuft called the glomerulus. The glomerular capsule, together with the glomerulus, forms the renal capsule. The complete functioning unit is the nephron, composed of the renal capsule, proximal convoluted tubules, loop of Henle, and distal convoluted tubule.

5. **Kidney regeneration:**

   a. Nephrons do not regenerate; however, life is possible with as little as 25 per cent of the total renal mass.

6. **Kidney transplantation:**

   a. Kidney transplants are becoming more common, although tissue rejection is still a factor in the success or failure of the transplant. Successful storage of organs at sub-zero temperatures is possible for short periods of time.

7. **Physiology of urine formation:**

   a. Urine composition: urine is 90 per cent water, containing metabolic wastes, salts, toxins, pigments, and hormones.

   b. Urine formation and excretion involve glomerular filtration, tubular reabsorption, and tubular secretion.

      (1) Filtration of substances (similar to plasma minus plasma proteins) from the blood by the glomeruli.

(2) Reabsorption of glucose, sodium, and potassium in the proximal tubule, and water reabsorption throughout the length of the tubules and the proximal portion of the collecting ducts.

(3) Secretion of substances by tubule cells. All the potassium is secreted in the distal tubule.

(4) Active reabsorption and secretion are transport processes requiring the expenditure of energy.

  c. Mechanisms regulating urine content and volume:

(1) Renal tubules under the influence of aldosterone regulate the concentration of sodium in the extracellular fluid. Low sodium concentration causes the suprarenal cortex to increase its secretion of aldosterone.

(2) The volume of water absorbed by the tubule cells determines the volume of urine formed. Distal tubules are stimulated to absorb water by ADH from the posterior hypophysis. Corticoids increase sodium reabsorption and therefore water reabsorption.

8. **Diseases associated with the kidney:**

  a. Essential hypertension: possibly a result of prolonged release of renin from the juxtaglomerular apparatus, causing constriction of the arterioles and chronic elevation of the blood pressure.

  b. Nephritis: a severe inflammation of the kidneys.

  c. Uremia: a disorder characterized by urea and other nitrogenous wastes in the blood.

9. **Dialysis:**

  a. The artificial kidney functions through the process of dialysis. Toxic substances are washed from the blood by the mechanism of diffusion.

URETERS

1. **Location and structure:** retroperitoneal, extending from the kidneys to the posterior part of the bladder. Ureters begin in the kidney as several calyces and unite to form a pelvis terminating in the bladder. The walls are of smooth muscle with mucous lining and a fibrous outer layer.

2. **Function:** to collect urine and convey it to the bladder.

3. **Double ureter:** a congenital abnormality resulting in partial or complete duplication of the ureter. Often this is a cause of incontinence if the opening occurs below the bladder sphincter.

URINARY BLADDER

1. **Location and structure:** located posterior to the symphysis pubis. The bladder consists of the trigone, with three openings (one urethral, two for the ureters), and the detrusor musculature.

2. **Function:**

  a. Storage of urine.

  b. Reservoir that expels urine from the body. The process of urination is called voiding or micturition.

URETHRA

1. **Location and structure:** a musculomembranous tube, lying behind the

symphysis pubis and extending through the prostate gland, triangular ligament, and penis in the male. It lies anterior to the vagina in the female.

2. Function:

   a. Male: passageway for expulsion of urine and semen.
   b. Female: passageway for expulsion of urine from the body.

STUDY QUESTIONS: THE URINARY SYSTEM

1. Describe briefly the embryologic development of the adult kidney.
2. Discuss the anatomy of the nephron.
3. Differentiate renal calyces, pyramids, and renal pelvis.
4. Describe the portions of the ureter and its enlargements and constrictions.
5. Describe the layers of the wall of the ureter.
6. Differentiate active transport, passive transport, and secretion in the tubular system of the kidney.
7. Explain the meaning of the term *clearance*.
8. Discuss dialysis.
9. Describe the mechanism of urine formation.
10. Name, locate, and describe the functions of the principal structures of the urinary system.
11. Briefly define the following terms:

    glomerulus
    loop of Henle
    trigone
    detrusor

12. What is meant by glomerular filtration rate?

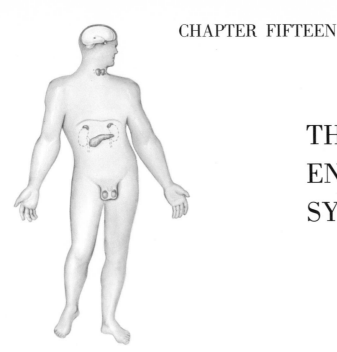

CHAPTER FIFTEEN

THE ENDOCRINE SYSTEM

TERMINOLOGY AND GENERAL FUNCTIONS

The glands of the endocrine system work in harmony with the nervous system to control and coordinate all the activities of the body. The substance secreted by an endocrine gland is called a *hormone.* Hormones serve three major functions:

1. *Integrative:* Hormones reach all the cells of the body and permit different tissue groups to act as a whole in response to internal or external stimuli.

2. *Homeostatic:* Hormones play a vital role in the maintenance of the internal environment.

3. *Growth:* Hormones control the rate and type of growth of the organism.

The glands of the body are classified either as exocrine, possessing ducts from which secretion is poured into some hollow organ, such as the intestine; or endocrine (ductless), pouring secretion directly into the blood.

Hormones pass directly into the blood through the capillaries draining each of the endocrine glands and are taken to other parts of the body. An organ specifically influenced by a certain hormone is referred to as a *target organ.* An excess or deficiency of a particular hormone may result in a specific disease state.

Eight glands of internal secretion will be discussed in this section; additionally, the placenta in the female, present only after fertilization of the ovum, serves an endocrine function (Fig. 349 and Table 42).

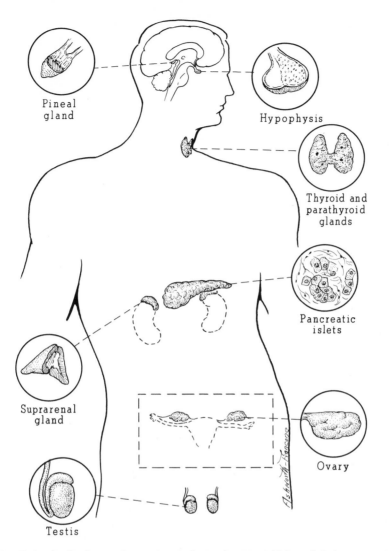

Fig. 349. Eight glands of internal secretion produce substances which work in harmony with the nervous system to control and coordinate all activities of the body.

TABLE 42.   Glands of Internal Secretion.

GLANDS	LOCATION
1. Hypophysis (pituitary)	Sella turcica of the sphenoid bone
2. Thyroid	Neck, with one lobe on each side of the trachea
3. Parathyroids (four)	Posterior aspect of the thyroid gland
4. Pancreatic islets	Scattered throughout the pancreas
5. Suprarenal glands (two)	Superior to each kidney
6. Ovaries (two)	In pelvis, one on each side of the uterus
7. Testes (two)	One in each side of the scrotal sac
8. Pineal	Above the superior colliculi of the midbrain

435

HYPOPHYSIS (PITUITARY GLAND)

The hypophysis is a mass of tissue about 1 cm. in diameter, weighing 0.8 gram in the adult. It consists of two divisions: the *adenohypophysis* and the *neurohypophysis*. The adenohypophysis includes the anterior and intermediate lobes. The posterior lobe is one part of a unit more properly termed the neurohypophysis and is connected with nuclei in the hypothalamus by axons which descend through the hypophyseal stalk.

The two component parts of the hypophysis are different in origin and histologic appearance. The adenohypophysis, consisting of the anterior and intermediate lobes, differentiates from Rathke's pouch, an outgrowth of the roof of the mouth. Embryologically, then, the adenohypophysis is an entodermal derivative. This pouch promptly meets the infundibulum (an outpocketing of the hypothalamus), and loses its connection with the buccal epithelium. The cavity of Rathke's pouch becomes the residual lumen of the hypophysis. The neurohypophysis, on the other hand, is a neural ectodermal derivative, taking its origin from the infundibulum. The resulting stalk permanently connects the neural lobe with the hypothalamus.

Neurohypophysis

Two well-defined polypeptides have been isolated from extracts of the neurohypophysis: oxytocin and vasopressin. *Oxytocin* (pitocin) stimulates the uterus to contract at the time of childbirth. It acts on the smooth muscle of the pregnant uterus to maintain labor. Commercial forms of oxytocin are sometimes employed to increase uterine contraction and decrease hemorrhage following delivery. Oxytocin also influences the lactating breast to release milk from the glandular cells into the ducts. Suckling by the infant, in turn, stimulates additional secretion of oxytocin.

Antidiuretic hormone, ADH (vasopressin, pitressin), acts on the circulation constricting the smaller arteries and capillaries. The major function of ADH is probably to enhance reabsorption of water from the distal renal tubule; additionally, it stimulates the smooth muscle of the gastrointestinal tract. The most important disorder associated with deficiency of the neurohypophysis is *diabetes insipidus,* a disease caused by a diminished production of antidiuretic hormone. Deficiency of ADH prevents the reabsorption of water by the distal renal tubules and

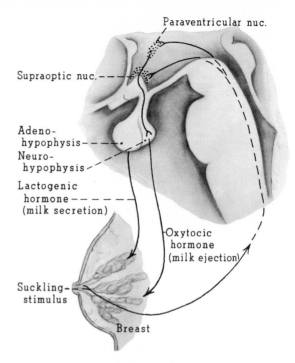

Fig. 350. Diagram illustrating interrelationships of neurohypophysis, adenohypophysis, and breast.

leads to the excretion of large volumes of urine—up to 20 liters a day.

Relationship between the hypothalamus and neurohypophysis. The hypothalamus and neurohypophysis are intimately connected. Nerve fibers from the supraoptic and paraventricular nuclei of the hypothalamus traverse the hypophyseal stalk, terminating in the neurohypophysis. Neurosecretory materials which represent a mixture of neurohypophyseal hormones and a carrier are found in the cell bodies of the supraoptic and paraventricular nuclei. These pass down the nerve axons and by cytoplasmic extensions reach the neurohypophysis, where they are stored until needed (Fig. 350).

Adenohypophysis (Fig. 351)

There are many different cell types comprising the anterior lobe of the hypophysis, of which four can be easily recognized by simple staining techniques. These are the chromophobes, basophils, eosinophils, and amphophils. *Chromophobes* are stem cells giving rise to the other three cell types, which are often referred to as chromophilic. The chromophobes are smaller than the chromophiles, and tend to be round in shape with a scanty cytoplasm practically devoid of granules. Chromophobes constitute 20 to 28

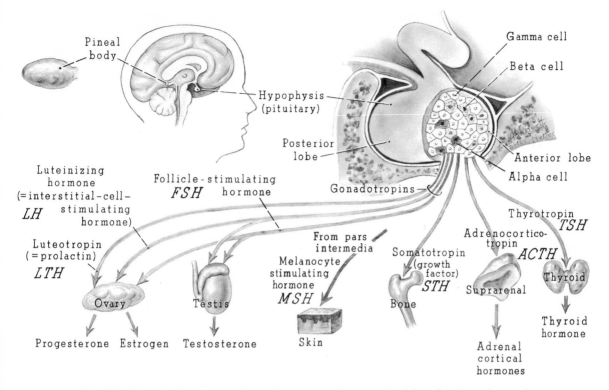

Fig. 351. The adenohypophysis includes the anterior and intermediate lobes of the hypophysis and produces several hormones controlling the activity of a number of endocrine glands.

per cent of the cells of the adenohypophysis. *Basophilic cells*, the largest cells in the adenohypophysis, constitute approximately 20 to 28 per cent of the cells in the adenohypophysis. The basophils produce follicle-stimulating and adrenocorticotropic hormones. Eosinophils make up 35 to 40 per cent of the cells and produce growth and lactogenic hormones. The fourth cell type is the amphophil, comprising 5 to 7 per cent of all cells. The amphophil, sparsely granulated and similar to the basophil in some of its staining qualities is a large cell believed to be responsible for secretion of the thyrotropic hormone.

FUNCTIONS OF THE ADENOHYPOPHYSIS. The adenohypophysis produces several hormones controlling the activity of a number of endocrine glands. The versatility of this part of the hypophysis is so well recognized that it has been termed "leader of the endocrine orchestra." Seven hormones have been isolated from the adenohypophysis including somatotropin (STH), or growth hormone; adrenocorticotropin (ACTH); thyrotropin (TSH); lactogenic hormone (prolactin); follicle-stimulating hormone (FSH); luteinizing hormone (LH), or interstitial cell-stimulating hormone (ICSH); and melanocyte-

stimulating hormone (MSH). All adenohypophyseal hormones are protein, and three—FSH, LH, and TSH—contain a carbohydrate as well as an amino acid.

Somatotropin (STH). The term somatotropin is derived from the Greek "soma" meaning body and "trophe" meaning nourishment. The mechanisms by which somatotropin accelerates growth are incompletely understood. It is thought to promote amino acid transport into cells. Recently, it has been shown that the transfer of amino acids from extracellular to intracellular loci can be influenced by growth hormone. Somatotropin also controls the growth of bone before closure of the epiphyseal cartilage.

Growth hormone from the hypophysis influences not only protein metabolism, but also lipid, carbohydrate, and calcium metabolism. An optimal cellular environment made possible by the presence of insulin is necessary for the anabolic action of growth hormone to become fully evident. When growth hormone is injected, there is a decrease in the proportion of fat in the body, along with other secondary manifestations of accelerated fat oxidation.

Over- or underproduction of growth hormone

results in characteristic deformities. In children underproduction is one cause of dwarfism. Underproduction of somatotropin in adult life, together with other tropic hormone deficiencies, produces hypophyseal *cachexia* (Simmonds' disease), a rare condition characterized by premature aging with marked atrophy of body tissues (Fig. 352). If there is an overproduction of growth hormone in children before the epiphysis of the long bone closes, *gigantism* results (Fig. 353). Overproduction of growth hormone in the adult results in *acromegaly*. Since bones cannot increase in length after the closure of the epiphyses in the adult, cancellous bones increase in thickness. As a result of acromegaly, the feet and hands become large and spade-like, while the bones of the face and skull become thicker (Fig. 354).

Adrenocorticotropin (ACTH). The adrenocorticotropic hormone (ACTH) controls cortisol (hydrocortisone) production by the suprarenal gland. Secretion of cortisol from the suprarenal gland, in turn, regulates ACTH release from the hypophysis by a feed-back device. ACTH does not influence adrenalin secretion by the medulla.

Thyrotropin (TSH). The thyrotropic hormone controls thyroxin (thyroid hormone) secretion by the thyroid gland. Secretion of thyroid

Fig. 353.   Gigantism; at 18 years of age this individual was 8 feet 3¼ inches tall and weighed 395 pounds. (Courtesy of Lisser and Escamilla: *Atlas of Clinical Endocrinology*, second edition. St. Louis, The C. V. Mosby Company, 1962.)

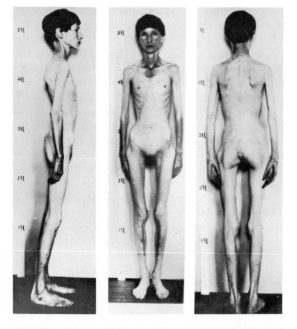

Fig. 352.   Simmonds' disease. (Courtesy of Escamilla and Lisser: California & West. Med., *48*:343, 1938.)

hormone and thyrotropin is reciprocally regulated by feedback device similar to the mechanism regulating the secretion of cortisol from the suprarenal gland. High blood levels of thyrotropin stimulate secretion of thyroid hormone. The subsequent elevated level of thyroid hormone inhibits the adenohypophyseal secretion of thyrotropin.

Prolactin luteotropic hormone (LTH). Prolactin promotes the growth of breast tissue and maintains lactation. It probably functions in the preservation of the corpus luteum, thereby stimulating secretion of progesterone. Secretion of prolactin is promoted by the nervous reflex of suckling.

Follicle-stimulating hormone (FSH) and luteinizing hormone (LH). FSH and LH are called gonadotropic hormones since they control the development of the ovaries in the female and the testes in the male. Follicle-stimulating hormone in the female stimulates the control of the graafian follicles in the ovary and the production of estrogen. FSH in the male influences the development of spermatozoa.

Luteinizing hormone (LH) in the male is also called interstitial cell-stimulating hormone (ICSH). It controls the testicular production of

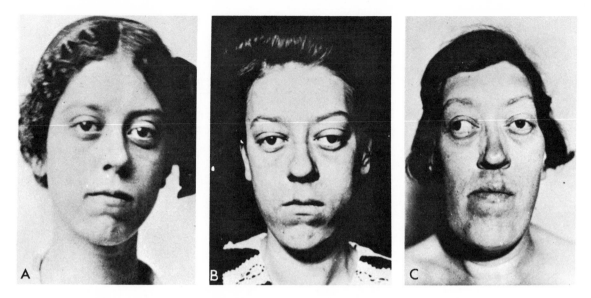

Fig. 354. Acromegaly; *A.* 16 years of age; *B.* 25 years of age; *C.* 44 years of age. (Courtesy of Lisser and Escamilla: *Atlas of Clinical Endocrinology,* second edition. St. Louis, The C. V. Mosby Company, 1962.)

testosterone. In the female, LH stimulates the production of progesterone by the ovary.

Melanocyte-stimulating hormone (MSH). It is well known that the pars intermedia of the adenohypophysis elaborates a hormone involved in the regulation of the pigment of the skin of Amphibia. This hormone probably assumes a similar role in human physiology.

NEURAL CONTROL OF ADENOHYPOPHYSIS. The neural control of the adenohypophysis is indirect rather than direct by way of nerve impulses. It is believed that axons or neurons in the hypothalamus release a substance into the blood which flows through a plexus of capillaries to the hypophyseal portal system from where it is in turn transported to and stimulates the adenohypophysis.

Many investigations have been conducted demonstrating the influence of the hypothalamus on adenohypophyseal function. For example, Greer has shown in rats that destruction of certain hypothalamic nuclei prevents goiter which normally follows administration of antithyroid compounds.

A summary of hypophyseal hormones is included in Table 43.

THE THYROID GLAND (Fig. 355)

The human thyroid is composed of two lobes lying on either side of the trachea and connected in the midline by a thin isthmus extending over the anterior surface of the trachea. In the adult, the thyroid weighs from 20 to 30 grams. It is encapsulated by two layers of connective tissue—the outer one continuous with the cervical fascia, and the inner one intimately adherent to the surface of the gland itself.

The ancients assigned the thyroid gland such functions as serving as a vascular shunt for cerebral circulation and beautifying the neck, especially when it enlarged into a "goiter."

The thyroid is an embryonic derivative of the entoderm (lining of the alimentary tract). It appears initially as a median evagination from the floor of the embryonic pharynx at the level of the first pair of pharyngeal pouches. The distal end of the outgrowth expands, gradually becoming bilobed, while the stalk narrows to form the thyroglossal duct. The branched terminal end of the primordium of the thyroid assumes a position on the anterior surface of the trachea. Normally the thyroglossal duct becomes obliterated. The foramen cecum, a depression at the root of the tongue, marks the point at which the thyroglossal duct emptied into the embryonic pharynx. If the duct does not become obliterated, a thyroglossal duct cyst may appear in the midline of the neck, requiring surgical removal. Occasionally, remnants of fetal thyroid are found at the base of the tongue.

MICROSCOPIC ANATOMY OF THE THYROID. The thyroid has a remarkable capacity to store

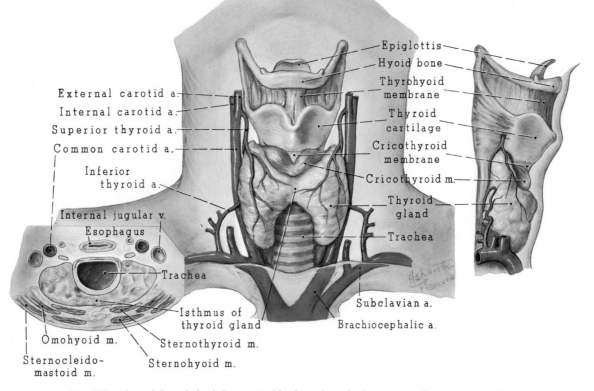

Fig. 355. Plate of thyroid gland showing its blood supply and relations to trachea; in cross section, anterior, and right lateral views.

secretions, as is reflected in its histology. Normally, the thyroid is composed of follicles of uniform size, each in effect a separate gland, and each about the diameter of a pinhead. These follicles are called *acini*. The sacs do not have external openings, but are richly supplied with minute blood and lymph vessels, bringing supplies of iodine and carrying away thyroid hormone. In the healthy gland the follicle consists of a single layer of cuboidal cells surrounding the cavity or lumen filled with a substance known as *colloid*. Colloid itself is a homogenous substance giving the gland its most distinguishing histologic characteristic. It is the storage product of the secretory epithelium. In iodine deficiency follicles become distended with colloid and the cells lining the acini become flattened. When the thyroid overacts, colloid stores become depleted and the acinar epithelium assumes a columnar shape. The stroma (delicate fibrous tissue), located between the acini, is denser in some areas than in others, creating fibrous septa traversing the gland.

PHYSIOLOGY OF THE THYROID. The thyroid is one of the most sensitive organs of the body. During puberty, pregnancy, and physiologic stress it increases in size, becoming more active. Changes in activity and size normally occur during the menstrual cycle.

Initially, iodine from the blood is converted into sodium iodide. Next, iodide ions are combined to form elemental iodine, a form in which iodine probably combines (through the mediation of an enzyme system) with tyrosine, one of the 20 amino acids from which body proteins are formed. Some of the tyrosine molecules take up one atom of iodine, producing monoiodotyrosine; some take up two, making diiodotyrosine. These iodinated tyrosines do not exhibit biologic activity until a coupling system combines two molecules to form iodothyronine which can have two, three, or four atoms of iodine. Among the iodothyronines secreted into the circulation, only thyroxine (tetraiodothyronine) and triiodothyronine possess significant biologic activity. Triiodothyronine is seven times as potent as

TABLE 43.   Hypophyseal Hormones.

NAME AND SOURCE	SYNONYMS	FUNCTION
Adenohypophysis (anterior lobe)		
TSH	Thyroid-stimulating hormone; thyrotropin	Stimulates thyroid growth and secretion.
ACTH	Adrenocorticotropic hormone; corticotropin	Stimulates adrenocortical growth and secretion
STH	Growth hormone; somatotropin	Accelerates body growth
FSH	Follicle-stimulating hormone	Stimulates growth of ovarian follicle and estrogen secretion in the female and spermatogenesis in the male
LH	Luteinizing hormone (in the female); interstitial cell-stimulating hormone ICSH (in the male)	Stimulates ovulation and luteinization of ovarian follicles in the female and production of testosterone in the male
LTH	Luteotropic hormone, luteotropin, prolactin, mammotropin, lactogenic hormone	Maintains the corpus luteum and stimulates secretion of milk
MSH	Melanocyte-stimulating hormone	Stimulates melanocytes causing pigmentation
Neurohypophysis (posterior lobe)		
Antidiuretic Hormone (ADH)	Vasopressin	Promotes water retention by way of the renal tubules and stimulates smooth muscle of blood vessels and digestive tract
Oxytocin		Stimulates contraction of smooth muscle in the uterus

thyroxine itself, although normally only small amounts are secreted.

Thyroxine and triiodothyronine are stored in the colloid of the thyroid follicle. The molecules of these substances attach to giant molecules of protein (thyroglobulin) which are so large that they normally cannot penetrate the wall of the follicle and escape into the blood. Thyroid hormone is released when the thyroglobulin splits.

Thyroid hormone is transported to cells in loose chemical combination with the globulin fraction of the serum protein. In this combination hormones can be precipitated from the patient's blood for measurement of *protein-bound iodine* (PBI), an index of the quantity of thyroid hormone in the circulation. Normally, the concentration of PBI is from 4 to 8 micrograms per 100 ml. Excess mono- and diiodotyrosine do not leave the follicle, but are rapidly deiodinated within the thyroid cell and reutilized for synthesis of thyroglobulin. The change is brought about by the enzyme deiodinase, for which only mono- and diiodotyrosine are substrates (Fig. 356).

Mechanism of action of thyroid hormone.

Several mechanisms of action for thyroid hormone have been proposed. This hormone functions in at least 20 enzyme systems. One of the major activities of thyroxine involves the acceleration of metabolic activity. It has been suggested that thyroxine does not directly influence oxidation, but merely stimulates processes such as protein synthesis which require oxygen. A most attractive theory is that thyroxine acts on the permeability of the mitochondrial membrane, influencing the transfer of enzymes. In the mitochondrial membrane system, thyroxine presumably acts as an oxidative catalyst.

General well-being depends upon the rate at which our bodies "live." The speed of virtually all the basic cellular processes of the body is regulated largely by the thyroid gland. Thyroid activity in turn is governed by the adenohypophysis which coordinates the work of other endocrine glands. Regulation of thyroid output by the adenohypophysis involves a release of thyrotropin, the thyroid-stimulating hormone.

When the adenohypophysis is removed from experimental animals, the thyroid shrinks, producing reduced quantities of hormone with

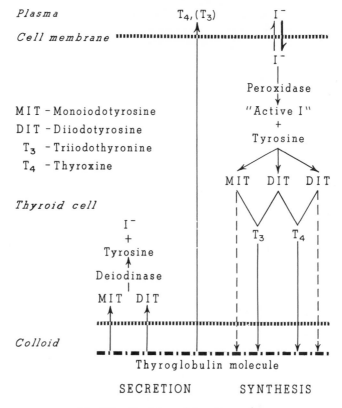

Fig. 356.   Physiology of thyroid secretion.

resulting hypothyroidism. The nervous system indirectly controls the thyroid through the agency of the hypothalamus. The final link in the chain of controls is established by a feedback from the thyroid itself. Thyroid hormone suppresses the production of thyroid-stimulating hormone. In contrast, if there is a deficiency of thyroid hormone, as occurs in some diseases of the thyroid gland itself, the adenohypophysis automatically secretes additional TSH, which in turn affects the thyroid and may result in the enlargement called "goiter."

Thyroid abnormalities usually manifest themselves in one of two ways: (1) the gland produces an excess of thyroid hormone with an increase in metabolic rate (hyperthyroidism); or (2) the gland produces a diminished output of hormone with a reduction in metabolic rate (hypothyroidism). Either condition may devastate the body, and either may be associated with goiter.

Increased secretion of thyroxine.   In hyperthyroidism, the patient becomes excitable and nervous, exhibiting a moist skin, rapid pulse, elevated metabolic rate, and exophthalmos (protrusion of the eyes) (Fig. 357). If a tracer dose of radioactive iodine is given, there is an increase

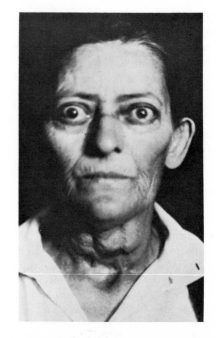

Fig. 357.   Exophthalmos. (Courtesy of Lisser: "Diseases of the Endocrine System," in Blumer, Ed., *Bedside Diagnosis*, volume III. Philadelphia, W. B. Saunders, 1928.)

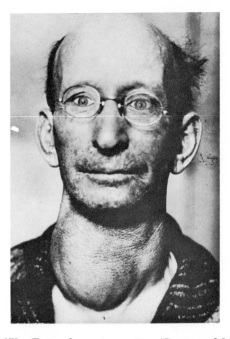

Fig. 358. Toxic adenomatous goiter. (Courtesy of Lisser: "Diseases of the Endocrine System," in Blumer, Ed., *Bedside Diagnosis*, volume III. Philadelphia, W. B. Saunders, 1928.)

tracts containing thyroid-stimulating hormone, even after the thyroid has been removed. The treatment of hyperthyroidism is well established. A physician can choose among the alternatives of surgery, actually removing large segments of the thyroid; administration of radioactive iodine to destroy segments of the gland, or the use of antithyroid drugs to block the production of thyroid hormone.

Reduced secretion of thyroxine. Hypothyroidism results in physical and mental sluggishness, with slowed circulation and other symptoms of a low "rate of living." If it appears in the child, changes in body proportion and face fail to occur. Formation and eruption of teeth are delayed, and cartilage is not converted to bone in the normal manner. The child with hypothyroidism exhibits a broad face with a large mouth and is usually mentally defective. These children have low metabolic rates; if the hypothyroidism is congenital, they are called *cretins*.

Adults with hypothyroidism show puffiness and dryness of the skin and functional changes in the heart. If the adult is a female, menstrual irregularities are common. Hypothyroidism in adults is called *myxedema*. The diagnosis of myxedema can be made by clinical findings, the thyroidal radioactive iodine (I^{131}) uptake, and measurement of serum protein-bound iodine. Hypothyroidism is treated by administration of thyroid hormone (Fig. 360).

Cancer of the thyroid. Cancer of the thyroid occurs in all age groups. Twenty-five years ago it was relatively common in infants following x-ray administration to the neck to combat an enlarged thymus. Treatment of thyroid carcinoma consists of surgical removal of the gland, or destruction

in thyroidal uptake in hyperthyroidism (Figs. 358 and 359). The administration of thyroid hormone in large quantities to animals produces many symptoms of hyperthyroidism, but not the protruding eyes. The adenohypophysis appears to play some role, since exophthalmos occurs in animals after the injection of hypophyseal ex-

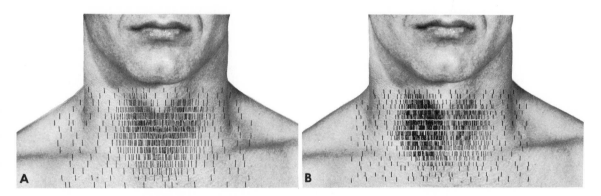

Fig. 359. The scintigram is an apparatus used for recording the intensity and distribution of radioactive tracer substances in the body. *A.* The distribution of radioactive iodine in a patient with a normally functioning thyroid gland. *B.* The pattern of radioactive tracer is demonstrated in increased thyroid activity in the hyperthyroid patient with toxic goiter.

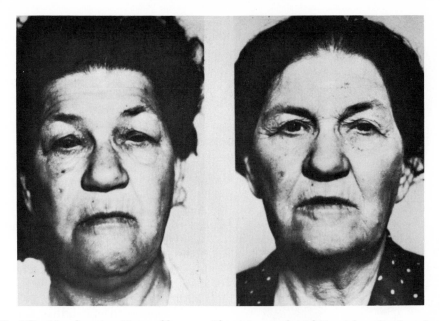

Fig. 360. Myxedema in a 61 year old woman. The picture on the right was taken after 7 weeks of thyroid treatment. (Courtesy of Lisser and Escamilla: *Atlas of Clinical Endocrinology,* second edition. St. Louis, The C. V. Mosby Company, 1962.)

by large doses of x-ray. Treatment with radioactive iodine holds hope for some patients in whom thyroid cancer has spread to other parts of the body.

SUMMARY OF FUNCTIONS OF THE THYROID GLAND. During the production of its hormone (thyroxine), two substances are taken from the blood by the thyroid gland; these are iodine as sodium or potassium iodide, and tyrosine, one of the five essential amino acids. The thyroid gland combines these two into a new product called diiodo- or monoiodotyrosine. Diiodotyrosine is acted upon by the thyrotropic hormone of the adenohypophysis, converting it into thyroxin which is then poured directly into the blood and subsequently carried to other parts of the body.

The amount of thyroxin released is dependent on the blood concentration of thyroxin through the mediation of the adenohypophysis. Thyroid hormone functions to regulate the rate at which the tissues of the body work.

THE PARATHYROID GLANDS

The parathyroid glands were unknown to the medical profession until 1880 when they were described by a Swedish anatomist. Surgeons have learned that the accidental removal of these structures at the time of a thyroidectomy results in a serious condition known as tetany.

The parathyroid glands are yellowish or reddish-tan, flattened, oval bodies, 6 mm. in length and 3 to 4 mm. in breadth; usually four in number, they are located on the posterior aspect of the lobes of the thyroid (Fig. 361). On histologic section, the parathyroid gland consists of two epithelial cell types: *chief* and *oxyphil.* The chief cell is the more numerous and has a large, vesicular, centrally placed nucleus embedded in a faintly staining cytoplasm containing glycogen. The oxyphil cell, characterized by eosinophilic granulation, does not contain glycogen, and is slightly larger than the chief cell. Parathyroid hormone is produced by the chief cells. The function of the oxyphil cell which appears after puberty is unknown.

PHYSIOLOGY OF THE PARATHYROIDS. The parathyroid gland secretes parathyroid hormone, a protein consisting of a single polypeptide chain composed of 83 amino acids with a molecular weight of 8000. Its function is closely linked with the homeostatic regulation of the calcium ion concentration of body fluids. The parathyroid responds to lower plasma concentrations of calcium by an increased output of parathyroid hormone. This removes calcium

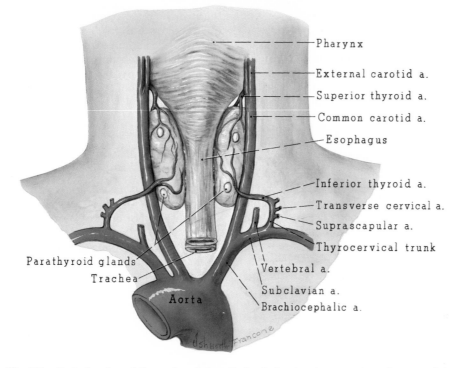

Fig. 361.   Posterior view of the neck and thyroid gland, showing the approximate location of the parathyroid glands.

from the bones and may result in cyst formation. The control of this mechanism operates by a negative feedback system; that is, the calcium ion concentration provides a stimulus for control of the activity of the parathyroid. The direct action of this hormone on bone has been shown by grafts of parathyroid tissue implanted adjacent to bone, resulting in local bone reabsorption.

METABOLISM OF CALCIUM AND PHOSPHORUS. Since the parathyroid hormone exerts an important regulating effect on calcium and phosphorus, it is essential at this point to review the metabolism of these minerals. Calcium serves four major functions; these are bone formation, coagulation of blood, maintenance of normal cell permeability, and maintenance of normal neuromuscular irritability. Since calcium is regulated by parathyroid hormone, normal parathyroid function is involved in all these roles.

Although calcium is present in all body fluids, 99 per cent is contained in bone. The normal adult requirement is 1 gram per day. During periods of active growth, such as pregnancy, this requirement may increase to approximately 2 grams per day. Calcium is absorbed chiefly in the duodenum, where its rate of absorption is modified by vitamin D and the hydrogen ion concentration of the intestine. The rate of absorption is also dependent on nutrients present in the gastrointestinal tract which may bind calcium and prevent absorption.

Calcium salts are more soluble in acid than in an alkaline medium; therefore, factors promoting acidity in the upper gastrointestinal tract tend to increase the absorption of calcium; factors promoting alkalinity decrease absorption. If the intake is less than the needs of the body, the deficit is made up by reabsorption of calcium from the bones into the blood. Once calcium is absorbed through the intestinal tract, it enters the circulation and is eventually deposited in bone or secreted by the kidneys.

Calcium balance is the difference between the quantity of calcium ingested and the amount excreted in the urine and feces. It is usually positive during growth and pregnancy and negative in diseases such as rickets. Calcium concentration varies inversely with the serum phosphorus level; the normal calcium content ranges from 9 to 11 mg. per 100 ml., and normal phosphorus from 2 to 4 mg. per 100 ml.

Phosphorus.   Phosphorus is present in all tissues and fluids and is an important mineral of the body, serving a role in the formation of bone and influencing the transfer of energy in the intermediary metabolism of carbohydrate and protein. The daily requirement of phosphorus is about 1 gram. Eight to 85 per cent of the body phosphorus is stored in the skeleton. Derangements in phosphorus metabolism are invariably associated with concomitant alterations in calcium and vitamin D levels; hence, no specific disease states are directly attributable to phosphorus alone.

DISEASES OF THE PARATHYROID GLANDS. *Hypoparathyroidism (tetany).* The signs of parathyroid underactivity include a drop in serum calcium and a rise in serum inorganic phosphorus. With parathyroid deficiency the urinary excretion of calcium diminishes. Common symptoms of parathyroid deficiency are increased excitability of the musculature to mechanical stimulation and fibrillary twitchings followed by jerky muscular contractions. The neuromuscular symptoms become more severe as the calcium level of the blood falls. Tetany is encountered following accidental removal or injury of the parathyroid glands when the thyroid has been surgically treated. One remaining parathyroid gland is thought to be sufficient to prevent the occurrence of tetany. Treatment of hypoparathyroidism must be considered from the point of view of acute and chronic phases. In the acute phase, which frequently occurs in the postoperative period following removal of the parathyroid with the thyroid, treatment is aimed at preventing muscle spasm and convulsions. This is accomplished by restoring the serum calcium level to normal by the intravenous injection of calcium salts.

During the chronic stage of hypoparathyroidism the major goal of treatment is to maintain the serum calcium level at normal, so as to prevent the symptoms and signs of tetany and to avoid future complications including cataracts. Vitamin D is given to enhance the absorption of calcium by the small intestine. Oral calcium salts are also of value.

Hyperparathyroidism. The basic problem in hyperparathyroidism is excess circulating parathyroid hormone, leading to increased serum calcium levels (hypercalcemia). Calcium is precipitated in the urinary tract and results in the formation of stones in the kidney. These in turn may cause obstruction of the ureter with accompanying pain and infection. Excess parathyroid hormone causes excess reabsorption of bone, producing pain, tenderness, fracture, and deformity. X-ray evidence of demineralization of bones is present; if the disease is severe or of long standing, bone cysts can occur. The laboratory findings in hyperparathyroidism include an increase in serum calcium, a decrease in serum phosphorus, and an increase in excretion of body calcium and phosphorus in the urine. Hyperparathyroidism is usually caused by a parathyroid tumor. Treatment consists of surgical removal of the tumor.

PANCREATIC ISLETS

The pancreatic islets are scattered throughout the pancreas (Fig. 362). The islets produce two polypeptide hormones, insulin and glucagon.

Structure of the islets. The pancreatic islets of the human contain at least three cell types: *alpha, beta,* and *delta,* distinguished on the basis of histologic characteristics. Insulin is formed by the beta cells of the islets and glucagon by the alpha cells. The function of the delta cells is unknown.

Insulin

Synthesis and storage of insulin by beta cells. The insulin molecule consists of 51 amino acids arranged in two polypeptide chains connected by two disulfide bridges. A number of essential amino acids are present, supplied by the diet. The other amino acids can be synthesized in the beta cells or transferred to the beta cells after

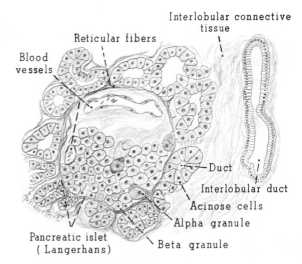

Fig. 362. Microscopic section of pancreas showing pancreatic islets (of Langerhans).

synthesis from other sites, including the liver. The sulfur-containing amino acids are important in the synthesis of insulin. A possible sequence for insulin synthesis is as follows. Energy in the form of adenosine triphosphate from mitochondria promotes amino acid transformation and peptide bond synthesis, the final synthesis being accomplished by the endoplasmic reticulum of the cytoplasm. Insulin enters the blood directly or can be stored in beta cells. The Golgi apparatus probably functions in concentrating and storing insulin in the beta cells. Zinc is present in these cells, but its role in storage and release of insulin is not clear. It is possible that insulin is stored as an insoluble zinc complex within the beta cell granules.

Function of insulin. For more than a third of a century, insulin has been one of the great puzzles of biology. Even today, over 40 years after the epic work of Banting and Best, its exact mechanism is unknown. When the systematic search for the mechanism of action of insulin was commenced, it was natural to assume that insulin acted on some key enzyme system. It was soon demonstrated that the function of insulin did not revolve around the internal machinery of the cell. Currently it is believed that when an animal ingests carbohydrate, sugar moves into the blood and raises the glucose level. This is the signal for the pancreas to secrete more insulin. The hormone travels by way of the blood to the cells and attaches itself to some specific point on the surface of the cells, thus opening the door allowing sugar to enter. Insulin secretion by the pancreas regulates the cellular uptake and blood sugar level. Lack of insulin results in coma and eventual death (Fig. 363). Recent evidence is consistent with the fact that skeletal muscle may also release an unidentified substance which can open this door. If insulin is the "gateman," scientists will soon be looking for other hormones acting as "engineers" controlling the flow of minerals in and out of the chemical factory of the cell.

Oral insulin substitutes. One of the difficulties in treating diabetes is that insulin cannot be given orally, since it is a protein partially inactivated in the gastrointestinal tract. However, several classes of oral substitutes for insulin are available today. These are helpful in individuals with diminished "effective" insulin (diabetes mellitus). The sulfonamide drugs were introduced in 1935. Soon afterward, observations were made that patients receiving the sulfonamides for infection showed a drop in blood sugar. In 1955, it was demonstrated that the sulfonamides could partially prevent hyperglycemia.

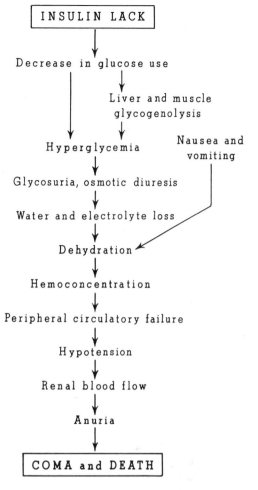

Fig. 363. Progressive symptoms due to lack of insulin. (From Tepperman: *Metabolic and Endocrine Physiology.* Chicago, Year Book Medical Publishers, 1962.)

Tolbutamide, a derivative of the sulfonamides, controls the symptoms of diabetes in individuals with remaining beta cell function, but not in the severe or juvenile diabetic. Tolbutamide, then, is not insulin, but a chemical stimulating release of insulin into the blood from the beta cell. The mechanism by which this occurs is unknown. Another class of oral compounds, the biguanides, is administered for the treatment of diabetes. Many patients cannot tolerate this class of compounds, since they produce gastrointestinal disturbances. The primary effect of the biguanides is exerted on the liver and not on beta cells. They apparently diminish gluconeogenesis and, therefore, reduce hepatic output of glucose.

Glucagon

Glucagon, a specific hormone produced by the pancreatic islets in the alpha cells, is a straight chain polypeptide consisting of 29 amino acids. The formation and release of glucagon is even less well characterized than is insulin itself. Recent studies have shown that measurable amounts of glucagon are present in circulating blood. The blood level of glucagon rises in response to *hypoglycemia*. Glucagon acts primarily on the liver to promote glycogen breakdown and glucose release.

The major stimulant, then, for the release of either insulin or glucagon, appears to be a change in the circulating blood glucose concentration. Physiologic elevation of blood glucose results in insulin release; similarly, a fall in blood glucose stimulates glucagon release. In the non-diabetic these control mechanisms operate smoothly. This precise control of normal fluctuation in blood sugar is lacking in patients with diabetes mellitus.

SUPRARENAL GLANDS (ADRENAL GLANDS)

There are two suprarenal glands, one superior to each kidney. Each resembles an admiral's cocked hat in shape and each is about 1½ inches in length and ½ inch in diameter. The suprarenal gland varies in weight in different age groups, the average in the adult being about 4 grams. Each suprarenal gland has a cortex, or outer portion, and a medulla, or inner portion. The cortex and medulla are different in both origin and function, with the cortex being derived from the mesoderm in close association with the developing gonads, and the medulla being neuroectodermal in origin.

Suprarenal Cortex

The cortex of the suprarenal gland is deep yellow in color and occupies three-quarters of the total width of the suprarenal gland in cross section. From the surface inward its component layers are the *zona glomerulosa*, the *zona fasciculata*, and the *zona reticularis*. The cells in the zona glomerulosa are arranged in loops, or whorls. Cells in the zona fasciculata form long cords running toward the center of the gland. Cells in the zona reticularis are found in order-

less masses. Cells of the suprarenal cortex possess little preformed hormone, but quickly elaborate steroids from cholesterol precursors within the cells. Since the cortex contains only about 20 micrograms of steroid hormone per gram, it is not possible to demonstrate cortical hormone by histochemical methods.

Three general types of substances are secreted by the cortex: mineralocorticoids, represented principally by *aldosterone;* glucocorticoids, represented chiefly by *cortisol (hydrocortisone)*; and androgens, represented by *testosterone*.

MINERALOCORTICOIDS. Aldosterone is the principal natural mineralocorticoid and is the most active substance known to promote sodium retention. It is secreted by the outer zone or zona glomerulosa of the cortex. DOCA, desoxycorticosterone, is a synthetic mineralocorticoid which at one time was employed in the treatment of patients with suprarenal insufficiency. The daily rate of aldosterone secretion in humans varies from 70 to 200 micrograms on a normal salt diet, compared with the secretion of 25 mg. of cortisol daily. The secretion of aldosterone can increase up to 900 micrograms per day in the face of severe sodium restriction. Aldosterone is an important link in the regulation of water and electrolyte metabolism. It increases the renal tubular reabsorption of sodium, thereby raising the sodium concentration and osmotic pressure of the extracellular fluid. Aldosterone also exerts extrarenal effects on electrolyte metabolism, decreasing sodium and increasing potassium concentration in saliva and sweat.

An understanding of the role of sodium in the cause of edema has led to the use of agents to reduce the high concentration of sodium found in edematous patients. These agents either inhibit tubular reabsorption of sodium by the kidney or block the renal tubular activity of aldosterone.

GLUCOCORTICOIDS. Glucocorticoids influence the metabolism of glucose, protein, and fat. Cortisol is the principal glucocorticoid and is formed by the zona fasciculata. Although there are several glucocorticoids secreted by the cortex, 90 per cent of the total activity is represented by cortisol.

The exact mechanism of the function of cortisol is unknown. One suggestion is that it increases the permeability of the cell membrane to amino acids. Cortisol increases the rate of amino acid metabolism and the conversion of protein and fats into glucose (gluconeogenesis).

ANDROGENS. Androgens, steroid hormones, produce masculinization. The most important androgen is testosterone secreted by the testis.

Suprarenal androgens are of minor importance, except when a suprarenal tumor develops, in which case excessive quantities of androgenic hormones are produced. This can cause a child or even an adult female to take on an adult masculine appearance, including growth of the clitoris to resemble a penis, growth of a beard, a change in the voice quality to bass, and increased muscular strength.

In summary, cortisol is particulary active in relation to carbohydrate metabolism and is hence known as a glucocorticoid. It is relatively inactive with respect to electrolyte metabolism. Aldosterone, on the other hand, has a limited effect on carbohydrate metabolism, but exerts a pronounced influence on electrolyte and water metabolism. Aldosterone is probably the principal biologic mineralocorticoid. Suprarenal androgen can be looked upon as a suprarenal by-product, assuming importance only when it is produced in excess.

ABNORMALITIES OF SUPRARENAL CORTEX FUNCTION. *Addison's disease,* a relatively rare disorder most common in middle life, occurs equally in both sexes. Addison's disease is a deficiency of function of the suprarenal cortex, with insufficient production of both glucocorticoids and mineralocorticoids, resulting in an incapacity of the renal tubules to adequately reabsorb sodium and chloride, and in other metabolic defects. There is, therefore, a loss of sodium and chloride and, with this loss, a secretion of large volumes of water. The plasma volume is reduced, followed by a drop in blood pressure and gastrointestinal symptoms. Pigmentation of the skin and mucosa is another diagnostic feature. The excessive melanin deposition is probably caused by a lack of suprarenal feedback to the hypophysis, with a resultant increased activity of ACTH. The outlook for patients with this disease is favorable with adequate substitution of suprarenal cortical hormones.

Cushing's disease, a primary disorder of the adenohypophysis, is excess production of ACTH with resulting suprarenal hyperfunction. The cortex can, however, be hyperfunctional without stimulation from the adenohypophysis (as in suprarenal tumors). Both these examples are characterized by obesity, elevated blood pressure, moon face, and acne (Fig. 364). Often there is an accompanying diabetes mellitus. The offending hyperfunctional tissue or tumor is removed when this condition is treated.

The adrenogenital syndrome is caused by defective cortisol production by the cortex. In an attempt to overcome this defect, the adenohypophysis secretes large amounts of ACTH, resulting in bilateral enlargement of the suprarenal glands and excessive androgen production. Masculinizing influences depend on age and sex of the patient.

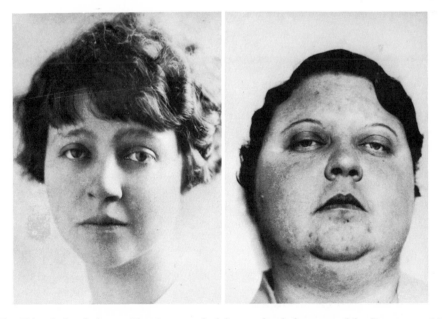

Fig. 364. Cushing's disease. The picture on the left was taken before onset of the disease at age 19. The picture on the right shows the same woman at age 28. (Courtesy of Lisser: J. Nerv. & Ment. Dis., 99:727, 1944.)

Suprarenal Medulla

Whereas the hormones of the cortex are steroids, those of the medulla are amines. The medulla, not essential to life, is composed of irregular masses of cells separated by sinusoidal-type vessels. The medulla elaborates the catechol-amines, epinephrine and norepinephrine (also known as adrenalin and noradrenalin respectively). The medulla contains about 1 mg. of catecholamines of which 90 per cent is epinephrine. Adrenomedullary extracts are composed of both epinephrine and norepinephrine, with constant proportions characteristic for a given species. The human medulla secretes ten times as much epinephrine as norepinephrine.

Epinephrine, in addition to other effects, elevates blood sugar. Two mechanisms are believed responsible—mobilization of carbohydrate stores from the liver, and enhanced transformation of muscle glycogen into lactic acid for the liver to manufacture into new carbohydrate.

The adrenal medulla functions in conjunction with the sympathetic nervous system. Medullary hormones are released in response to sympathetic stimulation. The two medullary amines appear to be released independently and to perform distinct roles in homeostasis. Epinephrine equips the organism to meet certain types of emergency situations and prevents hypoglycemia. Norepinephrine is found predominantly at sympathetic nerve endings and functions as a pressor hormone to maintain blood pressure.

OVARIES

The ovaries are two small bodies located in the pelvic portion of the abdomen and attached to the broad ligament in the female. The outer layer of the ovary consists of a specialized epithelium producing the ova. There are two types of hormones secreted by the ovary, estrogen and progesterone (see Chapter Seventeen for a more detailed description).

TESTES

The testes are small, ovoid glands suspended from the inguinal region by the spermatic cord and surrounded and supported by the scrotum.

Two major types of specialized tissue are found in testicular substance—tubules containing germinal epithelium functioning in the formation of spermatozoa; and interstitial Leydig's cells producing testosterone.

PINEAL GLAND

The human pineal is a small, conical organ, gray in color, lying at about the middle of the brain. It is attached anteriorly to the posterior wall of the third ventricle by the pineal stalk, located above the superior colliculi of the midbrain. The pineal is less than 1 cm. in its longest diameter and weighs approximately 0.1 to 0.2 gram. It is not a functionless vestige, as had been previously believed; recent evidence suggests that the epithelial cells of the pineal can regulate aldosterone secretion, although this is a controversial point. Prepubertal destruction of the pineal gland in the male results in precocious puberty.

PLACENTA

The placenta has been recognized as an endocrine organ since the earliest days of this century, when it was noted that the ovaries of

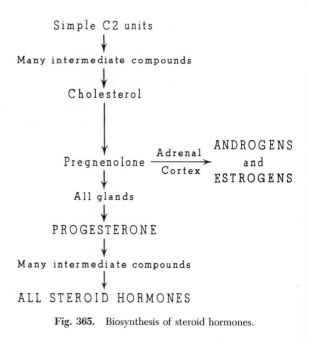

Fig. 365. Biosynthesis of steroid hormones.

pregnant women could be removed after 3 or 4 months of gestation without terminating pregnancy. Chorionic gonadotropin, estrogen, and progesterone are produced by the placenta. There is some evidence that the placenta secretes relaxin and aldosterone.

An understanding of the pathway of steroid biosynthesis provides an example of the versatility of the placenta in its own biosynthetic activity. Several types of steroids have a number of biosynthetic steps in common, from acetate to cholesterol. The cholesterol is metabolized through pregnenolone, which is the precursor of almost all steroid hormones. Progesterone is an intermediate in the synthesis of androgen and perhaps of corticosteroids (Fig. 365). A process utilizing the energy obtained by the energy-yielding reactions, such as the tricarboxylic acid cycle coupled with oxidative phosphorylation, takes place in the placenta. Thus, the placenta also has a means of converting glucose to fructose.

SUMMARY: THE ENDOCRINE SYSTEM

GENERAL FUNCTIONS

1. Correlation and control in harmony with the nervous system.

2. Endocrine glands: glands that pour secretions (hormones) directly into the blood.

3. Endocrine glands include the hypophysis, thyroid, parathyroids, pancreatic islets, suprarenals, ovaries, testes, and pineal; the placenta serves temporarily as an endocrine gland.

HYPOPHYSIS

1. Located in the sella turcica of the sphenoid bone, attached to the undersurface of the cerebrum.

2. Neurohypophysis (posterior hypophysis):
   a. Functions:
      (1) Secretion of oxytocin and ADH.
         (a) Oxytocin stimulates contraction of the uterus in pregnancy.
         (b) ADH controls water reabsorption by the distal tubules of the kidney and stimulates the smooth muscle of the digestive tract and blood vessels.
      (2) Control of neurohypophysis: impulses from the hypothalamus in combination with blood levels of oxytocin and ADH.

3. Adenohypophysis:
   a. Structure: consists of at least four cell types: chromophobes, basophils, eosinophils, and amphophils.
   b. Function:
      (1) Thyroid-stimulating hormone (TSH) stimulates thyroid growth and secretion.
      (2) Adrenocorticotropic hormone (ACTH) stimulates adrenocortical growth and secretion.
      (3) Somatotropic hormone (STH) accelerates body growth.
      (4) Follicle-stimulating hormone (FSH) stimulates growth of ovarian follicles in female and spermatozoa in the male.
      (5) Luteinizing hormone (LH) and interstitial cell-stimulating hormone ICSH (in the male). These hormones stimulate ovulation, the luteinizing of ovarian follicles in the female, and testosterone production in the male.
      (6) Luteotropic hormone (LTH) maintains the corpus luteum and stimulates secretion of milk.
      (7) Melanocyte-stimulating hormone (MSH) stimulates melanocytes.

Thyroid Gland

1. Structure: located in the neck below the larynx; composed of two lobes connected by an isthmus.

2. Function:

   a. Produces and secretes thyroid hormone which controls the metabolic turnover of oxygen, thus stimulating growth processes.
   b. Stores thyroglobulin.

3. Effects of abnormalities:

   a. Hyposecretion in childhood causes cretinism.
   b. Hypersecretion causes hypermetabolism.

Parathyroid Glands (Four)

1. Located on the posterior surface of the thyroid.

2. Structure: composed of two basic cell groups—chief cells and oxyphil cells.

3. Functions: control blood calcium level and neuromuscular tone by stimulating calcium reabsorption from bone.

4. Abnormalities:

   a. Hyposecretion causes hypocalcemia and in turn tetany.
   b. Hypersecretion results in replacement of bone with fibrous tissue.

Pancreatic Islets

1. Located throughout the pancreas.

2. Structure:

   a. The islets are composed of three cell types: alpha, beta, and delta.

3. Function:

   a. Beta cells secrete insulin, which acts as the "gateman" for normal carbohydrate metabolism.
   b. Alpha cells produce glucagon, which controls glycogenolysis.
   c. Function of delta cells is unknown.

4. Oral insulin substitutes: tolbutamides and the biguanides are effective only if there is some remaining function of the islets.

Suprarenal Glands

1. Located immediately superior to each kidney.

2. Structure:

   a. Composed of two parts: cortex (outer), derived from the mesoderm; and medulla (inner), derived from the neural ectoderm.

3. Function:

   a. Cortex:
      (1) Mineralocorticoids (aldosterone) regulate fluid and electrolyte balance by increasing renal tubule reabsorption of sodium, chloride, and water.
      (2) Glucocorticoids influence metabolism of glucose, protein, and fat.

(3) Androgens influence masculinization; usually an unimportant source unless production is increased over normal.

(4) Abnormalities of adrenal function: Addison's disease (deficiency of function of cortex); Cushing's disease (adrenal hyperfunction); and adrenogenital syndrome (masculinization due to excessive adrenal androgen production).

b. Medulla:

(1) Elaborates epinephrine and norepinephrine.

OVARIES

1. **Secrete estrogen and progesterone and liberate ova.**

TESTES

1. **Form spermatozoa and secrete testosterone.**

PINEAL GLAND

1. **Attached to third ventricle of brain; prepubertal destruction in male results in precocious puberty.**

PLACENTA

1. **Produces chorionic gonadotropin, estrogen, and progesterone.**

STUDY QUESTIONS: THE ENDOCRINE SYSTEM

1. List and give the location of each of the endocrine glands.
2. Name the hormone or hormones each gland secretes.
3. Give the origins of the two portions of the hypophysis.
4. Describe the hormonal control of uterine contraction.
5. Explain the control of the neurohypophysis.
6. Discuss in detail why the adenohypophysis has been called "the leader of the endocrine orchestra."
7. Follow, step by step, the biosynthesis of thyroid hormone.
8. How does thyroid hormone relate to mitochondria?
9. Name the conditions leading to the following states:

   a. Nervousness combined with moist skin, rapid pulse, and elevated metabolic rate.
   b. Puffiness and dryness of the skin and a low blood concentration of protein-bound iodine.
   c. Increased excitability of the musculature with jerky muscular contractions.
   d. Precipitation of calcium in the urinary system and bone wasting.

10. Explain the theory which states that insulin acts as a "gateman."
11. When are oral insulin substitutes practical?
12. List in detail the mechanisms of insulin and glucagon release from the pancreas.

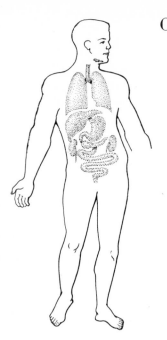

CHAPTER SIXTEEN

FLUIDS
AND
ELECTROLYTES

SURVEY

The 19th century physiologist Claude Bernard first advanced the concept that there existed within higher organisms a purposeful tendency toward the constancy of the internal fluid environment of cells. This concept of integration and dynamic equilibrium maintaining a normal body state is known as *homeostasis*. This relatively unvarying composition of the internal environment is assured by complex interactions of the respiratory, digestive, excretory, circulatory, endocrine, and nervous systems of the body.

After Bernard, understanding of the role of body electrolytes increased only slowly. More recently practical methods for the exact analysis of electrolytes in body fluids, and radioisotope techniques for determining the volume of the different types of body fluids have been associated with a marked increase in knowledge.

Body fluids have been "compartmentalized" by physiologists to help define their distribution. Fluids are in the *extracellular space* (outside cell membranes) or in the *intracellular space* (within cell membranes). The extracellular space is further divided into a *vascular* or *plasma compartment* (within blood vessels) and an *interstitial compartment* (between cells) (Fig. 366).

What percentage, then, by weight of an animal is represented by water? An early human

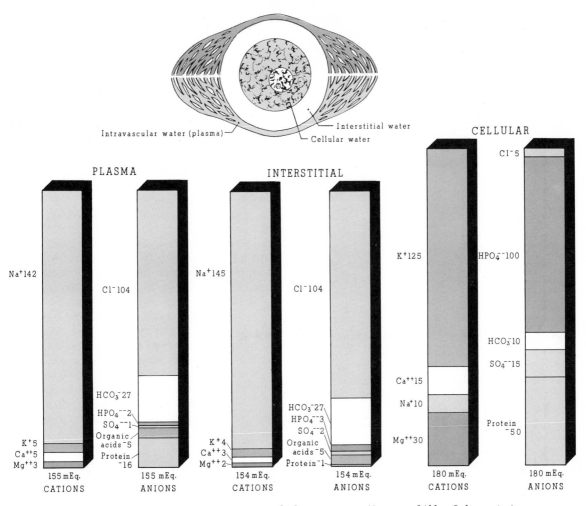

Fig. 366. Distribution of anions and cations in fluid compartments. (Courtesy of Abbott Laboratories.)

embryo is 97 per cent water; a newborn infant, 77 per cent water. Water constitutes 60 per cent of the weight of an adult male and slightly less than 54 per cent of the weight of an adult female. Since fat is essentially free of water, the less fat present the greater the percentage of body weight due to water.

Body water diffuses throughout the body without recognizing anatomic boundaries. For instance, water passes in a continuous manner across the connective tissue surface of the capillaries. If all the water molecules in the blood were suddenly labeled, perhaps only one-half of the labeled molecules would be present in the blood 1 minute later.

TERMINOLOGY

An *electrolyte* is a molecule which ionizes (dissociates into two or more charged particles called ions) in solution, rendering the solution capable of conducting an electrical current. An ion carrying a positive charge is known as a *cation;* an ion carrying a negative charge is an *anion.* Sodium chloride consists of positively charged sodium atoms (cations) and negatively charged chloride atoms (anions). However, electrical balance is always maintained. Both electrolytes and non-electrolytes are found in solution in body fluids. The non-electrolytes, such as dextrose and urea, do not ionize in water solutions.

A *molar* solution contains 1 gram molecular weight of a substance dissolved (solute) in enough solvent to make 1 liter. A *molal* solution, on the other hand, contains 1 gram molecular weight of a substance dissolved in 1000 grams of solvent.

Osmotic pressure refers to the force which solute particles exert to draw solvent across a semipermeable membrane. The basic unit used in expressing this force refers to the concentration of solute particles. This unit is the *osmol*. Clinically, $1/1000$ osmol, or 1 *milliosmol*, is a more useful unit. The osmotic pressure of a solution can be expressed as the osmolarity or osmolality of this solution, and the value is proportional to the molar and molal concentrations respectively.

A solution can be described as being *isotonic*, *hypotonic*, or *hypertonic*, which means it has the same, lower, or higher relative concentrations of the solute than is normal for the system with which the osmolarity is being compared (since the osmolar effect is related to the number of particles, rather than to the concentration in moles). An electrolyte solution, such as sodium chloride, which dissociates into two particles may be isotonic with a standard solution in a concentration of 0.15 M, while a glucose or urea solution, which does not dissociate, would be isotonic with the same standard in a concentration of 0.3 M.

The *equivalent* weight of a chemical substance is the amount of the substance in grams which will react with 1 gram of hydrogen or 8 grams of oxygen. A normal solution contains 1 gram equivalent weight of solute per liter. If the solute molecule has a valence of one, then the molarity and normality of the solution will be equal. If the valence is more than one, the gram equivalent weight is the gram molecular weight divided by the valence. A *milliequivalent* is $1/1000$ of an equivalent and is used as a common measure of all plasma electrolytes. The term *milligrams per cent* refers to the number of milligrams per 100 ml. of blood or plasma. To convert milligrams per cent to milliequivalents per liter, multiply milligrams per cent times ten, times the valence, and divide by the molecular weight. For example, calcium has a valence of two and a molecular weight of 40. To convert a report of 10 mg. per cent calcium to the value in milliequivalents per liter, simply multiply $10 \times 10 \times 2$ and divide this value by 40, equaling 5 mEq./liter.

Since osmotic pressure is a function of the number of particles in solution, the use of the milliequivalent system presents us with a convenient standard reflecting both the osmolarity and the chemical reactivity of a solute concentration (Fig. 367).

COMPOSITION OF BODY FLUIDS

The molecular weight of plasma proteins varies from less than 70,000 to more than 1,000,000. The osmotic pressure exerted by small particles is greater than that exerted by large particles. Proteins, therefore, exert an osmotic pressure of a magnitude in inverse proportion to weight. Thus, the concentration of plasma protein, about 7 grams per 100 ml. of plasma, represents an osmotic pressure of only 2 milliosmols per liter. Electrolytes, on the other hand, dissociate into ions and consequently exert osmotic pressures greater than their molar concentration, since they—NaCl, for instance—dissociate completely into sodium and chloride ions.

The fluid in each body compartment has a distinct distribution of electrolytes. The major cation in intracellular fluid is potassium; the major anion is phosphate. Sodium is the major cation in plasma and in interstitial fluid, while chloride is the major anion. Other ions, such as calcium, magnesium, carbonate, sulfate, and organic acids, are present in varying amounts in the different body fluids.

Gibbs-Donnan Equilibrium

The reason for these differences in distribution can be largely explained by the *Gibbs-Donnan equilibrium*. This states that, in the presence of a non-diffusible ion, the diffusible ions distribute themselves so that at equilibrium a product of the concentration of the ions on one side of a semipermeable membrane equals that on the other side. Thus, if there is an ion on one side of the membrane that cannot cross, distribution of other ions to which the membrane is permeable will occur in a predictable fashion. Since plasma protein does not readily pass through the wall of a capillary, the composition of the interstitial fluid differs from that of the plasma because of the Gibbs-Donnan membrane effect on ion distribution.

HOMEOSTASIS

Body water is regulated with precision. During a 24-hour interval the weight of a man varies

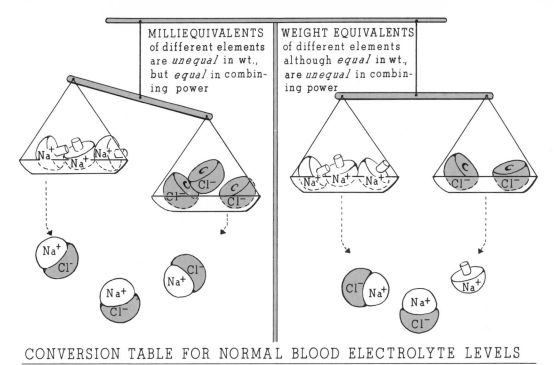

CONVERSION TABLE FOR NORMAL BLOOD ELECTROLYTE LEVELS

NORMAL RANGE

	Mg. per 100 cc.	Conversion Factor of Mg. to mEq.	mEq. per Liter
Na^+	317–340	0.435	137–148
K^+	15–21	0.257	4.1–5.4
$Ca++$	9–11	0.500	4.5–5.5
Mg^{++}	1.2–3.6	0.833	1–3
$HCO_3^-(CO_2/vol.\%)$	55–75	0.455	25–34
Cl^-	352–389	0.286	100–110
$PO_4=$	3–5	0.580	1.7–2.9
$SO_4=$	1.6–2.4	0.625	1.0–1.5
Protein (gm.%)	6.5–8.0	2.430	16–19

Fig. 367. Sodium and chloride ions combine equally on a milliequivalent basis but not on a weight basis. The conversion factor is multiplied times the mg. per 100 ml. value to yield the number of milliequivalents per liter. (After "Of Water, Salt and Life," Lakeside Laboratories, Inc.)

by approximately ⅓ pound. Normally, the body maintains a balance between intake of water and water loss (Fig. 368).

If the body loses water, it acts rapidly to compensate for this deficit. Urine volume diminishes and thirst is noted. Water is then taken into the body more rapidly than it is lost. Conversely, if there is an excess of water in the body, there is a speed-up of its elimination. The urinary output increases and soon exceeds the relatively constant gain of water produced from the oxidation of foodstuffs within the body.

Intake and Output

The approximate daily rates of water loss through the various possible avenues for the adult under basal conditions are skin, 500 ml.; expired air, 300 ml.; urine, 1000 to 1500 ml.; and feces, 200 ml. Water loss through the skin and lungs varies with the ambient temperature and humidity. With high environmental temperature, water loss through the skin and expired air may reach 20 liters per day. This vaporization of water from the surface of the skin is the chief

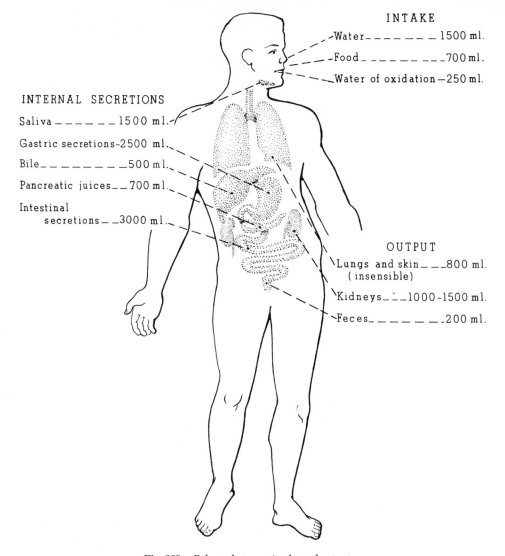

INTAKE

Water _ _ _ _ _ _ _ 1500 ml.

Food _ _ _ _ _ _ _ _ 700 ml.

Water of oxidation — 250 ml.

INTERNAL SECRETIONS

Saliva _ _ _ _ _ _ 1500 ml.

Gastric secretions - 2500 ml.

Bile _ _ _ _ _ _ _ _ 500 ml.

Pancreatic juices _ _ 700 ml.

Intestinal
    secretions _ _ 3000 ml.

OUTPUT

Lungs and skin _ _ _ 800 ml.
    (insensible)

Kidneys _ _ 1000-1500 ml.

Feces _ _ _ _ _ _ _ 200 ml.

Fig. 368.   Balance between intake and output.

protective mechanism against overheating when ambient temperature exceeds body temperature.

Loss of water by diffusion through the skin, independent of sweat gland activity, is termed *insensible perspiration.* At comfortable room temperature, water diffuses through the skin and evaporates as quickly as it is formed; thus, the skin appears dry. *Sensible perspiration,* on the other hand, refers to water appearing on the surface of the skin as a result of sweat gland activity.

Normally, the maintenance of the volume of body water is largely self regulated, provided there is free access to water. When losses are high, as with excessive sweating or diarrhea, the kidney conserves water by making less urine.

The neurohypophyseal antidiuretic hormone, ADH, in response to changes in osmotic tension of the blood, influences the kidney to conserve or excrete water (see Chapter Fourteen).

A rise of only 2 per cent in the total effective solute concentration of the serum is sufficient to stimulate a maximal release of ADH from the neurohypophysis. This, in turn, acts upon the renal tubules and results in increased reabsorption of water. When water is ingested, the decrease in solute concentration of the serum causes an inhibition of ADH release.

The appetite for water is under the control of the same mechanisms which regulate the solute concentration of body fluids; thus, an increase in solute concentration causes a stimulation of the thirst mechanisms originating in the hypothalamus, which in turn results in an increased ingestion of water. Experimentally the injection of hypertonic saline into the anterior hypothalamus of animals will stimulate the animal to drink to the point of water intoxication. Usually human beings must overcome a growing disgust for fluids if they seek to adjust to the ingestion of abnormally large quantities of water. Indeed, forced drinking, or the "water cure," was early recognized as a means of torture.

The lymphatic system plays an important role in fluid and electrolyte balance by returning to the vascular compartment water and solutes which have leaked from the capillaries.

REGULATION OF ELECTROLYTE BALANCE

Osmotic Pressure

Osmotic pressure in the intracellular fluid is regulated by the concentration of proteins and potassium. In the extracellular fluid, osmotic pressure is regulated by the concentration of proteins and sodium. If there is a loss or gain in either sodium or potassium concentration in one compartment, the osmotic pressure balance is disturbed and an increased amount of water will shift into the compartment of greater osmotic pressure.

Sodium Balance

Sodium is the principal cation of extracellular fluid. Its concentration is regulated by both the *hypophyseal-renal axis*, and the *hypophyseal-suprarenal axis*.

While the most sensitive regulator of sodium and water balance in normal subjects is the *neurohypophyseal-renal axis* mediated through ADH, other factors can enter into metabolism of sodium and water. For example, in advanced disease of the kidney inadequate glomerular filtration may occur, with the kidney unable to conserve water because of its lack of concentrating power. In advanced renal disorders there is often a tubular non-responsiveness to ADH. Another factor entering into the sodium and water metabolism is damage caused by injury or disease inside the body—particularly to the central nervous system—interfering with the ADH

secretion of the anterior hypothalamus and hypophysis.

Clinically the most important cause of sodium retention is a reduced glomerular filtration rate occurring secondarily to a drop in renal blood flow and seen in congestive heart failure, shock, or obstruction of the arterial supply to the kidney. Sodium is retained in the plasma, as are other solutes that would normally be filtered by the glomerulus with an adequate renal blood flow.

The hypophyseal-suprarenal axis is mediated through adrenocorticotropic hormone (ACTH) from the adenohypophysis, which directs the secretion of cortisone and related glucocorticosteroids by the suprarenal cortex. Among these steroids, corticosterone and desoxycorticosterone have a sodium-retaining effect and potassium-losing influence across the renal tubule, as well as other effects (see Chapter Fifteen).

The suprarenal hormone aldosterone, a mineral corticoid not mediated by a tropic hormone from the hypophysis, is of more importance in sodium-potassium exchange than are the glucocorticoids. Likewise, sodium is retained and potassium is excreted in the urine under the influence of this hormone.

Potassium Balance

The major fraction of exchangeable potassium is found within the cells. As a rule, the daily intake and output of potassium are well balanced. When undergoing stress, a patient having otherwise normal kidney function can excrete as much as 90 mEq. of potassium in 24 hours, even though the dietary intake of potassium is zero. In the postoperative period, as well as during other periods of stress, increased potassium loss can result indirectly from increased aldosterone production by the suprarenal cortex.

The potassium content of the cell depends upon its metabolic and structural integrity. In a healthy cell, there is a high potassium and a low sodium level. Cellular activity is also influenced by the concentration of potassium in the surrounding fluid. A high concentration of potassium, for instance, exerts striking effects upon cardiac muscle. Complete heart block occurs when the extracellular potassium level reaches 8 to 10 mEq. per liter. In the presence of a low extracellular potassium level, the patient experiences weakness and shows a loss of tone in both smooth and striated muscles because of a failure of normal conduction at the myoneural junction.

STARLING'S LAW OF CAPILLARIES

Factors regulating the flow of blood constituents between the interstitial and plasma compartments have been quantitatively stated in an equation known as Starling's law of capillaries. According to this concept, four measurable factors exist determining the flow of fluid between the two compartments (Fig. 369). Hydrostatic pressure of the blood tends to force fluids out of the capillary. This is "opposed" by hydrostatic pressure within the tissue spaces. Similarly, blood colloid osmotic pressure, tending to pull fluid into the capillary, is opposed by tissue colloid osmotic pressure, tending to pull fluid into the tissues.

Exchange of fluid occurs only across the wall of capillaries. Fluid is not exchanged across the walls of arterioles or venules. The transit time from the arterial end of the capillary to the venous end averages from 1 to 2 seconds. Fluid moves into the interstitial space at the arteriolar end under an effective driving force representing a difference between the net blood and tissue hydrostatic pressures and the net blood and tissue osmotic pressures. At the venular end, fluid moves back into the capillary from the interstitial space under an effective pulling force.

Molecules are exchanged across the capillary wall because of simple diffusion gradients. Since oxygen is in greater concentration in the capillary, it moves into the interstitial fluid. Carbon dioxide passes in the opposite direction from its higher concentration in the interstitial fluid to the lower concentration of the capillary.

The capillary endothelium acting as a semipermeable membrane permits free passage of crystalloids (but not of albumin) through pores in the cement substance between cells. Interstitial fluid contains approximately 0.6 per cent albumin, giving it a low osmotic pressure (2 to

STARLING'S LAW OF CAPILLARIES

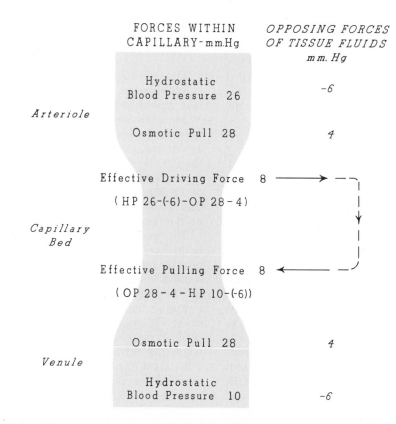

Fig. 369. Schematic representation of Starling's law illustrates the forces on both sides of the capillary driving fluid out at the arteriolar end and returning fluid at the venular end of the capillary.

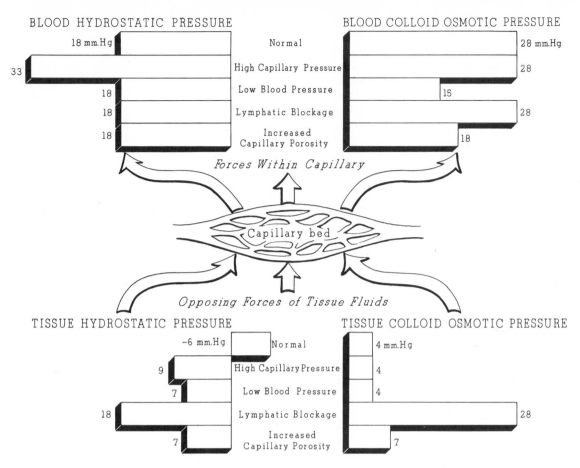

BLOOD HYDROSTATIC PRESSURE

18 mm.Hg	Normal
33	High Capillary Pressure
18	Low Blood Pressure
18	Lymphatic Blockage
18	Increased Capillary Porosity

BLOOD COLLOID OSMOTIC PRESSURE

28 mm.Hg	Normal
28	High Capillary Pressure
15	Low Blood Pressure
28	Lymphatic Blockage
18	Increased Capillary Porosity

Forces Within Capillary

Capillary bed

Opposing Forces of Tissue Fluids

TISSUE HYDROSTATIC PRESSURE

−6 mm.Hg	Normal
9	High Capillary Pressure
7	Low Blood Pressure
18	Lymphatic Blockage
7	Increased Capillary Porosity

TISSUE COLLOID OSMOTIC PRESSURE

4 mm.Hg	Normal
4	High Capillary Pressure
4	Low Blood Pressure
28	Lymphatic Blockage
7	Increased Capillary Porosity

Fig. 370. Starling's law operating under normal and abnormal conditions.

3 mm. of mercury). However, this tissue's colloid osmotic pressure does assist the hydrostatic pressure of the blood in moving fluid from the blood plasma to the tissue spaces.

Opposing the above forces is the colloid osmotic pressure of the plasma acting to hold fluid within the capillaries. The colloids of blood plasma exert an osmotic pressure of 25 to 30 mm. of mercury. This pressure is caused by the concentration of plasma proteins, including albumin, globulin, and fibrinogen.

The hydrostatic pressure of tissue fluid also tends to block the escape of water from plasma. Intercellular fluid exists under pressure because of the elastic properties of body tissue. The extent of this pressure varies in different regions. It has been demonstrated by fluid injection techniques that hydrostatic pressure of a fluid in the subcutaneous region about the malar areas (cheek) is six times greater than the fluid pressure in the subcutaneous region of the lower eyelids. This may help to explain why a swelling can be seen in the lower eyelid long before it becomes apparent over the cheek or other regions of the face.

EDEMA

An excess of extracellular fluid in the interstitial space is known as *edema*. Generalized edema is called *anasarca*. *Ascites* is an accumulation of fluid in the peritoneal cavity. *Hydrothorax* is an accumulation of fluid in the pleural cavity. *Hydropericardium* is an accumulation of fluid in the pericardial sac. Interstitial fluid volume must increase by at least 10 to 15 per cent for edema to be clinically evident.

Edema usually results from one or more of the following conditions: (1) an increase in blood (capillary) hydrostatic pressure, occurring with heart failure or venous obstruction; (2) a drop in blood (plasma colloid osmotic) pressure, as occurs with a decrease in plasma protein, particularly the albumin fraction; (3) obstruction of the lymphatic drainage, as is seen with tumor, inflammation, or injury; and (4) an increase in capillary permeability, as occurs with a toxin.

Any obstruction of the venous system may lead to edema. The superior or inferior vena cava can be obstructed by a tumor. The deep venous system of the lower extremity can be obstructed by a clot. Edema caused by abnormalities of the venous system actually results from an increased hyrostatic pressure in the capillaries.

Edema can be a prominent feature of renal disease. With certain types of kidney damage, the capillary endothelium of the glomerular tuft becomes abnormally permeable, permitting large amounts of albumin to escape into the urine. If the level of serum protein falls below 4 grams per 100 ml., edema occurs. Glomerular filtration rate may also be decreased with a consequent decrease in excretion of urea, sodium, potassium, and other electrolytes, leading to water retention in the tissues (edema).

Lymphedema follows obstruction of the lymphatic system by tumor or infection. Since the lymphatic system is closed, any obstruction causes an accumulation of lymph. The lymph vessels involved are in the dermis since the epidermis does not have lymphatics. Eventually the involved part becomes scarred and thickened.

Inflammatory edema develops because of increased capillary pressure from dilation of blood vessels and actual blockage of veins and capillaries. In this type of edema capillary walls are damaged by bacterial or toxic agents, and a fluid with a high protein content escapes.

GENERAL PRINCIPLES OF FLUID THERAPY

Fluids and electrolytes may be given to patients for one or more of the following reasons: to replace previous losses, to provide maintenance requirements, and to meet current losses. In addition to the primary objectives, it is necessary to provide for basic nutrition. Carbohydrates serve as a ready source of energy and are therefore frequently given to patients with an inadequate intake of food.

Treatment of Burns

A burned area will exude large amounts of plasma. Thus, the individual with a severe burn presents a difficult problem in fluid and electrolyte therapy. Fluid requirements in burned patients are related to the degree of burn and the total area of skin involved. This area must be carefully measured and is usually expressed as a percentage of total body surface which can be conveniently expressed by the *rule of nines*. In this rule the head equals 9 per cent of the surface area; each arm, 9 per cent; the trunk, anterior and posterior, a total of 36 per cent; each lower extremity, 18 per cent; and the genitalia, 1 per cent (Fig. 371). If an individual sustains second and third degree burns of one arm (9 per cent), the front of the trunk (18 per cent) and the front of one leg (9 per cent), 36 per cent of the skin area has been burned.

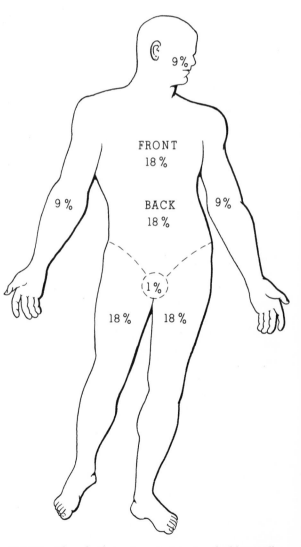

Fig. 371. The *rule of nines* is a convenient method for rapidly estimating the percentage of surface area loss following a burn.

Other Clinical Considerations

Knowledge of fluid and electrolyte therapy is important in all phases of patient treatment. For example, when water is used to irrigate a gastric tube, important ions can be washed out, and an electrolyte imbalance can occur. Multiple enemas can produce a drop in serum sodium concentration and a state of acidosis. Sodium chloride solution, 0.85 per cent (isotonic), or preferably a balanced salt solution (containing, in addition to NaCl, potassium and other ions), should be employed for irrigation of tubes. In general water and ice are not permitted by mouth in patients on continuous suction of the stomach, unless special provision is made to compensate for electrolyte losses.

ACID-BASE REGULATION

The problem of regulation of acid-base balance is essentially one of preventing alterations in hydrogen ion concentration secondary to the continuous formation of the acid end products of metabolism.

The acidity of a solution is determined by the concentration of hydrogen ions (H^+). Acidity is conveniently expressed by the symbol pH, which stands for the negative logarithm of the hydrogen ion concentration. Neutral solutions have a pH of 7. A strongly basic or alkaline solution has a pH as high as 14; an acidic solution has a pH which can be less than 1. The pH of extracellular fluid in health is maintained at a level between 7.35 and 7.45. This constancy of pH is made possible by buffer systems, by an exchange of ions between interstitial and intracellular fluid compartments, and by adaptations of respiratory and renal regulatory mechanisms. Each of these mechanisms will be considered in detail.

BUFFER ACTIVITY

A solution which has a tendency to resist changes in its pH when treated with strong acids or bases is called a *buffer*. A buffer solution contains a weak acid or base and a salt of this acid or base. In biologic fluids the bicarbonate-carbonic acid system, the phosphate system, the hemoglobin-oxyhemoglobin system, and the proteins act as the principal buffers in the regulation of pH.

Buffer Systems

THE BICARBONATE-CARBONIC ACID SYSTEM. The pH of a buffer system like the bicarbonate-carbonic acid system can be expressed by the familiar *Henderson-Hasselbalch equation*:

$$pH = pK_a + \log \left[\frac{\text{concentration of salt of weak acid}}{\text{concentration of weak acid}} \right]$$

For the bicarbonate buffer system, this becomes:

$$pH = 6.1 \pm \log \frac{BHCO_3}{H_2CO_3}.$$

The usual ratio of salt to acid in this system is 20:1, so that the equation becomes:

$$pH = 6.1 + \log \frac{20}{1}, \quad \text{or} \quad pH = 6.1 + 1.3 = 7.4$$

pH then depends on the salt: acid ratio. Large changes must occur in body concentrations to change the pH.

If a strong acid, such as HCl is presented to this buffer system, the following reaction occurs:

strong acid (HCl)
+ salt of weak acid ($NaHCO_3$) → salt (NaCl)
+ weak acid (H_2CO_3)

In turn, H_2CO_3 can become $H_2O + CO_2$, and the latter substance is removed by the lung during respiration. In this way buffer systems soak up the strong acid products of metabolism and keep the body pH at a remarkably constant level. In Fig. 372, the respective weights must be proportionately 20 and 1 in order to achieve balance. As long as the ratio remains 20:1, whether it be 40:2 or 10:0.5, the pH of blood remains normal. To appreciate how profound the derangement of electrolytes must be to alter the pH, Table 44 should prove useful.

THE PHOSPHATE BUFFER SYSTEM. The phosphate buffer system increases the amount of sodium bicarbonate in the extracellular fluids, making extracellular fluids more alkaline. The

TABLE 44.

pH	RATIO
7.8	50:1
7.6	30:1
7.4	20:1
7.3	16:1
7.2	13:1
7.1	10:1

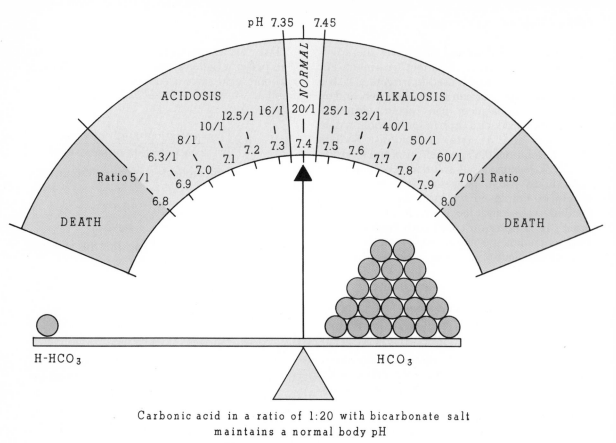

Carbonic acid in a ratio of 1:20 with bicarbonate salt
maintains a normal body pH

Fig. 372. Acidosis and alkalosis showing ratio between carbonic acid and bicarbonate ion.

quantity of Na_2HPO_4 in the glomerular filtrate is four times greater than NaH_2PO_4. Excess hydrogen ions combine in the tubules with Na_2HPO_4, forming NaH_2PO_4 which passes into the urine. Thus, the sodium liberated is absorbed from the tubules in place of the hydrogen ion.

THE HEMOGLOBIN-OXYHEMOGLOBIN BUFFER SYSTEM. Hemoglobin is an effective buffer, although the bicarbonate-carbonic acid system is more important because of its readiness for immediate action. Proteins are amphoteric (carry both an acidic and a basic charge), but function in blood as anions with considerable buffering capacity. Within the blood, oxyhemoglobin can neutralize more cations than reduced hemoglobin. Oxyhemoglobin is therefore a stronger acid than reduced hemoglobin. In arterial blood the CO_2 content and bicarbonate ion concentration are lower than in venous blood; nevertheless, the pH is the same, since the oxyhemoglobin inside the erythrocyte has taken over some of the anion function previously provided

by the excess bicarbonate in the venous plasma.

THE PROTEIN BUFFER SYSTEM. This system is found predominantly in tissue cells, but it also operates in the plasma. Proteins of the body act as anions in the alkaline pH of the body fluids. Since they are amphoteric, proteins can exist in the form of acids (H-protein), or alkaline salts (B-protein). In this way proteins are able to bind or release excess hydrogen ions as required.

REGULATION OF ACID-BASE EQUILIBRIUM BY ION EXCHANGE

An example of this mechanism can be seen when the serum concentration of carbon dioxide rises; CO_2 in its increased concentration diffuses into the red blood cell from the serum, where it combines with water to form H_2CO_3. This weak acid then dissociates, becoming HCO_3^- ion and H^+. The hydrogen ion is buffered by the hemoglobin of the red cell and the HCO_3^- moves back into the plasma as a chloride ion shifts into the cell to replace it. The net effect is a redistribution of anions in response to an increase in the concentration of carbon dioxide in this compartment.

Respiratory Regulation of Acid-Base Balance

The importance of the bicarbonate-carbonic acid buffer system has been stressed. The concentration of carbonic acid can be quickly altered by changes in respiration. Overbreathing will result in excessive removal of CO_2 from the blood and an increase in body pH, or *alkalosis*. Underbreathing results in increased blood concentration of CO_2, a decreasing preponderance of $BHCO_3$ in the Henderson-Hasselbalch equation, and thus a fall in body pH, or *acidosis*.

The central nervous system center which controls the rate and depth of respiration is sensitive to changes in blood pH or CO_2 concentration. A change toward acidosis will result in increased respiration to blow off more CO_2. A change toward alkalosis will result in depression of respiration.

Specialized nerve centers called chemoreceptors, located in the carotid arteries and the aortic arch, also sense changes in CO_2 concentration and pH. In turn, these stimulate the respiratory center and assist in homeostasis. Chemoreceptors in the arteries are not sensitive to changes in CO_2 concentration as is the respiratory center. They are, however, more sensitive to changes in oxygen concentration.

Urinary Regulation of Acid-Base Balance

Unlike the respiratory compensatory mechanisms, the kidneys actually remove hydrogen ion from the body in a selective manner. During the course of normal metabolism, an excess of acid is produced. The kidneys tend to compensate for this excess production by excreting acids and by returning bicarbonate to the plasma and extracellular fluid; therefore, the pH of urine is usually on the acid side, 5.5 to 6.5, whereas the pH of plasma and extracellular fluid is on the alkaline side.

There are three renal compensatory mechanisms (Fig. 373).

Acidification of phosphate buffer salts. An exchange mechanism occurs between the hydrogen ions of the renal tubular cells and the sodium salt (Na_2HPO_4) which appears in the tubular

urine. This salt dissociates into Na^+ and $NaHPO_4^-$ ions. The sodium ion moves into the tubular cell and the hydrogen ion moves out, uniting with $NaHPO_4$ ion to form a dihydrogen phosphate salt, NaH_2PO_4, which is excreted. In this way hydrogen ion is removed from the body.

Reabsorption of bicarbonate. Carbon dioxide is absorbed by the tubular cells from the blood and in the presence of carbonic anhydrase combines with water present in the cell to form carbonic acid. Carbonic acid in turn ionizes, forming H^+ and HCO_3^- ion. An exchange is then carried out between the sodium (Na^+) ion of the tubular urine and the hydrogen (H^+) ion of the tubular cells. The sodium next combines with the HCO_3^- to form sodium bicarbonate $NaHCO_3$, which is reabsorbed into the blood.

Secretion of ammonia. Ammonia, NH_3 is formed in the renal tubular cells by the oxidative breakdown of the amino acid glutamine in the presence of the enzyme glutaminase. Free ammonia is then transferred into the tubular urine, where it unites with hydrogen chloride (HCl) molecule and is excreted as ammonium chloride, NH_4Cl. Ammonia can also be converted into urea by the liver and excreted by the kidneys.

SUMMARY OF THE FOUR SYSTEMS OF pH CONTROL

In summary, four systems of pH control (buffers, ion exchange, respiratory, and renal) have been described. The buffer system is a mechanism which binds hydrogen ions so that they are no longer free or ionic. In essence a buffer is a "chemical sponge" soaking up and releasing anions or cations to neutralize imbalances as conditions dictate. The respiratory and urinary mechanisms, on the other hand, actually drain off fairly steady amounts of carbon dioxide and hydrogen ions respectively. The respiratory mechanism acts most quickly in the face of an emergency, while the renal mechanism is essential over extended periods of time. Finally, ion exchange facilitates both the buffer and urinary mechanisms via proper distribution of the ions.

CLINICAL CONSIDERATIONS IN ACID-BASE BALANCE

Defects in acid-base balance can be grouped under two major categories—*acidosis* and *alkalosis*. If there is too much acid in the body

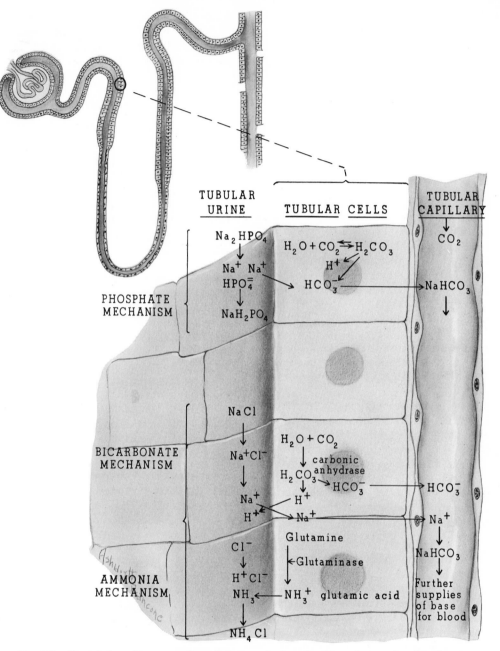

Fig. 373. The tubular cells carry on three distinct mechanisms for pH regulation: phosphate, bicarbonate, and ammonia. Note that the bicarbonate mechanism feeds hydrogen ions into the ammonia mechanism.

but the buffer systems, although depleted, have managed to keep the body pH within normal range, it is a "compensated" acidosis. If the pH has dropped, the acidosis is "uncompensated."

Acidosis can be caused by many abnormal conditions. When respiration is inadequate to blow off CO_2 (e.g., with lung disease or depression of respiration by drugs), a *respiratory acidosis* develops.

When the cause is an abnormal accumulation of acid products of metabolism (as in diabetes, kidney failure, etc.), or excessive losses of base (as in diarrhea), a metabolic acidosis is said to exist. With metabolic acidosis, the body attempts to compensate by increasing respiratory activity. In respiratory acidosis, the lung cannot adequately compensate, so the kidneys rid the body of the acid metabolites.

Counterparts of the above are found in alkalosis. In *respiratory alkalosis*, the lung has blown off excess CO_2 and has raised the pH. This occurs with *hyperventilation* (prolonged, rapid, deep breathing), caused by either anxiety or the toxic affect of drugs or diseases. Treatment consists of giving the patient air to breathe with a high CO_2 concentration, decreasing hyperventilation.

Metabolic alkalosis occurs when the body has lost excessive amounts of acid, as in vomiting, or when endocrine or renal diseases result in excessive loss of acid products or potassium in the urine. More unusual causes include the ingestion of excess alkali. Treatment consists of preventing further losses and replacement of chloride and potassium ions.

SUMMARY: FLUIDS AND ELECTROLYTES

SURVEY

1. Significance of fluid and electrolyte balance:
   a. The maintenance of balance between the three major fluid compartments—the plasma, interstitial fluid, and intercellular fluid—in terms of relative distribution of the total body water and electrolytes is involved in homeostasis.

TERMINOLOGY

1. A milliequivalent is 1/1000 of the molecular weight expressed in grams, divided by the valence or combining power.

2. An electrolyte is a substance which ionizes in solution.

COMPOSITION OF BODY FLUIDS

1. The major cation in the plasma and interstitial fluid is sodium, while the major anion is chloride.

2. The major cation in intracellular fluid is potassium, while the major anion is phosphate (PO_4^-).

3. The Gibbs-Donnan membrane equilibrium states that the concentration of a non-diffusible ion on one side of a semipermeable membrane essentially dictates movement of other diffusible anions and cations across the membrane barrier. The Gibbs-Donnan membrane effect is responsible for the distribution of electrolytes throughout the body's three fluid compartments.

HOMEOSTASIS

1. The water content of the body by weight is rigidly controlled.

2. Three avenues of fluid gain are ingested water, water with food, and water produced through metabolic degradation. The avenues of water loss in the body are the skin, expired air, urine, and feces.

3. Sensible perspiration is defined as perspiration appearing on the surface as the result of sweat gland activity; insensible perspiration is defined as the water which diffuses through the skin and evaporates immediately.

4. Antidiuretic hormone, ADH, regulates excretion of water by the kidneys.

5. When an excess of water has been lost, central nervous system receptors respond to elevated serum osmolarity by producing ADH to prevent further water losses.

REGULATION OF ELECTROLYTE BALANCE

1. Osmosis:

   a. Electrolytes influence not only acid-base balance but distribution of body fluids by their osmotic pressure.

2. Sodium balance:

   a. Sodium ion concentration is regulated by the neurohypophyseal-renal axis.
   b. A thirst center in the hypothalamus is stimulated by serum hypertonicity.
   c. Sodium can be excreted in the urine and feces and may be lost from the skin.

3. Potassium balance:

   a. Most potassium is found in intracellular fluid.

STARLING'S LAW OF CAPILLARIES

1. The four factors are: serum hydrostatic pressure, serum colloid pressure, tissue hydrostatic pressure, and tissue colloid pressure.

2. When combined into a single equation representing a balanced state and a net zero flow, (blood hydrostatic pressure) − (blood colloid osmotic pressure) = (tissue hydrostatic pressure) − (tissue colloid pressure). These factors represent Starling's law of capillaries.

EDEMA

1. Edema is defined as an excess of fluid in the interstitial spaces.

2. Edema usually results from one or more of the following conditions:

   a. An increase in capillary blood pressure, such as in heart failure or venous blockage.
   b. Low osmotic pressure caused by decreased plasma protein—for example, the diminished plasma albumin.
   c. Lymph blockage caused by secondary tumor or inflammation.
   d. Increased capillary permeability caused by toxins.

GENERAL PRINCIPLES OF FLUID THERAPY

1. In cases of severe burns the *rule of nines* is followed for determining surface area burned. Each arm equals 9 per cent; the head, 9 per cent; the trunk (front and back), 36 per cent; each lower extremity, 18 per cent; and the genitalia, 1 per cent.

2. Fluid therapy for burned patients is based on the percentage of body injury.

ACID-BASE REGULATION

1. pH is the negative logarithm of the hydrogen ion concentration.

BUFFER ACTIVITY

1. Buffer:

   a. A buffer is a solution of a weak acid or base and a salt of that acid or base which tends to resist any change in pH caused by the addition of stronger acids or bases.

b. The Henderson-Hasselbalch equation, $pH = pK_a + \log BA/HA$, is a mathematic expression of pH in which B is any cation and A is any acid; thus, BA is the salt of the acid HA. pK_a is the equilibrium constant of the acid. Thus, for bicarbonate-carbonic acid the buffer ratio in the blood is $NaHCO_3/H_2CO_3$. By simple calculations, we find that the ratio of these concentrations of $20:1$ is normal for healthy blood pH.

2. Buffer systems:

   a. The four major buffer pairs making up the buffer ratios are bicarbonate-carbonic acid, hemoglobin-oxyhemoglobin, phosphate, and protein systems.

   b. Carbonic acid produced by various metabolic pathways is buffered in the blood cells by hemoglobin-oxyhemoglobin, while bicarbonate-carbonic acid does the same in plasma and extracellular fluids.

REGULATION OF ACID-BASE EQUILIBRIUM BY ION EXCHANGE

1. **Respiratory regulation of acid-base balance:**

   a. Examples of exchanges of anions across membranes involve the red cells and cells of the proximal renal tubules.

   b. The principle is one of diffusion across cellular membranes in response to concentration gradients and maintenance of electrical neutrality.

   c. By removal of CO_2 the lungs produce a decrease in the carbonic acid content of the blood. The process is again one of diffusion.

   d. A system of chemoreceptors located in the carotid and aortic bodies detects alterations in arterial pCO_2 and stimulates appropriate changes.

2. **Urinary regulation of acid-base balance:**

   a. The kidney compensates for excessive acidity by excreting proportionately greater amounts of acid; thus, the characteristic acidity of urine.

   b. There are three major urinary compensatory mechanisms: reabsorption of bicarbonate, acidification of phosphate buffer salts, and secretion of ammonia.

SUMMARY OF THE FOUR SYSTEMS OF pH CONTROL

1. **The buffer system gives the most rapid response in emergencies, while urinary and respiratory compensatory mechanisms actually eliminate hydrogen ion and carbon dioxide respectively.**

2. **Ion exchange facilitates both the buffer and urinary mechanisms via proper distribution of the ions.**

3. **The respiratory mechanism is the first to act in an emergency.**

4. **The urinary is more variable and hence more significant than the respiratory mechanism.**

CLINICAL CONSIDERATIONS IN ACID-BASE BALANCE

1. **Metabolic acidosis is caused by either primary loss of bicarbonate or accumulation of acid.**

   a. The buffering of ketonic acids is followed by bicarbonate reabsorption in the urinary tubules.

2. **Metabolic alkalosis is caused by an excess of bicarbonate not neutralized by an equivalent increase in CO_2.**

   a. Hypoventilation and increased secretion of bicarbonate in the urine are the major compensatory mechanisms.

3. **Respiratory acidosis is caused by an inadequate elimination of CO_2 by the lungs (for example, in emphysema).**

   a. Buffering is the major compensatory mechanism.

4. **Respiratory alkalosis is caused by hyperventilation and the ensuing drop in CO_2 concentration.**

   a. Attacks of respiratory alkalosis tend to be so short that only buffering and slowed respiration occur to compensate for the imbalance.

STUDY QUESTIONS: FLUIDS AND ELECTROLYTES

1. List and define the three major fluid compartments.
2. If sodium, Na, has an atomic weight of 23 and a valence of one, what is the weight in grams of 1 mEq.?
3. Describe the Gibbs-Donnan membrane effect. How does it influence the difference in composition of plasma and interstitial fluid?
4. Differentiate sensible and insensible perspiration.
5. What roles do ADH and the lymphatic system play in fluid and electrolyte equilibrium?
6. What is the principal cation of extracellular fluid, and how does the neurohypophyseal-renal axis regulate its concentration?
7. Describe Starling's law of capillaries.
8. List four major causes of edema.
9. Match each of the following types of edema with one of the four major causes you have described in question 8: lymphedema, cardiac edema, inflammatory edema, and pulmonary edema.
10. If an individual has burns on his head, the front of one arm, and the front of one leg, what percentage of his body surface has been burned according to the rule of nines?
11. How does pH differ from pCO_2?
12. Describe a buffer pair in terms of chemical composition and function.
13. What do the BA and HA represent in the general formula of the Henderson-Hasselbalch equation?
14. How do we arrive at a ratio of 20:1 as the proportion of bicarbonate anion to carbonic acid which constitutes a normal acid-base balance in the blood? Discuss.
15. Define *acidosis* and *alkalosis* in terms of pH which is normal for blood.
16. What are the major buffer systems?
17. Describe the relationships between the medulla and the lungs in the respiratory compensatory mechanism.
18. List the three renal compensatory mechanisms.
19. What are the distinctive qualities of the four systems of pH control—buffer, ion exchange, respiratory, and renal?
20. Characterize metabolic acidosis and metabolic alkalosis.
21. What is the relationship between hyperventilation and respiratory alkalosis?

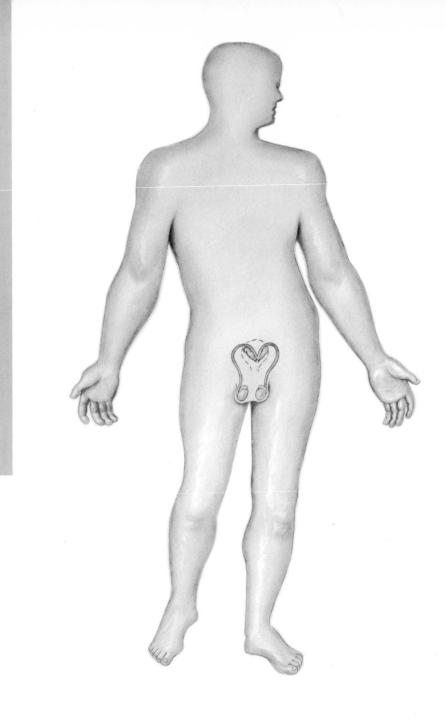

REPRODUCTION

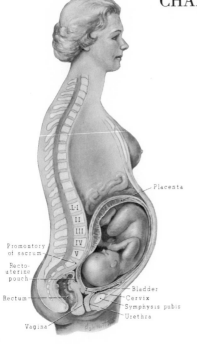

CHAPTER SEVENTEEN

Placenta

L-1
II
III
IV
V

Promontory of sacrum

Recto-
uterine
pouch

Rectum

Vagina

Bladder
Cervix
Symphysis pubis
Urethra

THE REPRODUCTIVE SYSTEM

HISTORICAL DEVELOPMENT

Many early scientific explanations of reproduction were more mystical than scientific. Hippocrates believed that "seeds from all parts of the male and female bodies flowed together to unite and form the fruit." Aristotle opined that the male factor provided movement and the female factor substance, with the sex of the baby depending upon which factor predominated. In 1672, de Graaf observed the follicles of an ovary and mistakenly thought they were ova. The actual ovum was not seen until 1827, when von Baer traced its course along the uterine tube into the uterus. Spermatozoa were so named because they were originally thought to be "small parasitic animals." In 1853, fertilization was properly described as the entry of the spermatozoon into the ovum; however, the vast knowledge at our disposal today concerning reproduction came about largely as the product of investigation during the last four decades.

EMBRYOLOGY (Fig. 374)

The reproductive system is unique among organ systems in that its component parts vary between the two sexes. During embryologic de-

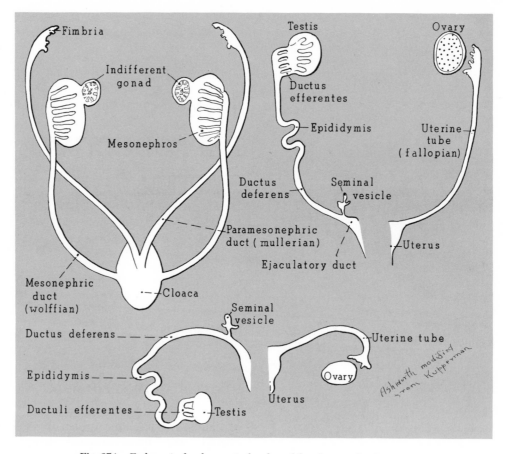

Fig. 374. Embryonic development of male and female reproductive systems.

velopment, special cells are set apart from the general body mass for perpetuation of the species. These grow and develop into what are called sex cells or gametes. The organs containing gametes are termed *gonads*. The testes (male gonads) contain large numbers of spermatozoa, or male gametes. The ovaries (female gonads) contain the ova, or female gametes.

Despite the difference between male and female sex organs, they appear morphologically similar until the seventh week of development. The gonads are first present as two longitudinal accumulations of cells, the genital ridges, located medial to the mesonephros in a 4-week embryo. These ridges consist of condensed mesenchyme covered by mesothelium. The mesothelium differentiates by growing rapidly and developing into *germinal epithelium*. By the sixth week, distinct primordial germ cells from the wall of the yolk sac migrate toward and penetrate the genital ridge. The proliferating germinal epithelium

forms cord-like masses surrounding the invading germ cells and develops into the primitive sex cords. At this stage of development, the male and female gonads are indistinguishable.

Male development. If the embryo is a male, the primitive sex cords continue to proliferate and penetrate the medulla of the primitive sex gland during the seventh or eighth week of development. They anastomose with one another to form the cords of the testes. The testicular cords then become separated from the surface epithelium by a dense layer of fibrous connective tissue, the *tunica albuginea*, which eventually forms the capsule of the testis. The supporting Sertoli's cells and interstitial cells of Leydig develop from the adjacent mesenchyme and surround the testicular cords. The cords become hollow and form the seminiferous tubules which eventually join with the ductus deferens.

Female development. In the developing female embryo, the primitive sex cords are replaced by vascular stroma, but the surface epithelium remains thickened and continues to proliferate, giving rise to a second generation of cords, the *cortical cords*. These then split into clusters of cells, each containing several primordial germ cells. Each primordial germ cell develops into an oogonium; the surrounding epithelial cells form a follicle, the primary ovarian follicle.

Descent of gonads. As the gonads continue to develop and grow, they change their relative position in the body. At the third month, the ovaries descend bilaterally to a point just below the brim of the true pelvis, where they remain. The testes descend through their respective inguinal canals into the scrotal sac, guided by the tractional force of the ligamentum gubernaculum of the testis. If this ligamentum fails to close, an indirect inguinal hernia can result.

Development of ductile system. The ductile system of the reproductive organs is derived from either one of two pairs of embryonic genital ducts: the mesonephric (wolffian) ducts and the paramesonephric (müllerian) ducts. In the male embryo, the paramesonephric ducts degenerate and form only the appendix testis and prostatic utricle, while the mesonephric ducts persist to give rise to the paradidymis, epididymis, ductus deferens, ejaculatory ducts, and seminal vesicles.

In the female embryo the mesonephric ducts degenerate, and the pair of paramesonephric ducts develop into the uterine tubes and fuse caudally to form the uterus and vagina.

Table 45 summarizes the embryonic structures developing into definitive and homologous forms in the male and female reproductive systems.

MALE REPRODUCTIVE SYSTEM

External Organs (Figs. 375 to 377)

SCROTUM AND PENIS. The scrotum and penis are the external male organs of reproduction. The scrotum is a pouch suspended from the pubis in the anterior midline; it hangs behind the penis. It is a continuation of the abdominal wall and is divided by a septum into two sacs, each containing and supporting one of the testes with its epididymis. After adolescence the skin of the scrotum is more heavily pigmented than the covering of the general body and is covered with pubic hair. Scattered in the subcutaneous tissue of the scrotum are fibers of smooth muscle (the dartos layer). The fibers of the dartos layer contract in the presence of reduced ambient or body temperature, and give an increased wrinkled

TABLE 45. Embryonic and Adult Structures of Male and Female.

INDIFFERENT EMBRYONIC STRUCTURE	MALE	FEMALE
Genital ridge	Testis Rete testis	Ovary Rete ovarii°
Mesonephric tubules	Ductuli efferentes Paradidymis°	Epoophoron° Paraoophoron°
Mesonephric duct (Wolffian duct)	Epididymis Ductus deferens Ejaculatory duct Seminal vesicle	Gartner's duct
Paramesonephric duct (Müllerian duct)	Prostatic utricle Appendix testis	Uterine tubes Uterus Vagina
Urogenital sinus	Urethra	Urethra Vagina Vestibule
	Bulbo-urethral glands (Cowper's)	Greater vestibular glands (Bartholin's)
Genital tubercle	Glans penis	Clitoris
Genital folds	Prepuce of penis	Labia minora
Genital swellings	Scrotum	Labia majora
Urethral budding	Prostate gland	Para-urethral glands (Skene's)

° Rudimentary.

appearance to the scrotum. This wrinkling causes the testes to be positioned close to the perineum, where they can absorb body heat and maintain a temperature compatible with the viability of spermatozoa. Under conditions of normal temperature, muscle fibers are relaxed, the scrotum is pendulous, and the walls are relatively free from wrinkles.

The penis, the male organ of copulation, is a flaccid structure when not stimulated. It is attached to the anterior and lateral walls of the pubic arch in front of the scrotum, and is composed of three longitudinal columns of erectile tissue bound together by fibrous bands and covered with skin. The skin of the penis, like that of the scrotum, is more highly pigmented than the skin of the remainder of the body, but is not covered with hair except at its base. Two of the longitudinal columns are located laterally and are called the *corpora cavernosa* of the penis. They are sponge-like in nature and contain large venous sinuses (Fig. 378).

The phenomenon of *erection* occurs with sexual stimulation. The arteries supplying the penis dilate, and a large quantity of blood under pressure enters the cavernous spaces of the erectile tissue. As these spaces expand, they compress the veins supplying the penis, thus retaining all the entering blood. This causes the penis to become firm and erect and facilitates its penetration into the female vagina during sexual intercourse. When the arteries constrict, more blood leaves the penis than enters, and the organ returns to its flaccid state.

The third longitudinal column of the penis is also erectile tissue and it too becomes engorged with blood during erection. This column, known as the *corpus spongiosum* or *corpus cavernosum urethrae,* is the medial column and lies between the corpora cavernosa. It contains the urethra which transmits urine as well as semen, the male sexual secretion. At its distal end, the corpus cavernosum urethrae is larger, forming the glans penis upon which the urethral orifice is located. Overhanging the glans is the prepuce, a loose skin folded inward and then backward upon itself. In current practice this foreskin is usually removed in newborn boys by the simple surgical procedure known as *circumcision* (Fig. 379).

The penis may be the site of several abnormalities noted at birth (Fig. 379). Two of these are *hypospadias* and *epispadias.* Malformations of the urethral groove and urethral canal sometimes create abnormal openings either on the ventral surface of the penis (hypospadias) or on the dorsal surface (epispadias). Such abnormalities are generally associated with a failure of normal descent of the testes and with malformations of the urinary bladder. Both hypospadias and epispadias should be surgically corrected.

Phimosis. When the orifice of the prepuce is too narrow to permit retraction over the glans penis, the condition is known as phimosis. Phimosis prevents cleanliness and permits accumulation of secretions under the prepuce favoring the development of secondary bacterial infection. Circumcision obviates phimosis and possibly protects against the development of tumors by lessening the accumulation of secretions, minimizing the tendency to irritation and infection.

Internal Organs

The internal organs of reproduction in the male can be divided into three groups. First there are the male gonads, or testes. The second group consists of a series of ducts, including the epididymis, ductus deferens, and urethra. The third group of internal organs is the accessory glands: seminal vesicles, prostate, and bulbourethral (Cowper's) glands. The spermatic cords serve as the internal supporting structures (Figs. 380 and 381).

Testes. The testes correspond to the ovaries in the female. Each is an oval organ about 2 inches in length, lying within the abdominal cavity in early fetal life. About 2 months prior to birth the testes leave the abdomen and descend with the spermatic cord along their respective inguinal canals into the scrotum; occasionally the testes do not descend, but remain in the abdomen, giving rise to a condition known as cryptorchism. This can happen unilaterally or bilaterally.

The cause of cryptorchism is poorly understood. In a small percentage of cases it is believed to be an hereditary abnormality; but in most instances it is an isolated anatomic abnormality or mechanical obstruction to descent. When cryptorchism is discovered before the age of puberty, the testes are usually normal in size but in an abnormal location. When the condition is discovered at or after the age of puberty, the testes have already commenced to atrophy and decrease in size. A concomitant hernia in the inguinal area can accompany the abnormal position of the testes. Such a position in the inguinal canal is particularly susceptible to trauma by crushing against ligaments and bones.

The outer layer of the testis is known as the *tunica albuginea,* a dense layer of white fibrous tissue. At its posterior border it is reflected into the testis, forming an incomplete vertical septum

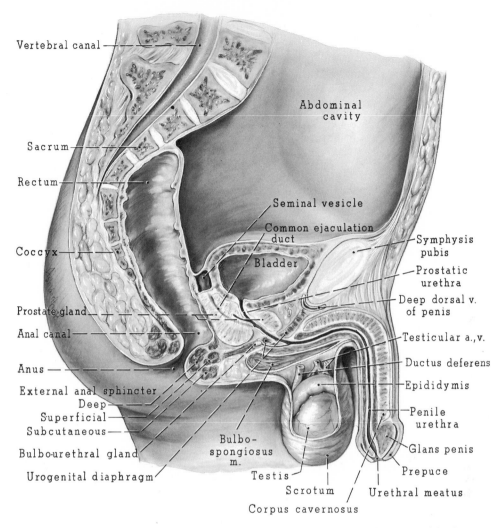

Vertebral canal
Abdominal cavity
Sacrum
Rectum
Seminal vesicle
Common ejaculation duct
Symphysis pubis
Bladder
Coccyx
Prostatic urethra
Deep dorsal v. of penis
Prostate gland
Anal canal
Testicular a.,v.
Ductus deferens
Anus
Epididymis
External anal sphincter
Deep
Penile urethra
Superficial
Subcutaneous
Bulbo-spongiosus m.
Glans penis
Bulbo-urethral gland
Prepuce
Urogenital diaphragm
Testis
Scrotum
Urethral meatus
Corpus cavernosus

Fig. 375. Mid-sagittal section of the male pelvis and external genitalia. (The course of the ductus deferens is shown in Fig. 347.)

known as the *mediastinum testis*. Fibrous septa extend into the substance of the testis, dividing it into about 250 wedge-shaped lobes. Each lobe contains from one to three narrow coiled tubes known as *seminiferous tubules*. If uncoiled, a tubule would measure 2 feet in length. Male reproductive cells at different stages of development are found within these tubules. The maturing spermatozoa are usually seen in the center of the tubule, and the premature spermatogonia and primary spermatocytes at the periphery of the tubule nearer the germinal epithelium.

In addition to reproductive cells, supportive and nutritive cells known as Sertoli's cells are found in the testis. These cells supply nutrients to the spermatozoa. Interstitial cells of Leydig

are scattered among the tubules and are responsible for the production of male hormones.

The seminiferous tubules unite to form a series of larger straight ducts, which in turn form a network known as the *rete testis*. It is into the rete testis that the seminiferous tubules empty their spermatozoa. About 20 small, coiled ductules leave the upper end of the rete testis, perforate the tunica albuginea, and open into the epididymis (Fig. 382).

Epididymis. The epididymis is the first part of the ductile system of the testis. It is a coiled tube lying on the posterior aspect of the testis and extending from the upper end downward for about 1½ inches. About 16 feet of tube are coiled within this short distance.

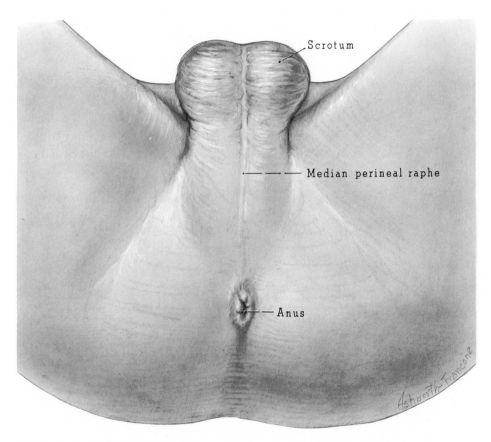

Fig. 376. Superficial view of the male perineum (subject in supine position with thighs fully abducted).

478

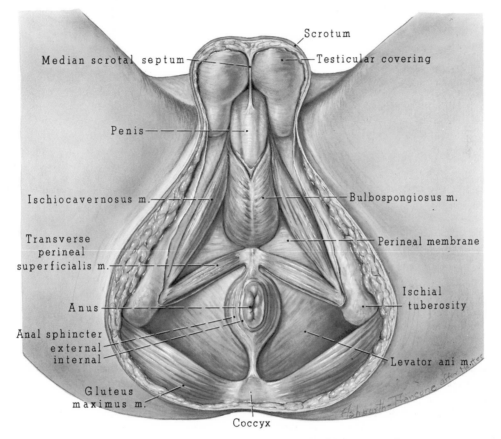

Scrotum

Median scrotal septum — Testicular covering

Penis —

Ischiocavernosus m. — Bulbospongiosus m.

Transverse perineal superficialis m. — Perineal membrane

Anus — Ischial tuberosity

Anal sphincter external internal — Levator ani m.

Gluteus maximus m.

Coccyx

Fig. 377. Male perineum with skin and superficial fascia removed.

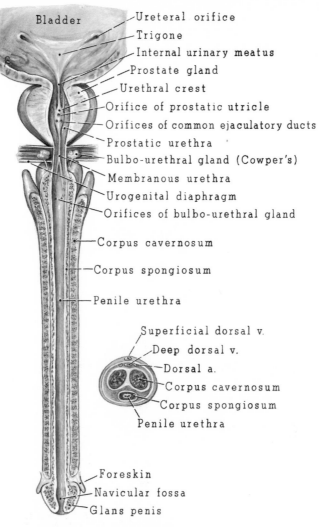

Bladder

Ureteral orifice
Trigone
Internal urinary meatus
Prostate gland
Urethral crest
Orifice of prostatic utricle
Orifices of common ejaculatory ducts
Prostatic urethra
Bulbo-urethral gland (Cowper's)
Membranous urethra
Urogenital diaphragm
Orifices of bulbo-urethral gland

Corpus cavernosum
Corpus spongiosum
Penile urethra

Superficial dorsal v.
Deep dorsal v.
Dorsal a.
Corpus cavernosum
Corpus spongiosum
Penile urethra

Foreskin
Navicular fossa
Glans penis

Fig. 378.   Section through the bladder, prostate gland, and penis.

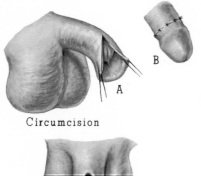

B

A

Circumcision

Hypospadias

Epispadias

Phimosis

Fig. 379.   In *circumcision* the prepuce is removed. *A* shows incision in the prepuce. Closure of the wound after removal of the prepuce is shown in *B*.

The penis may be the site of several abnormalities at birth. Among these are *hypospadias,* in which the urethral opening is on the ventral surface of the penis; *epispadias,* in which the urethral opening appears on the dorsal surface; and *phimosis,* in which the orifice of the prepuce is too narrow to permit retraction over the glans penis.

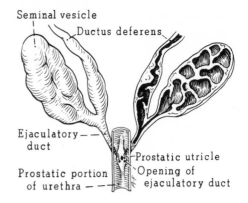

Fig. 380. Seminal vesicle and related parts. On the left the vesicle and duct are intact; the right side is sectioned to show internal detail.

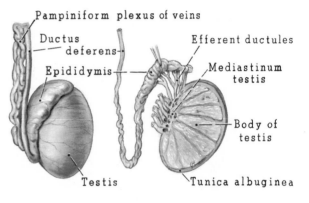

Fig. 381. Male testis, entire and sectioned views.

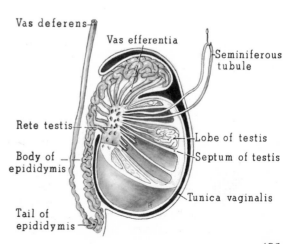

Fig. 382. Diagram of a section of the male testis showing detail of a seminiferous tubule.

481

Ductus deferens. The ductus deferens is a straight tube leading from the lower portion of each epididymis. It ascends for about 18 inches along the posterior border of the testis through the inguinal canal to enter the abdomen. The ductus deferens consists of an inner mucous layer, a middle muscular layer, and an outer fibrous layer. It can be considered as a continuation of the epididymis and has been described as "the excretory duct of the testis." The ductus deferens, together with nerves, lymphatics, and blood vessels, forms the *spermatic cord.*

Seminal vesicles. There are two seminal vesicles, membranous pouches lying posterior to the bladder near its base, each consisting of a single tube coiled upon itself. The seminal vesicles secrete a fluid giving motility to the spermatozoa. The tube of each seminal vesicle ends in a straight, narrow duct joining the ductus deferens to form the *ejaculatory duct.* The ejaculatory duct is a tube about 1 inch in length penetrating the base of the prostate gland and opening into the prostatic portion of the urethra. This duct actually ejects the spermatozoa and seminal vesicle fluid into the urethral lumen.

Prostate. The prostate gland is a conical body about the size of a chestnut lying inferior to the bladder. It surrounds the first inch of the urethra and secretes an alkaline fluid aiding in the motility of sperm cells. In older men a progressive enlargement of the prostate commonly obstructs the urethra and interferes with the passage of urine. This condition calls for the surgical removal of a part of the prostate gland. The prostate is also a frequent site of cancer in elderly men.

The *bulbo-urethral glands* (Cowper's) are two glands about the size of a pea located inferior to the prostate on either side of the urethra. These secrete alkaline fluid as a part of the semen.

The *male urethra* is a tube-like organ responsible for transmitting both semen and urine. It extends from the internal urethral orifice in the urinary bladder to the external urethral orifice at the distal end of the penis (see Chapter Fourteen).

Endocrinology

The testes perform two functions which to a large extent are complementary—proliferation of spermatozoa and secretion of male sex hormones. The male steroid hormones determine the physiologic state of the accessory ducts and glands, contain 19 carbon atoms, condition the appearance of secondary male sex character-istics, and promote protein anabolism. Androgens are produced not only by the testes, but also by the suprarenal cortex and even the ovaries. Testosterone, the most potent androgen, is formed by the interstitial cells of Leydig within the testes. The secretory capacity of the cells of Leydig is regulated by the gonadotropins of the adenohypophysis.

FEMALE REPRODUCTIVE SYSTEM
(Fig. 383)

External Organs

Vulva. The external female reproductive organs are collectively known as the vulva, which includes the mons pubis, labia majora, labia minora, clitoris, vestibule, vestibular glands, and hymen. The vulva extends from the mons pubis anteriorly to the central tendinous point of the perineum posteriorly (Fig. 384).

Mons pubis and labia majora. The most anterior of the anatomic structures of the vulva is the mons pubis (mons veneris), a firm, cushion-like elevation of adipose tissue over the symphysis pubis, covered by pubic hair. The labia majora are two rounded folds of adipose tissue with overlying skin; they extend from the mons pubis downward and backward to encircle the vestibule. The outer surfaces of these folds are covered with hair, while the inner surfaces are smooth and moist, containing sebaceous follicles. The labia majora unite anteriorly with the mons pubis to form the *anterior commissure* and posteriorly to form the *posterior commissure* located on the anterior margin of the perineum. The labia majora are homologues of the scrotum in the male.

Labia minora. The labia minora are two folds of skin lying medial to the labia majora and enclosing the vestibule. Anteriorly the labia minora divide into two layers. The upper folds join just in front of the clitoris to form the prepuce, while the lower folds are attached to the inferior aspect of the glans of the clitoris to form its frenulum. Posteriorly, the labia minora become less distinct and appear to join the labia majora in a transverse fold of skin, the posterior fourchet. A depression known as the fossa navicularis is located between the fourchet posteriorly and the posterior margin of the vaginal orifice.

Clitoris. The clitoris is a pea-shaped projection of erectile tissue, nerves, and blood vessels occupying the apex of the vestibule anterior to the vagina. It is partially covered by the anterior

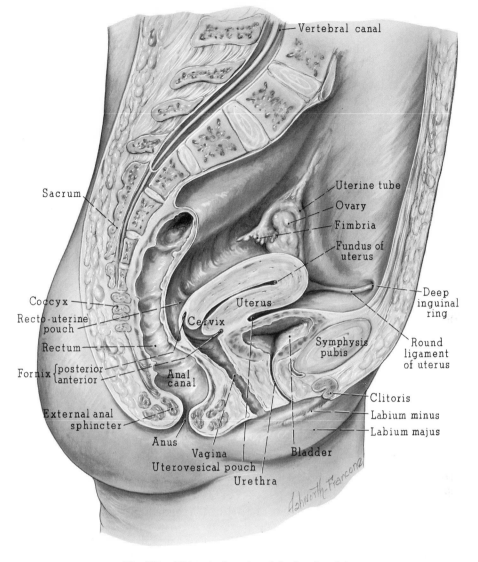

Fig. 383. Mid-sagittal section of the female pelvis.

ends of the labia minora and is highly sensitive to tactile stimulation. The clitoris is important in the sexual excitation of the female and represents the homologue of the penis in the male, but is not traversed by the urethra.

Vestibule. The vestibule is an almond-shaped area between the labia minora extending from the clitoris to the fourchet. Situated within the vestibule are the hymen, the vaginal orifice, the urethral orifice and the openings of the vestibular glands. The urethral orifice is an opening 4 to 6 mm. in diameter, located about 1 inch posterior to the clitoris. Multiple small paraurethral glands (Skene's) surround the orifice and are homologous to the prostate in the male.

These glands open by way of a pair of ducts placed laterally in the submucous layer of the urethra at its orifice.

The vaginal orifice occupies the greater portion of the posterior two-thirds of the vestibule. On either side of the vaginal orifice, deep within the perineal tissues, are the two greater vestibular glands (Bartholin's glands) (Fig. 385). Each opens by means of a duct placed laterally in a groove between the hymen and the labium minus. The greater vestibular glands, homologous to the bulbo-urethral glands in the male, elaborate a mucous secretion which acts as a lubricant during sexual intercourse.

Hymen. The hymen is a thin fold of vascu-

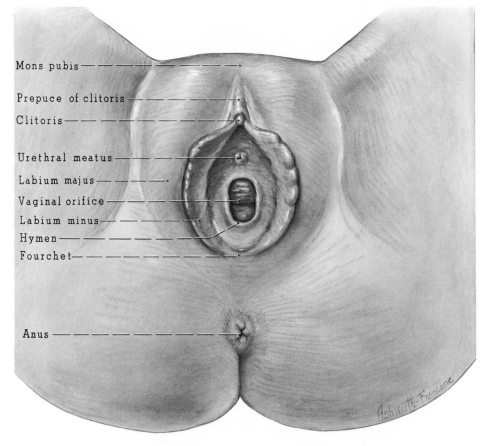

Mons pubis

Prepuce of clitoris

Clitoris

Urethral meatus

Labium majus

Vaginal orifice

Labium minus

Hymen

Fourchet

Anus

Fig. 384. Female external genitalia.

larized mucous membrane separating the vagina from the vestibule. It can be entirely absent or can cover the vaginal orifice partly or completely. If the hymen completely covers the vaginal orifice, it is known as an imperforate hymen. Anatomically neither its absence nor presence can be considered a criterion for virginity (Fig. 386).

Perineum. The perineum is the inferior outlet of the pelvis bounded anteriorly by the symphysis pubis, anteriolaterally by the inferior rami of the pubis and the ischial tuberosities, and posteriorly by the tip of the bony coccyx. When the thighs are fully abducted, the perineum assumes a diamond shape which is further divided into anterior and posterior regions by a line drawn between the two ischial tuberosities. The triangle anterior to the line is called the *urogenital triangle,* and contains the external urogenital organs. The triangle posterior to the line is the rectal triangle, containing the anus.

The perineal structures are sometimes torn during childbirth. Tears can extend from the vaginal orifice posteriorly through the perineum and damage the anal sphincters. To avoid this danger an incision is deliberately made in the perineum just prior to the passage of the fetus through the vagina. This incision (episiotomy) allows enough room for the infant to pass and thus minimizes perineal damage.

Internal Organs (Fig. 387)

Vagina. The internal organs of reproduction include the vagina, uterus, uterine tubes, and ovaries. The vagina is a tubular canal 4 to 6 inches in length, directed upward and backward and extending from the vestibule to the uterus. It is situated between the bladder and the rectum. The vaginal wall consists of an internal membranous lining and a muscular layer capable of constriction and enormous dilatation, separated by a layer of erectile tissue. The mucous membrane forms thick transverse folds and is kept moist by cervical secretions. The vaginal walls

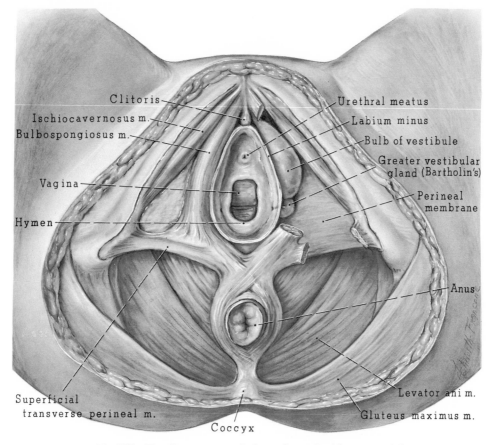

Clitoris
Ischiocavernosus m.
Bulbospongiosus m.
Vagina
Hymen
Urethral meatus
Labium minus
Bulb of vestibule
Greater vestibular gland (Bartholin's)
Perineal membrane
Anus
Superficial transverse perineal m.
Coccyx
Levator ani m.
Gluteus maximus m.

Fig. 385. Female perineum with skin and superficial fascia removed.

are normally folded in close apposition to each other, forming a collapsed tube. The vagina serves as part of the birth canal and represents the female organ of copulation.

Uterus. The uterus is a pear-shaped, thick-walled, muscular organ suspended in the anterior part of the pelvic cavity above the bladder in front of the rectum. In its normal state it measures about 3 inches in length and 2 inches in width. The uterine tubes enter into its upper end, one on each side, and the lower end projects into the vagina. The lower part of the uterus (the *cervix*) corresponds to the stem of an inverted pear. The corpus or body of the uterus is superior to the cervix; it is the upper rounded portion of the organ lying between the two uterine tubes, and is known as the fundus. The uterus, tilted forward and projecting above the bladder from behind, is freely movable; consequently, its position varies with the state of distension of the bladder and rectum (Fig. 388). The uterine cavity is normally triangular and flattened anteroposteriorly, making the cavity

appear as a mere slit when it is observed from the front.

The uterus is covered with a layer of peritoneum and is attached to both sides of the pelvic cavity by means of two double sheets of peritoneum, or *broad ligaments,* through which the uterine arteries course (Fig. 389). The principal supports of the uterus, the cardinal ligaments, lie in the base of the broad ligaments. There are also two round ligaments, attached on either side and near the uterine tubes, which hold the uterus in its anterior position. The two uterosacral ligaments are fibrous bands curved along the floor of the pelvis from the cervix to the sacrum. The uterosacral ligaments aid in supporting the cervix and maintaining its position.

The wall of the uterus consists of three layers. The outer layer is a peritoneal investment of the organ, continuous on each side with the peritoneum of the broad ligament. The middle layer, *myometrium,* a thick, muscular layer, consists of bundles of interlaced, smooth muscle fibers embedded in connective tissue. The myometrium

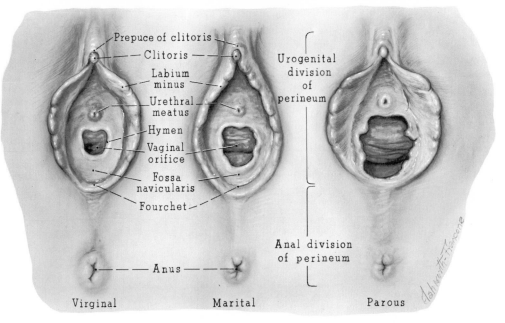

Prepuce of clitoris
Clitoris
Labium minus
Urethral meatus
Hymen
Vaginal orifice
Fossa navicularis
Fourchet
Urogenital division of perineum
Anal division of perineum
Anus
Virginal   Marital   Parous

Fig. 386. Vulva (virginal, marital, and parous states).

in turn is subdivided into three ill-defined but intertwining muscular layers, the middle of which contains many large blood vessels of the uterine wall. It is this intertwining arrangement of muscles that presses against the blood vessels and stops them from bleeding during the violent contractions of labor.

During pregnancy, there is a marked increase in the thickness of the myometrium. This occurs not only because of hypertrophy (actual enlargement of existing fibers) but also because of the addition of new fibers derived from transformation and division of mesenchymal cells. The inner coat of the uterine wall is the mucous membrane, or *endometrium*. It consists of an epithelial lining and connective tissue called the endometrial stroma. The stroma supports the tubular epithelial glands opening into the uterine lumen. Two types of arteries supply blood to the endometrium. The straight arteries supply the deeper layer and the coiled type supplies the superficial layer. The coiled arteries are important in menstruation when the superficial portion of the endometrium sloughs.

Uterine tubes. The uterine tubes (fallopian tubes) are two flexible, trumpet-shaped, muscular tubes approximately 4½ inches in length, extending from the fundus of the uterus on either side toward the pelvic brim. The uterine tubes are suspended by a mesenteric-peritoneal fold called the *mesosalpinx*. The wall of the tube is

composed of the same three layers as the uterus —mucous, smooth muscle, and serous layers. The mucous or internal layer is lined with ciliated epithelium and is continuous with the epithelium of the uterus as well as with the peritoneum in the abdominal cavity. One end of the tube, the isthmus, opens into the endometrial cavity and is continuous with the ampulla. The ampulla is the dilated, central part of the tube curving over the ovary, and is in turn continuous with the *infundibulum* which opens into the abdominal cavity.

The infundibulum is surrounded by finger-like projections or *fimbriae*. The fimbriated portion of the uterine tube curves about the ovary and is adjacent to but not necessarily in direct contact with it. When an ovum is expelled from the ovary, the fimbriae work like tentacles to draw the ovum into the tube where fertilization may occur. Then, by muscular peristaltic contractions and ciliary activity, the tube conducts the ovum to the uterine cavity.

Ovaries. The ovaries, often referred to as the primary reproductive organs of the female, are two oval-shaped structures about 1½ inches in length; they are located in the upper part of the pelvic cavity, one on each side of the uterus. The ovaries are suspended from the broad ligament of the uterus by the *mesovarium*, a fold of peritoneum, and are anchored to the uterus by the ovarian ligament. The infundibulopelvic or

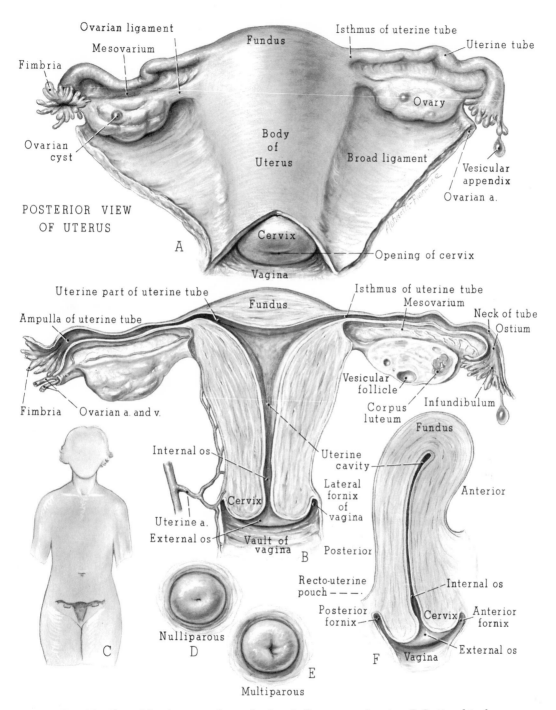

POSTERIOR VIEW OF UTERUS

Ovarian ligament
Mesovarium
Fimbria
Fundus
Isthmus of uterine tube
Uterine tube
Ovary
Ovarian cyst
Body of Uterus
Broad ligament
Vesicular appendix
Ovarian a.
Cervix
Opening of cervix
Vagina

A

Uterine part of uterine tube
Ampulla of uterine tube
Fundus
Isthmus of uterine tube
Mesovarium
Neck of tube
Ostium
Fimbria
Ovarian a. and v.
Vesicular follicle
Corpus luteum
Infundibulum

Internal os
Uterine cavity
Fundus
Anterior
Cervix
Lateral fornix of vagina
Uterine a.
External os
Vault of vagina
Posterior
B

Nulliparous
D
Multiparous
E

C

Recto-uterine pouch
Posterior fornix
Internal os
Cervix
Anterior fornix
External os
F
Vagina

Fig. 387. Plate of female organs of reproduction. *A.* Uterus, posterior view. *B.* Sectioned to show internal structure. *C.* Position in body. *D* and *E.* Shape of cervix before and after childbirth. *F.* Right lateral sagittal view.

487

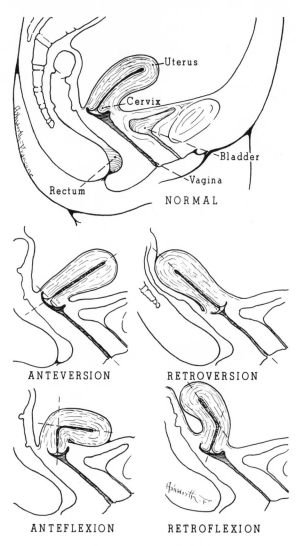

Fig. 388. Normal and abnormal positions of the uterus.

suspensory ligament of the ovary extends from its upper pole to the pelvic wall.

A thin layer of columnar cells, the germinal epithelium, covers each ovary. The inner structure or stroma of the ovary consists of a meshwork of spindle-shaped cells, connective tissue, and blood vessels. Minute vesicular follicles (graafian) at various stages of development are present within each ovary. The ova develop within these follicles. The two major functions of ovaries are development and expulsion of the female ova and elaboration of female sex hormones.

Mammary Glands

The two mammary glands, or breasts, are accessory reproductive organs. The breasts of pregnant women secrete milk available for nourishment of the newborn. Each breast is located anterior to the pectoral muscles and extends as a convex structure from the lateral margin of the sternum to the anterior border of the axilla (Fig. 390).

The nipples containing the openings of the milk ducts are located near the center of the breasts. A wider circular area of pigmented skin,

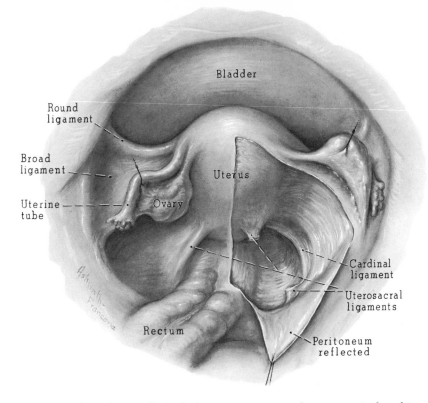

Fig. 389. View from above and behind of uterine structures as they are seen in the pelvic cavity. The peritoneum has been reflected on the right side, and the uterosacral ligament has been cut to expose the cardinal ligament found in the base of the broad ligament.

known as the *areola*, surrounds each nipple. There are from 15 to 20 lobes of glandular tissue arranged radially within the breast. Each is embedded in fat and connective tissue and each has its own excretory duct, the lactiferous duct. The lobes converge toward the areola, beneath which they form the ampulla, which serves as a reservoir for milk.

FURTHER DEVELOPMENT. Increasing titers of ovarian hormones and a conspicuous growth and branching of the ductal system, along with an extensive deposition of fat, occur at puberty. In the postpubertal virginal female, slight fluctuations in breast size may be correlated with changes in the reproductive cycle. A characteristic differentiation of glands of the breast occurs during pregnancy. The duct system branches extensively, and the terminal twigs end in secretory alveoli. The alveolar lining constitutes the secretory surface from which milk arises. After parturition (childbirth) the secretion of milk begins; the gland then gradually involutes until lactation ceases. Breast tissue atrophies,

becoming less prominent at the time of the menopause.

PHYSIOLOGY OF THE MAMMARY GLAND.

Two components of mammary gland physiology will be described—development of the glands and the formation and evacuation of milk.

DEVELOPMENT TO A FUNCTIONAL STATE. Experimental studies in animals have shown that prolactin from the hypophysis, as well as the ovarian hormones, estrogen and progesterone, are all essential for normal growth and development of the breast. Ovarian hormones exert specific control over growth of the breast and its development. Estrogen stimulates the development of the ducts; progesterone influences the growth of the alveoli.

There are cyclic changes in the mammary glands associated with a rise and fall of hormonal titers during the menstrual cycle. Many women notice fullness, tightness, heaviness, and, occasionally, pain in the breast just before the time of menstruation. This correlates with the observed

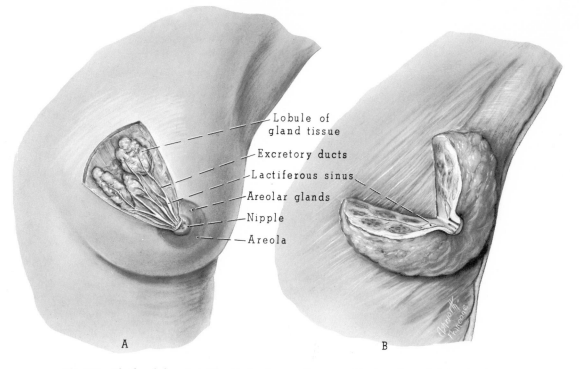

Lobule of
gland tissue

Excretory ducts

Lactiferous sinus

Areolar glands

Nipple

Areola

A   B

Fig. 390. The female breast. *A*. The skin has been partly removed to show the underlying structures. *B*. A section has been removed to show the internal structures in relation to the muscles.

limited growth of ducts and alveoli and also with swelling in the connective tissues of the breast just prior to the time of menstruation. Regression occurs after menstruation, and the connective tissue becomes more fibrous.

During pregnancy, the rapid increase of estrogen and progesterone produced by the ovary and later by the placenta causes alterations in the mammary glands more marked than the premenstrual changes. Each breast becomes larger with an increase in the number of ducts and the complexity of the alveoli. The color of the areola darkens.

FACTORS CONTROLLING LACTATION. Lactation is a complex process requiring the interplay of various hormonal and nervous factors. The exact mechanisms underlying the sudden onset of lactation after childbirth have not been fully explained. It is apparent, however, that the hypothalamus, hypophysis, suprarenal cortex, and thyroid are important control centers for initiation and maintenance of secretion of milk. Prolactin elaborated by the adenohypophysis appears to be the prime factor.

After parturition, there is a fall in the circulating estrogen and progesterone levels and a rise in the level of prolactin. High levels of progesterone and estrogen inhibit the output of prolactin, thus preventing lactation during the period of pregnancy. A low level of estrogen stimulates prolactin and induces lactation after childbirth.

Suckling stimulus. Maintenance of lactation involves the suprarenal cortex, the thyroid, and the growth hormone of the adenohypophysis. These organs regulate gluconeogenesis and fat metabolism to sustain normal milk synthesis. There is a well-recognized nervous factor in the maintenance of normal lactation—that is, the suckling stimulant to the mother's breast by the infant. Suckling by the newborn stimulates nerve endings at the nipple, and impulses are carried through the hypothalamic region to the neurohypophysis. There, oxytocin is released and taken by the blood to the mammary glands. Oxytocin causes contraction of the myoepithelial cells surrounding the alveoli, forcing the contents into the lactiferous ducts to be made available to the infant. It has been shown that failure of the ejection reflex eventually leads to a failure of lactation.

Endocrinology

Estrogen and progesterone are the two essential ovarian hormones secreted by the thecal cells of the vesicular follicles and the granulosa cells of the corpus luteum respectively. Their secretion occurs in response to two specific trophic hormones produced in the adenohypophysis— the follicle-stimulating hormone (FSH), and the luteinizing hormone (LH), also termed interstitial cell-stimulating hormone (ICSH). A third anterior hypophyseal hormone, luteotropic hormone (LTH) is directly concerned with secretions of the corpus luteum, especially in maintaining the secretion of progesterone.

Just before puberty, the hypothalamic gonadotropic centers reach maturity. Hypothalamic cells secrete a substance which is carried through the hypophyseal portal venous system to the anterior hypophysis, stimulating it. Under this stimulation the hypophysis produces FSH in ever-increasing amounts, and increased numbers of follicles appear in the ovary. Enhanced development of ovarian thecal cells and estrogen secretion are initiated. With the formation of additional estrogen, FSH is suppressed and release of LH stimulated.

Under the influence of LH, the precursor substance of progesterone (presumably cholesterol) is laid down on the granulosa cells; progesterone secretion in the proliferative phase causes a further release of LH, thus initiating ovulation.

Following ovulation, the granulosa cells become luteal in type and are organized to form the corpus luteum. Under the stimulation of luteotropic hormone, the corpus luteum secretes progesterone and some estrogen. In the absence of pregnancy, functional degeneration of the corpus luteum begins 8 to 10 days after ovulation. The life span of the corpus luteum is apparently fixed by the amount of precursor substance laid down prior to ovulation. As luteal function degenerates, estrogen and progesterone cease to be excreted. The decreasing amounts of the two ovarian hormones cause the uterine endometrium to degenerate, initiating menstruation and removing the inhibitory influence of the corpus luteum on the hypophysis, allowing FSH to be secreted in increasing amounts. The rising titer of FSH stimulates the growth of young follicles; thus, the ovarian cycle starts again (Fig. 391).

Functions of estrogen. In summary, then, estrogens are natural steroid hormones containing 18 carbon atoms, produced by the developing vesicular follicles and later by the corpus luteum. Estrogens are responsible for the increased uterine growth and growth of the vagina at puberty; development of secondary sex characteristics, such as the female figure; thickening of the lining of the cavity of the uterus in preparation for implantation of the blastocyst; and repair of the endometrium following menstruation.

Estrogen causes water retention by the endometrium and exercises partial control over breast development and function. In pregnancy and puberty, estrogen stimulates the formation of ducts in the mammary glands. These hormones inhibit lactation by preventing prolactin secretion by the hypophysis. When the placenta is shed following delivery, the tremendous elevations of circulating estrogen present during pregnancy abruptly disappear. This decrease precipitates prolactin production and stimulates lactation. Estrogen inhibits the production of FSH and LTH from the adenohypophysis. There is evidence that estrogen plays a significant role in normal sexual desire. Diminished secretion of estrogen produces irregularity of the menses and underdevelopment or atrophy of the breast and uterus.

Functions of progesterone. Progesterone is secreted by the corpus luteum and placenta. It prepares the already partially thickened uterine endometrium for embedding of the blastocyst and is responsible for the process of implantation. Progesterone maintains the development of the placenta and prevents the ovary from producing more ova during pregnancy. It is responsible for enlargement of the breast during pregnancy and for development of the milk-secreting cells of the mammary glands. During the secretory phase of the menstrual cycle, progesterone causes the spiral arteries in the uterus to dilate and coil and promotes a decrease in myometrial contraction. Diminished secretion of progesterone leads to menstrual irregularities in non-pregnant women and spontaneous abortion in pregnant women.

Menstrual Cycle and the Menopause

THE MENSTRUAL CYCLE. Menstruation commences at the age of puberty (menarche) and continues until the menopause, approximately 35 years later. The day of onset of the menstrual flow is considered the first day of the cycle. The

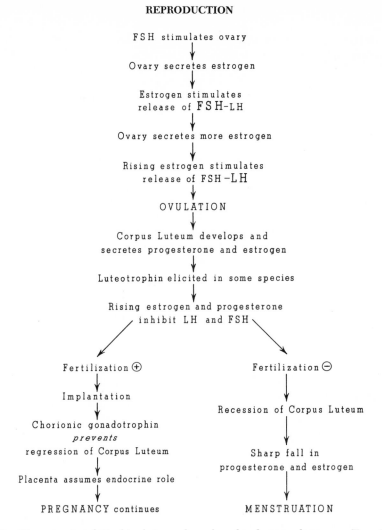

Fig. 391. Diagrammatic relationships between hypophyseal and ovarian hormones. (From Tepperman: *Metabolic and Endocrine Physiology.* Chicago, Year Book Medical Publishers, 1962.)

cycle ends on the last day prior to the next menstrual flow. Normally the cycle is 28 days in duration, but it can vary from 22 to 35 days. Three phases of the menstrual cycle are distinguished—menstrual, proliferative, and secretory.

Menstrual phase. The menstrual phase lasts from the first day to the fourth day of the cycle. Menstruation occurs when the expectation of implantation of the fertilized ovum is not fulfilled. The endometrial lining is destroyed and is rebuilt for the next possible implantation. When the ovum is not fertilized, the corpus luteum regresses; the subsequent deficiency of ovarian hormones causes the uterine endometrium, which is unable to maintain its nutrition, to regress and disintegrate. Predecidual cells from the

solid sheaths below the surface epithelium and leukocytes invade the tissue; necrotic changes occur in the stroma, and the uterine glands involute. Eventually the superficial functional layer of the endometrium is sloughed, and bleeding occurs into the uterine cavity (Fig. 392).

Proliferative phase. The proliferative phase, characterized by estrogen stimulation, begins at about the fifth day of the cycle and extends through ovulation, which usually occurs near the midpoint of the cycle (fourteenth day). The endothelium thickens as estrogen secretion rises. There is a rapid proliferation of both glands and stroma, so that the glandular and vascular patterns are gradually restored.

The ovulatory process is initiated by a signifi-

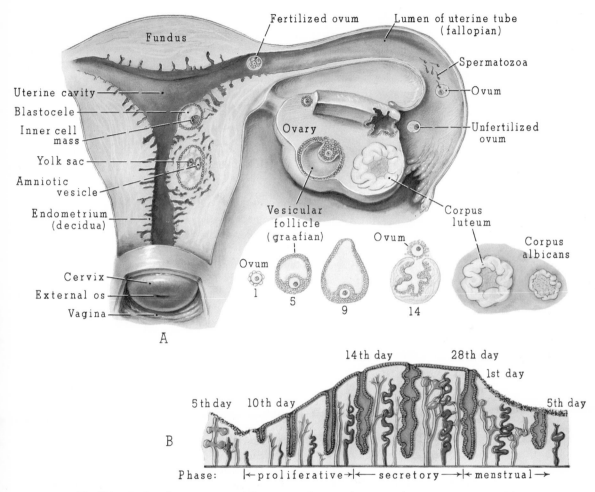

Fundus

Fertilized ovum

Lumen of uterine tube
(fallopian)

Spermatozoa

Ovum

Uterine cavity

Blastocele

Inner cell
mass

Yolk sac

Amniotic
vesicle

Endometrium
(decidua)

Ovary

Unfertilized
ovum

Vesicular
follicle
(graafian)

Ovum

Corpus
luteum

Corpus
albicans

Cervix

External os

Vagina

Ovum
1

5

9

14

A

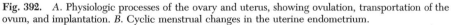

14th day

28th day

1st day

5th day   10th day

5th day

B

Phase: |← proliferative →|← secretory →|← menstrual →|

Fig. 392.   *A.* Physiologic processes of the ovary and uterus, showing ovulation, transportation of the ovum, and implantation. *B.* Cyclic menstrual changes in the uterine endometrium.

cant drop in the serum level of estrogen before progesterone begins to appear. Conspicuous changes do not occur in the endometrium at this point. A distinct rise in basal body temperature occurs at ovulation and remains high until the onset of the next menstrual period. The presence of progesterone accounts for this temperature fluctuation.

Secretory phase. During the secretory (progestational) phase, progesterone levels gradually rise; there is a concomitant but lesser rise in estrogen. The endometrium differentiates into a tissue capable of fulfilling the requirements for implantation of the embryo. The stroma becomes vascular and edematous, the mucosa thickens, and the glands take on a coiled and tortuous appearance. The endometrium must be a secretory type before a fertilized ovum can implant and develop. If implantation does not occur, the corpus luteum decreases in functional activity, degenerative changes are observed in the uterine endometrium, and the menstrual phase starts again.

MENSTRUAL PROBLEMS. The delay of the menarche, infrequent or irregular menstruation, prolonged menstruation, and menstrual pain are among the most frequent menstrual problems, particularly during adolescence.

In the adolescent girl amenorrhea (absence of menstruation) takes one of two forms; either there is a delay in the menarche beyond the age of 16, or after one or several periods the patient has only an occasional menstruation between long intervals (oligomenorrhea). Absence of the menarche after the age of 16 is rarely normal. On the other hand, menstrual irregularity, characterized by scanty or heavy flow at intervals of several months or even less than 28 days, is quite common during adolescence. It is usually associated with failure of ovulation. Dysmenorrhea, or menstrual pain, is sometimes experienced by young, apparently healthy women, although their periods tend to be regular and normal in amount and duration. No specific causes are known.

MENOPAUSE. The menopause marks the cessation of menstrual activity in the female. It occurs generally between the ages of 45 and 50, often gradually, but sometimes with a sudden change in body physiology. The most common symptoms consist of characteristic flushes involving the head, neck, and upper parts of the thorax, and the so-called "flashes," typified by hot, tingling sensations over the entire body. Perspiration, weakness, and elevation in blood pressure occur, accompanied by emotional depression. Most women take these changes in stride. Symp-

toms are severe enough in 20 per cent to necessitate medical advice and care. Generally reassurance is all that is required.

Menopausal symptoms are believed to be the result of ovarian failure, preceded by a period of ovarian deterioration. Unlike other endocrine glands, the ovary has a limited span of functional life, lasting about 35 years. In the majority of women, an increase in hypophyseal gonadotropins occurs coincident with ovarian failure. The normal reciprocal relationship between the ovary and adenohypophysis is interrupted. Since the atrophic ovary is unable to produce enough hormone to inhibit the production of hypophyseal gonadotropic substances, a high excretion of hypophyseal gonadotropins results.

PHYSIOLOGIC PROCESSES RELATED TO REPRODUCTION

Gametogenesis (Fig. 393)

Gametogenesis, or maturation of sex cells, can be considered the first phase of reproduction. It occurs by two processes of cell division, the first being *mitosis,* the usual type of cell division for somatic cells in which each daughter cell receives a complete set of chromosomes (see p. 29). The second step is *meiosis,* a two-stage type of cell division peculiar to reproductive tissue. In meiosis the chromosome number is reduced by one-half, so that the sex cells (gametes) receive only half as many chromosomes as somatic cells. In man the sex cells have 23 chromosomes (the *haploid* number). After the two gametes unite in the fertilization process, the normal (*diploid*) chromosome number, 46, is reconstituted.

SPERMATOGENESIS. Spermatogenesis is the development of spermatozoa. It takes place in the seminiferous tubules of the testis. In the embryo primordial germ cells differentiate and appear in the region where the reproductive organs form. As the primordial germ cells multiply by mitotic cell division, some differentiate and form the youngest male gametes, or spermatogonia. Others are organized to form the seminiferous tubules in which young germ cells grow and develop. The designated spermatogonia then multiply several times and enter a growth period. After birth, through infancy and childhood, these remain in a relatively quiescent state. At the time of sexual maturity they again become active and mature to form primary spermatocytes. This usually occurs at the age of 12 to 15 in the adolescent male.

Each primary spermatocyte divides by meiosis

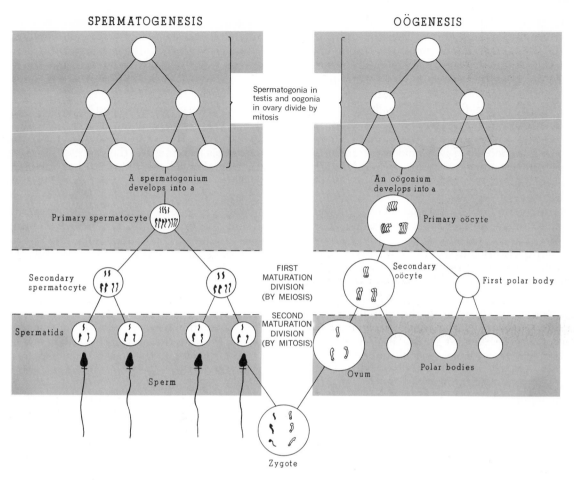

Fig. 393. Gametogenesis.

to give rise to two cells called secondary spermatocytes that contain the haploid chromosome number. These in turn divide, this time by mitosis, to produce four small haploid cells known as spermatids. Without further division, the spermatids are gradually transformed into four mature spermatozoa. The process of maturation occurs in the seminiferous tubules of the testes and requires about 2 weeks. It should be noted that the process of spermatogenesis proceeds at different rates in different parts of the seminiferous tubules. It is common in the human to find different developmental stages in adjacent areas within the same tubule.

Spermatozoa. The mature spermatozoon is microscopic in size and is often described as a tadpole in appearance. It consists of an oval head containing a nucleus, a middle section of cytoplasm, and a long tail which aids in motility of the cell by its lashing movements. Spermatozoa are bathed in fluid and stored in the epididymis. During ejaculation, the spermatozoa and seminal and prostatic secretions are transported in the ductus deferens to the ejaculatory duct through the urethra and are deposited in the vagina close to the cervix.

Semen. During transit the fluid receives ingredients from the secretion of seminal vesicles and prostate and bulbo-urethral glands, forming the final product called semen. These secretions buffer the acidity encountered in the female genital tract. Normally the volume of semen in a single discharge is about 2 to 3 ml., and the number of spermatozoa between 200 to 300 million.

The most important factors influencing the fertility of male spermatozoa are the actual number of spermatozoa (sperm count), the percentage of abnormal forms, and the motility. The actual number is the most important. A minimum of 60 million spermatozoa per milliliter is required for fertilization of the ovum.

OOGENESIS. Oogenesis is the development of the ovum. The process takes place in the cords of the ovary. As in the male, the female primordial germ cells are derived from the germinal epithelium in the embryo. These multiply and form primitive ova or oogonia. Maturation of the oogonia follows essentially the same course as that described for the spermatogonia, with certain differences. As in spermatogenesis, the mitotic division of the oogonia results in daughter cells with a diploid (46) number of chromosomes. The cells formed in the final mitotic division enter a period of growth and are transformed into primary oocytes with the diploid number of chromosomes. It is believed at present that the formation of oogonia is restricted to the intra-uterine period of life and that all cells produced by the female during reproductive life are derived from oocytes already present in the ovaries at birth. Meiotic division of the primary oocytes follows, with the production of cells containing the haploid (23) number of chromosomes. Here, unlike the corresponding stage of spermatogenesis, the division of the cytoplasm is unequal, producing the large and functional secondary oocyte and the small, non-functional first polar body, which usually undergoes rapid degeneration but which can occasionally undergo meiotic division forming two functionless cells. The secondary oocyte divides by mitosis, again in an unequal division, to produce a mature ovum and a second polar body. Thus, from each primary oocyte only one mature ovum is produced, while each primary spermatocyte gives rise to four mature spermatozoa.

The mature ovum is large in comparison with the spermatozoon. It is non-motile and barely visible to the naked eye. The nucleus of the ovum is surrounded by cytoplasm containing a small quantity of nutritive material in the form of yolk granules.

Ovulation. During the entire process of growth and maturation in the ovaries, the oocytes are surrounded by a layer of cells which have separated from the columnar epithelium within the stroma. These are known as the first or primitive follicles; they develop to form the vesicular ovarian (graafian) follicles—200,000 at birth in each ovary. As these mature under hormonal control (FSH and LH), two additional layers of cells are derived from the stroma and develop around the original layer. A cavity soon appears separating the mass of follicular cells into two parts.

The cavity, or antrum, is filled with fluid (liquor folliculi) believed to be secreted by the cells of the follicle. The oocyte remains embedded at one side of the vesicular follicle and is separated from the surrounding layer of cells by a transparent membrane known as the *zona pellucida.* As the follicle matures, it becomes distended by an accumulation of contained fluid and moves outward to the surface of the ovary. Once a month, usually about the middle of a 28-day menstrual cycle, the process of ovulation occurs.

A mature follicle ruptures and the ovum slowly oozes out of the ovarian surface in a stream of follicular fluid. Studies of ovulation in a variety of mammals indicate that the process is initiated by a neural mechanism in the hypothalamus stimulating the release of hypophyseal gonadotropins at the opportune time. The ovulation-inducing hormone is believed to be principally LH, but the exact manner in which it brings about rupture of the ovarian follicle is incompletely understood. It does not appear likely that increased intrafollicular tension arising from the accumulation of fluid within the antrum is the immediate cause of rupture of the mammalian follicle.

Once ovulation has occurred, definite changes take place within the ovary. First, there is minimal hemorrhage into the ruptured follicle, forming a blood clot, the *corpus hemorrhagicum.* Then the cells lining the ruptured follicle multiply and create a mass known as the *corpus luteum* (yellow body) which absorbs the corpus hemorrhagicum. It is the corpus luteum which secretes progesterone, the hormone responsible for preparing the uterus for the reception of the fertilized ovum. It is also responsible for placental development. If fertilization occurs, the corpus luteum continues to increase until about the third month of pregnancy, when the placenta takes over its function and it begins to slowly degenerate. It is still present in the ovary at the time of birth. If fertilization does not occur, the corpus luteum immediately degenerates and menstruation follows in about 14 days. The location of the old corpus luteum is marked by an area of white scar tissue in the ovary known as the *corpus albicans.*

Fertilization (Fig. 394)

After its discharge from the ovary, the ovum begins a 6- to 8-day journey, with its destination, the uterus, more than 3 inches away. It does not have any means of locomotion and must be transported through the uterine tube by peristaltic contractions of smooth muscles and by the activity of cilia present in the tube.

Fertilization normally occurs when the ovum is about one-third of the way down the tube. Spermatozoa, if present, should by this time have

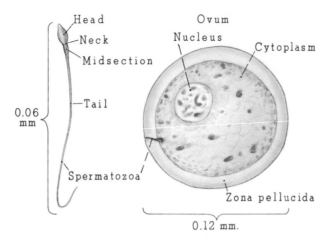

Fig. 394. Size relations of sperm and ovum.

reached the infundibulum. The mechanism by which the spermatozoon travels from the cervix to the uterine tube is still uncertain. Some believe it is caused by the lashing movement of the tail of the cell, while others maintain that the spermatozoon is transported passively by muscular contractions of the uterus. The spermatozoon must pass through a preparatory period lasting from 4 to 6 hours in the genital tract before it is able to fertilize the ovum. This process is known as *capacitation*, in which activation of an enzyme capable of acting upon the zona pellucida is thought to occur.

When the sperm reaches the ovum, it releases an enzyme, hyaluronidase, which is capable of breaking down hyaluronic acid (the cement substance used to hold together the granulosa cells surrounding the ovum). Thus, the sperm gains entrance to the ovum by dissociating and by wiggling through the granulosa cells. Normally only one sperm enters the ovum. As soon as penetration has occurred, the sperm sheds its tail and the chromosomal material forms the male pronucleus. Simultaneously, the ovum becomes impenetrable to other spermatozoa and prevents fertilization by several sperm.

The presence of the male pronucleus induces the ovum to proceed with the second maturation division, and it casts off the second polar body to form the female pronucleus. The two pronuclei approach each other and join into one. The union of the two gametes restores the chromosome number to 46, and the fertilized ovum (also known as the *zygote*) begins its first cleavage in the process of development (Fig. 395).

There is a short period of time each month during which fertilization can occur. This fol-

lows ovulation when the ovum is being carried down the uterine tube to the uterus. If fertilization does not occur in the outer third of the uterine tube, the ovum continues on to the uterus, where it usually undergoes rapid degeneration.

Determination of Sex

The prediction of sex of a developing fetus has always been a topic for speculation. Despite recent knowledge, such a prediction is not yet practical; however, the sex chromatin pattern in cells of aspirated amniotic fluid has been used to predict sex with some success. The nuclei of female cells have a distinctive nuclear appendage (chromatin body).

There are 23 pairs of chromosomes in man. Twenty-two of these are known as autosomes; the remaining pair, sex chromosomes, are commonly designated as either X or Y. In the female, there is a pair of X-chromosomes, while males have an X and a Y. During meiosis of the sex cells, each daughter cell receives only one-half the diploid number of chromosomes, so each ovum formed will have 22 autosomes and one (X) sex chromosome. Each spermatozoon will also have 22 autosomes, but either one X or one Y sex chromosome. If a sperm with an X-chromosome fertilizes the ovum, the embryo will develop into a female with a pair of X-chromosomes. If the ovum is fertilized by a sperm bearing a Y-chromosome, a male will develop with the genetic constitution of XY. It seems obvious that the sex of the zygote, either male or female, should be a 50-50 chance; but for reasons that are un-

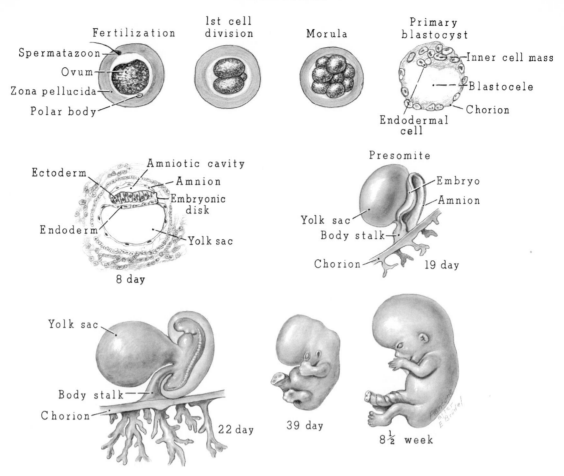

Fig. 395. Fertilization, cleavage, implantation, and fetal development.

known, slightly more males than females are born.

CLINICAL CONSIDERATIONS OF ABNORMALITIES OF SEX. Development of male external genitalia occurs in response to androgens during embryonic life; however, male genital development may also occur in genetic females exposed to androgens from some other source, such as overactive suprarenal glands, drugs, or tumors. The resulting individual is known as a female pseudohermaphrodite. A *pseudohermaphrodite* is an individual with the genetic constitution and gonads of one sex and the external genitalia of the other, while a *true hermaphrodite* is an individual with the gonads of both sexes. On the other hand, there is a condition known as male pseudohermaphrodism, in which the female external (and even internal) genital development occurs in genetic males. In this condition the

embryonic testes are defective and deficient in androgens. The female development fails to be inhibited. Pseudohermaphrodism is treated with hormonal therapy and plastic surgery.

CHROMOSOMAL ABNORMALITIES. Abnormalities of sexual development can be caused by genetic or hormonal disorders, as well as by other influences. Non-dysjunction is an established defect in gametogenesis. In this defect a pair of chromosomes fails to separate, and both go to one of the daughter cells during meiosis. The three types of abnormal zygotes that can form as a result of non-dysjunction of one of the sex chromosomes during gametogenesis are 44/XO, 44/XXX, and 44/XXY. The XO and XXY patterns, but not the XXX patterns, can occur as a result of non-dysjunction during spermatogenesis. In individuals with the XO chromosomal pattern, the gonads are rudimentary or absent, so that the female external genitalia are present. Stature is short and maturation does not occur at puberty. This symptom complex is referred to as ovarian agenesis (absence of the ovaries) or Turner's syndrome.

Individuals with the XXY pattern have the genitalia of the normal male, and testosterone production at puberty is often sufficient for the development of male characteristics; however, seminiferous tubules are abnormal, and there is a higher than normal incidence of mental retardation. This syndrome is known as Klinefelter's syndrome. A few individuals with XXX patterns have been reported; this is associated with mental retardation, oligomenorrhea (diminished menstruation), and, sometimes, sterility.

Cleavage

Immediately following fertilization, the zygote begins to undergo rapid cell division or mitosis. First two, four, then eight cells and so forth are formed, each containing 46 chromosomes. The 16-cell stage is reached about 96 hours after ovulation. This process of cell division is called cleavage.

At first the cells, called *blastomeres*, form a solid sphere; the cell mass is known as the *morula*. Successive cleavages produce cells of smaller size, so that the developing morula is only a little larger than the original zygote. As the cells of the morula continue to multiply, they form a hollow ball of cells known as the *blastocyst*. The blastocyst contains a thin layer of cells, the *trophoblast*, forming a cavity filled with fluid and containing an inner cell mass. It is from this inner cell mass that the three germ layers of the embryo will be derived. The trophoblast plays no direct part in the formation of the embryo, but is concerned with implantation and development of the fetal membranes.

Twinning. Identical twins are the result of a division of a single fertilized ovum into two masses, each becoming a separate embryo. If the division occurs at the two-celled stage, each embryo can have separate membranes. If division does not occur until the formation of the inner cell mass, then both embryos usually have a single placenta. This is known as monovular twinning. Binovular twinning follows fertilization of two separate ova, resulting in fraternal twins. Both shed at approximately the same time, and each developing individual has his own membranes and placenta.

Implantation

Six to 8 days after fertilization, the blastocyst, having traveled down the uterine tube, enters the uterus and becomes embedded in the endometrium on the posterior wall of the fundus. This process is called *implantation*. The lining of the uterus has been thickened in preparation for about 3 weeks. The zona pellucida of the blastocyst begins to dissolve, exposing the trophoblast which is able to digest or liquefy the tissues it contacts. Thus, the trophoblast burrows into the endometrial lining and carves out a nest for the blastocyst, which then sinks into the underlying connective tissue. The uterine vessels and glands in the penetrated area disrupt; the fluid thus formed furnishes nourishment for the implanted zygote. The epithelium heals over, and the embryo develops within the tissues of the uterine wall—not in the cavity, as occurs in most lower animals. This connective tissue in which the embryo rests is called the *decidua basalis*, and the mucosa covering it, the *decidua capsularis*. These tissues will be described subsequently in relation to the formation of the placenta.

Ectopic pregnancy. Occasionally the fertilized ovum becomes implanted in the uterine tube, a serious condition known as an *ectopic pregnancy*. Ectopic pregnancy includes all cases in which the fertilized ovum becomes implanted at a site other than the decidua of the normal uterine cavity. The most common site for this to occur is the uterine tube; but there are also other regions, such as the ovary, cervix, broad ligament, and peritoneal cavity. The uterine tube must either expel the ovum from its implantation cavity in the tubal mucosa into its lumen (tubal abortion), or the tube must give way (tubal rupture). This mishap frequently occurs before the embryo reaches the age of 6 weeks; it endangers the life of the mother.

Fetal Membranes and the Placenta of Pregnancy

Immediately following implantation, the embryo with its fetal membranes, together with the well-prepared uterine endometrial lining, begins formation of the placenta, which functions in the exchange of gaseous, nutritive, and excretory products between fetal and maternal systems. The definitive placenta consists of two layers of fetal membranes, the amnion and chorion. The decidua is the endometrial lining of the mother

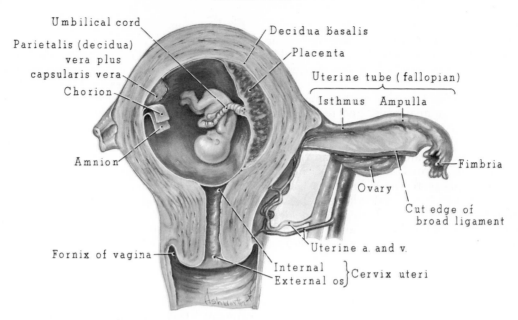

Fig. 396. Frontal section of pregnant uterus showing associated structures and fetal membranes.

on which the fetal placenta is implanted (Fig. 396).

Amnion. The amnion is derived from the inner layer of the trophoblast reinforced by mesodermal cells. It appears at an early stage as a small sac with an amniotic cavity covering the dorsal surface of the embryo. The amnion gradually enlarges to completely surround the embryo, coming into apposition with the inner surface of the chorion. The amniotic cavity is filled with amniotic fluid bathing the embryo. This serves to cushion the fetus against possible injury, to maintain the constancy of its temperature, and to furnish a medium in which the developing individual can readily move.

Chorion. The chorion, the second layer of the placenta, is derived from the ectodermal cells in the wall of the blastodermic vesicle. The wall of the blastocyst, at first entirely smooth in development, forms finger-like projections called trophoblastic buds. Irregular spaces, trophoblastic lacunae, are located between the projections. Initially these buds are solid epithelial sheets, but they are later penetrated by a core of vascularized mesenchyme to form chorionic villi. Simultaneously, the epithelial cells differentiate into two distinct layers, with an inner layer of smaller cuboidal cells covered by a layer of nondistinct, syncytial cells. These villi grow into the endometrial tissues and branch out to form a tree-like structure. The amnion, together with the chorionic villi, constitutes the fetal portion of the placenta. The embryo is connected with the connective tissue layer of the chorion by the forerunner of the umbilical cord, and in it the fetal blood vessels develop.

The decidua. The decidua is the mucous membrane of the uterus that has undergone certain changes under the influence of progesterone to prepare it for implantation and nutrition of the ovum. It is usually divided into three parts: the *decidua basalis*, that portion beneath the embryo between the chorionic vesicle and the myometrium of the uterus; the *decidua capsularis*, a thin layer of endometrium covering the embryo, which expands as the embryo grows, obliterating the uterine lumen; and the *decidua parietalis*, the remaining part of the uterine endometrium.

By the third month of pregnancy, the placenta is completely formed by the infiltration of the chorionic villi into the decidua basalis. These villi enlarge, multiply, and branch to the point that each is bathed in a pool of maternal blood.

Actually, there is no exchange of blood between the fetal and maternal portions of the placenta. The maternal placenta receives its blood from the uterine arteries, and blood is returned by way of the uterine veins. The fetal placenta is bathed in maternal blood and receives nutrients ingested by the mother by diffusion through the villi. Oxygen from the mother's blood also diffuses into the blood of the fetus. The waste products diffuse from the fetal blood and are eliminated by the excretory organs of the mother. Thus, the placenta forms the only means by which the nutritional, respiratory, and excretory functions of the fetus are possible.

Functions of placenta. The placenta also serves as an effective barrier against diseases of bacterial origin; however, viruses and some blood-borne diseases such as syphilis affect the fetus. Antibodies are transmitted by the mother to the developing embryo and fetus to build up immunity against various diseases. (For discussion of the Rh factor, see Chapter Ten.) This immunity is necessary during the first few months of life before the time when the infant can produce its own antibodies. The placenta, in addition to its protective function, is capable of forming estrogen and progesterone; it takes over the functions of the corpus luteum at late pregnancy. The mature placenta is a circular disc 8 inches in diameter and nearly 1 inch in thickness, weighing approximately 1 pound. The fetal surface is smooth and glistening, beneath which can be seen many large vessels. The maternal surface is red and flesh-like. At delivery, after the fetus is born, the placenta becomes detached from the uterus and is the "afterbirth" (Fig. 397).

DISORDERS OF PREGNANCY. *Abortion* is any interruption of pregnancy prior to the period when the fetus is viable. Abortion can be either spontaneous or induced. The fetus is considered viable when it weighs 500 grams or more and the pregnancy is over 20 weeks in duration. When infection occurs, the process is known as a septic abortion. Women who abort repeatedly

are said to be habitual abortors. To the laity the term *miscarriage* merely means a spontaneous interruption of pregnancy—as distinguished from *abortion*, which the lay individual infers as a criminal emptying of the uterus. This is a misconception; miscarriage is not a correct medical term. Abortion is, as we have seen, any interruption of pregnancy prior to the period when the fetus is viable.

Laboratory diagnosis of pregnancy. Chorionic gonadotropin is produced by the placenta shortly after implantation and is excreted in the maternal urine. It is readily detectable because of its effect on the rodent ovary and on the gonads of various amphibians. A large number of pregnancy tests are based on this influence.

Calculation of term. On the assumption that the gestation period totals 280 days from the beginning of the last menstrual period, the date of confinement is estimated by adding 7 days to the date of the last menstrual period and subtracting 3 months (Fig. 398).

Labor

The mechanisms involved in the onset of labor are complex and poorly understood. It is certain that labor is not initiated by a single event; it must be regarded as a consequence of many developments occurring during the course of gestation. The uterus is relatively quiescent during gestation, but as labor approaches, there are signs of increasing myometrial irritation. There is also increased sensitivity of the uterine musculature to hormones, in preparation for the forceful muscular contractions required to expel the fetus.

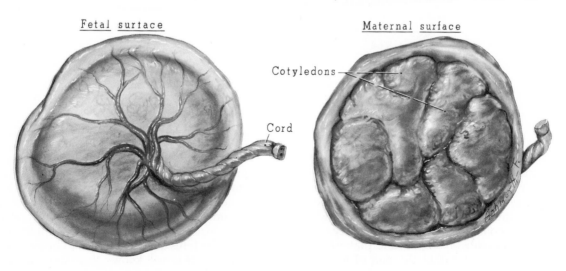

Fetal surface   Maternal surface

Cotyledons

Cord

Fig. 397. Placenta (fetal and maternal surfaces).

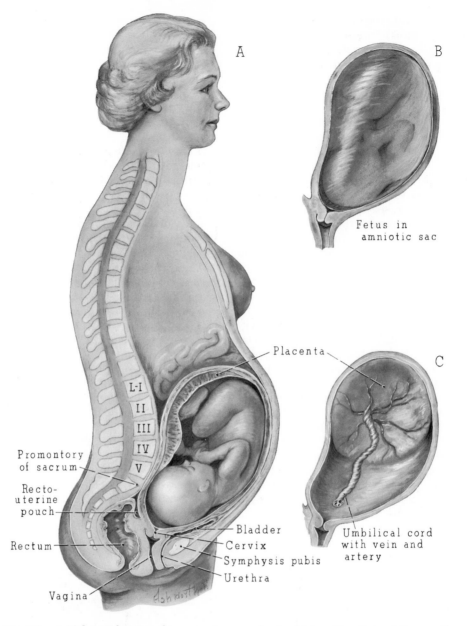

Fig. 398. *A.* Mid-sagittal section of a pregnant woman showing fetal position. *B.* Amniotic sac with fetus. *C.* Placenta in uterus with fetus removed.

The hormones generated from the placenta and ovaries are known to play key roles in determining the onset of labor. Progesterone exerts a pregnancy-stabilizing effect. Labor cannot occur until its influence is effectively diminished. Estrogens promote rhythmic contractility of the uterus. It is probably significant that estrogen increases in amount until the end of gestation, when secretion diminishes.

Oxytocin from the neurohypophysis is known to exert a powerful effect on uterine contractility. Relaxin is a hormone of pregnancy secreted by the placenta as well as the ovary. It acts to relax the ligamentous structures. Without proper hormonal balance and timing, labor would not occur, or the fetus and mother would be injured. For example, it is well known that labor may be precipitated by administering large doses of oxytocin; however, if the cervical canal is not softened and the pubic ligaments not relaxed by the action of relaxin, violent uterine contractions would kill the fetus and rupture the uterus instead of expelling it through the vagina.

The stages of labor are conveniently described in three phases (Fig. 399). In the first stage, there are regular contractions, rupture of the membranes, and complete dilatation. The obstetrician follows the course of labor by frequent rectal examinations. Complete dilatation of the cervix is synonymous with the cervical dilatation of 10 cm. The second stage extends from the time of complete cervical dilatation to delivery. In the third stage, the "afterbirth" is delivered.

A dependable sign of impending labor is the so-called "show." This is the vaginal discharge of a small amount of blood-tinged mucus representing the extrusion of mucous blood which has filled the cervical canal during pregnancy. It is a late sign, and labor usually ensues within 24 hours. The quantity of blood escaping with the mucus (show) amounts to only a few milliliters. Any substantial loss of blood at this time should be regarded as suggestive of an abnormal condition.

True labor must be distinguished from false labor. In true labor the pains occur at regular intervals; the intervals gradually shorten, and the intensity of pain increases. The pain is located in

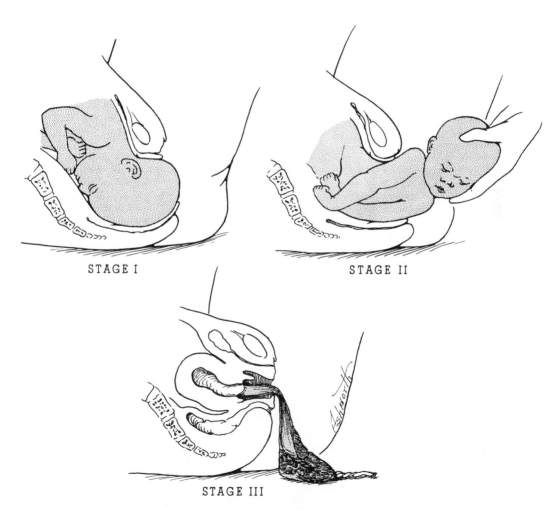

STAGE I

STAGE II

STAGE III

Fig. 399.   The stages of labor can be described as follows. The first stage is characterized by regular contractions, rupture of the membranes, and complete dilatation; the second stage extends from the time of complete cervical dilatation to delivery; during the third stage the "afterbirth" is delivered.

the back and is intensified by walking. "Show" has occurred and the cervix dilates.

In false labor, pains occur at irregular intervals, the intervals remain long, intensity remains unaltered, pain is located in the abdomen, and walking either has no effect or can relieve the pain. In false labor there is no show, and the cervix remains closed.

SUMMARY: REPRODUCTIVE SYSTEM

EMBRYOLOGY OF THE REPRODUCTIVE SYSTEM

1. Organs of both sexes develop from indifferent genital ridges.

2. The male embryo forms cords of the testis which develop into seminiferous tubules.

3. The female embryo develops secondary ovarian cords containing primary ovarian follicles.

4. Gametes develop from primordial germ cells which penetrate the genital ridges.

5. Ductile systems arise from the two pairs of distinct embryonic ducts.

MALE REPRODUCTIVE SYSTEM

1. External organs:

   a. Scrotum—a pouch supporting the testes.
   b. Penis—the male organ of copulation; it consists of three columns of erectile tissues.
   c. Congenital abnormalities of the penis—hypospadias and epispadias.
   d. Clinical consideration of the penis—circumcision and phimosis.

2. Internal organs of the male reproductive tract:

   a. Male gonads—testes:
      (1) Structure and location—250 wedge-shaped lobes containing coiled seminiferous tubules.
      (2) Functions of reproductive cells and supporting cells inside the tubules, as well as interstitial cells between the tubules.
      (3) Congenital defect—cryptorchism.
   b. Series of ducts:
      (1) Epididymis—a coiled tube lying on the posterior aspect of the testis.
      (2) Ductus deferens—continuous with the epididymis and joins the duct of the seminal vesicle.
      (3) Ejaculatory duct—tube for depositing semen into the urethra.
      (4) Urethra transmits semen and urine (see Chapter Fourteen).
   c. Accessory glands add alkaline contents to the semen.
      (1) Seminal vesicles are membranous pouches lying posterior to the bladder.
      (2) Prostate gland surrounds the first part of the urethra; it can obstruct flow of urine in aged.
      (3) Bulbo-urethral glands—located below the prostate.

3. Endocrinology of the testis:

   a. Two functions of the testis are proliferation of spermatozoa and secretion of male sex hormones.
   b. Androgens are produced chiefly by the testis, also formed by the suprarenal cortex.
   c. Testosterone is secreted by interstitial cells; secretion is regulated by the gonadotropins.

    d. Chemical structure of androgens—all contain 19 carbon atoms, similar to steroid hormones.

    e. Functions of androgens:

        (1) Promote protein metabolism, causing true storage of nitrogen as tissue protein.

        (2) Stimulate secondary sex characteristics.

        (3) Diminished secretion of testosterone causes a failure in development of male characteristics.

FEMALE REPRODUCTIVE SYSTEM

1. External organs—vulva:

    a. Mons pubis—adipose tissue over the symphysis pubis.

    b. Labia majora—rounded folds of adipose tissue, uniting anteriorly and posteriorly to form commissures; homologous to scrotum.

    c. Labia minora—two smaller medial folds, surrounding the vestibule.

    d. Clitoris—a small projection of erectile tissue, sensitive to tactile stimulation and homologous to the male penis.

    e. Vestibule—the region between the labia minora containing the vaginal orifice and urethral orifice.

        (1) The para-urethral glands are adjacent to urethral orifice.

        (2) The greater vestibular glands are adjacent to vaginal orifice.

    f. Hymen—mucous membrane separating the vagina from the vestibule. Can be present or absent in virginity.

    g. Perineum—inferior outlet of the pelvis, contains the urogenital triangle and rectal triangle; of clinical importance in childbirth.

2. Internal organs:

    a. Vagina—tubular canal.

        (1) Structure—three layers.

        (2) Location—between bladder and rectum.

        (3) Function—forms part of the birth canal and represents the female organ of copulation; capable of constriction and enormous dilatation.

    b. The uterus:

        (1) Location—between the bladder and rectum.

        (2) Consists of three parts—cervix, corpus, and fundus.

        (3) Supporting ligaments:

            (a) Cardinal ligaments—principal support of the uterus.

            (b) Broad ligaments—to both sides of the pelvic cavity.

            (c) Round ligaments—hold the uterus in a forward tilted position.

            (d) Uterosacral ligaments—support the cervix.

        (4) Wall of uterus—divided into three layers.

            (a) Outer serous layer of peritoneum.

            (b) Middle muscular layer, myometrium, divided into three ill-defined intertwining layers, the middle of which is thickest and contains large blood vessels.

            (c) Inner mucous layer, endometrium, subject to regulation by ovarian hormones and responsible for menstruation and implantation; superficial layer sloughs off during menstruation.

    c. The uterine tubes—a pair of flexible, muscular tubes.

        (1) Location—extend from the upper angle of the uterus on either side toward the side of the pelvis.

        (2) Attachment—suspended by peritoneal fold, mesosalpinx.

        (3) Structure—three layers: mucous, smooth muscle, and serous; mucous layer is lined with ciliated epithelium.

        (4) The infundibula with the fimbriae open to the abdominal cavity.

       (5) Function—to convey the ovum to the uterus by muscular contraction and ciliary action.

          (a) Fertilization takes place in the uterine tube.

    d. Ovaries—primary reproductive organs of the female.

       (1) Location—in upper part of pelvic cavity.

       (2) Attachment—by peritoneal folds; attached to the broad ligament by the mesovarium, anchored to the uterus by the ovarian ligament.

       (3) Structure—almond-shaped, 1½ inches in length.

          (a) Germinal epithelium covers the ovary.

          (b) Stroma—a meshwork of spindle-shaped cells.

          (c) Minute vesicular follicles at different developmental stages.

       (4) Functions:

          (a) Development and expulsion of ova.

          (b) Elaboration of female sex hormones.

3. Accessory organs—mammary glands secrete milk.

    a. Location—anterior to the pectoral muscles of the chest.

    b. Structure—a convex structure of adipose tissue and ducts.

       (1) Nipple or circular area of pigmented skin (areola).

       (2) Fifteen to 20 lobes arranged radially within the breasts, embedded in fat and connective tissue.

       (3) Each lobe has its alveoli and own excretory duct (lactiferous duct).

    c. Further development after puberty:

       (1) Growth and branching of ductile system.

       (2) Intensive deposition of fat.

       (3) Fluctuation of breast size correlates with reproductive cycle.

       (4) After menopause breast tissue atrophies and becomes less prominent.

    d. Physiology of mammary glands:

       (1) In development to a functional state prolactin, estrogen, and progesterone are important.

          (a) Estrogenic hormones stimulate development of ducts.

          (b) Progesterone influences growth of alveoli.

          (c) Cyclic changes during menstrual cycle are associated with rise and fall of hormones.

          (d) During pregnancy progesterone causes exaggerated premenstrual activation of glands.

       (2) Factors controlling lactation—neural and hormonal:

          (a) Lactation is initiated by prolactin from the adenohypophysis, the output of which is regulated by ovarian hormones.

          (b) Maintenance of lactation depends upon factors influencing milk secretion—gluconeogenesis and fat metabolism.

          (c) Suckling stimulant is also responsible for maintenance of lactation. The stimulus is carried through the hypothalamus and adenohypophysis to release oxytocin.

4. Endocrinology:

    a. Ovarian hormone secretion is dependent on three sex hormones produced by the adenohypophysis.

       (1) Follicle-stimulating hormone (FSH).

       (2) Luteinizing hormones (LH or ICSH).

       (3) Luteotropic hormones (LTH).

    b. Mode of action of different sex hormones:

       (1) FSH is secreted by hypophysis, stimulates follicle growth.

       (2) LH stimulates ovarian thecal cells to produce estrogen.

       (3) Ratio of FSH and LH is essential in inducing ovulation.

    c. Functions of estrogen:
      (1) Growth of uterus and vagina.
      (2) Development of secondary sex characteristics.
      (3) Preparation of uterine wall for implantation.
      (4) Stimulates formation of ducts in mammary glands.
      (5) Inhibits lactation by preventing production of prolactin.
      (6) Hyposecretion causes irregularity of menses and atrophy of breast and uterus.
    d. Functions of progesterone:
      (1) Further prepares uterine endometrium.
      (2) Responsible for process of implantation.
      (3) Maintains development of placenta.
      (4) Develops mammary alveoli.
      (5) Stimulates spiral arteries in uterus.
      (6) Diminished secretion leads to menstrual irregularities and spontaneous abortion.

MENSTRUAL CYCLE AND MENOPAUSE

1. Menstrual cycle normally requires 28 days.

    a. Three phases of menstrual cycle:
      (1) Menstrual—day 1 to 4: sloughing off of superficial endometrium.
      (2) Proliferative—day 5 to 14: rebuilding of endometrial wall.
      (3) Secretory—day 14 to 28: preparation for implantation.

2. Menstrual problems:

    a. Amenorrhea: absence of menses.
    b. Dysmenorrhea: menstrual pain.

3. The menopause between ages 45 and 50; permanent cessation of menstrual activity.

    a. Symptoms are related to deprivation of estrogen.
    b. Psychological influence on women.
    c. Physiological considerations:
      (1) Deterioration of function of ovary.
      (2) Increase in hypophyseal gonadotropins.
      (3) Decrease of ovarian hormones, especially estrogen.

ESSENTIAL PHYSIOLOGIC PROCESSES OF REPRODUCTION

1. Gametogenesis: maturation of sex cells.

    a. Cell division:
      (1) Mitosis retains the diploid number of 46 for humans; common in somatic cells.
      (2) Meiosis acquires the haploid number of 23; unique to sex cells.
    b. Spermatogenesis: development of spermatozoa.
      (1) Formation of primary spermatocyte from spermatogonia.
      (2) Formation of spermatozoa from one spermatocyte through two meiotic divisions.
      (3) Structure of spermatozoa: head, neck, and tail.
      (4) Composition of semen: contributions from the seminal vesicle and prostate and bulbo-urethral glands.
      (5) Fertility factors: sperm count most important.

    c. Oogenesis and ovulation:
- (1) Maturation division of primary oocyte—process essentially the same as spermatogenesis, except for unequal distribution of cytoplasm.
- (2) Formation and structure of vesicular follicles.
- (3) Process of ovulation is initiated by neural mechanisms.
- (4) Formation of corpus luteum from ruptured follicle.

2. Fertilization:

- a. Transportation of ovum: peristalsis and ciliary flagellation.
- b. Site of fertilization: one-third of the way down uterine tube.
- c. Transportation and capacitation of spermatozoa.
  - (1) Lashing movement of spermatozoa.
  - (2) Contraction of uterus.
  - (3) Activation of proteolytic enzymes.
- d. Penetration of spermatozoa, hyaluronidase, and wriggling movement.
- e. Union of gametes to form zygote.

3. Determination of sex:

- a. Uncertainty in prediction of sex of newborn.
- b. Genetic make-up of male and female gametes:
  - (1) Male: 22 autosomes + XY.
  - (2) Female: 22 autosomes + XX.
- c. If the ovum is fertilized by sperm with an X-chromosome, a female fetus develops; if the ovum is fertilized by sperm with a Y, a male fetus results.
- d. Clinical considerations of abnormalities of sex caused by abnormal action of sex hormones:
  - (1) Pseudohermaphrodite: male or female.
  - (2) True hermaphrodite: rare.
- e. Chromosomal abnormalities—caused by non-dysjunction:
  - (1) Turner's syndrome: female with absence of ovaries.
  - (2) Klinefelter's syndrome: male with abnormal seminiferous tubules.

4. Cleavage—cell division of an embryo:

- a. Morula stage with blastomeres.
- b. Blastocyst: a hollow ball of cells with a thin layer of trophoblast.
- c. Implantation at blastocyst stage.
- d. Twinning:
  - (1) Monovular twinning: identical twins—division of a single fertilized ovum into two masses.
  - (2) Binovular twinning: fertilization of two separate ova, giving rise to fraternal twins.

5. Implantation: 6 to 8 days after fertilization.

- a. Site: posterior wall of fundus.
- b. Burrowing of blastocyst.
- c. Formation of decidual layers—decidua basalis and decidua capsularis.
- d. Ectopic pregnancy: implantation outside uterus.
  - (1) Common sites: uterine tube and broad ligament.
  - (2) Expulsion of fetus: tubal abortion and tubal rupture.

6. Fetal membranes and the placenta of pregnancy:

- a. Two layers of the placenta from fetal membranes—amnion and chorion.
- b. Formation and structure of amnion:
  - (1) Amniotic cavity and amniotic fluid.
  - (2) Functions of amniotic fluids.

    c. Formation and structure of chorion:
- (1) Trophoblastic buds.
- (2) Primary chorionic villi.
- (3) Formation of true chorion.

    d. Decidua: mucous membrane of uterus:
- (1) Three layers of decidua: decidua basalis, decidua capsularis, and decidua parietalis.

    e. Physiology and function of the placenta:
- (1) Exchange of food, gas, and waste products without actual exchange of blood.
- (2) Effective barrier against bacteria.
- (3) Transmission of antibodies.
- (4) Production of estrogen and progesterone.

    f. Shape and structure of mature placenta after birth.

    g. Disorders of pregnancy:
- (1) Abortion: interruption of pregnancy.
- (2) Miscarriage: layman's term.

    h. Laboratory diagnosis of pregnancy: detection of chorionic gonadotropin by action on rodent ovary.

    i. Calculation of term: (seven days + date of last menstrual period) − 3 months = date of confinement.

7. Labor:

    a. A complex, poorly understood process.
- (1) Actomyosin increases in quantity by the end of gestation.
- (2) Increased sensitivity of uterine musculature.
- (3) Progesterone exerts a stabilizing effect.
- (4) Estrogen and oxytocin increase uterine contraction.
- (5) Relaxin relaxes ligamentous structures.
- (6) Balance of the above factors bring about labor and parturition.

    b. Three stages of labor: period of dilatation, complete cervical dilatation to delivery, and delivery of "afterbirth."

    c. Show: vaginal discharge of blood-tinged mucus.

    d. True labor: pains at regular intervals; intervals shorten; pain increases; pain in back; and show.

    e. False labor: no show; pain at irregular intervals; pain located in abdomen; and cervix closed.

STUDY QUESTIONS: THE REPRODUCTIVE SYSTEM

1. Describe the embryologic development of the testes.
2. List the structures derived from the embryonic genital ducts of both the adult male and adult female.
3. Name the erectile tissues of the penis. How do they function?
4. Review the congenital abnormalities related to the development of the penis.
5. List the accessory glands of the male reproductive system and their functions.
6. If the testes fail to descend, what is the name of the clinical condition?
7. Specify the cells, other than sex cells, found in the testes. List their functions.
8. Describe the ductus deferens.
9. Discuss androgens.
10. List the structures included in the vulva.
11. Describe the structure and function of the clitoris.
12. Discuss the structures of the perineum.

13. List the internal organs of the female reproductive system.
14. Describe the wall of the uterus.
15. List the functions of the uterus.
16. Describe the structures of the mammary glands.
17. Name the three phases of the menstrual cycle.
18. Describe the function of progesterone.
19. Discuss spermatogenesis.
20. How does the spermatozoon gain entrance into the ovum?
21. Name and describe briefly the different layers of the placenta.
22. Describe the process of implantation.
23. Discuss the function of estrogen in the female.

SUGGESTED ADDITIONAL READING

THE CELL:

Brachet, J.: The living cell. Scientific American, 205:50–61, 1961.
Stanbury, J. B., Wyngaarden, J. B., and Fredrickson, D. S. (Eds.): The Metabolic Basis of Inherited Disease. New York, McGraw-Hill Book Co., 1960.
West, E. S., and Todd, W. R.: Textbook of Biochemistry. New York, The Macmillan Co., 1961, Chaps. 1–10.

TISSUES:

Arey, L. B.: Human Histology. Philadelphia, W. B. Saunders Co., 1963.
Asboe-Hansen, G.: Connective tissue. Annual Review of Physiology, 25:45–60, 1963.
Gillison, M.: A Histology of the Body Tissues. Baltimore, Williams & Wilkins Co., 1962.
Ham, W. A., and Leeson, T. S.: Histology. Philadelphia, J. B. Lippincott Co., 1961.

SKIN:

Cahn, M. M.: The skin from infancy to old age. American Journal of Nursing, 60:993–996, 1960.
Lobitz, W. C., Jr., and Daniels, F., Jr.: Skin. Annual Review of Physiology, 23:207–228, 1961.
Mackay, J.: Emotion and the skin. Nursing Times, 58:669–700, 1962.
Montagna, W.: The Structure and Function of the Skin. New York, Academic Press, 1962.
Pillsbury, D. A., Shelley, W. B., and Kligman, A. M.: A Manual of Cutaneous Medicine. Philadelphia, W. B. Saunders Co., 1961.

THE SKELETAL SYSTEM:

Shapiro, R., and Janzen, A. H.: The Normal Skull. New York, Paul B. Hoeber, 1960.
Warren, R.: Surgery. Philadelphia, W. B. Saunders, 1963, Chap. 13.

THE ARTICULAR SYSTEM:

Frost, H. M.: Introduction to joint biomechanics. Henry Ford Hospital Medical Bulletin, 8:415–432, 1960.
Smyth, C. J.: Rheumatism and arthritis. Review of American and English literature of recent years (Fourteenth Rheumatism Review). Annals of Internal Medicine, 56(5) Pt. 2:1–119, 1962.

THE MUSCULAR SYSTEM:

Basmajian, J. V.: Muscles Alive. Baltimore, Williams & Wilkins Co., 1962.
Bourne, G. H.: Structure and Function of Muscles. New York, Academic Press, 1962.
Burnstock, G., and Horman, M. E.: Smooth muscle: autonomic nerve transmission. Annual Review of Physiology, 25:61–90, 1963.
Haupt, R. E., and Wall, D. M.: High speed cinematography of muscle contraction. Science, 137:132, 1962.
Huxley, A. F.: Muscle. Annual Review of Physiology, 26:131–152, 1964.
Podolsky, R. J.: Kinetics of muscular contraction. Nature, 188:666–668, 1960.

THE NERVOUS SYSTEM:

Chusid, J. G., and McDonald, J. J.: Correlative Neuroanatomy and Functional Neurology. Los Altos, Calif., Lange Medical Publications, 1962.
Epstein, B. S.: The Spine, A Radiological Text and Atlas. Philadelphia, Lea and Febiger, 1962.
Frank, K., and Fourtes, M. G. F.: Excitation and conduction. Annual Review of Physiology, 23:357–386, 1961.
Manter, J. T., and Gatz, A. J.: Essentials of Clinical Neuroanatomy and Neurophysiology. Philadelphia, F. A. Davis Co., 1962.
Nachmansohn, D.: Chemical factors controlling nerve activity. Science, 134:1962–1968, 1961.
Wyburn, G. M.: The Nervous System: An Outline of the Structure and Function of the Human Nervous System and Sense Organs. London, Academic Press, 1960.
Zacks, S.: The Motor Endplate. Philadelphia, W. B. Saunders Co., 1964.

SPECIAL SENSES:

Bing, H. I.: Studies in cutaneous sensation. Acta Neurologica Scandinavica, 37:86–103, 1961.
DeWeese, D. D., and Saunders, W. H.: Textbook of Otolaryngology. St. Louis, C. V. Mosby Co., 1964.
Gordon, D.: Diseases of the eye. CIBA Clinical Symposia, 14:115–142, 1962.
Hawkins, J. E., Jr.: Hearing. Annual Review of Physiology, 26:453–480, 1964.
Kalmus, H., and Hubbard, S. J.: The Chemical Senses in Health and Disease. Springfield, Ill., Charles C Thomas, 1960.
Myers, D., Schlusser, W., and Winchester, R.: Otologic diagnosis and the treatment of deafness. CIBA Clinical Symposia, 14:39–73, 1962.
Terkildsen, K.: Conduction of sound in the human middle ear. Archives of Otolaryngology, 73:69–79, 1961.
Weddell, G., and Miller, S.: Cutaneous sensibility. Annual Review of Physiology, 24:199–222, 1962.

THE CIRCULATORY SYSTEM:

Berne, R. M., and Levy, M. N.: Heart. Annual Review of Physiology, 26:153–189, 1964.
Bohr, D. F.: Peripheral circulation. Annual Review of Physiology, 23:295–320, 1961.
Copley, A. L., and Stainsby, G.: Flow Properties of Blood. New York, Pergamon Press, 1960.
D'Alonzo, C. A.: Heart Disease, Blood Pressure and Strokes. Houston, Gulf Publishing Co., 1961.
Loki, K.: Clotting of fibrinogen. Scientific American, 206:66, 1962.
Macfarlane, R. G., and Robb-Smith, A. H. T.: Function of the Blood. New York, Academic Press, 1962.
Murray, J. F.: Systemic circulation. Annual Review of Physiology, 26:389–420, 1964.
Reich, C.: The cellular elements of the blood. CIBA Clinical Symposia, 14:79–109, 1962.
Talmage, D. W., and Cann, J. R.: The Chemistry of Immunity in Health and Disease. Springfield, Ill., Charles C Thomas, 1961.
Zucker, M. B.: Blood platelets. Scientific American, 204:58–64, 1961.

THE LYMPHATIC SYSTEM:

Csaba, G., Mold, K., and Toro, I.: Some new data concerning the functional duty of the lymphatic system. Acta Anatomica, 48:114–121, 1962.
Rebuck, J. W.: Lymphocyte and Lymphatic Tissue. New York, Paul B. Hoeber, 1960.
Ruszynyak, I.: Lymphatics and Lymph Circulation. New York, Pergamon Press, 1960.

THE RESPIRATORY SYSTEM:

DuBois, A. B.: Respiration. Annual Review of Physiology, 26:421–452, 1964.
Rossier, R. H.: Respiration. St. Louis, C. V. Mosby Co., 1960.
Tenney, S. M.: Respiration. Annual Review of Physiology, 23:123–152, 1961.
Von Hayek, H.: The Human Lung. New York, Hofner Publishing Co., 1960.
West, E. S., and Todd, W. R.: Textbook of Biochemistry. New York, The Macmillan Co., 1961, Chap. 16.

THE DIGESTIVE SYSTEM:

Bogert, L. J.: Nutrition and Physical Fitness. Philadelphia, W. B. Saunders Co., 1960.
Bollman, J. L.: Liver. Annual Review of Physiology, 23:183–206, 1961.
Davenport, H. W.: Physiology of the Digestive Tract. Chicago, Year Book Publishers, 1961.
Grossman, M. I.: The digestive system. Annual Review of Physiology, 25:165–194, 1963.

THE URINARY SYSTEM:

Smith, D. R.: General Urology. Los Altos, Calif., Lange Medical Publications, 1964.
Ullrich, K. J., and Marsh, D. J.: Kidney, water, and electrolyte metabolism. Annual Review of Physiology, 25:91–142, 1963.
West, E. S., and Todd, W. R.: Textbook of Biochemistry. New York, The Macmillan Co., 1961, Chaps. 17–33.

THE ENDOCRINE SYSTEM:

Cooley, D. G.: Hormones: your body's chemical rousers. Today's Health, 40:28–33, 1962.
Danowski, T. S.: Clinical Endocrinology. Vols. 1–4. Baltimore, Williams & Wilkins Co., 1962.
Ezrin, C.: The pituitary gland. CIBA Clinical Symposia, 15:71–100, 1963.
Forsham, P. H.: The adrenal gland. CIBA Clinical Symposia, 15:3–21, 1963.
Levine, R.: Diabetes mellitus. CIBA Clinical Symposia, 15:103–152, 1963.
Purshottam, N., and Purshottam, S.: Hormonal assays and gonadal function. Annual Review of Medicine, 13:261–272, 1962.
Williams, R. H.: Textbook of Endocrinology. Philadelphia, W. B. Saunders Co., 1962.

FLUIDS AND ELECTROLYTES:

Chinard, F. P.: Kidney, water, and electrolytes. Annual Review of Physiology, 26:187, 1964.
Weisberg, A. F.: Water, Electrolyte and Acid-base Balance. Baltimore, Williams & Wilkins Co., 1962.

THE REPRODUCTIVE SYSTEM:

Allan, F. D.: Essentials of Human Embryology. New York, Oxford University Press, 1960.
McPhedran, M.: The Maternity Cycle. Philadelphia, F. A. Davis Co., 1961.

ADDITIONAL REFERENCES:

Anthony, C. P.: Textbook of Anatomy and Physiology. St. Louis, C. V. Mosby Co., 1963.
Arey, L. B.: Developmental Anatomy. Philadelphia, W. B. Saunders Co., 1965.
Bell, G. H., Davidson, J. N., and Scarborough, H.: Textbook of Physiology and Biochemistry. Baltimore, Williams & Wilkins Co., 1939.
Best, C. H., and Taylor, N. B.: The Physiological Basis of Medical Practice. Baltimore, Williams & Wilkins Co., 1961.
Chaffee, E. E., and Greisheimer, E. M.: Basic Physiology and Anatomy. Philadelphia, J. B. Lippincott Co., 1964.
Davison, H., and Eggleton, M. G. (Eds.): Starling and Evans' Principles of Human Physiology. Philadelphia, Lea and Febiger Co., 1962.
Francis, C.: Introduction to Human Anatomy. St. Louis, C. V. Mosby Co., 1964.
Ganong, W.: Review of Medical Physiology. Los Altos, Calif., Lange Medical Publications, 1963.
Guyton, A. C.: Textbook of Medical Physiology. Philadelphia, W. B. Saunders Co., 1961.
Magle, D. F.: Gastrointestinal Physiology. Springfield, Ill., Charles C Thomas, 1962.
Rhodin, J.: An Atlas of Ultrastructure. Philadelphia, W. B. Saunders Co., 1963.
Ruch, T. C., and Fulton, J. F. (Eds.): Medical Physiology and Biophysics. Philadelphia, W. B. Saunders Co., 1960.
Selkurt, E. E. (Ed.): Physiology. Boston, Little, Brown & Co., 1962.
Tuttle, W. W., and Schottelius, B. A.: Textbook of Physiology. St. Louis, C. V. Mosby Co., 1962.

GLOSSARY*

a--: a prefix meaning absent or deficient.

abdomen: the portion of the body lying between the diaphragm and the pelvis.

abduct: to draw away from the median line.

absorption: the taking up of fluids or other substances by the skin, mucous surfaces, or vessels.

acidosis: a condition marked by a lowered pH of the blood due to excess concentration of hydrogen ion or lowered bicarbonate.

acuity: sharpness or clearness, especially of vision.

adduct: to draw toward a center or toward a median line.

adeno--: a combining form meaning glandular.

adhesion: abnormal union of two surfaces as a result of inflammation.

ad libitum: freely; as much as wanted.

adventitia: the outermost covering of a structure not forming an integral part of it.

aerobic: growing only in the presence of molecular oxygen.

afferent: conveying toward a center.

aldehyde: any one of a large group of compounds derived by the oxidation of primary alcohols, containing the CHO group.

--algia: a combining form meaning pain.

alimentary: pertaining to food or nutritive material.

alkalosis: a condition in which there is an excessive proportion of alkali in the blood.

alveolus: a small cavity.

amino acid: an organic compound with an NH_3 and a COOH group in its molecule, and having both acid and basic properties. Amino acids are the structural units from which proteins are built.

amorphous: having no definite form; shapeless.

amphoteric: having opposite characteristics; capable of acting either as an acid or as a base; combining with both acids and bases.

ampulla: a sac-like dilatation of a tube or duct.

an--: a prefix meaning absent or deficient.

anabolism: any constructive process in which simple substances are converted by living cells into more complex compounds, such as conversion of simple compounds into protoplasm.

anaerobic: growing only in the absence of oxygen.

analgesia: loss of sensitivity to pain.

anaphylaxis: an exaggerated reaction of the organism to a foreign protein.

anastomosis: a connection between vessels or between parts of a tube, such as the stomach to the small intestine.

° Reference source: Dorland's Illustrated Medical Dictionary, 24th edition. Philadelphia, W. B. Saunders Co., 1965.

anesthesia: loss of sensation.

aneurysm: a sac formed by the dilatation of the wall of an artery or of a vein and filled with blood.

angina: any disease characterized by spasmodic, choking, or suffocative pain.

antrum: a cavity or chamber, especially one within a bone.

aperture: an opening or orifice.

apex: the top or pointed extremity of a conical part.

aphasia: defect or loss of the power of expression by speech, or loss of the ability to use or understand words.

aponeurosis: a white, flattened or ribbon-like tendinous expansion.

appendage: a thing or part affixed or attached.

aqueduct: a channel in a body structure or organ, especially a canal for the conduction of liquid.

arthro--: a combining form pertaining to one or more joints.

arthrosis: a joint or articulation.

articular: of or pertaining to a joint.

articulation: the site of union or junction between two or more bones of the skeleton.

asphyxia: loss of consciousness due to deficient oxygen supply.

aspirate: to remove fluids or gases from a cavity by suction.

ataxia: loss of muscle coordination.

atrium: a chamber or cavity.

atrophy: a wasting away or diminution in the size of a cell, tissue, organ, or part.

autonomic: self-controlling; functionally independent.

axial: of, or pertaining to, the axis of a structure or part.

benign: not malignant; not life-threatening.

biceps: a muscle having two heads.

bifurcate: forked; divided into two like a fork.

bilateral: pertaining to both sides of the body.

binovular: pertaining to or derived from two distinct ova.

blast: an immature stage in the formation of a blood cell before the development of the definitive characteristics of the cell.

bolus: a rounded food mass of soft consistency.

brachial: pertaining to the arm.

buccal: pertaining to the cheek.

buffer: a substance in a fluid medium which lessens the change in hydrogen or hydroxyl ion concentration when an acid or base is added.

cachexia: a profound and marked state of constitutional disorder, usually associated with loss of fat stores and muscle mass.

calorie: a unit of heat, being the amount of heat required to raise 1 gram of water from 15 to 16° C.

canal: a tubular and relatively narrow passage or channel.

canaliculus: a small canal or channel.

cancellous: a lattice-like bony structure.

carbohydrate: organic compounds containing carbon, hydrogen, and oxygen in certain specific proportions.

carpal: of or pertaining to the wrist.

cast: a mold of a body part.

catabolism: any process by which complex substances are converted by living cells into simpler compounds.

catalyst: a substance which changes the velocity of a reaction but does not form part of the final product.

caudal: denoting a position more toward the tail.

celiac: pertaining to the abdomen.

cellulose: a carbohydrate polymer forming the skeleton of most plant structures and plant cells.

centimeter: a unit of linear measure of the metric system, being $\frac{1}{100}$ meter or about $\frac{2}{5}$ inch.

cephalic: pertaining to the head or superior end of the body.

cervix: the neck or any neck-like part.

chiasm: an X-shaped crossing.

cholesterol: an organic fatty alcohol present in bile, blood, and various tissues.

chondrification: the formation or transformation into cartilage.

choroid: skin-like.

chylomicron: a particle of emulsified fat found in the blood during the digestion of fat.

cilia: minute, hair-like processes attached to the free surface of a cell.

cochlea: having a spiral form; part of the inner ear.

coenzyme: a non-protein substance actuating an enzyme.

collagen: an albuminoid, the main supportive protein of skin, tendon, bone, cartilage, and connective tissue.

collateral: accompanying; running by the side of; accessory.

colloid: a state of matter in which matter is dispersed throughout a medium called the dispersion medium; the matter dispersed is termed the disperse phase. The particles are larger than a crystalloid molecule, but are not large enough to precipitate under the influence of gravity. They range in size from 0.1 micron to 1 micron.

coma: profound unconsciousness.

commissure: the band of fibers joining corresponding opposite parts, mainly in the brain and spinal cord.

concha: a structure resembling a shell in shape.

condyle: a rounded projection on a bone, usually for articulation with another bone.

congenital: existing at, and usually before, birth.

conjugation: the act of joining together.

contraction: a shortening, as of a muscle in the normal response to a nervous stimulus.

contralateral: situated on or pertaining to the opposite side.

convoluted: rolled together or coiled.

coracoid: like a raven's beak in form.

coronary: encircling in the manner of a crown; a term applied to vessels, nerves, and ligaments.

corpus: the body as a whole, or the main part of any organ.

corpuscle: any small organ or body.

cortex: the outer layer of an organ as distinguished from its inner substance.

costal: pertaining to a rib or ribs.

cribriform: perforated like a sieve with small apertures.

cricoid: ring-shaped.

cruciate: shaped like a cross.

crypt: a minute, tube-like depression opening on a free surface.

crystalloid: a non-colloid substance which in a solvent passes readily through animal membranes.

cubital: pertaining to the ulna or to the foramen.

cutaneous: pertaining to the skin.

cyanosis: a bluish appearance of the skin or nails secondary to deficient oxygenation of blood.

deamination: a chemical reaction in which the amino group is split from an amino acid.

debilitating: lacking or losing strength.

deciduous: not permanent, cast off at maturity.

decussation: a crossing over, particularly a band of nerve fibers crossing the median plane of any part of the central nervous system.

deferens: carrying away.

dehydration: removal of water from the body or a tissue, or the condition which results from undue loss of water.

deltoid: having a triangular outline.

dendrite: a branched and tree-shaped protoplasmic process from a nerve cell conducting impulses toward the cell body.

dentate: having teeth or projections like saw teeth on the edges.

denticulate: having fine marginal teeth.

derma--, dermato--: combining forms pertaining to the skin.

dia--: a combining form meaning through, between, across, or apart.

diagnosis: the process of determining which disease is present.

dialysis: the process of separating crystalloids and colloids in solution by the difference in their rates of diffusion through a semipermeable membrane; crystalloids pass through readily, colloids slowly or not at all.

diaphragm: a membrane or partition separating one thing from another.

diarthrosis: a freely movable articulation.

differential diagnosis: a diagnosis made by closely comparing a case with several diseases producing similar symptoms, so as to exclude as many alternatives as possible.

diffusion: dialysis through a membrane.

digit: a finger or toe.

dissect: to cut, separate, and expose body structures, especially for anatomic study.

distal: remote, farther from any point of reference.

diurnal: occurring during the day.

diverticulum: a pouch or pocket from a main cavity or tube.

dorsal: denoting a position toward the back or posterior.

duct: a tube for the passage of excretions or secretions.

--dynia: a combining form meaning pain.

dys--: a prefix meaning disordered, difficult, or painful.

dystrophy: defective or faulty nutrition.

ecto--: a combining form meaning a surgical removal.

ectopic: out of the normal place.

edema: the presence of an abnormally large volume of fluid in the interstitial spaces of the body.

effector: a responding organ.

efferent: conveying away from the center.

effusion: the escape of fluid into a part or tissue.

electrocardiogram: a graphic record of the electric current produced by the contraction of heart muscle.

electroencephalogram: a record of the electric currents developed in the brain, made by means of electrodes applied to the scalp or directly to the surface of the brain.

electrolyte: any solution conducting electricity by means of its ions.

electron: a minute, negatively charged particle.

elimination: the act of expulsion or of extrusion, especially expulsion from the body.

embryo: the early or developing stage of any organism.

emesis: vomiting.

empirical: based on knowledge derived solely from experience.

empyema: accumulation of pus in a cavity of the body, especially in the chest.

endo--: a combining form meaning interior.

endocrine: applied to organs functioning to secrete substances into the blood or lymph producing a specific affect on another organ or part.

energy: capacity for doing work.

entero--: a combining form pertaining to the intestines.

enuresis: involuntary urination.

enzyme: a protein capable of accelerating or producing by catalytic action some change in a specific substrate.

epimysium: the fibrous sheath about an entire muscle.

epiphysis: a segment of bone separated from the long bone early in life by a piece of cartilage, but later becoming part of the larger bone.

erectile: capable of being made rigid and elevated.

ethmoid: cribriform; sieve-like.

etiology: the study of cause, especially of disease.

evagination: an outpouching of a layer or part.

eversion: a turning inside out.

excoriation: a superficial loss of substance, such as is produced on the skin by scratching.

exocrine: secreting into a duct.

extrapyramidal: outside the pyramidal tracts.

extravasation: escape of blood, lymph, or serum from a vessel into tissue spaces.

extrinsic: originating outside.

exudate: any substance deposited in or on a tissue by a vital process or a disease.

facilitation: the effect produced in nerve tissue by the passage of an impulse.

fascia: a sheet or band of fibrous tissue covering the body under the skin and investing muscles and other organs.

fasciculus: a small bundle, chiefly of nervous or muscular fibers.

febrile: pertaining to fever.

fiber: an elongated, thread-like structure of organic tissue.

filiform: thread-shaped.

filtration: the passage of a liquid through a straining device.

fimbria: any fringe-like structure.

fissure: any cleft or groove, normal or other.

flaccid: weak and soft.

follicle: a small excretory or secretory sac or gland.

foramen: a natural hole or passage, especially one into or through bone.

fossa: a pit or depression.

fovea: a fossa, or cup; applied to various depressions in the structure of the body such as the fovea centralis.

frenulum: a small fold of the integument or of mucous membrane, especially one that limits the movements of an organ or part of an organ.

fundus: the base or part of a hollow organ most remote from the entrance.

fusiform: spindle-shaped.

gamma: a microgram.

ganglion: any collection or mass of nerve cells.

gastro--: a combining form pertaining to the stomach.

gastrointestinal: pertaining to the stomach and intestines.

genitalia: the reproductive organs.

genu: the knee or any structure bent like a knee.

gestation: pregnancy.

gland: an organ that produces a specific product or secretion.

globus: a sphere or ball.

glomerulus: a coil of blood vessels.

glossal: pertaining to the tongue.

gluteal: pertaining to the buttocks.

glycogen: a polysaccharide which is the chief carbohydrate storage material in animals.

graafian follicle: a small, spherical vesicular sac embedded in the cortex of the ovary, which contains an egg cell or ovum. Each follicle contains a liquid, liquor ovarii, supplied with the hormone folliculin or estrin.

groin: the lowest part of the abdominal wall, near its junction with the thigh.

gyrus: a convoluted ridge.

hallucination: a perception not founded on reality.

hema--, hemato--, hemo--: combining forms pertaining to blood.

hemiparesis: muscular weakness of one side of the body.

hemiplegia: paralysis of one side of the body.

hemorrhage: a copious escape of blood; bleeding.

hepar: the liver, or a liver-like or liver-colored substance.

heredity: transmission of characteristics from a parent to a child.

hilum: a depression or pit in an organ where the vessels and nerves enter.

histology: anatomy dealing with the minute structure, composition, and function of the tissue.

homeostasis: a tendency to uniformity or stability in an organism.

homogenous: having a similarity of structure.

homologous: corresponding in structure, position, and origin. In transplantation, tissues or organs are exchanged between two non-identical individuals of the same species.

hormone: a substance secreted by a ductless gland regulating the functions of other organs.

horn: any horn-shaped projection or extension.

hyaline: glassy; transparent or nearly so.

hydro--: a combining form pertaining to water or hydrogen.

hydrostatic: pertaining to a liquid in a state of equilibrium.

hyoid: shaped like the letter U.

hyper--: a prefix meaning above, beyond, or excessive.

hyperplasia: the abnormal multiplication or increase in the number of normal cells in normal pattern.

hypertonic: pertaining to or characterized by excessive tone, tension, or activity.

hypertrophy: the enlargement or overgrowth of an organ or part due to an increase in size of its constituent cells.

hypo--: a prefix meaning beneath, under, or deficient.

hypochondriac: pertaining to the upper lateral region of the abdomen below the lowest ribs.

hypodermic: applied beneath the skin.

hypoxia: low oxygen content in inspired air.

impermeable: not permitting a passage, as for fluid.

impulse: a sudden pushing force.

inferior: situated or directed below.

inflammation: a series of reactions produced in the tissues by an irritant, marked by an erythema with exudation of serum and leukocytes.

infundibulum: a funnel-shaped structure or passage.

inguinal: pertaining to the groin.

inhalation: the drawing of air or other vapor into the lungs.

inhibition: restraint of a process.

in situ: in the normal place or confined to the site of origin without invasion of neighboring tissues.

inter--: a prefix meaning between.

intercostal: situated between the ribs.

interstitial: pertaining to or situated in the spaces or gaps of a tissue.

intima: innermost.

intra--: a prefix meaning within.

intravascular: within the blood vessels or the lymphatics.

intrinsic: situated within or pertaining exclusively to a part.

invaginate: to infold one portion within another portion of the same thing.

inversion: turning inward.

in vitro: within a glass; observable in a test tube.

in vivo: within the living body.

involuntary: performed independently of the will.

involution: retrograde or degenerative change.

ion: an atom or a group of atoms having a charge of positive or negative electricity.

ipsilateral: pertaining to the same side.

irritability: the quality responding to stimuli.

isotonic: having the same concentration.

--itis: a suffix meaning inflammation.

keratin: an insoluble protein containing sulfur which is the principal constituent of hair and nails.

ketone: any compound containing the carbonyl group CO.

kilogram: a unit of weight of the metric system, being 1000 grams.

labium: a lip or lip-shaped organ.

lacrimal: pertaining to the tears.

lacuna: a small pit, hollow, or depression.

lamella: a thin leaf or plate, as of bone.

lamina: a thin, flat plate or layer.

lateral: denoting a position toward the side and farther away from the median plane.

lemniscus: a longitudinal band of sensory fibers in the medulla and pons.
lesion: any pathologic discontinuity of tissue or loss of function of a part.
ligament: any tough, fibrous band connecting bone or supporting viscera.
lipid: fat and fat-like compounds.
liter: the volume occupied by 1 kilogram of pure water at its temperature of maximum density and under standard atmospheric pressure. It is the equivalent of 1.0567 quarts liquid measure.
lobe: a well-defined portion of any organ.
--logist: a suffix meaning a specialist.
--logy: a suffix meaning a study or a field of medicine.
lumbar: pertaining to the loins.
lumen: the cavity or channel within a tube or tubular organ.

macroscopic: visible with the unaided eye or without the microscope.
macula: a spot.
mal--: a prefix meaning disordered.
malignant: virulent; tending to go from bad to worse.
mammary: pertaining to the breast.
mammillary: like or pertaining to a nipple.
manometer: an instrument for measuring the pressure or tension of liquids or gases.
mass: a body made up of cohering particles.
mastoid: nipple-shaped.
matrix: the ground substance in which cells are embedded.
meatus: a passage or channel, especially the external opening of a canal.
medial: pertaining to the middle; nearer the median plane.
mediastinum: a median septum or partition.
medulla: the central portion of an organ as contrasted with its cortex.
megakaryocyte: the giant cell of bone marrow, believed to form blood platelets.
membrane: a thin layer of tissue covering a surface or dividing a space or organ.
meno--: a combining form pertaining to menstruation.
mesenteric: pertaining to mesentery.
mesentery: the peritoneal fold attaching the intestine to the posterior abdominal wall.
mesial: situated in the middle; nearer the middle of the body.
mesothelium: a layer of flat cells, which in the adult forms a squamous-celled layer of epithelium covering the surface of all serous membranes.
meta--: a prefix meaning after or changing.
metabolism: the sum of all the physical and chemical processes by which living organized substance is produced and maintained, and also the transformation by which energy is made available for the use of the organism.
metachromic: tissue in which different elements take on different colors with the same dye.
metastasis: the transfer of disease from one organ or part to another not directly connected to it.
meter: the basic unit of linear measure of the metric system, equivalent to 39.371 inches.
microgram: $\frac{1}{1,000,000}$ gram (10^{-6} gram).
micron: a unit of linear measure in the metric system, being 10^{-3} millimeter, or 10^{-6} meter.
microscopic: visible only by the aid of the microscope.
micturition: the passage of urine.
milliosmal: $\frac{1}{1000}$ osmol.
mitral: shaped somewhat like a miter (a headdress worn by bishops).
ml.: abbreviation for milliliter; interchangeable with cc. (cubic centimeter).
monovular: pertaining to or derived from a single ovum.
morbid: pertaining to disease.
mucosa: a mucous membrane.
multiparous: having had two or more pregnancies resulting in viable offspring.
muscle: an organ which by contraction produces movement.
myeloid: pertaining to, derived from, or resembling bone marrow.
myo--: a combining form pertaining to muscle.
myotome: the muscle plate or portion of the somite developing into the voluntary muscles.

navicular: boat-shaped.
necrosis: death of a cell or of a group of cells.
neuro--: a combining form denoting relationship to a nerve or nerves, or to the nervous system.
neuron: a nerve cell with its processes and collaterals regarded as the structural unit of the nervous system. Lower motor neutrons—peripheral neurons whose cell bodies lie in the ventral gray column of the spinal cord. Upper motor neurons—neurons in the cerebral cortex which conduct impulses from the motor cortex to the motor nuclei of the cerebral nerves.
nuchal: pertaining to the back of the neck.
nucleoside: one of the glycosidic compounds into which a nucleotide is split by the action of nucleotidase.
nucleotide: one of the compounds into which nucleic acid is split by the action of nuclease.
nulliparous: having never given birth to a viable child.

occiput: the back part of the head.
odontoid: like a tooth.
olfactory: pertaining to the sense of smell.
ophthalmic: pertaining to the eye.
orbicular: circular or rounded.
orifice: the entrance or outlet of any body cavity.
os: bone.
--osis: a combining form meaning a condition or a process, especially one that is abnormal.
osmol: the standard unit of osmotic pressure.
osseous: of the nature or quality of bone; bony.
ossicle: a small bone.
ossification: conversion of fibrous tissue or cartilage into bone, or bony substance.
osteo--: a combining form pertaining to one or more bones.
oxidation: the increase of positive charges on an atom through the loss of electrons.

palliative: affording relief, but not cure.
papilla: a small nipple-shaped projection or elevation.
para--: a prefix meaning beside, beyond, accessory to, apart from, against, etc.
parenchyma: the essential or functional elements of an organ.
paresthesia: morbid or perverted sensation; an abnormal sensation, as burning, prickling, etc.
parietal: of or pertaining to the walls of a cavity.
parotid: situated near the ear.
--pathy: a suffix meaning abnormality.
pCO$_2$: symbol for carbon dioxide pressure (tension).
pectineal: pertaining to the pubic bone.
pectoral: pertaining to the breast or chest.
peduncle: a neural fiber tract extending from the cerebellum to the brain.
pelvis: any basin-like structure.
pennate: shaped like a feather.
peri--: a prefix meaning around.
peripheral: situated at or near the outward part or surface.
peroneal: pertaining to the fibula or to the outer side of the leg.
perspiration: sweating; the excretion of sweat.
petrous: resembling a rock; hard; stony.
pH: the symbol commonly used in expressing hydrogen ion concentration, the measure of alkalinity and acidity. It signifies the logarithm of the reciprocal of the hydrogen ion concentration in gram molecules per liter of solution. pH 7 is the neutral point; above pH 7 alkalinity increases, below pH 7 acidity increases.
phagocyte: any cell ingesting microorganisms, foreign particles, or other cells.
phalanges: bones of the fingers or toes.
phlebo--: a combining form meaning venous.
--phobia: a suffix meaning morbid fear.
phrenic: pertaining to the diaphragm.
pilo--: a combining form denoting relationship to hair.
pilomotor: causing movements of hair.
pineal: shaped like a pine cone.
piriform: pear-shaped.
pisiform: like a pea in shape and size.
plantar: pertaining to the sole of the foot.
plexus: a network, especially of nerves, veins, or lymphatics.
plica: a fold or ridge.
pneuma--, pneumato--: prefixes pertaining to air or gas, or breathing.
pneumo--: a prefix pertaining to lung tissue or the lungs.
poly--: a prefix meaning many.
polymer: a compound, usually of high molecular weight, formed by the combination of simpler molecules.
polymorphonuclear: having a nucleus deeply lobed or so divided that it appears to be multiple.
pons: any slip of tissue connecting two parts of an organ.
popliteal: pertaining to the posterior surface of the knee.
post--: a prefix meaning after.
posterior: situated behind or toward the rear.
pre--: a prefix meaning before.
primordium: the earliest discernible indication during embryonic development of an organ or part.
prognosis: a forecast of the probable outcome of an illness.
prolapse: the falling down of an organ or other part.
proliferation: the reproduction or multiplication of similar forms, especially of cells.
protuberance: a projecting part, process, or swelling.
proximal: nearest; closer to any point of reference.
psoas: pertaining to the loin, the part of the back between the ribs and hip bones.

psycho--: a combining form meaning mental.
psychosomatic: pertaining to both mind and body, or physical conditions resulting from mental causes.
ptosis: prolapse of an organ or part.
pyo--: a prefix pertaining to pus.

racemose: resembling a bunch of grapes on its stalk.
ramus: a branch, as of an artery, bone, nerve, or vein.
reflection: the throwing back of a ray of light from a surface it does not penetrate.
reflex: a reflected action or movement.
refraction: the bending of a ray of light as it passes from one medium into another of different density.
renal: pertaining to the kidney.
reticulum: a network, especially a protoplasmic network in cells.
retinaculum: a special fascial thickening helping to retain an organ or tissue in its place.
rigidity: stiffness or inflexibility.
rostral: having to do with a beak-like appendage; toward the nose.
--rrhea: a suffix denoting a flow or discharge.
rugae: ridges, wrinkles, or folds.

saccule: a little sac.
salpinx: a tube.
sarcoma: a tumor, often malignant, arising from connective or non-epithelial tissue.
sciatic: pertaining to the ischium.
sclero--: a combining form meaning hard.
semilunar: resembling a crescent, or half-moon.
senescence: the process or condition of growing old.
septum: a dividing wall or partition.
serous: producing or containing serum.
serratus: saw-toothed.
serum: the clear portion of any animal liquid separated from its more solid elements.
sesamoid: resembling a grain of sesame.
sigmoid: shaped like a letter S.
sine: without.
sinus: a recess, cavity, or hollow space.
skeleton: the bony framework of the higher vertebrate animals.
soleus: pertaining to the sole.
somatic: pertaining to the framework of the body, as distinguished from the viscera.
spasticity: increased muscle tone producing stiffness.
sphenoid: wedge-shaped.
sphincter: a ring-like muscle enclosing a natural orifice.
splanchnic: pertaining to the viscera.
squamous: scaly or plate-like.
stasis: a stoppage of the blood or any other body fluid in any part.
stenosis: narrowing or stricture of a duct or canal.
stimulus: any agent, act, or influence producing a reaction in a receptor.
stomato--: a prefix pretaining to the mouth.
--stomy: a suffix meaning surgical opening.
stratum: a layer.
striated: striped; provided with streaks or lines.
stroma: the tissue which forms the ground substance, framework, or matrix of an organ.
sub--: a prefix meaning under, near, almost, or moderately.
subcutaneous: beneath the skin.
sulcus: a groove, trench, or furrow.
super--: a prefix meaning over.
superior: situated or directed above.
syndrome: a group of symptoms and signs occurring together in such a way as to indicate the existence of a common cause.
synthesis: putting together parts to form a more complex whole.

tegmentum: a covering.
tela: any web-like tissue or any thin anatomic membrane resembling a web.
temporal: pertaining to the temple.
tension: the condition of being stretched.
therapy: medical treatment.
thoraco--: a prefix pertaining to the chest.
thyro--: a combining form denoting relationship to the thyroid gland.
titer: the amount of one substance required to correspond with a given amount of another substance.
--tomy: a suffix meaning surgical cutting.
toxic: harmful to the body; poisonous.

transudation: the passage of serum or other fluid through a membrane.
trauma: a wound or injury.
trochlear: resembling a pulley.
trophic: of or pertaining to nutrition.
--tropic: a suffix denoting turning, changing, or tending to turn or change.
tube: an elongated hollow cylindrical organ or instrument.
tubercle: a nodule or small eminence.
tumor: a swelling.
tunica: a membrane or other structure covering or lining a body part or organ.
turbinate: shaped like a cone or spiral.

ulcer: a loss of substance on a cutaneous or mucous surface.
unilateral: pertaining to one side of the body.
unipennate: shaped like one-half of a feather.
--uria: a suffix denoting a condition of the urine or of presence in the urine.
utricle: a little sac.

vagina: a sheath-like structure.
vagus: wandering; tenth cranial nerve.
valence: the number of hydrogen atoms with which a single atom of an element can combine.
valve: a membranous fold in a canal or passage preventing the reflux of its contents.
vas: a vessel or duct.
vascular: pertaining to or full of vessels.
vastus: wide; of great size.
ventral: denoting a position more toward the belly surface than some other object of reference.
ventricle: any small cavity.
vermiform: shaped like a worm.
vestibule: a space or cavity at the entrance to a canal.
villus: a small vascular protusion, especially such a structure growing on mucous surface.
viscera: the internal organs.
visceral: pertaining to internal organs.
viscous: pertains to sticky or gummy fluid which flows with difficulty.
volar: pertaining to the palm or sole.

xiphoid: shaped like a sword.

INDEX

Note: *Italicized* page numbers refer to illustrations.